The Scientific Management of
Animal and Plant Communities
for Conservation

The Scientific Management of Animal and Plant Communities for Conservation

The 11th Symposium of
The British Ecological Society
University of East Anglia, Norwich
7–9 July 1970

edited by
E. Duffey

The Nature Conservancy
Monks Wood Experimental Station
Abbots Ripton, Huntingdonshire

and
A.S.Watt

Botany School
Cambridge University

Blackwell Scientific Publications
Oxford, London and Edinburgh

© 1971 by Blackwell Scientific Publications
5 Alfred Street, Oxford
3 Nottingham Street, London, W1
9 Forrest Road, Edinburgh

ISBN 0 632 08010 0

First published 1971

Distributed in the USA by
F.A.Davis Company, 1915 Arch Street,
Philadelphia, Pennsylvania

Printed and bound in
Great Britain by
W & J Mackay Ltd,
Chatham, Kent

Contents

xi   Introduction

xv   Acknowledgements

Part 1
The Dynamic Structure of
Plant and Animal Communities

3   The dynamic structure of plant communities in relation to the objectives of conservation
V.Westhoff, University of Nijmegen, The Netherlands

15   Grazing, fertilizers and pesticides in the management of grasslands
John L.Harper, School of Plant Biology, University College of North Wales, Bangor

33   Techniques for long-term diagnosis and prediction in forest communities
H.C.Dawkins, Department of Forestry, University of Oxford

45   Plant species diversity in relation to management
E. van der Maarel, Botanical Laboratory, University of Nijmegen, The Netherlands

65   The use of nutrients in the control of the floristic composition of grassland
I.H.Rorison, Nature Conservancy Grassland Research Unit, Department of Botany, University of Sheffield

79   The experimental alteration of a *Kobresia*-rich sward in Upper Teesdale
D.W.Jeffrey, Department of Biological Sciences, University of Lancaster. Present address: School of Botany, Trinity College, Dublin

91   *Calluna* heathlands: use and conservation in the light of some ecological effects of management
C.H.Gimingham, Department of Botany, University of Aberdeen

105   Importance of soil toxicity in relation to the stability of plant communities
R.K.Robinson, Department of Forestry, University of Oxford

115   The mechanism of acidification of soil by *Calluna* and *Ulex* and the significance for conservation
P.J.Grubb and M.B.Suter, Botany School, University of Cambridge

Part 2
Factors regulating the Numbers of
Individuals in a Community

137   Factors controlling the floristic composition of some plant communities in Breckland
A.S.Watt, Botany School, University of Cambridge

153   The influence of burning and grazing on the growth and development of *Rubus chaemamorus* L. in *Calluna-Eriophorum* bog
K.Taylor and T.C.Marks, Department of Botany and Microbiology, University College London

167   Comparative autecology as a guide to plant distribution
F.H.Whitehead, Imperial College London

177   Conservation and the genetical constitution of populations
R.J.Berry, Royal Free Hospital School of Medicine, London

207   A self-regulation to density-independent continuum in Australian parrots, and its implication for ecological management
John le Gay Brereton, Department of Zoology, University of New England, Armidale, New South Wales, Australia

Part 3
Conservation Problems in Freshwater

225   Eutrophication
J.W.G.Lund, Freshwater Biological Association, Ambleside

241   Dynamic balance between plant species in South Moravian reed-swamps
K.Fiala and J.Květ, Czechoslovak Academy of Sciences, Institute of Botany, Brno

271   Some effects of organic enrichment on benthic invertebrate communities in stream riffles
H.A.Hawkes and L.J.Davies, Department of Biological Sciences, University of Aston in Birmingham

295   The role of introduced fish in fish production in Ceylon's freshwaters
C.F.Fernando, Department of Biology, University of Waterloo, Waterloo, Ontario, Canada

311   Water management in nature reserves
L.W.G.Higler, Research Institute for Nature Management, Leersum, The Netherlands

Part 4
Habitat Management for Wildlife in Africa

319   African grassland management—burning and grazing in Murchison Falls National Park, Uganda
D.H.N.Spence and A.Angus, Department of Botany, University of St. Andrews, Fife

333   Destruction or utilization of a wildlife habitat?
R.M.Lawton, Land Resources Division, Directorate of Overseas Surveys, Tolworth, Surrey

337   The seed biology of *Themeda triandra* Forsk. in relation to fire
J.M.Lock, Nuffield Unit of Tropical Animal Ecology, P.O. Queen Elizabeth Park, Lake Katwe, Uganda
T.R.Milburn, Department of Botany, Makerere, University College, P.O. Box 7062, Kampala, Uganda

351   Comparative food preferences of five East African ungulates at different seasons
D.R.M. and J.Stewart, Research Division, Kenya Game Department, P.O. Box 241, Nairobi, Kenya

367   The effect of creating additional water supplies in a central African National Park
J.S.Weir, Department of Zoology, University of Leicester

387   Influence of indigenous animals on the dynamics of vegetation in conservation areas
R.Knapp, Institute of Botany, University of Giessen, Germany

Part 5
Ecological Studies on the Conservation and
Control of Large Mammals

393   The ecological and economic basis for game ranching in Africa
I.S.C.Parker and A.D.Graham, Wildlife Services Ltd, P.O. Box 30678, Nairobi, Kenya

405   Field trials of the line transect method of sampling populations of large herbivores
Patrick Hemingway, College of African Wildlife Management, Tanzania

413   A behavioural approach to the management of wild ungulates
V.Geist, Environmental Sciences Centre, The University of Calgary, Calgary 44, Alberta, Canada

425   Controlled fire in the management of North American Deer
Richard D.Taber, College of Forest Resources, University of Washington, Seattle
James L.Murphy, Pacific North West Forest and Range Experiment Station, U.S. Forest Service; and College of Forest Resources, University of Washington, Seattle

437   Some effects of a change in estate management on a deer population
V.P.W.Lowe, The Nature Conservancy, Merlewood Research Station, Grange-over-Sands, Lancashire

Part 6
The Influence of Biotic Factors
on Wildlife Conservation

459   The effects of public pressure on the vegetation of chalk downland

at Box Hill, Surrey
D.T.Streeter, University of Sussex

469   Some effects of walking and skiing on vegetation at Cairngorm
Neil G.Bayfield, The Nature Conservancy, Blackhall, Banchory, Kincardineshire

487   The influence of sheep grazing on limestone heath on the Baltic island of Öland
Erik Sjögren, University of Uppsala, Sweden

497   A comparison of the effects of sheep grazing and mechanical cutting on the structure and botanical composition of chalk grassland
T.C.E.Wells, The Nature Conservancy, Monks Wood Experimental Station, Abbots Ripton, Huntingdonshire

517   Some effects of grazing on the population ecology of the Cinnabar Moth
J.P.Dempster, The Nature Conservancy, Monks Wood Experimental Station, Abbots Ripton, Huntingdonshire

527   The management of grassland for the conservation of invertebrate animals
M.G.Morris, The Nature Conservancy, Monks Wood Experimental Station, Abbots Ripton, Huntingdonshire

Part 7
Management Policy and Practical Problems
of Conservation

555   The size and surroundings of nature reserves
M.D.Hooper, The Nature Conservancy, Monks Wood Experimental Station, Abbots Ripton, Huntingdonshire

563   Historical studies and woodland conservation
Oliver Rackham, Corpus Christi College, Cambridge

581   The management of Woodwalton Fen: a multidisciplinary approach
E.Duffey, The Nature Conservancy, Monks Wood Experimental Station, Abbots Ripton, Huntingdonshire

599   The management of plant and animal communities in the Tatra
       Mountains National Park
       *Adam Łomnicki, Nature Conservation Research Centre, Polish
       Academy of Sciences, Krakow, Poland*

605   The conservation of ecological diversity of Mediterranean eco-
       systems through ecological management
       Z.Naveh, Technion, Israel Institute of Technology, Haifa

Indexes

625   Author Index

634   Subject Index

Introduction

In recent years much has been written and discussed about the subject of conservation, its aims, its social significance for town-dweller and country-dweller alike and its administrative machinery, but nearly all of it stops short at the point where technical knowledge of plant and animal communities is necessary to translate ideas into practice. Indeed, until recently, there was little awareness of this gap in our knowledge and, in fact, it was often assumed that the necessary scientific information was available.

The idea that wildlife communities may need to be managed is still difficult for some ecologists to accept. A policy of 'hands off nature' is quite unrealistic. It arises from a failure to appreciate that, beginning with the entry of Neolithic man with his crops and stock, the influence of agricultural, pastoral and industrial man on plant and animal life has become so extensive, both in space and in time, that at present there is no part of the earth's surface, land or water, entirely free from the effects of his activities. The degree of the effect varies from the negligible to the radical (for example, snow patch vegetation to cultivated crops replacing original forest): and what was of little and local significance yesterday may become serious and widespread tomorrow (erosion, pollution, trampling). Because of man's pervasive influence no area can be completely isolated from his direct or indirect influence.

Further, man's influence has been largely destructive in displacing or exterminating species of animals and plants, and in replacing communities which fully exploit the climatic potential, by others which do not. At the same time he has altered the relative numbers of individuals of the surviving species, provided conditions for greater genetic diversity for many, and increased the number and variety of assemblages of plants and animals. Much that is admired and appreciated for a variety of values, and is regarded as desirable and worthy of retention, is of man's making, and only by a continuation of his influence can it be preserved.

The realization that man is a world power in the field of nature does not mean that he will exercise it more than is necessary to achieve a defined objective. As far as possible he will leave the achievement of that objective to natural forces, but for some objectives management is a necessary means to the end. So that whatever views are held about the nature of the plant and animal community, the kind of knowledge required and the methods to be used in management become important.

'You may have what you wish', said the late Professor W.H.Pearsall in a similar context, and the graded series of diminishing control of the environment by man in glasshouse, zoo, garden, farm, pasture, forest, game-park and range bears witness to it. Common to the management of all these is a knowledge of the organisms concerned, plant and animal. Although the relevant facts about wild plants and animals are few, compared with those for the cultivated or domesticated species, there is no reason to suppose that, in the extension of control to the more complex natural or semi-natural community, the problems to be faced are inherently different.

Full knowledge of the thousand and one ecological facts in a community and of the complexity of the relationships between them is an ecologist's dream, the part-realization of which forms the stepping stone to the next stage in its analysis. First he aims to find out what is there (this emphasizes the importance of more organized ecological survey in conservation work, because there are still big gaps in our knowledge particularly of the lower groups of organisms) and then, what is happening. We need to know the processes at work, the relationship between plant and plant, plant and animal, animal and animal and both to the inorganic environment, so that an understanding of what is going on provides a guideline for what has to be done. On the basis of this understanding the ecologist interprets the existing situation and extrapolates to reconstruct the past and predict the future in given circumstances.

The real test of one's understanding of a community is the possession of knowledge on how to control its floristic and faunistic composition. Most research on this subject is limited in its scope; it is fragmentary and conditioned by the duration and place of residence of the worker as well as by his interests. And he is fortunate indeed if his local colleagues, specialists in other branches, are sufficiently interested in the same objective so that the work may be co-ordinated and focused upon the central issue. Institutional and team work, better communication and exchange of information are recent improvements towards this end. Also continuity of experiment over longer periods of time is essential.

Conservation implies not only the preservation of the desirable in our heritage, as we find it today, but also an appreciation of what can be created in the future. The subjective element in conservation is strong, and when values or requirements change, ecologists must have the information necessary to meet this challenge. This Symposium is a first attempt to review the state of our knowledge in several different fields of conservation research. It begins with contributions on some fundamental characteristics of community structure and dynamics, is followed by experimental results on management treatments and some ecological effects of man's activities, leading finally to some practical problems of management on nature reserves and national parks. It is clear that not only is our knowledge very inadequate on all subjects but that a good deal of effort is required to interpret and apply existing ecological data in a conservation context. The meeting did not set out to provide answers to specific types of practical management problems, but to examine the progress and extent of research, applicable to an ecological understanding of conservation. In addition, by bringing so many approaches and points of view to focus on this subject, it was hoped to make participants more aware of its complexity and the urgent need to foresee the problems of the future in a rapidly changing world.

Acknowledgements

Over 400 people attended all or part of the 11th Symposium meeting, at which forty-two papers were read, arranged under seven subject headings. All except one of the contributions are included in this volume.

A meeting of this size and complexity required a great deal of careful preparation and organization, which was very capably dealt with by the local organizer Dr R.L.Jefferies of the School of Biology in the University of East Anglia, assisted by his colleagues Dr J.Barkham, Dr R.James, Mr G.Byers, Mr A.J.C.Cooke and Mrs Janet Crook. The Society deeply appreciates their untiring efforts to ensure the success of the meeting and the comfort of the participants.

Our thanks are due to the Principal and University of East Anglia for receiving the Society at Norwich and for making available the Halls of Residence, Lecture Theatres, Refectory and other facilities. The Vice-Principal, Mr F.Thistlethwaite, welcomed the Society on the first day and our President, Professor J.L.Harley, opened the first session. We are grateful to the following who acted as chairmen: Professor J.L.Harley, Professor J.L.Harper, Mr H.C.Gilson, Dr D.R.M.Stewart, Dr R.Laws, Dr M.E.D.Poore, Dr K. Mellanby and also to Professor P.J.Newbould who summed up the work of the Symposium on the last day. At the Symposium dinner the President welcomed as guests participants from the Netherlands and Czechoslovakia, in recognition of the hospitality which members of the Society had received in their countries in 1965 and 1967 respectively.

After the lecture programme the Society organized tours of nature reserves and research sites in Scotland and calcareous grassland reserves in southern England. There was also a series of day excursions to places of scientific interest in East Anglia. The Society is especially grateful to Dr F.B.Goldsmith who was responsible for the booking arrangements, and to the individual tour organizers, Dr M.George and colleagues in the Nature Conservancy East Anglian Regional Office, Mr T.C.E.Wells and Dr M.G. Morris of the Lowland Grassland Research Section at the Monks Wood Experimental Station and to Dr N.Bayfield, Mr E.M.Matthew, Mr A.Currie and their colleagues in the Conservation and Research branches of the Nature Conservancy Scottish Headquarters.

Miss Gillian Searle helped us in many ways with the preparation of the programme and during the meeting and Mrs Rita Duffey assisted at the meeting and was also responsible for the preparation of the index to this volume as well as doing much of the proof-reading. We are also grateful to Dr R.M.Laws for his help with the editing of the papers for parts IV and V of this volume and with the index. Finally we would like to thank the forty-two Symposium contributors, many of whom came from overseas, for their enthusiastic participation.

Eric Duffey

A.S.Watt

Part 1
The Dynamic Structure of Plant and Animal Communities

Part I

The dynamic structure of plant communities in relation to the objectives of conservation

V. WESTHOFF *University of Nijmegen, Netherlands*

In the western European countries perhaps the most important new viewpoint on nature conservation during the past thirty years is the better understanding of the effect of man on pattern and process of ecosystems. Until a quarter of a century ago nature preservation implied that man must be kept out. Human influence was considered to be an undesirable disturbance; nature should be left to look after itself. In the western European countries this viewpoint is nowadays considered to be an outdated idea. Ecological research has elucidated scientifically what field practitioners had already known long before: man and his impact are part of the ecosystem, and they are not necessarily undesirable or even harmful.

A large number of biotic communities would not be able to persist or even to exist without a major human impact. Nevertheless, many of them require preservation, especially the semi-natural ones. Nature does not need defending against man himself, but against the deterioration caused by modern technical production and cultivation methods, which are levelling down the variety of environmental sites, strongly diminishing the original richness of flora and fauna, and aiming at the maintenance of only a very restricted number of cultivated species.

Contrary to this process and in reaction to it, nature conservation has to maintain and to increase environmental variety.

Categories of landscape

Pursuing the matter further we need to realize that there are different levels of human impact on the landscape and its biotic communities. Four categories can be distinguished, not based primarily on historical research but on ecological criteria. We use, for that purpose, the concepts of *flora* and *vegetation*.

3

We consider whether the given flora is native, naturalized, adventitious or cultivated, and we use our experience about the diagnostic value of pattern and process in vegetation in relation to the rate of human influence on it. We come, next, to the four main categories: the natural landscape, the subnatural landscape, the semi-natural landscape and the cultivated landscape. In the *natural* landscape flora and fauna are native and spontaneous, and the vegetation is undisturbed by man. This type no longer occurs in western and central Europe and will be left out of consideration.

In the *subnatural* landscape the flora and the fauna are native and spontaneous too, although there may be some minor exceptions. The basic vegetation appearance and structure are not quite undisturbed: they have to a certain extent been influenced by man. But they are closely related to the potential natural vegetation, and belong to the same formation type as the original landscape, and share the latter's physiognomy.

In the *semi-natural* landscape the flora and the fauna are again, at least to a large extent, native and spontaneous, but the vegetation has been essentially changed by human influence. The result is a vegetation structure which is quite different from that of the potential natural vegetation. It presents a different physiognomy, and belongs to another formation type. To this category belong nearly all dry pastures, hayfields, mown lands and downs, provided they have not been artificially manured, drained, levelled down or otherwise disturbed. Other examples are heaths and moorlands, carr, reed swamps, litter fen, the older coastal dunes, hedges, coppice and scrub. In western and central Europe this type constitutes the greater part of all those areas and biotic communities which are essential for the variety of the landscape and therefore need to be preserved.

In the *cultivated* landscape both the composition of flora and fauna and the vegetation are essentially controlled by man. For nature conservation in a strict sense, this category is of minor importance only.

It must be stressed that in the Middle Ages and until the end of the nineteenth century the semi-natural landscapes predominated in western and central Europe. They covered a much larger surface than either the subnatural or the cultivated landscape. This situation prevailed for many centuries. Human influence was much more positive than negative; it was enriching and beneficial, not impoverishing. Differentiation outweighed levelling down.

Stability and diversity

During the last decades it has become clear that man has a positive influence on diversity as long as his action aims at stabilization; on the other hand, by disturbance, he is impoverishing nature by increasing the amount of instability. For the means and ends of nature conservation, the basic relation in pattern and process of vegetation, is the positive correlation between stability and diversity of ecosystems. Margalef in 1958 was the first to stress this correlation, an approach accepted by E.P.Odum (1963, 1969), di Castri & Covarrubias (1966) and Whittaker (1965, 1969).

In the past 25 years C.G.van Leeuwen and myself have regularly studied the succession phenomena on about 500 permanent sample quadrats in nature reserves all over our small country. We formulated the results in a theory of pattern and process dealing with the relations between diversity in space and stability in time. Isolation versus communication has been taken as a fundamental antithesis. It could be shown that isolation leads to enrichment, variation and diversity; communication, on the contrary, to levelling down, monotony and impoverishment. It became obvious that diversity in space is conditioned by stability in time and, the reverse, that concentration, monotony, uniformity and poverty in species are conditioned by discontinuity in time, that is to say by disturbances, by instability. We developed these views mainly by the study of ecological gradients in transitional zones, focusing our attention on the dynamics of vegetation boundaries.

From these considerations two main types of boundaries can be discerned which we have called *limes convergens*—characterized by spatial concentration and instability in time and *limes divergens*—characterized by spatial dispersion and stability in time. Their main respective qualities are the following.

The *limes convergens* is in its pattern characterized by coarse granulation and sharp, often straight border lines: it presents an 'all-or-nothing' situation. It is marked by unstable conditions on the inside, coupled to a low amount of internal variety-in-space. Conditions in border areas of this kind show a high degree of instability, while the vegetation is poor in species, most of them represented by many individuals showing large primary production. We have suggested restricting the concept of 'ecotone' to this boundary type, considering stress or tension as an aspect of instability.

A *limes divergens*, on the contrary, shows a fine granulation in its pattern together with faint lines of demarcation: it presents a 'more-or-less' situation. It is marked by stable conditions on the inside, coupled to a high amount of variety-in-space. The vegetation of such gradual transition zones between differing environments is rich in species, many of them represented by only a few individuals. The concept of 'ecocline' seems appropriate to the *limes divergens* (cf. van der Maarel 1966, and this symposium).

Both types of boundary zonation gradients accommodate their own organisms and communities. Some of the plant species characteristic of the *limes convergens*, i.e. the unstable situation, are: *Ranunculus repens, Potentilla anserina, Rumex crispus, Trifolium repens, Juncus inflexus, J. maritimus, Carex hirta, C.otrubae, Elytrigia repens* and *Festuca arundinacea*, all bound to one higher vegetation unit in the continental classification, viz. the class of Planta-gineta maioris. The plant communities assigned to this class live in habitats which, at first sight, seem to be rather different, but which show one important feature in common; strong and often irregular, temporal variation in the habitat as caused by alterations between wet and dry, between salt and fresh or between situations poor and rich in nutrients. These often sudden and marked changes may result in soil compaction.

Natural and subnatural surroundings favourable to plant communities of the *limes convergens* are met with along sea coasts and river banks, on flat areas now-and-then inundated, on boundary lines between eutrophic and oligotrophic habitats where rich-in-nutrients dominates over poor-in-nutrients.

Next to these natural and subnatural possibilities, man-made landscapes are pre-eminently suited for the *limes convergens* and its vegetation types, particularly at the present. Modern technical civilization more and more favours the *limes convergens* by making sharp lines of demarcation, monotonous vegetation, barrages, metalled roads, straight canals, and by soil compaction. A number of *limes convergens* biotypes are characteristic and suitable habitats for the snail *Limnaea truncatula*, the specific host of the liver fluke, *Fasciola hepatica*.

Environments of the *limes divergens*, the stable gradient type with its fine-grained pattern and vague delimitations, accommodate quite another set of plants, among which, are for example: *Botrychium lunaria*, *Silene nutans*, *Dianthus superbus*, *D.armeria*, *Pinguicula vulgaris*, *Lathyrus nissolia*, *Trifolium medium*, *Agrimonia eupatoria*, *Origanum vulgare*, *Polygonatum odoratum*, *Carex dioica*, *C.pulicaris*, *C.hostiana*, and most species of orchids. In many examples the total number of individuals belonging to these species, present in a certain area, may be no more than one or two, the circumstances required being limited to almost one single spatial point. The internal stability of the situation ensures the survival of such tiny populations for tens of years.

Typical environments of the natural *limes divergens* may be expected in similar areas where the *limes convergens* is found; but in the former case is nearly always confined to sites where gradual differences in height or great distances between the extremes are available as a requisite for stable types of gradual transition zones. They are found on border areas between salt-marshes and fresh dune valleys; on slopes of dry and rather poor sand dunes never inundated, shading off into wet and clayey soils often inundated; and on boundaries between eutrophic and oligotrophic environments where 'poor-in-nutrients' dominates over 'rich-in-nutrients', the last situation being just opposed to what has been mentioned in the *limes convergens*. Instructive examples of this situation are shown in the lagg-zone of bogs on limestone; in swamps and quaking bogs where oligotrophic water, running down from a higher level, reaches a eutrophic environment; and on the slopes of limestone hills which at their top are covered by poor sandy soils.

The ecological culminating point of the *limes divergens* is found in the gradual transition-in-space between woodland and non-woodland, specifically represented by scrub and tall forb communities.

In contrast with the present, the former agricultural and mining systems automatically led to greater spatial diversity in habitats. This greater diversity was mainly the result of three sets of factors.

1 For centuries the methods did not change. By this stability the variety-in-space steadily increased.

2 Isolation by distance gave a gradually increasing restriction to human influence on the landscape. This restraint was minimal near the dwelling-places in the centre of the action radius and maximal at the outside with all possible degrees of influence between the extremes.

3 Our ancestors moved slowly and on a small scale. By this dispersion-in-time, which has the same effect as dispersion-in-space, the spatial variety increased still more.

Though, in general, the positive correlation between diversity and stability may be obvious, we need a critical examination of its overall applicability. Biological laws tend to be rules with exceptions, and it is the very exception which may throw new light on a problem.

Whittaker (1969) discusses a number of examples of diversity in plant communities. He confirms the previous statements (Margalef 1958, Odum 1963, Daubenmire 1968) about increase of diversity in the course of succession, together with an increase of stability. On the other hand he mentions some temperate grasslands, and even some semi-deserts, presenting a large alpha diversity compared with temperate forests. Environments favouring lower strata may, also in relatively unstable situations, induce a higher alpha diversity than is to be found in forests at similar latitudes, altitudes and soils.

In Whittaker's opinion there is an obvious overall tendency to decreasing diversity of cormophyte communities in unstable or extreme environments, but this tendency is influenced and modified by stratification, life forms and the effect of dominants on the composition and the diversity of the relevant communities. As an example, coniferous forests are poorer in species than deciduous forests in similar climatic and edaphic situations.

An apparent contradiction can be observed in cultivated land on post-glacial cover sands very poor in nutrients, not uncommon in the Dutch pleistocene area. Its potential natural vegetation is the oak-birch-woodland, Querceto-Betuletum. Frequently in such areas small oak coppice woodlands can be observed which consist of a small number (e.g. 10) of species of woody plants, herbs and mosses together, and which, apparently, present no larger diversity or even a smaller one than that of the surrounding arable land and pastures. Nevertheless, in the latter case the degree of stability is much lower. This contradiction may be explained by our using the number of cormophyte species only on a given area as a diversity parameter, whereas, in reality, the diversity is determined by the relatively large number of fungi and animals (soil fauna and terrestrial invertebrates).

Not all contradictions, however, are as easily explained away. Oligotrophic moorland pools undisturbed by man are stable, but they are very poor in species too and seem to present a low diversity (species–area relationship). One might be inclined to say that we should not compare such different ecosystems as a raised bog and, for example, a chalk grassland, but that we should rather consider the result of enlarging versus reducing stability within a given ecosystem (or a complex of ecosystems). However, also in such a case an increase of instability does not necessarily bring about a decrease of diversity. The contrary may seem to the the case if we start from a habitat extremely poor in nutrients. An example can be observed in the nature reserve 'Hatertse Vennen' near Nijmegen. Here all transitions can be observed from undisturbed, extremely oligotrophic habitats to eutrophic (guanotrophic) pools manured by gull colonies (*Larus ridibundus*). The undisturbed, oligotrophic communities are the more stable ones, but at the same time they are very poor in species: they do not consist of more than 10, mostly even not more than 5, species of cormophytes, mainly *Sphagnum cuspidatum, Eriophorum angustifolium, Rhynchospora alba* and *Molinia caerulea*. On the other hand, in the guanotrophic, unstable vegetation the species–area relationship increases, and continues to do so as the rate of disturbance increases. The main invading components are highly productive, fast growing, partly annual nitrate and phosphate indicators (such as *Bidens cernuus, B. tripartitus, Polygonum hydropiper, Typha latifolia, Oenanthe aquatica*), together with a number of more mesotrophic disturbance indicators as *Juncus effusus, Lycopus europaeus, Peucedanum palustre, Hydrocotyle vulgaris* and *Ranunculus flammula*.

The question has to be posed, however, whether it is correct to use the species number on say 10 m² or 100 m² as a diversity parameter. Comparing the diversity on very small plots the opposite result is obvious. In the oligotrophic ecosystem the usual relationship is more than one species to one dm², whereas in the disturbed area we used to observe one species on one dm² only. We are dealing with a difference in pattern granulation and, therefore, in the extent of boundary. In the latter case, the individuals of any given species form larger patches than in the former. The estimate of diversity depends on the scale of observation. The oligotrophic, undisturbed, stable pools present a '*limes divergens*' situation, the guanotrophic ones a '*limes convergens*'. In relation to the low number of species able to thrive at all in a hyperoligotrophic habitat, the latter nevertheless presents a high diversity, providing the diversity parameter is chosen in the right scale.

Problems of reserve management

We will discuss now some ecological problems of reserve management in relation to the successional changes which may or may not occur. These changes have to be studied, firstly with the help of periodical, qualitative, quantitative and structural analyses of vegetation samples on permanent quadrat plots, a type of research already mentioned, and furthermore by periodically repeated floristic and faunistic inventories as well as by vegetation mapping. It has been shown, for example, that when a rather detailed vegetation map on a scale of 1 : 2500 in a calcareous dune area with a complicated vegetation pattern is repeated after about 10 years, the comparison between them gives valuable information on the course of succession. This kind of information allows us to generalize the results of the periodical (by preference yearly) vegetation analyses of sample plots. A similar 10 years' interval is adequate in the succession of reed and sedge swamps.

It appears, then, that four main situations can be observed.

1   There may be no short-term succession at all, though in the course of centuries certain changes may become obvious. This case is much more widespread than was formerly supposed, when, apart from the climax, succession was thought to be a universal and omnipresent phenomenon. This is not so. If we are dealing with a physiographically stable site with a constant balance between primary and secondary production, as between herbs and herbivores, the vegetation pattern also presents a high degree of stability. This is also the case in a large part of the subnatural and semi-natural British and Irish landscape, such as many moorlands, bracken fields and blanket bogs, although they cannot claim to be climax communities.

2   We may have to deal with disturbances coming from outside, mostly from man, and resulting either in changing the present stability into a new and undesirable development, or changing the course of the present succession. The effluent of eutrophic water into an oligotrophic environment and changes in the water table are the most widespread examples.

3   In the semi-natural landscape, disturbances are mostly the result of a sudden change in the management, as by cessation of mowing, grazing, burning or treading. Then a succession sets in which is partly allogenic and partly autogenic; it is a result of an interaction between short-term autogenic effects brought about by the organisms which are part of the ecosystem itself, e.g. humus accumulation and increase of shade, and continuous long-term influences from outside such as the climatically conditioned leaching of the soil. In all cases, such sudden disturbances lead to a severe impoverishment in species which for the most part has not been expected by the owners or managers of the reserve.

4   Finally we may have to deal with dynamic ecosystems which do show a

measurable succession without disturbance as an effective agent. We may discern then cyclic successions, proceeding successions and terminating successions.

Time does not allow discussion of all these eventualities. We will discuss now only the third and the fourth cases, beginning with the semi-natural landscapes.

In semi-natural ecosystems, which constitute by far the major conservation problem, a sudden disturbance brings about a succession which leads to homogenization, levelling down, decrease of differentiation and impoverishment of species. Such a process starts as soon as the former management practice is stopped or changed. This implies that the flora and fauna of semi-natural landscapes can be preserved *only* by continuation of the former agricultural use. Some examples may be given. In litter fen—in German called Riedern und Streuwiesen—human activity consisted in mowing once a year in high summer; in heath it consisted in burning, sheep grazing and sometimes periodical mowing (not every year), and in moist heath by cutting sods. In dry semi-natural downs and pastures (in German called Triften und Halden) rural activity consisted of extensive grazing, alternating with burning. Reed beds are mown in winter and in brackish *Sphagnum* reed swamps, the *Sphagnum* is usually collected. The cutting of coppice is another example of long-established land use.

In the history of nature conservation in the first half of this century, it was usual in such cases to have farmer tenants, who hired the land and worked on it. This had a double advantage: the Society for the Preservation of Nature Reserves got money, and the reserve was well-kept too. The theoretical objections of the scientific non-interventionists have ceased, but the previous solution is more and more difficult to apply, because the modern farmer wants to use up-to-date agricultural methods. These very modern methods, however, destroy the value of the reserve: they consist of artificial manuring, draining, levelling down the surface, and the increasing use of herbicides and insecticides. The owner, that is to say the reserve manager, may forbid the tenant farmer to use such methods, but in an increasing number of cases the farmer then is no longer interested in using that land. The consequence is, that the manager has to manage the land himself with the aid of employed labourers. In Great Britain and in the Netherlands this is done in certain cases but is usually very expensive. Consequently one has to select very carefully which areas are of sufficient importance to be managed in that way and which other areas can be left to develop in their own way. This selection again requires research, especially vegetation mapping.

We next come to certain dynamic biotopes presenting a succession without any intervention or disturbance. In the first place we are dealing with a cyclic or a proceeding succession. These two concepts indicate that all or most biotic communities of such an area are continuously rising and falling; at any one moment all being present, but changing in time at a given place. The classical example of a cyclic succession is the living raised bog. Perhaps a better example is the aeolian rejuvenation in shifting sea dunes behind the coastal range by parabolization of the dune system, as it has been described by Van Dieren (1934) for the Westfrisian island of Terschelling. In the dune subclimax, Violo-Corynephoretum, troughs are blown out by the wind, in which is a cycle of secondary Ammophiletum and a *Carex arenaria* phase, a new Corynephoretum arises. Since the classical work of Watt (1947) on pattern and process of vegetation we know that cyclic processes in succession are much more frequent than was supposed before. For the objectives of nature conservation it is important to analyse and recognize them. Principally such development should be left to itself; management should restrict itself to the elimination of disturbing influences. Practical considerations, however, may require another type of management. If, for example, a closed *Calluna* heath, not showing a tendency to develop to woodland, is left to itself, it may gradually change into a cyclic pattern of ling, grasses, lichens, which does not please the lover of *Calluna* dominance. If, for any reason, preponderance of *Calluna* is the object of management, regular burning every 12–15 years is required.

Examples of a 'proceeding succession' can be observed where new land continually arises out of the sea. Young embryo dunes with *Elytrigia juncea* are succeeded by higher dunes with *Ammophila arenaria*, which may develop into dune shrub, dry grassland or open xerophytic communities; but new embryo dunes arise where the old ones have developed into other systems. On the saltings, the open *Salicornia stricta* community is succeeded by a closed turfy grass mat of Puccinellietum maritimae and this again by the high salt marsh with *Armeria maritima*, *Festuca rubra* and *Juncus gerardii*, which may develop into fresh pastures or into fresh, wet, dune valley vegetation; but at the same time a new Salicornietum occurs. Nature reserves consisting of such ecosystems are self-supporting but for one important point: the absence of large herbivorous mammals. Apart from that, they maintain their dynamic character without any other management than the elimination of disturbance.

The problem of grazing may be illustrated by salt marsh. Nearly all European salt marshes are grazed by cattle or sheep. This might be considered unnatural and the question arises, what would be the result of a succession without grazing. This is *not* the same as experimentally putting an end to grazing and studying the effect: in the latter case, we are introducing a severe disturbance with disastrous results. What we want to know is the successional pattern in saltings which *never* have been grazed by ruminants, but only by rabbits and geese. There are some of these areas in Europe; the major part of the nature reserve Boschplaat on the Westfrisian island of Terschelling,

Netherlands. This reserve has offered an ideal example of studying adjacent grazed and ungrazed ecosystems. The author studied the succession of the Boschplaat during 25 years; since 1966 this reserve is the main Dutch area of research on production ecology within the framework of the International Biological Programme. When the silt content of the soil is high, the grazed salt marsh bears the well-known hemicryptophyte communities of Puccinellietum maritimae and Juncetum gerardii. In the ungrazed ecosystem however the grasses are kept down by other life forms, firstly *Limonium vulgare* and chamaephytes like *Halimione portulacoides*. Only in terminal stages do some grasses achieve dominance, viz. *Festuca rubra* and *Elytrigia pungens*, forming a monotonous turf, very poor in species. When the silt content of the soil is low and the soil sandy, the situation is different, but in this case it is still more obvious that the grazed vegetation presents a larger diversity in species than the ungrazed one. The herbivores are adapted to the grass formation as this formation is adapted to the herbivores.

Since it is impossible to restore the original extensive grazing by elk and aurochs, the best management in such instances is to preserve an adjacent ungrazed area together with an adjacent one grazed by sheep, cattle and horses.

Most subnatural landscapes however do not present a cyclic or a proceeding succession, but a terminating one, since all their communities finally develop into a woodland climax or subclimax. The most important examples are shallow waters ('broads'), swamps and fens. Another example is a stabilized dune system. In such a system the problem of the maintenance of the diversity of biotic communities arises, and is solved only if a rejuvenating factor intervenes. This factor can deflect the succession or may cause retrogression. In the older dune system rabbits produce this result. As regards the swamp and marsh areas it is interesting to compare a western european situation, for example in the Netherlands, with an eastern european one, such as in Poland. Poland has large mesotrophic swamp areas showing a tendency to succession to woodland which is certainly not less than the western one. Nevertheless the diversified mosaic pattern maintains itself in Poland much better than in Holland, and that without any special management to this effect. Examples are the nature reserves Grzedy near Ciszewo and Bialowieza in eastern Poland, where beautiful and large sedge communities of *Carex appropinquata, Carex hudsonii, Carex caespitosa, Carex lasiocarpa, Carex buekii* and others alternate with stands of *Salix rosmarinifolia* and *Betula humilis*. This difference between Poland and the Netherlands is caused by the activities of the elk. In these Polish reserves a production balance between vegetation and herbivorous mammal fauna, chiefly the elk, is obvious. The elk is a characteristic swamp animal. It is regrettable that the ecological niche characterized by the elk is not filled in western Europe. Reintroduction of elk would meet too strong objections. The only comparable influence in Holland is that of the naturalized swan, *Cygnus olor*, but this bird influences only the first succession stages and not the later ones. Consequently, the management of swamp reserves in the Netherlands aims to prevent the monotony of the carr wood as the only resulting climax stage by digging out the peat regularly on carefully selected plots at intervals indicated by succession research.

Guiding Rules for Management

The problems and solutions presented here may be summarized in six basic rules for the management of nature reserves (van Leeuwen, 1966b).

1   The preservation of the botanical richness of a nature reserve is most assured if its treatment follows as near as possible the methods applied formerly, and is later on subject to as little change as possible.

2   If the character and size of a nature reserve are suitable, its internal regulation can be amplified by furthering the development of ecoclines based on the degree of human influence within the area.

3   Our controlling operations have to be done gradually and on a small scale.

4   The external protection of nature reserves situated in landscapes with a coarse-grained pattern has to be based on their form and size. The more concentric the form and the larger the surface, the safer the areas will be from alterations threatening them from the outside.

5   If the extent of a nature reserve is sufficient the controller has to take advantage of the ecolines, which develop along the outskirts, by the interaction of internal and external influences. In this connection it is necessary that oligotrophic conditions predominate over eutrophic ones.

6   If alterations are induced from the outside the internal botanical control has to be directed by delaying the processes evoked by them.

In conclusion, nature presents two major types of environment, stable and unstable. In temperate Europe, man, as such, is not an enemy of nature. He only becomes an enemy in his modern technical aspect of communication and of furthering monotony and uniformity. By doing so, he throws nature out of balance, because he stimulates the unstable ecosystem and destroys the stable. Therefore ecological research for the sake of nature conservation has one main object—to study the role of man in changing the face of the earth. On this basis, nature conservation itself has one main end, to preserve the stability of the ecosystem where such is required, thus maintaining the diversity of biotic communities necessary for the preservation of all organisms living on earth.

References

CASTRI F.DI & COVARRUBIAS R. (1966) *Symposium on ecology of sub-arctic regions.* Unesco, Helsinki (MS 31 pp.).

DAUBENMIRE R. (1968) *Plant Communities.* Harper & Row, New York and London.

GABRIELSON I.N. (1957) Management of nature reserves on the basis of modern scientific knowledge. *Tech. Meet. int. Un. Conserv.Nat. nat. Resour.* 6th, 27–35.

MARGALEF D.R. (1958) Information theory in ecology. *Gen. Syst.* 3, 36–71.

ODUM E.P. (1963) *Ecology.* Holt, Rhinehart & Winston, New York.

ODUM E.P. (1969) Strategy of ecosystem development. *Science, N.Y.* 164, 262–70.

VAN DER MAAREL E. (1966) Dutch studies on coastal sand dune vegetation, especially in the Delta region. *Wentia* 15, 47–82.

VAN DIEREN J.W. (1934) *Organogene Dünenbildung, eine geomorphologische Analyse der westfriesischen Insel Terschelling mit pflanzensoziologischen Methoden.* Dissertation, Amsterdam, Den Haag.

VAN LEEUWEN C.G. (1966a) A relation theoretical approach to pattern and process in vegetation. *Wentia* 15, 25–46.

VAN LEEUWEN C.G. (1966b) Het botanisch beheer van natuurreservaten op structuur-oecologische grondslag (with summary in English). *Gorteria* 3, 16–28.

WESTHOFF V. (1952). The management of nature reserves in densely populated countries considered from a botanical viewpoint. *Int. Tech. Conf. Prot. Nat.* 2nd, 77–82.

WESTHOFF V. (1968) Die ausgeräumte Landschaft. Biologische Verarmung und Berei-cherung der Kulturlandschaften. In *Handbuch für Landschaftspflege und Naturschutz,* ed. Buchwald K. & Engelhardt W. Vol. 2, 1–10. Munich–Vienna.

WESTHOFF V. (1969) Die Reste der Naturlandschaft und ihre Pflege. In *Handbuch für Landschaftspflege und Naturschutz,* ed. Buchwald K. & Engelhardt W., Vol. 3, 251–65. Munich–Vienna.

WESTHOFF V. (1970) New criteria for nature reserves. *New Scient.* 46, 108–13.

WHITTAKER R.H. (1965) Dominance and diversity in land plant communities. *Science, N.Y.* 147, 250–60.

WHITTAKER R.H. (1969) The evolution of diversity in plant communities. *Brookhaven Symp. Biol.* 22, 178–96.

Grazing, fertilizers and pesticides in the management of grasslands*

JOHN L.HARPER *School of Plant Biology,*
University College of North Wales, Bangor

From the time that man ceased to be a nomad and farmed from settled communities, he has managed vegetation to his own ends. This management has become increasingly sophisticated and offers many lessons to the conservationist. In the practices of agriculture, forestry and horticulture, a relatively deep understanding of the ecological requirements of useful and decorative species has been acquired to the end that specific vegetation may be produced at will. The autecological information available for cultivated plants exceeds that of almost all wild species and has been gained with the deliberate intent of increasing the sensitivity with which the species can be managed. Management has usually been by manipulation of edaphic conditions (liming, fertilizer applications and cultivations) together with more or less control of biotic factors (grazing animals, pests, disease organisms and competitors). In agriculture, forestry and commercial horticulture the aim has usually been to create pure stands of a single species, often a single cultivar, and this has proved successful only where alien species (weeds) have been controlled and the forces of vegetational succession deliberately arrested. Although much of the interest at this conference will be directed to maintaining species diversity, and much of agriculture and forestry aims at monoculture, it must be remembered that the weed-free environment remains a pipe dream and even the farmer who cultivates continuous wheat crops does so in a background of many other species which at best are not eliminated but controlled at such a level that the crop succeeds.

Amongst the complicated multi-species communities manipulated by man, grassland systems are probably the best known. Their manipulation has an intriguing history. Through the eighteenth and early nineteenth centuries

*Parts of this paper represent a précis of a more detailed study of the role of predators in vegetational diversity (Harper 1969).

farmer naturalists acquired and published relatively detailed accounts of very many herbage species (for example, Lisle 1713, Anon 1808). Indeed the desirability of particular components in a pasture was argued vigorously and often elegantly as in the 'Ode to Dr. Richardson' a long poem in classical style published in 1845 by a group of farmers (S. T. 1815) poking fun at a Dr Richardson who believed that *Agrostis tenuis* was the ideal pasture grass:
'The bard who thy rare merit sings
Should boast a harp of fiorin strings'.

With the rapid development of an appreciation of the varied qualities of the species present in 'natural' grassland, the idea of deliberately creating ideal swards by sowing mixtures of many desirable components became obvious. The Clifton Park mixture of grass seeds is one of the famous early recommendations. This contained eight species of grass and eight dicotyledonous species. The mixture was sown at high density (40lb/acre) and had the great advantage that it produced something useful to a farmer under a wide variety of conditions. However, it produced differently composed pastures in different areas; even in the same area when sown at different times. Usually many of the species included failed to establish successfully or were suppressed by what proved locally to be more vigorous species in the mixture and were eventually seen to be insurance inclusions to make it a general purpose mixture that seldom failed. From this stage historical development has seen a progressive narrowing of the range of species deliberately sown in mixtures and a search for ecologically compatible species which, sown together, will grow and persist together. It was the work of Martin Jones (1933), referred to in more detail later, which demonstrated how completely the pattern of species composition resulting from sowing a mixture of species could be changed by modification of grazing practice, and the Cockle Park experiments (Gilchrist 1906) on the application of phosphates showed that the species composition of pastures could be profoundly altered by changing the nutrient status, in this case by strongly favouring the development of *Trifolium repens* in a sward.

Images of the ideal balance between species in mixed swards tended to become important amongst farmers and from 1930 to 1960 it often seemed as though the most sophisticated farmers were managing their pastures to produce some idealized botanical composition rather than managing them for the production of livestock or milk! This period was even marked by the holding of county competitions for the best grassland management in which the proportions of *Trifolium repens* to grasses and the relative proportions of *Phleum pratense* to *Festuca pratensis* or of *Phleum pratense* to *Dactylis glomerata* were the qualities that lead to prize winning. Parallel with this concern for maintaining and controlling the balance of species within sown pastures was a concern to change the composition of naturally occurring permanent grasslands towards an agronomically improved but still complex floristic composition. The Park Grass experiments at Rothamsted (Thurston 1969), the classic experiments of Milton (1940, 1947) on upland pastures in Cardiganshire and Martin Jones's experiments at Jeallott's Hill (Jones 1933) demonstrated that both controlled variation in nutrient supply and regulation of the activity of grazing animals could change the composition of grasslands almost at will.

Fashions in grassland agronomy have changed in the period 1950–70 towards the maintenance as far as possible of two species mixtures, one grass with one legume, which brought rather simpler problems of maintaining the balance of species (Davies 1960) and ultimately towards stands of single species so that grassland has become treated more as a monoculture crop and even white clover seen as a weed. The new fashion favours many species managed in single species stands (Woodford 1966) but the great grassland revolution of 1930 to 1950 largely pioneered by Sir George Stapledon represents an outstandingly successful example of the manipulation of vegetational diversity and has involved some of the greatest ecological experiments of all time.

The concept of dominant control

Putwain & Harper (1970) and Harper (1967) have discussed the ways in which the symbolic representation of niche relationships in grassland may be used to clarify problems of species diversity within a community (Fig. 1). In the mixed plant population, the growth and multiplication of individuals lead to shortage of growth requirements. Two species having similar requirements at the same time and in the same state enter into an exclusive struggle for existence in which superiority (or chance) determines a winner. This process leads to the ousting of one species by another. At the same time by virtue of differences in requirements (for example due to differences in phenology, growth form or nutritional needs) species may evade such a direct struggle for existence and 'interniche' or 'annidate' in such a way that they persist together. In Fig. 1a species A and B annidate completely and C and A partially. The extent of such annidative relationships determines the diversity of species in a stable state. The model illustrates the effect of management directed at A on the other components of the flora. Many of the examples of management of grassland systems given in the remainder of this paper represent a variety of ways in which the populations of aggressive exploiters of a habitat are controlled allowing a change in the composition of the community. Thus a basic model can be made accounting for the composition of, for example, a grassland community in which the deliberate suppression of one aggressive species leaves resources unexploited which other previously suppressed or excluded species may themselves now exploit. This model represents floristic interaction in a homogeneous physical environment and is of course made much

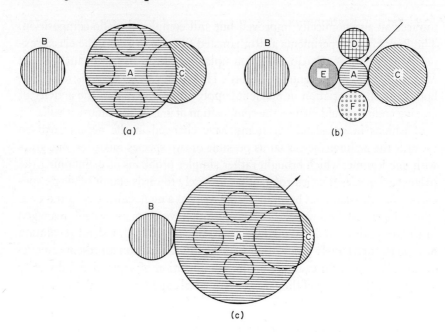

Figure 1. Venn diagram of species relationships in a hypothetical mixed community. Each circle describes in 2-dimensional simplification, the fundamental niche of a species (expressed as its mass, productivity or population size). Continuous lines outline realized niches.

Species B, by virtue of differences in the manner in which its population is regulated, cohabits with A and neither excludes the other. Species C has a partial niche overlap with A, so that in the presence of A it is unable to develop its full population size (or range). Removal or partial suppression of A permits C to increase. D, E and F represent species whose fundamental niche lies wholly within that of the more aggressive A. Their presence depends on the removal or suppression of A. Thus the selective suppression of A, Fig. 1b (e.g. by grazing, fertilizers, herbicides), or its encouragement, Fig. 1c, largely determines the floristic composition of the community.

more complex if a heterogeneous background is present and maintained in the habitat. In this respect the localized distribution of dung, mole-hills, ant hills, hoofmarks, etc., provide small-scale heterogeneity in the habitat which the agriculturist would normally try to avoid but the conservationist may well wish to use as tools in vegetational management.

The management of grassland by mineral nutrition

Amongst the vast literature on the role of nutrient application in determining the composition of grasslands are two classic experiments: the Park Grass experiment at Rothamsted Experimental Station and Milton's experiment on hill land in Cardiganshire.

A. The Park Grass experiments at Rothamsted

In 1856 an experiment was started to determine the effects of regular application of fertilizers on the yield of permanent meadow grasslands. The results of this experiment have been published at intervals since 1880 and most recently by Thurston in 1969 who gives a full bibliography.

The area on which the experiment was performed was on a freely drained silty-clay soil and had been maintained under permanent grassland for several hundred years before the experiment was started. As an experiment it suffers from the defects of its time in being unreplicated and unrandomized. Annual applications were made of nitrogen, phosphorus, potassium, sodium and magnesium, and from 1903 onwards applications of lime were made to half plots. From 1965 an even more intricate design was superimposed to maintain pH values of 4, 5, 6 and 7 on quarter plots of the more acid treatments. Applications of dung or of fish-meal every fourth year were also included in the experiment.

The sward was initially managed by taking a hay cut in June and following this by grazing with sheep. From 1873 a second hay cut has been taken in the autumn and there has been no grazing so that the present composition of the sward is not accounted for by effects of grazing. Marked floristic changes have occurred in the plots and these have largely stabilized (except where new experimental treatments, e.g. liming, have recently been applied). It is particularly striking that each plot has settled down to a unique species composition differing markedly from the control. The control plots contain some 60 species of flowering plants and no new species have invaded any of the fertilized plots as a result of the treatments. The changes in floristic composition associated with treatments are so marked and precise that plot boundaries are sharply defined. Particularly conspicuous species changes have been in, for example, *Taraxacum officinale*, which has become very abundant on plots receiving potassium and having a pH of more than 6.0. The effects of regular applications of ammonium sulphate without lime or other fertilizers are also very pronounced. Marked acidification of the soil has occurred and a species-poor sward has developed largely composed of *Agrostis tenuis*, *Festuca rubra*, and occasionally *Potentilla reptans* and *Rumex acetosa*. In contrast, where no nitrogen has been given, phosphorus, potassium, sodium and magnesium seem to have encouraged members of the Leguminosae. Where nitrogen was applied as sodium nitrate and acidity did not develop, grass development was strongly favoured. The records of the experiment show many other highly interesting floristic changes but the main conclusion that is relevant to the present symposium is that the species composition of a floristically very rich grassland has been sensitively manipulated simply by changes in fertilizer application and liming against a background of otherwise constant management. (I have suggested elsewhere (Harper, 1966) that miniature Park Grass experiments could well form part of a teaching programme for schools and that a small area on the edge of a school football pitch can be used to illustrate the role that soil nutritional factors play in determining the balance of plant communities.)

Management practices that influence the balance of species in vegetation are, of course, also likely to exert selective forces within the species and recent experience of the speed with which natural selection can operate leads one to expect that genetic change will be the norm rather than the exception. Snaydon (1963) has shown that both morphological and physiological differentiation has occurred within *Anthoxanthum odoratum* living in different plots of the Park Grass experiment.

B. *Milton's experiments at Llety-ifan-Hên*

An experiment somewhat similar to Park Grass was started by W.E.J.Milton in 1930 on a hill farm at Llety-ifan-Hên in north Cardiganshire, central Wales, 9–10 miles east of Aberystwyth. He treated native hill pastures with artificial fertilizers and lime and grazed the herbage with sheep, both under a controlled system involving fenced plots and under uncontrolled conditions of free access. At Llety (900 ft) two contrasted areas were chosen, one with a *Festuca/Agrostis* dominated sward and the other a sward of *Molinia caerulea*. Fertilizer applications were made every year, and changes in the botanical composition of the areas were followed until 1946. The communities studied were floristically poor, and the records of these experiments show astonishing changes in their floristic composition associated both with fertilizer treatments and the degree of control of grazing (Fig. 2). One of the most striking observations was that in plots provided with Ca, P, K and N fertilizer the composition of the grassland changed to resemble a low-land pasture with a rich flora. Dominance was changed from the original 1 to 2 grass species to a more mixed grassland community with 12 or more associated dicotyledonous species. These changes, however, were pronounced only when grazing by the sheep was controlled in a graze-rest-graze-rest cycle. Under these circumstances the sheep are forced to graze most of the plant species present, and all the plants are allowed to recover from a somewhat similar degree of defoliation during the period of rest. In contrast, when the same fertilizer treatments were applied to areas to which the population of hill sheep had free access, relatively little change occurred in the composition of the sward. This example of management makes a number of important points. Firstly that the

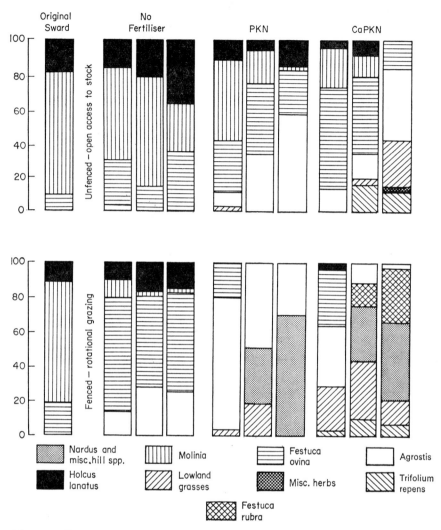

Figure 2. Changes in the botanical composition of an upland fescue sward due to lime and fertilizer applications (redrawn from Jones 1967).

unrestricted access of grazing animals may prevent floristic changes that might otherwise be expected as a result of nutrient addition. Unrestricted access by livestock, in this case sheep, tended to maintain the relative floristic poverty of the sward. It seems clear that this is because new volunteer species which find niches in the community after the change in nutrient status are, for the most part, much more palatable to sheep than the original sward and are avidly searched for and eaten. The fullest floristic diversity was developed in those experimental conditions in which both lime, phosphorus and potassium applications were regularly made and in which grazing was controlled by

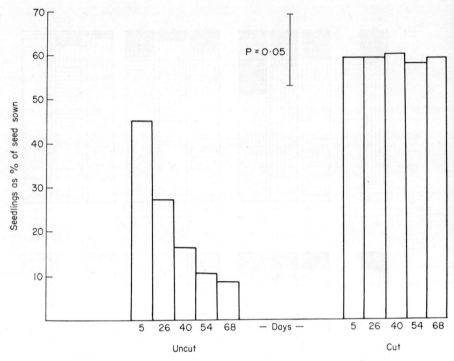

Figure 3. The influence of time of sowing and cutting regime on the establishment of *Bellis perennis* in a sown sward of *Lolium perenne* in 6 in (15 cm) pots in a greenhouse. *B.perennis* sown 5, 26, 40, 54 and 68 days after *L.perenne*. Counts made 96 days after the start of the experiment. Cut swards were defoliated to within $\frac{1}{2}$–1 in of the soil surface at 6–14 day intervals.

   Fiducial limit shown at P=0·05. (From Foster 1964.)

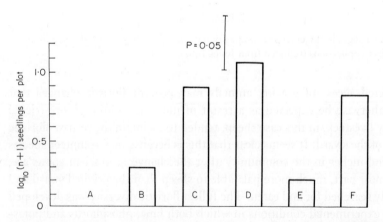

Figure 4. The influence of defoliation of permanent grassland on the establishment of

alternating periods of relatively heavy stocking with periods of rest. Plots which were freed from the influence of the grazing animal and were regularly taken for hay became relatively species-poor. Milton's experiments contrast interestingly with the Park Grass experiments in which defoliation was by mowing machine and the starting point of the management exercise was a species rich community. At Park Grass the various nutritional treatments resulted in changing the balance of the pre-existing species with many extinctions. In Milton's experiments the initial communities of the experimental area were species poor and the effect of nutrient application on controlled grazing was the establishment of a complex of new species. The Park Grass experiment illustrates management for specific locally adapted floras. Milton's experiments represent, at least in part, management for increased floristic diversity.

Management involving the timing of non-selective defoliation

The mowing machine is a non-selective grazer but alterations in the timing of a mowing operation may change the balance of species present in a sward by favouring those which have largely completed their growth cycle at the expense of those which are growing vigorously. A cut made at a critical time (and height) may also favour the establishment of seedlings of species which would not have tolerated the conditions in a tall growing sward. The density of established seedlings of *Bellis perennis* is strongly modified by the type of mowing regime imposed on permanent grassland (Figs. 3 and 4). In an experimental sward established by sowing *Bellis perennis* and *Lolium perenne*, Foster (1964) delayed sowing *Bellis* from 5–68 days after sowing the grass. In half the treatments he cut the sward at 6–14 day intervals to a height of $\frac{1}{2}$–1 in. The remainder of the treatments were allowed to grow freely. Although the establishment of *Bellis* was seriously hindered in the uncut sward, especially if sowing was delayed, frequent defoliation maintained a highly favourable environment for seedling survival. It is well known in agronomic practice that frequent cutting (as for dried grass or ensilage) leads to a floristic composition different from that resulting from one or two cuts per annum, as in hay making.

Bellis perennis from seed. Plot size 18 in (45 cm) square.
A No defoliation.
B One defoliation in early summer.
C Regular defoliation every time the sward reached *c.* 15 cm height.
D As C, but the sward maintained short throughout May.
E Frequent cutting—as D but maintained short throughout the year.
F Vegetation treated with paraquat before seed of *Bellis* was sown.
   Fiducial limit shown at $P = 0.05$. (From Foster 1964.)

The management of grassland composition involving selective defoliation by grazing animals and other predators

Whereas Milton's experiment demonstrated that the role of a grazing animal could determine the magnitude of response of grassland to nutrient application, a series of experiments by Martin Jones (1933) showed that management of the grazing animal alone was sufficient to make major shunts in the composition of a sward. He used both artificial grassland, into which he had deliberately sown mixtures of grasses and legumes, and long-established permanent pastures which had a naturally established flora of some considerable complexity. On to these pasture systems he imposed grazing regimes primarily involving sheep and he varied the time at which the most intense defoliation occurred. He was particularly interested in systems of controlled grazing in which animals were introduced onto the pasture and allowed to remain until it had been grazed to a particular predetermined state and the pasture was then allowed to recover before stock were reintroduced. This rotational grazing was contrasted with a system of continuous and heavy overgrazing and with systems that allowed for either minimal winter grazing or minimal spring grazing. The data are presented in an essentially agronomic form in which the species are often grouped into categories that do not permit precise statements about diversity.

The sort of information obtained is illustrated in Fig. 5 in the form of tiller counts. The type of livestock management had profound influences on

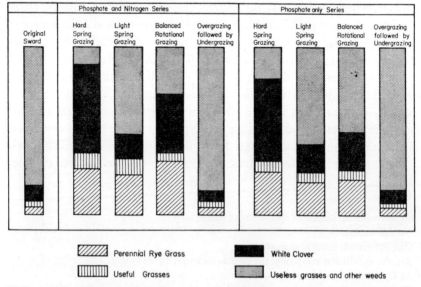

Figure 5. The influence of two years of grazing management on the composition of an old permanent grassland sward fertilized with nitrogen plus phosphate or with phosphate only. (Redrawn from Jones 1933.)

floristic composition and these were achieved rapidly, often being apparent within three months of the start of a particular grazing regime. Hard spring grazing allowed the grassland system to become largely dominated by a single species, *Trifolium repens*. Maximal floristic richness, including some of the sown species and a wide range of natural invaders, occurred when overgrazing in the winter and spring was followed by undergrazing during the peaks of growth in the early summer. This latter treatment is, in a sense, the most natural, reflecting a condition in which the grassland supports a relatively constant population of herbivores which are underfed and therefore overgraze during the periods of low plant productivity, but are unable to cope with the main flush of summer production, which is therefore undergrazed. These experiments make the point very clearly that the action of a predator on the composition of grassland depends in part on the length of the feeding life of the herbivore, relative to the periodicity of the cycle of herbage production. Clearly management of this type calls for sophisticated knowledge of the behaviour of the grazing animal and of the growth cycles and palatabilities of the species co-habiting in the pasture.

Controlled grazing can change the composition of hill grasslands even in the absence of applied fertilizer. Figure 6 shows the results of only 2 years of

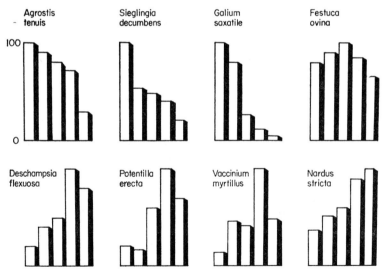

Figure 6. The influence of two years of grazing and mowing treatments on the *relative* numbers of tillers of various species in an *Agrostis*-Fescue upland pasture. (Redrawn from Jones 1967.)

varied grazing regimes applied to an *Agrostis/Festuca* sward at 950 ft in Cardiganshire (Jones 1967).

Many of the changes in grassland that are brought about by grazing management can be explained by the ways in which differences in their growth cycles expose species differentially to damage by grazing at different times (Jones 1930) and by marked contrasts in the palatability of the species (Milton 1933). A pilot attempt to design a computer simulation programme to predict changes in vegetation subject to grazing has recently been made by Goodall (1967). It involves using arbitrary values for the palatability and growth cycles of hypothetical species but is an important signpost to the degree of sophistication that predictive ecology and rational management may be expected to achieve.

Grazing management, like fertilizer application, selects in favour of some species and against others and this applies also to genotypes within the species. The genetic composition of populations of a single species after grazing management reflects that management (Charles 1961, 1964).

Great subtlety in the management of the plant/animal interface is implied in recent demonstrations by Cantlon (1969) that seedlings of *Melampyrum lineare* are consumed in Michigan woodlands by nymphs of a Katydyd (*Atlanticus testaceous*) and that a yearly spring application of 2 lb per acre of the insecticide aldrin plus regular weekly applications in the first two years of a 50:50 mixture of malathion and DDT to the foliage of moderate to high density populations of *Melampyrum* led to spectacular increases in the population of the plant. 'One year after the experiment began spring starting populations of *Melampyrum* were twice as large in the treated plots as in the controls, and after 2 years they were 3 times as large. The 3rd year the 3-fold difference persisted, and the 4th year the seedling populations on the treated plots are clearly more than 3 times as large as in the control plots.' Cantlon's experiments suggest that there may be an opportunity for the management of specific plant species by invoking the chemical control of their predators and a similar approach is also suggested by the experiments of Foster (1964) who attempted to discover ways of increasing the density of *Bellis perennis* within grassland systems. Treatment of the seed of the daisy with the fungicide thiram or the insecticide dieldrin produced no significant changes in seedling establishment, but seeds dressed both with thiram and dieldrin significantly increased the establishment of daisies in the field. Populations were also increased by treating the sward with the molluscicide metaldehyde. Although the application of pesticides to natural vegetation is repugnant to many ecologists, they may yet provide the most powerful and sensitive management tool yet available for specific acts of conservation.

The management of grassland composition by the use of selective herbicides

In grassland communities the species most often becoming dominant are, needless to say, grasses and where grazing pressures have been reduced as, for example, after damage to rabbit populations by myxomatosis (Harper 1969), a floristically rich vegetation often gives way to a sward dominated by a few grass species, for example on chalk grassland *Zerna erecta*, *Brachypodium pinnatum* and/or *Festuca rubra*. These dominant grasses may be selectively killed or partially suppressed by the use of herbicides such as Dalapon (2,2-dichloropropionic acid) or Paraquat (1,1-dimethyl-4, 4-bipyridylium 2A). There has been much argument between agronomists on the relative roles of management by (*a*) herbicides and (*b*) grazing and fertilizer management, as means of changing the composition of grasslands. This argument was pursued by William Davies (1953) and Maxwell Davies (1953) in the First British Weed Control Conference and was raised again by A.H.Charles & G.P.Allen in the 9th British Weed Control Conference of 1968. Charles (1968) showed that *Lolium perenne* could be favoured at the expense of *Poa trivialis* by livestock management (hard and frequent grazing up to the end of June followed by long rest intervals between defoliation in the autumn) or by changed nitrogen status (again favouring *Lolium perenne*). In the same symposium Allen (1968) discussed the ways in which Dalapon may be used selectively to suppress *Agrostis stolonifera*, *Poa trivialis* and *Holcus lanatus* in favour of *Lolium perenne*. Rather than being treated as alternatives, the various techniques of management are probably best employed in conjunction. The combination of controlled grazing, fertilizer application and judicious herbicide usage can produce both quick and lasting changes in the balance of the community. The herbicide gives speed to the process of change and the fertilizer and stock management ensure that the change persists.

Herbicide treatment of grassland may often permit major flushes of growth by dicotyledonous species. Watkin and Winch (1970) have chemically suppressed *Poa pratensis* in Ontario grasslands and found increases in the density of 31 broad leaved species (6 not previously recorded in the area). Experiments which demonstrate the use of herbicides in increasing the presence of specific dicotyledonous species are those of Sagar & Harper (1961) on *Plantago lanceolata* in neutral grasslands (Fig. 7) and of Putwain & Harper (1970) on *Rumex acetosella* and *Rumex acetosa* in hill grazings. Herbicide application reduced grass density and permitted increased vegetative reproduction by *Plantago* (Dalapon) and *Rumex* (Paraquat) and in the case of *Plantago lanceolata* also increased the chances of seedling survival and the reproductive output of the individual plants. The herbicide tolerances and susceptibility of many common grassland species are now well known (Fryer and Evans 1968). Few rare species have been screened; but so great are the selective subtleties of the range of modern herbicides that it is reasonable to expect that they can become useful tools in locally increasing the abundance of rare and valuable species simply by suppressing their most important competitors and aggressors. It is perhaps important that, whereas management by controlling the grazing animal or the nutrient status involves the manipulation of the whole complex of a plant community and may therefore be difficult and require recondite knowledge of the competitive interactions between species, herbicides by virtue of their much greater specificity may often be the more quickly effective.

I have tried to emphasize in this paper that the agronomist has a series of techniques which not only can be, but have been, successfully used in the management of quite complex vegetation. The aims of the agronomist are

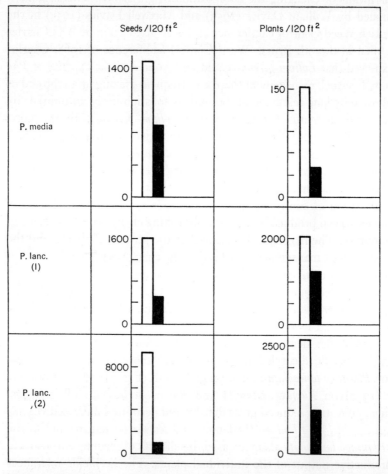

Figure 7. The effects on *Plantago media* and *P. lanceolata* of the controlled herbicidal removal of grasses from mixed communities on permanent grassland. Plots were sprayed with 2:2-dichloropropionic acid on 3 October 1957. Open columns indicate sprayed plots and black columns unsprayed plots. The sites treated in this experiment were at Lockinge, nr. Wantage, Berks, which is a seldom-grazed calcicolous grassland community, and H.F. Riverside, which is an alluvial meadow flooded by the Thames and subject to intense summer grazing. (After Sagar 1960.)

usually different from those of the conservationist, but the principles and techniques available are the same and readily adaptable. The agronomist has provided the evidence that multi-species communities may be manipulated largely at will. The success of this manipulation has depended on deep autecological and synecological knowledge of the vegetation involved and a very clearly defined set of aims. It is difficult to see how the conservationist can achieve comparable success in managing vegetation without aims as firmly defined and as well informed.

In the management of both natural and artificial grasslands the agronomist has had a quite clearly defined aim: to maintain high productivity of livestock. This has been achieved either by bringing together a number of species known separately to have desirable qualities or by deliberately imitating the floristic composition of naturally occurring pastures that are known empirically to have high qualities in livestock production (a good example is the deliberate attempt to mimic the character of Millfield, Medbourne, regarded as probably the most productive permanent pasture in the fattening districts of the midlands (Williams & Davies 1954).

I imagine that the conservationist will usually have at least one of four aims in managing vegetation: (i) management for species diversity, if only because variety is 'a good thing' in itself, (ii) management to imitate or maintain some specific vegetational *status quo*, not necessarily natural (the maintenance of hedgerows is a good example of this ideal), (iii) management to preserve or increase specific desirable species, because they are either rare or beautiful, (iv) management to preserve natural assemblages as a museum of vegetation types. The fourth aim, management for naturalness, is the most difficult because of necessity it is the least well defined, and of course vegetation ceases to be natural as soon as it is managed to that end.

Unfortunately most of the information that ecologists have collected about vegetation which they now wish to conserve is inappropriate as a guide to its management. In particular there is deep ignorance of basic actuarial data for most herbaceous plants and yet it is on life tables that the best predictive theories of the effect of management are likely to depend. The mechanisms by which most wild plant populations are naturally regulated (including the causes of mortality) are almost always obscure, and yet it is by manipulating natural regulation that the most sensitive management is likely to be achieved. As a consequence of our ignorance of the mechanisms controlling natural vegetation, attempts to manage it are bound for some time to be largely empirical. However, if a typical lowland multispecies sward can be created on a bleak siliceous mountain, there seems no reason why the floral complex of Teesdale should not be recreated on the South Downs. When we understand how to achieve such aims ecology will have graduated to a predictive science.

References

ALLEN G.P. (1968) The potential role of selective herbicides in grassland improvement. *Proc. 9th Br. Weed Control Conf.* 1231–7. British Crop Protection Council, London.

ANON (1808) *The Complete Grazier, or The Farmer and Cattle-Dealer's Assistant.* B.Crosby & Co, London.

CANTLON J.E. (1969) The stability of natural populations and their sensitivity to technology. In *Diversity and stability in ecological systems,* ed. Woodwell G.M. & Smith H. H. *Brookhaven Symp. Biol.* 22, 197–203.

CHARLES A.H. (1961) Differential survival of grass cultivars of *Lolium, Dactylis* and *Phleum. J. Br. Grassld Soc.* 16, 69–75.

CHARLES A.H. (1964) Differential survival of plant types in swards. *J. Br. Grassld Soc.* 19, 198–204.

CHARLES A.H. (1968) Control of weed grasses by the selective effects of fertilizer application and management. *Proc. 9th Br. Weed Control Conf.* 1223–30. British Crop Protection Council, London.

DAVIES M. (1953) The place of herbicides in grassland management. *Proc. 1st Br. Weed Control Conf.* 158–65. British Crop Protection Council, London.

DAVIES W. (1953) Good husbandry and the control of grassland weeds. *Proc. 1st Br. Weed Control Conf.* 155–7. British Crop Protection Council, London.

DAVIES W. (1960) *The Grass Crop,* 2nd edn. Spon, London.

FOSTER J. (1964) *Studies on the population dynamics of the daisy,* Bellis perennis *L.* Ph.D. thesis, University of Wales.

FRYER J.D. & EVANS S.A. (1968) *Weed Control Handbook,* 5th edn. Blackwell Scientific Publications, Oxford.

GILCHRIST D.A. (1906) Manures for pastures. *Bull. Northumb. Co. agric. Exp. Stn.* 8.

GOODALL D.W. (1967) Computer simulation of changes in vegetation subject to grazing. *J. Indian bot. Soc.* 46, 356–62.

HARPER, JOHN L. (1966) The teaching of experimental plant ecology. In *The Teaching of Ecology,* ed. Lambert J.M. *Symp. Brit. Ecol. Soc.* 7, 135–45. Blackwell Scientific Publications, Oxford.

HARPER, JOHN L. (1967) The regulation of numbers and mass in plant populations. In *Population Biology and Evolution,* ed. Lewontin R.C. University Press, Syracuse.

HARPER, JOHN L. (1969) The role of predation in vegetational diversity. *In Diversity and Stability in Ecological Systems* ed. Woodwell G.M. & Smith H.H. *Brookhaven Symp. Biol.* 22, 48–61.

JONES Ll.I. (1967). Studies on hill land in Wales. *Tech. Bull. Welsh Plant Breed. Sta.* 2, 1–179.

JONES M.G. (1930) The effect of varying the periods of rest in rotational grazing. *Bull. Welsh Pl. Breed. Sta.* Series *H,* 11.

JONES M.G. (1933) Grassland management and its influence on the sward. *Emp. J. exp. Agric.* 1, 43–57, 122–8, 223–34, 360–6, 366–7.

LISLE E. (1713) *Observations in Husbandry.* G.Faulkner, London.

MILTON W.E.J. (1934) The relative palatability of seed-mixtures, and a study of the influence of fertilizers on natural hill pastures. *Emp. J. exp. Agric.* 2, 51–64.

MILTON W.E.J. (1940) The effect of manuring, grazing and liming on the yield, botanical and chemical composition of natural hill pastures. *J. Ecol.* 28, 326–56.

MILTON W.E.J. (1947) The composition of natural hill pasture, under controlled and free grazing cutting and manuring. *Welsh J. Agric.* 14, 182–95.

PUTWAIN P.D. & HARPER J.L. (1970) Studies on the dynamics of plant populations. III. The influence of associated species on populations of *Rumex acetosa* L. and *R. acetosella* in grassland. *J. Ecol.* **58**, 251–64.

S.T. (1815) Ode to Dr Richardson. *The Agricultural Magazine*, **5** (N.S.), 171–8.

SAGAR G.R. (1959) *The biology of some sympatric species of grassland*. D.Phil. Thesis, University of Oxford.

SAGAR G. R. & HARPER J. L. (1961) Controlled interference with natural populations of *Plantago lanceolata*, *P. major* and *P. media*. *Weed Res.* **1**, 163–76.

SNAYDON R.W. (1963) Morphological and physiological population differentiation of *Anthoxanthum odoratum* on the Park Grass Experiment, Rothamsted. *Heredity*, **18**, 382.

THURSTON J.M. (1969) The effect of liming and fertilizers on the botanical composition of permanent grassland, and on the yield of hay. In *Ecological Aspects of the Mineral Nutrition of Plants*, ed. Rorison I.H. *Symp. Brit. Ecol. Soc.* **9**, 3–10. Blackwell Scientific Publications, Oxford.

WATKIN E.M. & WINCH J.E. (1970) Assessment and improvement of roughland pasture in Ontario. *Ontario ARDA Project 25021 & 6011*.

WILLIAMS T.E. & DAVIES W. (1954) Cattle fattening in permanent grass and leys. *J.R. agric. Soc.* **115**, 98–111.

WOODFORD E.K. (1966). The need for a fresh approach to the nature and purpose of a ley. *J. Br. Grassld Soc.* **21**, 109–15.

Techniques for long-term diagnosis and prediction in forest communities

H.C.DAWKINS *Department of Forestry, Oxford University*

Introduction

The purpose of this paper is to review some of the methods which foresters are finding useful for the long-term quantitative observation of large areas of woodland. To anyone concerned with management, forest or otherwise, one of the greatest lacunae in the wider conservation field is information on how the community has changed and particularly its rate of change in the present—from which some diagnosis of past events and prediction of trends is possible.

This kind of information has long been sought with some success (Johnston & Bradley 1964) in plantations, partly because of the relative simplicity of dealing with large, unitary and stationary life forms but mostly because of its clear material and financial importance. However in the past three decades we have begun to tackle quite large areas of polyspecific unevenaged forest with low fraction sampling, as opposed to the extremely tedious 'total enumerations' employed in the classical and intensive systems of Europe (Schlich 1895).

The concept of continuous inventory

The newer techniques are known as 'recurrent' or 'continuous forest inventory' (CFI). The term clearly conveys a detailed list of contents, continuously updated and maintained in a form designed to be easy of reference. Its objects include:

1 estimation of present population, allowing for the fact that it will have changed since the last assessment,

2 detection of trends and prediction of future population for the planning of control or remedial operations,

3 provision of a continuous record of changes in performance to assist diagnosis of causes.

The data collected include distribution, dimensions, recruitment, performance, health and mortality of each species, but other parameters could of course be observed for other life-forms.

Early systems of forest inventory took no account of individuals but listed every tree in the wood (or sample-plot) by diameter (and/or height) classes, to give a 'stand-table', i.e. a size-class frequency distribution.

Similar records at regular intervals permit calculation of growth (Meyer 1953)—but only under certain stringent conditions:

1   size-classes must be arranged so that no individual can move up more than one class between measurements, and

2   all losses and recruits during the interval must be known by size classes.

If either condition is violated then calculation of growth is either impossible or misleading. At the extreme, two successive and identical stand-tables may indicate anything from total stagnation to rapid growth with heavy mortality and recruitment. There is one obvious way to get over this difficulty: all individuals must be individually identified from one measurement to the next, allowing precise measures of growth, recruitment and mortality and a study of their relation to age, microsite, pathology, etc., which is essential for accuracy of prediction. Nothing new in this—but it was not considered practicable over large areas until modern statistical data handling methods showed that low fraction sampling gives sufficiently accurate estimates for most of the purposes of management (Hasel 1938).

Design of recurrent sampling

In any system of sampling, the first problem is how to design and distribute the sample units. The earliest extensive forest sampling systems were for static information only, not intended to be repeated, and were conducted along systematically spaced transects. Later and with more critical work demanding less labour and unbiassed sampling errors, distribution became stratified random and much work was done comparing continuous or interrupted transects with scattered plots. Not surprisingly and within a wide range of practicable plot sizes it was found that a given sampling error required a larger sampling fraction from a system of transects than from a scatter of plots. But because a greater area of transect can be covered for a given cost the ratio of observation-time within plots to access-time between them was obviously critical. In recurrent sampling, particularly in polyspecific or uneven-aged forest (still more so in general conservation areas where more than trees must be recorded), the labour ratio within-plot/ between-plot is much greater than in once-only stocktaking, so that scattered plots are likely to be more economical than transects for quantitative long-term studies.

Present-day recurrent inventory systems in managed forest use many plot sizes, from the zero-area point-samples of the Bitterlich (Bitterlich 1947 et seq.) system through demarcated plots of 0·01 to 1·0 hectares, circular, square or oblong (Shain & Rudolph 1965). In general, larger usually rectangular plots are used in more irregular forest, smaller and often circular plots (or point-samples) in even-aged plantations. Distributions vary from systematic to random with the customary wrangles over which system to employ; this however is a minor problem compared with that of keeping the initial sample 'representative'. The paradox is this: a permanent plot recurrently observed is likely to become atypical due to physical interference by the observers—yet only by such recurrence on the same entities and ground can the required predictive observations be obtained. In forestry and conservation practice there is the further danger that silvicultural workers may, when recognizing a plot, act with special assiduity or timid avoidance or even downright sabotage.

Another difficulty in permanent low-fraction inventory is that the sample, because it is unbiased—random or systematic—may by chance be a poor one, failing to contain certain important communities or having an unexpectedly high variance. Fortunately both this and the representation paradox may be mitigated if not overcome by the technique of 'sampling-with-partial-replacement' (SPR). This takes advantage of the fact (at least in dealing with perennials) that temporary once-only sampling is cheap but recurrent is expensive, and that correlation between successive resamplings of identified plots is high while between successive independent samples is apt to be low (Ware & Cunia 1962). It is therefore possible to use comparatively few re-measured plots to connect, by regression, two or more otherwise unconnected occasions of more numerous temporary plots. Carrying on through second, third, fourth and further re-assessments (Cunia & Chevrou 1969) the system must gradually creep over the whole area, steadily reducing sampling errors by increasing the sampling fraction and degrees of freedom.

We are still left with the problem of initial distribution. The argument systematic versus stratified-random used to be simple (Finney 1948):

systematic samples risk coincidence with periodic variation in the field and overestimate sampling error, but if no such coincidence occurs tend to produce means closer to the true mean than do random samples, and are more useful for cartographic interpolation;

stratified random samples, if well designed, produce the lowest sampling errors of all and without bias, and are therefore more reliable and can be reduced to lower intensities for a given precision—with saving in cost.

However in present circumstances, namely vegetation under management, permanent stratified random sampling may develop defects in the long term because of changes in the criteria of stratification. Management needs are likely to arise which cut across or modify past vegetation or site groupings, thus leading to inefficient distribution of the initial system of plots. Apart from unrestricted randomization which is not efficient over large areas, only a systematic layout can be unaffected by changes in management and pattern of variation over long periods. Since both its risks—periodic variation and inflated sampling error—may be neutralized by subsequent recurrent and randomized SPR and because of its cartographic efficiency in new conservation areas, it is reasonable that a long-term system of vegetation inventory should indeed start with a systematic layout and continue with stratified random SPR.

Not all the inventory needs of vegetation management can be met by objective SPR. It is also necessary to record rare or especially interesting sites or communities, which must by definition be sought in special, subjectively selected plots. It should be obvious that unless an objective, representative sample also exists, it will be impossible to assess the status of the special sites—their frequency, stability, potential spread or degree of hazard. It has been our fortunate experience in tropical forests that supposedly rare species or communities crop up surprisingly frequently in any extensive but highly dispersed, low-fraction system of sampling.

There is plenty of published information on successful systems of woodland inventory (Spurr 1952), with and without SPR, mostly from relatively simple communities or at least taking account only of a simple component— the larger trees. Extensive work with many more species but less publicity also exists in tropical rain-forest (Loetsch & Haller 1964) notably Borneo (Fox 1967), Malaya (Cousens 1957), Ghana, Uganda (Dawkins 1958). From this emerge some useful experiences and principles of value to conservation inventory generally.

Perhaps the most important is that of continuity—sometimes known cryptically in forest research as the 'bus' factor. The originator of any long-term work, however brilliant or enthusiastic, is nevertheless a potential victim or one-way passenger under or in the proverbial bus, in short he must some time go out of the system with or without adequate notice. His work is futile unless his plots and the plants within them are individually re-locatable by his successors. To ensure this requires subtlety. Too flamboyant monumentation (a New World term) of plots or plants will draw attention to them and hasten their atypical treatment, but obscurity can also be overdone. The rule must be: difficult to recognize for those who do not know where it is, easy to find for those who do and are looking for it. This can be achieved by inconspicuous but permanent marks in the ground—sunken cement or metallic posts for instance—coupled with precise co-ordinates and directions on the maps and charts showing positions of individuals within each plot.

An experience which surprised most of us was the adequacy of information from low sampling fractions, even of very complex communities over large areas. In fact the sampling fraction is a parameter of little account, what matters is the number of independent sampling units—plots in this case—available. Thus 50 one-hectare plots on a stratified random design will give almost as good estimates of a widespread species from 20,000 hectares of forest as from 5,000, provided the stratification is as carefully done.

Application of the Poisson distribution

It is axiomatic that without some knowledge of variation, preferably from exploratory sampling, it is impossible to predict what sampling errors may be expected and therefore how many samples will be required in any new situation.

In forest sampling we already have 'some knowledge' of a general nature allowing at least an intelligent guess. First we find the greater frequency leads to lower sampling errors or requires fewer samples for the same error —it is therefore the lower frequencies which are critical and their sampling can at least be planned, if not calculated, on the Poisson hypothesis. Secondly we find that sampling errors on areas (basal, crown, leaf, etc.) and volumes are similar to or less than those on frequency.

For the first, a randomly distributed population, especially if sparse or sampled by small plots, random or systematic, is likely to observe the following relation:

$$E = \frac{100\,t\,\sqrt{\bar{y}(1-f)/n}}{\bar{y}} \tag{1}$$

where E = sampling error per cent
$\quad n$ = number of sampling units
$\quad \bar{y}$ = means occurrence per sampling unit (i.e. frequency)
$\quad t$ = student's t
$\quad f$ = sampling fraction

The relation is due to the variance of Poisson-distributed observations being equal to their mean frequency.

If sampling is at less than 10 per cent the expression approximates closely to:

$$\left.\begin{aligned} E &= 100t/\sqrt{(n\bar{y})} \\ \text{or } \log E &= \mathrm{Log}\,(100t/\sqrt{n}) - 0.5\log\bar{y} \end{aligned}\right\} \tag{2}$$

And if we are content with 95 per cent confidence limits and have more than twenty sample units it simplifies further to:

$$E = 200/\sqrt{n\bar{y}} \tag{3}$$

Equation (2) is conveniently expressed as a nomogram (Fig. 1) from which not only the number but the size of sampling units may be planned for any critical frequency, using the following arguments.

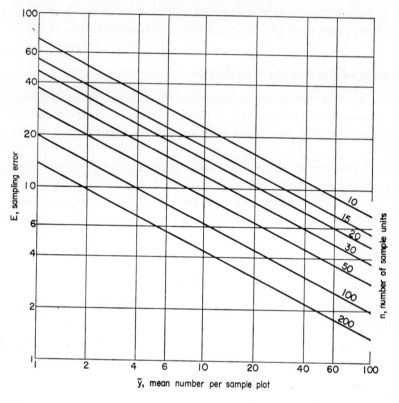

Figure 1. Nomogram for a randomly distributed population sampled at less than 10% by random or systematically distributed sample units. E, sampling error %; t, student's t (taken on the nomogram at 95% probability); n, the number of sampling units; $\bar{y}$, the mean frequency of individuals per sample unit.

Because: the Poisson estimation (PE) is valid only for a randomly distributed population sampled by random or systematic plots,

and: occurrence of species is unlikely to be random because of site and seral preferences,

Therefore:

1   stratified random sampling designed with knowledge of site and seral variation should give lower than PE sampling errors,

2   unstratified or systematic sampling should give higher than PE sampling errors,

3 purely geographical stratification, the most convenient and commonest situation, is likely to give higher than PE sampling errors but could, if chancing to coincide with site variation, give similar or even lower errors.

The Poisson distribution may therefore be used to suggest an upper or lower limit to the intensity of sampling required, whether the distribution exists or not, according to which of the three sampling strategies are employed. Note that these arguments justify the layout of the initial series of permanent plots of a recurrent inventory system on a systematic grid, since their expected higher-than-PE sampling errors will be corrected by the subsequent stratified random SPR. The latter can be made very efficient because the initial sample will have collected the information necessary for effective, site-based stratification.

I can produce no extensive inventories from British woodlands, recurrent or otherwise, to support these suggestions. However we have worked at Oxford on a score of rainforest inventories from a dozen tropical countries, all of which exhibit a straight-line Log E on Log $\bar{y}$ relation, but with exponents varying around -0.45 rather than -0.5 (equation (2)) and with constants almost all greater than $100t/\sqrt{n}$. The latter was to be expected (though perhaps not to the degree that we found) on arguments (2) and (3) because all our work has been with geographical stratification or unrestricted randomization. The greater exponent is harder to explain; it could be due to increasing divergence from the Poisson distribution at the higher frequencies, where perhaps the Normal is a better approximation. Data are very rarely sufficient or so nicely distributed as to make tests of fit worth while. The consequence in any case is that PE sampling errors underestimate the empirical ones more in the greater frequencies than in the lesser, and more when samples are large or few than when many and small. Indeed at the one-per-plot frequency level the PE sampling errors from small-plot systems are usually close to the observed, at 10-per-plot they may be only 50 per cent of the observed, and at 100-per-plot sometimes even lower. Fortunately it is the lower frequencies with high sampling errors which are critical in the planning stage. A few examples are given in Table 1; they have been selected to show the extreme range from small to large plots and under- to overestimation (by the Poisson hypothesis) of sampling error. We are left in little doubt that 100 small-plot samples will rarely find sampling errors over 20 per cent on frequencies of tree populations averaging one or more individuals per plot, and better may be expected with careful stratification.

The nature of predictive information

So far we have discussed sampling only because it is the most critical part of long-term inventory in woodland. The samples will eventually produce

Table 1. Comparison of observed sampling errors with the Poisson prediction. From inventories carried out by numerous field workers, the data processed and statistics calculated at Oxford.

Mean frequency per sample unit		1		3		10		30		100	
E% Predicted: / Empirical:		P	E	P	E	P	E	P	E	P	E

Sample units

No.	Size :ha.	1 P	1 E	3 P	3 E	10 P	10 E	30 P	30 E	100 P	100 E
Malaya 66	8	·		·		7·8		4·5		2·5	
			·		·		11		7·4		4·6
Ghana 60	0·8	26		15		8·1		·		·	
			18		12		7·1		·		·
Sabah 32	0·8	·		21		12		6·6		·	
			·		39		25		17		·
Solomons 30	2	·		22		12		6·9		·	
			·		19		13		8·4		·
St Lucia 26	3	·		24		13		7·4		4·1	
			·		44		28		18		11
B. Honduras 24	16	·		·		14		7·7		4·5	
			·		·		36		22		13
B.Honduras 24	8	·		·		14		7·7		4·5	
			·		·		55		37		24
Malaya 12	8	·		·		20		12		6·4	
			·		·		30		19		12
Uganda 10	1·0	·		40		22		13		·	
			·		59		32		18		·

statistics of recruitment and mortality as well as growth curves for obvious dimensions such as height and crown spread. The former, being prone to wide variations in time are principally of diagnostic value, by correlation with preceding events. Incidentally it has frequently to be brought to the notice of ecologists that correlation is not causation; diagnoses must be followed by experiment or verified prediction if causal inferences are required. Growth curves although diagnostic are of great predictive value, so much so that the typical patterns for European trees form the main basis of practical forecasting of both crop behaviour and the need for silvicultural treatment. Here it is the discrepancy between expected (i.e. tabulated and published) and actual growth which alerts the manager to some factor or condition which must be investigated. In less well-known forests the lifelong growth curves may be predicted (though with more pitfalls than was at first realized) from data collected over perhaps only a tenth of the lifespan, by an evolution of methods well described by Osmaston (1956). Most rainforest management is based on such predictions, though all too often some of the safeguards have been overlooked (Keay 1961).

Of recent years several useful but not-so-recent hypotheses have come near to verification, for the prediction of structure, density and woody production of forest communities. It seems, however, that these techniques have rarely escaped from forest literature. For instance it now appears that the alleged exponential fall-off of stem density with size in stable communities (de Lioucourt 1898) may be better explained by a hyperbolic equation. It is certainly so in some African rainforests (Pierlot 1966) and is one of the consequences of Reineke's (1933 et seq.) widely substantiated logarithmic stand-density equation:

$$\text{Log } N = k - b \log d \tag{4}$$

where $N =$ frequency, individuals (of diameter d) per unit area;

$\quad d =$ their mean diameter, in practice diameter-class;

$\quad b =$ coefficient, of diminution of N;

$\quad k =$ a constant, namely the log of frequency when $d = 1$.

Reineke found and numerous later workers have confirmed that the relation is almost unaffected by age or site, and in even-aged woods arising artificially or naturally from windblows, burns or clearing the exponent generally lies between -1.6 and -1.7, varying little even between species. Uneven-aged relatively stable so-called 'natural' communities show exponents near to -2, the value at which all diameter-classes are of equal basal-area and at which spacing between trees remains proportional to their diameter.

Given some knowledge of growth curves, Reineke's hypothesis allows a reasonable prediction of stem density for as far ahead as the growth curves are themselves predictable.

Another useful phenomenon is the markedly linear relation between crown and bole diameters in trees (Duchaufour 1903). This relation is all but inflexible in light-demanders, varying little with site or age, and is distinct though less rigid in shade-bearers (Dawkins 1963). Crown area being therefore clearly related to basal-area (bole section), it is possible to predict an upper limit to stem density for any size—and perhaps age—of community or stratum of light-demanders. With shade-bearers, the crown/bole-diameter relation yields a useful index of competitive pressure, first described by Krajicek *et al.* (1961) but often used later. This expresses the area of crown which a community would be expected to have if all its individuals were growing free, as a percentage of the ground area actually occupied. Obviously an obligate light-demander such as *Terminalia superba* cannot exceed (nor in practice reach) 100 per cent, whereas a shade-bearer such as *Pseudotsuga* may exceed 200 per cent, the observed value forming a clear index of community pressure.

Proceeding from stem or basal-area density to volume and therefore weight, it has rarely been appreciated by ecologists how predictable tree and forest volume and volume production can be, with the minimum of fuss (Dawkins 1961). Tree total volume is a surprisingly precise linear function of basal-area times height and both have several well-known constraints. Thus height growth of the dominants of a community is closely related to fertility or at least productivity of the site, and may be used to predict yield well before the peak of growth. This is the basis of Eichhorn's hypothesis and much of the European forest yield prediction system. The other dimension, total community basal-area, also has an upper level for any particular assemblage of species controlled by site. This observation finds expression in Assmann's (1961) hypothesis and is a well-known feature of forest inventory (Johnston & Bradley 1963).

It is impossible to describe here all the methods available for 'stand-prediction' of the tree element of woodland communities; they are available in numerous standard texts and among the quoted references. It is, however, quite clear that the vegetation manager cannot do without them if he is to anticipate changes over large areas of polyspecific communities, in which trees are the dominants and the principal anchors of the food-chain.

The writer is at present attempting to introduce such an inventory and predictive system to a woodland conservation area in Britain—the Warburg Reserve—owned by BBONT (Berks., Bucks. and Oxon Naturalists' Trust). Having an area of only 100 hectares, the sampling fraction will need to be greater than in many very much larger tropical reserves but at least the botanical problems will be simpler. The initial sample, of 100 systematically distributed 1–are (0.01 ha) plots is not expected to show sampling errors below 20 per cent on species less frequent than 100 per hectare (Fig. 1). The initial sample is, however, only the first—if SPR becomes accepted in conservation forestry as well as in the commercial.

Summary

The efficient management of vegetation requires quantitative prediction of trends, particularly when valuable communities or species are under threat. Prediction depends on hypotheses based on past behaviour and, in woodland at least, this may be recorded over very large areas by the well-tried technique of recurrent or continuous inventory, using low-fraction sampling-with-partial-replacement. By this method, a series of systematic and randomized permanent and temporary plots linked by regression gradually creeps over the whole area, all measurements being made on permanently locatable individuals. It is shown how the Poisson distribution may help to plan such samples even when neither the population nor sample is randomly distributed. Useful predictive hypotheses include the properties of height- and diameter-growth curves, hyperbolic diminution of frequency with size, the concept of limiting basal-area and its relation to production, the linear relation of crown to bole-diameter and the consequent measure of competitive pressure. A recurrent inventory system is being started in a woodland nature reserve owned by a County Naturalists' Trust.

References

ASSMANN E. (1961) *Waldertragskunde*. BLV Verlagsgesellschaft München.

BITTERLICH W. (1947) Die Winkelzahlmessung. *Allg. forst- u. holtzw. Ztg* 58, 94–6.

COUSENS J.E. (1957) The sampling of regenerated forest in Malaya. Paper for Brit. Comm. For. Conf. 1957. Pp. 22.

CUNIA T. & CHEVROU R.B. (1969) Sampling with partial replacement on three or more occasions. *Forest Sci.* 15, 204–24.

DAWKINS H.C. (1958) *The management of natural tropical high forest with special reference to Uganda*. Institute Paper 34, Comm. For. Inst. Oxford, Pp. 155.

DAWKINS H.C. (1961) Estimating total volume of some Caribbean trees. *Caribbean Forester*, 22, 62–3.

DAWKINS H.C. (1963) Crown diameters, their relation to bole diameter in Tropical forest trees. *Comm. For. Rev.* 42, 318–33.

LIOUCOURT F. de (1898) L'aménagement des sapinières. *Bull. Soc. for. Franche-Comté*, 8, 396–409.

DUCHAUFOUR A. (1903) L'aménagement de la forêt de Compiegne. *Revue. Eaux Forêts* 42, 65–78.

FINNEY D.J. (1948) Random and systematic sampling in timber surveys. *Forestry* 22, 64–9.

FOX J.E.D. (1967) An enumeration of lowland dipterocarp forest in Sabah. *Malay. Forester* 30, 263–79.

HASEL A.A. (1938) Sampling error in timber surveys. *J. agric. Res.* 57, 713–36.

JOHNSTON D.R. & BRADLEY R.T. (1963) Forest management tables. *Comm. For. Rev.* 42, 217–27.

JOHNSTON D.R. & BRADLEY R.T. (1964) Developments in yield control and inventory in British forestry. *Forestry* 37, 21–30.

KEAY R.W.J. (1961) Increment in the Okomu forest reserve, Benin. *Niger. For. Inform. Bull.* (n.s.) 11, pp. 34.

KRAJICEK J.E., BRINKMAN K.A. & GINGRICH S.F. (1961) Crown competition, a measure of density. *Forest Sci.* 7, 35–42.

LOETSCH F. & HALLER K.E. (1964). *Forest Inventory* Vol. I Statistics of forest inventory and information from aerial photographs. BLV Verlagsgesellschaft, München.

MEYER H.A. (1953) *Forest Mensuration*. Penns Valley Publishers, pp. 357.

OSMASTON H.A. (1956) Determination of age girth and similar relationships in tropical forestry. *Emp. For. Rev.* 35, 193–7.

PIERLOT R. (1966). Structure et composition des forêts denses d'Afrique Centrale spécialement celles du Kivu. *Acad. r. des Sci. d'Outre-mer NS.* 16–4, Bruxelles.

REINEKE L.H. (1933) Perfecting a stand-density index for even-aged forests. *J. agric. Res.* 46, 627–38.

SCHLICH W. (1895) *A Manual of Forestry* Volume 3, Forest Management. Bradbury and Agnew, London, pp. 397.

SHAIN W.A. & RUDOLPH V.J. (1965) Continuous forest inventory in American forest management. *Q. Bull. Mich. St. Univ. agric. Exp. Stn* No. 47, 387–429.

SPURR S.H. (1952) *Forest Inventory.* Ronald Press, New York, pp. 476.

WARE K.D. & CUNIA T. (1962) Continuous Forest Inventory with partial replacement of samples. *Forest Sci. Monogr.* 3.

Plant species diversity in relation to management

E.VAN DER MAAREL *Botanical Laboratory,*
University of Nijmegen, Netherlands

Introduction

The material in this contribution is derived from a study on some Dutch nature reserves of the diversity of plant species in relation to management. The vegetation types, of which the diversity will be described, include a machair-type dune grassland complex, a desalinated dune slack under rabbit grazing; and a limestone heath and a Molinietum-type grassland, which are both mown annually.

These communities all belong to the semi-natural landscape in which the flora and fauna are to a large extent native and spontaneous, but in which community structure has been changed by human influence (Westhoff 1970). In this type of landscape man and domestic animals keep the vegetation in a kind of semi-steady state. The plant communities here may be very rich in species, but the balance is subtle and slight changes from outside the community may rapidly reduce the diversity. Diversity values may reach levels that are known only from tree strata of tropical forests (Poore 1964). For example, in the dune grassland complex, situated in the inner dunes of Voorne, 220 species of vascular plants are found in an area of 1 ha (van der Maarel 1966*a*, *b*). Similar figures can be obtained in limestone areas containing a mosaic of grassland, scrub and woodland. In only 2,000 m² within the Voorne grassland over 130 species have been recorded. Records on smaller areas from my own observations are: 90 species on 200 m² of mature dune scrub, 70 species on 10 m² of an open dwarf scrub community in a dune hollow, both in the Voorne dunes, 40 species on 2 m² in dune slack and dune grassland types and 30 species on only 625 cm² in a dune slack on Schiermonnikoog (Thalen 1969).

It is not clear to what extent general statements on the origin and evolution of diversity in community succession (Odum 1969, Whittaker 1969) are

45

applicable to these semi-natural types, or to put it more simply to what extent general succession theories (e.g. Dansereau 1957) are erroneously based on observations or speculations on semi-natural communities. It is perfectly clear, however, that management is very much involved in the dynamic structure of these types. It may be said that in the first place the main objective of management in semi-natural landscapes should be the strict maintenance of the traditional pattern of human influence. Direct experiments to prove this and other statements on diversity are rather scarce in our country, but there is circumstantial evidence from which conclusions can be drawn. Still the main theme of this contribution will be the background of diversity and the ways in which it can be maintained or enlarged.

This will lead to some general remarks on evaluation and planning of nature reserves, which are relevant to Part 7 of this symposium, management policy. These remarks are concerned with recent developments in the Netherlands which I would like to mention here and which bring me to a slightly more general title than was originally proposed.

Plant species diversity in relation to environmental gradients in some Dutch nature reserves

The first example is the dune grassland complex, mentioned earlier. It forms part of the coastal dune system known as the Voorne dunes, one of the most interesting dune systems of north-west Europe (Adriani & van der Maarel 1968), lying west of Rotterdam and being threatened by harbour and industry developments. The dune grassland forms a zone at the inner side of a rather markedly zoned dune system with gradients of carbonate content, humus content, soil moisture and airborne salt (van der Maarel & Westhoff 1964, van der Maarel 1966a, Sloet & Heeres 1969).

In 1963 a detailed study of a very variable part of this dune grassland was performed (van der Maarel 1966b). The investigated area measures 2,000 m² and was characterized by two small dunes separated by a flat dune hollow, through which a footpath ran. The dune tops bore an open vegetation with *Corynephorus canescens* (L.)P.B. and *Cladonia foliacea* (Hds.) Schaer. The upper sides of the gentle slopes were characterized by a community with *Festuca tenuifolia* Sibth and many species of the association Festuco-Galietum maritimi (Onno 1933) Br.Bl et De Leeuw 1936, such as *Galium verum* L. var. *maritimum* DC, *Polygala vulgaris* L., *Hypnum cupressiforme* Hedw. var. *lacunosum* Brid., *Lotus corniculatus* L. ssp. *corniculatus* and *Thymus pulegioides* L. The hollow was partly vegetated by a tall grassland with *Calamagrostis epigejos* (L.)Roth, *Anthoxanthum odoratum* L. and species of the alliance Agropyro-Rumicion crispi Nordh. 1940 em R.Tx. 1950, e.g. *Potentilla reptans* L., *Hydrocotyle vulgaris* L. and *Leontodon autumnalis* L. Along the path fragments of the Lolio-Cynosuretum (Br.Bl. et De Leeuw 1936) R.Tx. 1937 em. Van Leeuwen et Westhoff 1965 and Poo-Lolietum De Vries et Westhoff 1965 occurred. For full information on the phytosociological units mentioned in this paper, see Westhoff & den Held 1969. When species are referred to as 'species of the alliance' or 'characteristic species of the association', etc., they may be considered as either faithful species or as local differential species of that community type.

During this study I investigated the pattern of species diversity which appeared to be well defined. Bands of high diversity values, corresponding to species numbers of 25–30/m² occurred on the slopes, i.e. in intermediate zones within topographical gradients. Height differences between tops and hollows were 2·5 m with the lowest places well under ground water influence. Lowest diversity values, 5–10 species/m² occur in the central flat part of the grassland, where treading was very frequent. The remarkable influence of the main path on the diversity of its borders should be noted. Where the path ran along a zone with high diversity, these values continued to increase, where it ran through the species-poor central part, the diversity is further reduced. Thus diversity is determined by the gradient structure of the environment (van Leeuwen 1966b). This result is also in accordance with the general law formulated by Odum (1963) stating that the greatest diversity occurs in the moderate or middle range of a physical gradient.

Within this grassland a number of permanent transects were laid down in 1963. The main objective of the study of these transects is the careful description and subsequent interpretation of the relation between pattern and process of the dune grassland, which had been free from major biotic influences since 1940 after some centuries of grazing and ten years of golfing. First of all the dynamic structure of this community series under stable management conditions should be known. In addition mowing experiments were started in 1969.

Within each transect, structure and species composition of each homogeneous site were described from year to year. Some of the results of these analyses in the years 1963–6 will be discussed below.

The diversity pattern in 1966 was similar to that in 1963. The diversity trend also follows a pattern: some of the species-rich zones become richer, others remained in the original diversity class. The change, 'instability', measured as the average annual qualitative shift in species composition, as in 'information-theory', shows a distinct pattern. By means of a chi square test it was found that the original species-rich sites were significantly (slightly) more stable than the poorer ones. This pattern may be obscured by the interference of two environmental tendencies: the area as a whole is very slowly becoming more densely vegetated after the cessation of grazing and heavy treading, and a very slow deterioration of the area occurred as a result of modest but continuing drainage by local gardeners.*

In the period 1964–6 the ground-water table fell some 75 cm because of low rainfall after some very wet years. The effects of these changes are shown in Fig. 1. This is a two-dimensional ordination model showing the relation-

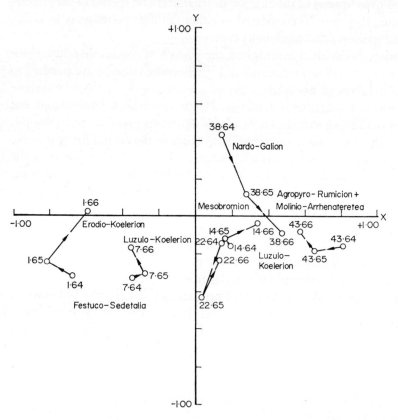

Figure 1. Ordination of successional relationships in a permanent transect within a dune grassland based on the 1964, 1965 and 1966 relevés of six permanent plots, taken from van der Maarel (1969).

ship between six typical vegetation spots from the main transect in three successive years, 1964, 1965 and 1966. In this model isocenes (van der Maarel 1969) are drawn, i.e. lines connecting points of equal percentage distribution of all species characteristic for a certain phytosociological unit. The main line of variation is from Erodio-Koelerion on one of the dune tops towards Agropyro-Rumicion crispi in the adjacent hollow. The second dimension

* Figures as well as discussion concerning these diversity studies are given in van der Maarel & van Leeuwen 1967.

suggests a variation from Luzulo-Koelerion to Violion caninae=Nardo-Galion. By connecting points representing a stand in successive years we may get an idea of the 'phytosociological dynamics'. It appears that there is a marked tendency towards convergence into the alliance Agropyro-Rumicion crispi, a unit characteristic for unstable transitions of the *limes convergens* type (see part 4, general discussion). In the years after 1966 this tendency has been reversed. The correlation between this change in community structure and the temporal deterioration mentioned above is obvious! This figure illustrates the dynamics within gradient-rich ecosystems under stable management conditions which should be known first before management experiments can be interpreted properly. At the same time it suggests the applicability of ordination methods in succession studies.

The second example is the *Drosera* valley on the West Frisian island of Schiermonnikoog having a dune system with a small amount, up to 1 per cent, of carbonates, (the other West Frisian islands like Terschelling are much poorer in carbonates). In 1966 a transect was laid down across the edge of a desalinated dune slack irregularly flooded with sea water from the Wadden Sea. This transect has been described in some detail by van der Maarel & Leertouwer (1967). A considerable part of this valley bore a hygrophytic cal-cicole vegetation with *Schoenus nigricans* L. and other species of the alliance Caricion davallianae Klika 1934, but still with facultative halophytes like *Juncus maritimus* Lamk. and *Glaux maritima* L. On slight elevations calci-fuge species occur, e.g. *Drosera rotundifolia* L., after which species this part of the slack was named.

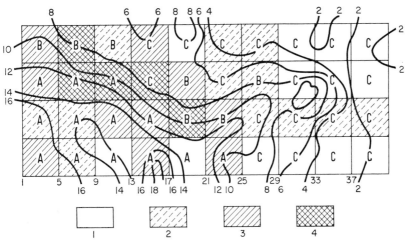

Figure 2. Distribution of species diversity, vegetation types and height (2 cm contours) in a transect within a dune slack. Diversity class 1:17–25 species/m²; 2:26–30 sp.; 3:31–35 sp.; 4:36–43 sp. A: *Radiola linoides* type; B: *Linum catharticum* type; C: *Parnassia palustris* type. Redrawn from van der Maarel & Leertouwer (1967).

The transect originally measured 10 × 4 m, but was enlarged to 16 × 4 m. Vegetational structure, species composition and some environmental factors were described per m². The vegetation within the transect could be classified into three local types, which were called after *Radiola linoides* Roth, *Linum catharticum* L. and *Parnassia palustris* L. The *Radiola* type occurred on the higher side of the transect and was characterized by species such as *Drosera rotundifolia* L. and species of relatively dry sites like *Festuca tenuifolia* Sibth. The *Parnassia* type occurred on the lower side and contained species such as *Schoenus nigricans*. The intermediate zone was characterized by *Gentiana amarella* L., *Euphrasia borealis* Wettst. and particularly *Linum catharticum* L.

The height difference in the transect was only 14 cm, but a considerable variation in pH, from 4·2–7·0 was found, more or less parallel to the elevation gradient. Figure 2 shows the pattern of species diversity, measured as species number per m² (including mosses and lichens). A small band with species numbers of over 36/m² lies between contours 8 and 14 cm above the lowest point of the transect. This zone of greatest diversity varied in pH from 5·1–5·7. In 1967 Thalen (1969) found exactly the same pattern of diversity, but even more pronounced: species numbers per $\frac{1}{16}$ m² in the transect varied from under 5 to over 26, the latter values being reached only within the intermediate zone. The characteristic species of vegetation type B mostly followed the zone. The faithful species *Linum catharticum* L. behaved rather strikingly in this respect, as is shown in Fig. 3, where its distribution over the $\frac{1}{16}$ m² grid is presented.

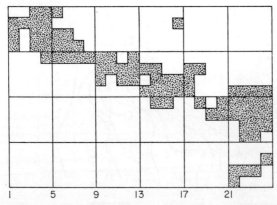

Figure 3. Distribution of *Linum catharticum* in a grid of $\frac{1}{16}$ m² quadrats in part of the transect shown in Fig. 2. Data from Thalen (1969).

A third example comes from a limestone grass heath in a nature reserve near Winterswijk in the eastern part of the Netherlands. Here a heath field was cleared from open *Pinus* woodland ten years ago and has since been mown annually. The grass heath, which was widely known (Westhoff 1938) for some very rare plant species, was re-established more or less in its original structure. The most remarkable species, *Selinum carvifolia* (L.)L., a continental plant characteristic for the Eu-Molinion coeruleae W.Koch 1926, still occurred in the area, which is now the only locality in the Netherlands with a large population. It occurred especially in places where the limestone outcrop came near to the surface. The topography of the area as a whole is rather varied. On the drier parts a *Calluna* heath with *Vaccinium vitis-idaea* L. was found under normal acid conditions in the top soil layer. In the wetter parts, 3–5 dm lower, basic conditions favoured the development of a marsh-like community with species like *Lysimachia vulgaris* L. The intermediate zones were vegetated by a Nardo-Galion grass heath with elements of the Molinietalia W.Koch 1926. Characteristic species were *Selinum carvifolia* L., *Carex pulicaris* L., *Carex hostiana* DC, *Gentiana pneumonanthe* L. and *Platanthera bifolia* (L.)Rich.

In this area a transect was laid down, measuring 16×4 m². The upper side of the transect was characterized by *Erica tetralix* L., *Vaccinium vitis-idaea* and *Festuca ovina* L. s. str. The lowest part was characterized by the species combination mentioned above, especially by *Selinum carvifolia*. The other end of the transect lay somewhat higher and showed species of the heathland. The vegetation pattern was coarser than it was in the situations described above, which means that fairly large patches of dominant species occurred, e.g. *Vaccinium vitis-idaea, Molinia caerulea* (L.) Moench and *Agrostis canina* L. Fig. 4 illustrates the pattern of species diversity of the two species *Carex pulicaris* and *Selinum carvifolia*, as well as the distribution of pH and Mg content values. Greatest diversity values occurred at either side of the lowest part of the transect with pH values mainly between 5·5 and 6·0 and Mg values of 60–100 ppm. Again the diversity maximum occurred at intermediate pH levels. It may be expected that continuation of the present management directive, viz. annual mowing, may result in a further enrichment of this intermediate zone. This process may be induced by a refinement of the patchy structure mentioned earlier. The final example is again a Molinietalia-type grassland. It formed part of a nature reserve near Nijmegen. The investigated area, analysed by Mrs W.Th.L.Driessen-van Oss and Miss M.J.A.van Nies from the University of Nijmegen, was cleared of *Salix-Myrica* scrub some 10 years ago and has been mown annually since. The vegetation still has a coarse structure with relatively large patches of species such as *Molinia caerulea*, but the grain of the pattern was finer than it was in the cleared limestone heath. The diversity level in this area was comparable to that of the heath. The greatest diversity found here was 45 species on the unit area of investigation, viz. 16 m². The grassland as a whole was inundated in winter and under ground water influence throughout the

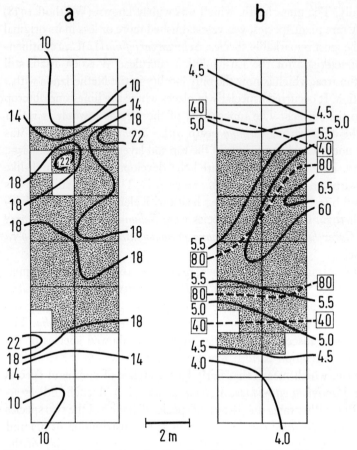

Figure 4. Distribution of species diversity, pH, Ca and Mg within a transect in a limestone grassheath. Data from Hofstad & Derksen (1969). a. Contours of species diversity (as number of species/m²) and distribution of *Carex pulicaris* (shaded); b. Contours of pH (———) and Mg content in ppm (– – – –), and distribution of *Selinum carvifolia*.

summer. The effect of this influence varied with the topography of the area, which lies on a very gentle slope with a height difference of only 30 cm over 100 m. The variation in pH was relatively small, between 5 and 6. The variation in vegetation was considerable, which must be mainly attributed to the variation in topography. The higher zone was characterized by an optimum development of Nardo-Galion species, the lower zone by Caricion curtae-nigrae W.Koch 1926 em. Nordh. 1936 and Calthion palustris R.Tx. 1937 em. 1951, whilst the intermediate zone had the largest amount of species from the Junco-Molinion Westhoff 1969. This zone had the greatest diversity as well as the maximum of rare species like *Carex pulicaris* and *Platanthera bifolia*.

Some effects of management on species diversity

As mentioned, few experiments have been set up so far in the Netherlands to study the effect on the diversity of plant species of certain management measures. Nevertheless quite a number of observations have been made and some experiments with a different aim have been done from which relevant conclusions may be drawn. The following survey summarizes the available information on Dutch situations. Extensive information based on experiments can be found in British literature. Especially the research done at Cambridge, Bristol, Sheffield and Rothamsted in this field has been very useful for general reference. Various contributions to this symposium, both from University departments and Nature Conservancy Research Stations, show the continuing importance of British experimental work on management.

Addition of fertilizers

One of the most drastic intervention measures is the addition of nutrients to the soil of species-rich communities. Willis (1963) reports a rapid growth of *Festuca rubra* L. and *Poa pratensis* L. in dry dune grasslands and of *Agrostis stolonifera* L. in dune slacks, when full nutrient supply was added. At the same time the total number of species decreased considerably. Without N, fertilizers had little effect, without P, only some *Carex* and *Juncus* species showed a slight response.

Similar experiments with comparable results have been carried out in the dunes of Voorne by Freysen and Heeres. The Park Grass plot experiments gave basically the same results; manuring with N led to species poor grasslands. In untreated vegetation, with high numbers of species, very low levels of phosphates and nitrates are generally found. These results lead to the conclusion that great species diversity in these semi-natural communities is associated with low levels of primary nutrients, especially N and P, and readily disappears after the addition of fertilizers.

Grazing

Many gradient situations of the type described in section 2 are, or recently were, under a grazing regime: dune grasslands with horses, cattle and/or rabbits, dune slacks with cattle or sheep, high salt marshes with cattle or sheep, limestone grasslands with cattle.

Observations and some experiments in Dutch nature reserves show that a sudden stop in grazing may lead to a drastic reduction of the species diversity together with a rapid growth of some potentially dominant grass species such as *Festuca rubra*. An obvious parallel exists with the effect of fertilizers!

Many data are available on the effect of the disappearance of rabbits after myxomatosis. In dune grasslands and dwarf shrub communities a decrease in rabbit grazing intensity leads to a coarser vegetation pattern with a tendency towards dominance of grasses like *Festuca rubra* and *Calamagrostis epigejos* (L.) Roth and/or the shrub species *Salix repens* L. and *Hippophae rhamnoides* L. This was demonstrated in fencing experiments by van Leeuwen within permanent plots in the former dunes of the nature reserve De Beer, north of Voorne, now eliminated by the Rotterdam harbour Europoort (see van der Maarel & van Leeuwen 1967) and by van der Laan in dune slacks on Voorne and in many other observations (cf. Ranwell 1960). Watt (1960a, b) found similar developments in acidiphilous grasslands.

There are exceptions to this rule. In very young stages of succession rabbits may keep the diversity (or rather the development of diversity) on a lower level. In vegetation mosaics with different structures, e.g. dune grasslands and types of scrub, rabbits maintain the boundaries between grassland, Tortulo-Phleetum arenarii (Massart 1908) Br. Bl. et de Leeuw 1936 and scrub, Hippophae-Ligustretum Meltzer 1941 em. Boerboom 1960. An almost bare zone borders the scrub with characteristic species such as *Cynoglossum officinale* L. After the disappearance of rabbits a gradual structural transition between grassland and scrub may develop which tends to increase total species diversity (van Leeuwen & van der Maarel 1970).

Watt (1962) described a gradual increase in the number of species in a calcicolous grassland after protecting it from rabbit grazing and concluded that some of the 'new' species were palatable to grazing. One should note that in these two situations a certain over-grazing, which means an under-diversity, occurred at the beginning of the observations. Perhaps a general interpretation of these changes in the grazing regime is that the effect of the change depends on the level of stability of the system prior to the change.

Mowing

The effect of mowing is rather similar to that of grazing; it keeps the standing crop at a low level and enables the development of a fine-grained vegetation pattern. In gradient-rich environments it may lead to species-rich communities.

A change in the mowing regime, for example, cessation, in ecosystems that have become adapted to this type of management, leads to a similar change in the community structure as described under grazing. On the other hand the introduction of mowing in a vegetation with a high structure (tall grassland, dwarf scrub) will finally lead to a lower structure (low grassland) with a greater diversity.

Treading and trampling

It may be said that the effects of these activities on diversity are generally negative although few quantitative data are available (cf. Perring 1967, van der Werf 1967). As I explained earlier moderate treading within gradient situations may increase species diversity, but in this case the positive effect has been noticed after a balanced situation has developed. Sudden introduction or increase in treading will practically always lead to an impoverishment of the flora whilst a sudden stop of heavy treading will, at least temporarily, result in an enrichment.

Management of the ground-water table

The effect of deterioration in ecosystems under ground-water influence is well known as may be concluded from observations in many Dutch dunes where water catchment for urban water supplies has lowered the (fresh) ground-water table by several meters.

On a more local scale the effect may be followed in permanent plots during a period in which considerable changes in weather occur. In dune hollows and slacks I could trace a certain decrease in species diversity after both a considerable increase and a decrease of the free water table by at least some dm. In one permanent plot in a secondary dune slack, containing the only population of *Teucrium scordium* L. left in the Netherlands, three species appeared to be potential dominants: *Rubus caesius* L. was dominant in the very dry year 1959 when the summer ground-water table fell well under 1 m below the surface, *Carex disticha* Huds. became the dominant species in wet years, e.g. 1962 when the summer ground-water level was near to the surface, whilst in 'intermediate' years *Calamagrostis epigejos* took over the dominance, which coincided with slightly higher diversity values.

General discussion

In conclusion we may say that in Dutch semi-natural vegetation types plant species diversity seems to be determined by the gradient structure of their environment and any kind of management that keeps their standing biomass on a low level and their stability on a high level.

This conclusion is in accordance with observations and statements on diversity (e.g. Margalef 1958, 1968, Odum 1963, 1969, Whittaker 1965, 1969). We must realize, however, that these ecosystems are of a special kind as far as their evolutionary status and their sensitivity to change are concerned. When we try to interpret these semi-natural communities with the help of the scheme of Odum (1969), giving trends of change in 24 ecosystem attributes during succession from early development to mature stages, we come to the following tentative survey. Community energetics partly indicate the 'development' stage, but management artificially causes a mature-like stage, for example, in net community production. The community structure, including life history of species, is partly immature, in that total organic matter and the development of stratification are low, but partly mature-like, in that life cycles of species tend to become long and niche specialization leads to narrow niches. Species diversity tends to be high, i.e. mature-like, but this seems to hold only for the variety component; the equitability component is still 'low'. In addition the overall homeostasis is intermediate in value: information is high and entropy is low, but stability in the sense of resistance to external influence is also low.

In this 'stabilized' type of ecosystem environmental variety seems to be the main source of diversity. Environmental variety again is largely bound to the gradient structure of the environment. Van Leeuwen (1965, 1966a, b) approached this structure in a system-theoretical way and introduced a main division into two types of environmental boundary situation, which he called the *limes convergens* and the *limes divergens* types. The *limes convergens* environment is characterized by sharp boundaries between contrasting adjacent environments which are fluctuating in time. The pattern of vegetation belonging to this type of environment is coarse-grained, the species diversity is low. The *limes divergens* environment is characterized by a gradual change from one environmental type into another. Within this zone numerous small stable boundaries occur. The corresponding vegetation has a fine-grained pattern and a high species diversity. After consulting the original papers and in subsequent discussion with van Leeuwen I proposed the term ecotone= tension belt=stress zone as an adequate synonym for *limes convergens*, whilst the term ecocline was suggested as synonymous with *limes divergens* (van der Maarel 1964, 1966a). This proposal has probably not been noticed, so it may be repeated here. Apart from the linguistic argument—the terms ecotone and ecocline are more easily understood and pronounced—I should mention that in discussions with colleagues there is often some confusion over whether we are dealing with a boundary in the literal sense of the word (limes) or else with a boundary zone. There may also be some difficulty in understanding which attributes of the environment are said to be converging and which, diverging.

Recently van Leeuwen (1968) in a Dutch publication on species-rich grasslands distinguished three main environmental gradient types in these grasslands, viz.
acid over basic-rich
organic over mineral
dry over wet.

As van Leeuwen pointed out each of these gradients can only develop as such, when the first mentioned extreme is at the upper end of a topographical gradient. Through rain, and connected downward infiltration, a gradual transition zone is developed. When the second mentioned extreme is at the upper end no gradient develops, but an ecotone-type situation is established, which van Leeuwen calls disturbance.

Van Leeuwen evaluated these three gradients in the supposed multiplicity of micro-boundaries (niche formation possibilities) with (fully arbitrary) values 3, 2 and 1. Of course these gradient situations may occur simultaneously and amplify their individual diversification potentials. I proposed, in van der Maarel & Leertouwer (1967), the term ecological amplification for those inter-acting ecological diversification factors. Van Leeuwen gives a scheme of possible combined gradient situations. In Fig. 5 this scheme has been redrawn

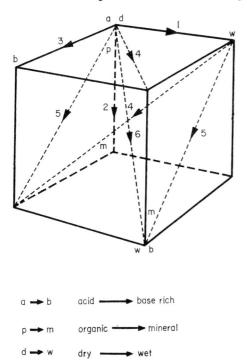

Figure 5. Three-dimensional scheme of main complex gradient situations, redrawn after van Leeuwen (1968).

in the form of a cube model whose diagonals represent the complex gradients. This model is used in ordination studies (e.g. Loucks 1962) and it is probably the most convenient scheme.

The 'diversity potential value' of each complex gradient, as a simple addition of single values, is given in the model. This is, of course, nothing more than a suggestion for a possible hierarchy of diversity potentials. However the gradient from acid-organic-dry over base-rich-mineral-wet is considered the most important integrated gradient. This may be actually found in the situation of dry, acid peaty hummocks in mineral limestone marsh, a situation only met with in arctic-alpine or oceanic limestone areas.

This brings us to Teesdale, and the status of its rarities. Van Leeuwen and I visited this famous area in 1966 with Professor Pigott who kindly acted as guide. We feel strongly that the occurrence of peculiar gradient structures within the area together with the other features mentioned, particularly a low nutrient level and a low standing biomass level, forms the best hypothesis for the occurrence of rare plant species (cf. van Leeuwen 1970). This possibility does not seem to be recognized by Pigott (1956), Bellamy et al. (1969) and Jeffrey (this volume). It may be worthwhile publishing this hypothesis elsewhere in more detail.

Species diversity in nature reserves and larger areas

So far species diversity on the community level has been discussed. With Whittaker (1965) we call this α-diversity—actually in some cases Williams's (1964) α measure has been used.

Patterns of species diversity on a much larger scale have also been analysed including some studies on the scientific value of nature reserves. Here we are dealing with γ diversity, species diversity of a larger community complex, based on α diversities of the component communities and a β diversity of environmental types (cf. Whittaker).

Figure 6 shows the diversity pattern within the Voorne dune system. Here diversity is measured as total species number in landscape units with an average of 16 ha. Greatest values—up to 280 species per unit area—occur in the inner middle and inner dunes as well in the transition zone between the primary dune slacks in the north-east part of the dunes and the adjacent salt marsh area (see Adriani & van der Maarel 1968 for further discussion).

The species richness, of an area as a whole, can be measured by comparing the species number with the average number on an area of that size. The comparison is based on a species-area relationship for the Dutch flora which appeared to be a straight line in a log-log plotting with Preston's (1962) z-value=0·28.

This method was introduced in Adriani & van der Maarel (1968) and will be further discussed in a future paper.

Figure 7 gives the position of Voorne and a number of other natural areas towards the 'standard-line'. The diversity value is then determined by the quotient of species number and average species number. Perhaps in this way diversity can be quantitatively approached. Such methods may be success-

Figure 6. Distribution of species richness in dune landscape units in the dunes of Voorne, taken from Adriani & van der Maarel (1968); white: species number less than 160; lightly shaded: 160–240 species; heavy shaded: over 240 species.

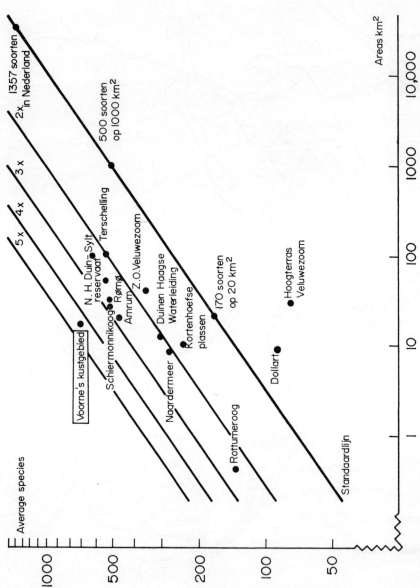

Figure 7. Species richness of the coastal area of Voorne and other natural areas compared with the standard line for the species-area relationship for the Netherlands, obtained by plotting log values of average species number against log value of areas of various sizes. (From Adriani & van der Maarel 1968.)

fully used in conservation policy (cf. Sukopp 1970 for Germany and Hooper, this volume, for Britain).

The same method has been applied in a multidisciplinary study of the future biological status of the south-west Netherlands, the so-called Delta area. Maps of species diversity for various groups for the entire area have been made and will be published in the near future (Anonymous 1970).

The general pattern of plant species diversity may be described as follows: greatest diversity values (species number over 4x average) are found along the coastline with top values on the coastal dunes and salt marshes of Voorne and Goeree; diversity values of 3–4x average occur in and along estuaries, particularly west Schelde and Haringvliet, and the fresh water tidal areas Biesbos and Oude Maas.

In this study the relation between diversity and management comes into the sphere of planning. The biotic diversity pattern of an area can be used as a biological basis for the planning of that area. Planning authorities are rapidly developing an interest in this approach which deals with the relation between diversity and management on a large scale; a trend which is both hopeful and encouraging for nature conservation.

Acknowledgement

The help of Dr Eric Duffey in preparing my part in this symposium and in improving the English text, and of Mr J.Gerritsen and his staff in drawing Figs. 2–5, is gratefully acknowledged.

References

ADRIANI M.J. & MAAREL E.VAN DER (1968) *Voorne in de Branding.* Stichting Weten-schappelijk Duinonderzoek, Oostvootne.

BELLAMY D.J., BRIDGEWATER P., MARSHALL C. & TICKLE W.M. (1969) Status of the Teesdale rarities. *Nature, Lond.* **222**, 238–43.

ANON. (1970) Biologische rÿkdommen in Zuid-West Nederland. *Biol. Station Oostvoorne* (in press).

DANSEREAU P. (1957) *Biogeography: an ecological perspective.* Ronald Press Comp., New York.

HOFSTAD J.G.L. & DERKSEN J.W.M. (1969) De vegetatie van het natuurreservaat Willinksweust en Heksenbos. Doct. verslag, Botanisch Laboratorium, Nijmegen.

LEEUWEN C.G.VAN (1965) Het verband tussen natuurlijke en anthropogene landschaps-vormen, bezien vanuit de betrekkingen in grensmilieu's. *Gorteria* **2**, 93–105.

LEEUWEN C.G.VAN (1966a) Het botanisch beheer van natureservaten op structuur-oecologische grondslag (with a summary). *Gorteria* **3**, 16–28.

LEEUWEN C.G.VAN (1966b) A relation theoretical approach to pattern and process in vegetation. *Wentia* **15**, 25–46.

LEEUWEN C.G.VAN (1968) Soortenrijke graslanden en hun milieu. *Kruipnieuws* 30–1, 16–28.

LEEUWEN C.G.VAN (1970) Onderzoek aan structuur en dynamiek van vegetaties. In 'Het verstoorde evenwicht', *Oosthoek, Utrecht*, 125–38.

LEEUWEN C.G.VAN and MAAREL E.VAN DER (1971) Pattern and process in dune vegetations. In 'Historic and dynamic aspects of coastal dune vegetation in the Netherlands'. *Acta bot. neerl.* **20**, 191–8.

LOUCKS O.L. (1962) Ordinating forest communities by means of environmental scalars and phytosociological indices. *Ecol. Monogr.* **32**, 137–66.

MAAREL E.VAN DER (1964) Review of J.T.Curtis: *The vegetation of Wisconsin. Acta bot. neerl.* **13**, 438–40.

MAAREL E.VAN DER (1966a) Dutch studies on coastal sand dune vegetation, especially in the Delta region. *Wentia* **15**, 47–82.

MAAREL E.VAN DER (1966b) On vegetational structures, relations and systems, with special reference to the dune grasslands of Voorne, the Netherlands. Thesis, Utrecht.

MAAREL E.VAN DER (1969) On the use of ordination models in phytosociology. *Vegetatio* **19**, 21–46.

MAAREL E.VAN DER & LEERTOUWER J. (1967) Variation in vegetation and species diversity along a local environmental gradient. *Acta bot. neerl.* **16**, 211–21.

MAAREL E.VAN DER & LEEUWEN C.G. VAN (1967) Beziehungen zwischen Struktur und Dynamik in Ökosystemen. *Int. Symposium Syndynamik*, Rinteln, W. Germany (in press).

MAAREL E.VAN DER & WESTHOFF V. (1964) The vegetation of the dunes near Oostvoorne, the Netherlands. *Wentia* **12**, 1–61.

MARGALEF R. (1958) Information theory in ecology. ('La teoria de la informacion en Ecologia'). *Gen. Syst.* **3**, 36–71.

MARGALEF R. (1968) *Perspectives in ecological theory.* The University of Chicago Press, Chicago.

ODUM E.P. (1963) *Ecology.* Holt, Rinehart and Winston, New York.

ODUM E.P. (1969) The strategy of ecosystem development. *Science, N.Y.* **164**, 262–70.

PERRING F.H. (1967) Changes in chalk grassland caused by galloping. In: *The biotic effects of public pressures on the environment.* Ed. E.Duffey, Monks Wood Exp. Station, Huntingdon.

PIGOTT C.D. (1956) The vegetation of Upper Teesdale in the North Pennines. *J. Ecol.* **44**, 545–86.

POORE M.E.D. (1964) Integration in the plant community. *J. Ecol.* **52** (supp.), 213–26.

PRESTON F.W. (1962) The canonical distribution of commonness and rarity. *Ecology* **43**, 185–215, 410–32.

RANWELL D.S. (1960) Newborough Warren, Anglesey. III. Changes in the vegetation on parts of the dune system after the loss of rabbits by myxomatosis. *J. Ecol.* **48**, 385–95.

SLOET VAN OLDRUITENBORGH C.J.M. and HEERES E. (1969) On the contribution of air-borne salt to the gradient character of the Voorne Dune area. *Acta bot. neerl.* **18**, 315–24.

SUKOPP H. (1970) Charakteristik und Bewertung der Naturschutzgebiete in Berlin (West). *Natur Landsch.* **45**, 133–9.

THALEN D. (1969) *Soortdiversiteit en variatie in enkele duin- en kweldervegetaties op Schiermonnikoog in relatie tot variatie tot het milieu.* Doct. verslag, Lab. Plantenoecologie, Groningen.

WATT A.S. (1960*a*) The effect of excluding rabbits from acidiphilous grassland in Breckland. *J. Ecol.* 48, 601–4.

WATT A.S. (1960*b*) Population changes in acidiphilous grassheath in Breckland. *J. Ecol.* 48, 605–29.

WATT A.S. (1962) The effect of excluding rabbits from grassland A (Xerobrometum) in Breckland 1936–1960. *J. Ecol.* 50, 181–98.

WERF S.VAN DER (1967) De invloed van recreatie op vegetatie en milieu, in het bijzonder in Meyendal en op de Hoge Veluwe. *Rapport RIVON, Zeist.*

WESTHOFF V. (1938) Zwerftochten door Weust en Heksebos. In: *Kotten, zoals de NJN het zag*, p. 85–102, Utrecht.

WESTHOFF V. (1970) New criteria for nature reserves. *New Scient.* 46, 108–13.

WESTHOFF V. & HELD A.J.DEN (1969) *Plantengemeenschappen in Nederland.* Thieme, Zutphen.

WHITTAKER R.H. (1965) Dominance and diversity in land plant communities. *Science, N.Y.* 147, 250–60.

WHITTAKER R.H. (1969) Evolution of diversity in plant communities. In: *Diversity and stability in ecological systems.* Brookhaven Symp. Biol. 22, 178–96.

WILLIAMS C.B. (1964) *Patterns in the balance of nature.* London, New York.

WILLIS A.J. (1963) Braunton Burrows: The effects on the vegetation of the addition of mineral nutrients to the dune soils. *J. Ecol.* 51, 353–74.

The use of nutrients in the control of the floristic composition of grassland

I.H.RORISON *Nature Conservancy Grassland Research Unit, Department of Botany, University of Sheffield*

Introduction

Mineral nutrients have a strong influence on the floristic composition of plant communities such as those which grow in acidic, calcareous and saline conditions. These communities represent complex and probably delicately balanced systems which would need subtle handling to achieve anything but gross changes. For example, the addition of major nutrients leads to a more productive site with the gradual exclusion of slow-growing species and a drift towards monoculture.

This is particularly important to remember when we plan to conserve some of our semi-natural grasslands in which species numbers may be 40/m² or more and grasses are outnumbered by forbs. Many species which comprise these grassland communities are slow-growing and are surviving towards the limit of their edaphic range. Their survival is due more to tolerance of polyvalent cations and/or mineral nutrient imbalance than to high nutrient requirements. They will usually grow far better in a fertile soil of intermediate pH (Rorison 1967) but not well enough to compete with fast growing species.

A simplified relationship between nutrients and floristic composition might be stated as:

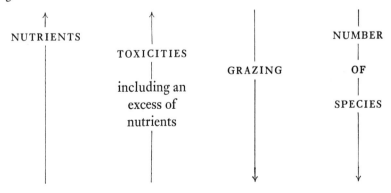

High levels, whether of essential or toxic elements, lead to a decrease in the number of species; low levels of essential elements lead to an increased number of species.

Evidence that floristic composition can be controlled, or at least influenced, by nutrients comes from the following sources.

1   Surveys of plant distribution in the field—surveys which also record soil type, nutrient content, topography and management.

2   Experiments involving the addition of nutrients in the field.

From (1) and (2) we should be able to describe the conditions with respect to nutrients in any one community at one point *in* time, and to note gross changes in floristic composition *with* time.

3   Autecological studies of species which occur in fertile, in infertile or edaphically extreme habitats.

These enable us to measure growth response over a wide range of nutrient levels from the minimum for survival to optimum levels. Laboratory experiments can extend this knowledge of requirements, of efficiency of uptake, and of utilization of individual nutrients, and should essentially include a study of mycorrhizal associations (Harley 1969).

Information from these three sources may be used to assess the species' ability to survive in a habitat with or without competition from other species. For the sake of simplicity, it is assumed, unless otherwise stated, that for any given plant community the physical conditions and system of management remain constant. The influence of management is particularly important, but it will be only briefly noted, since it is given detailed consideration by Harper and by Wells (this volume).

Field surveys

Floristic surveys confirm that certain species and groups of species are limited to certain soil types and that the number of species present may also vary (Ellenberg 1963, Hundt 1966, Olsen 1923, *inter alia*). Three aspects of species distribution in relation to nutrient status will be considered:

Species density

A general picture emerges that:

Few species tend to occur in level sites which suffer from surface leaching because leaching may lead to the increasing availability of toxic polyvalent ions, an imbalance of nutrients and various nutrient deficiencies. Few species occur in level and very fertile soils but these are usually reserved for agriculture. Few species occur on slight slopes of moderate fertility, particularly if ungrazed.

Many species tend to occur in open sites and on steep slopes where there is little leaching but where fertility is low and there may be nutrient imbalance such as in calcareous soils. A certain pressure of grazing helps maintain a high number of species in such communities.

Perhaps the best single guide to nutrient status of a soil is its pH and to test the relationship between pH and species density, data from a survey of the grasslands of the Sheffield area (Lloyd *et al.* 1971) have been sorted to give the mean number of species per metre square according to pH and from each of six geological strata. Six hundred and thirty sites and 298 species were involved and a composite picture emerges (Fig. 1). The two lines show

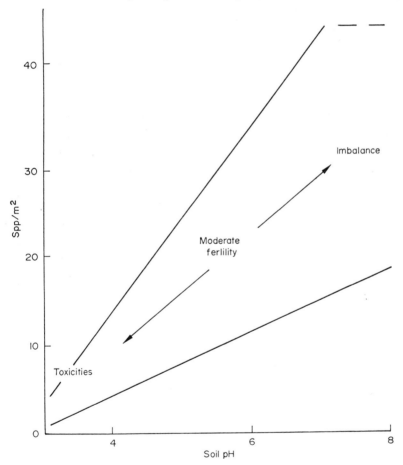

Figure 1. The relationship between species' density and soil pH at 0–3 cm depth. The two lines show the approximate upper and lower limits of scatter from 630 individual sites.

the approximate upper and lower limits of species density when data from 630 sites are plotted. Predominant mineral nutrient conditions are indicated in the three critical pH ranges of less than 4·0, 4·0–6·5 and more than 6·5. The slope of the curves may vary according to the pressure of environmental factors (M.Spray, in progress). Optimum density is achieved at around pH 6·5.

Relative growth rates

There are scattered reports in the literature that plants growing in edaphic extremes have low optimum relative growth rates and those typical of fertile conditions (including ruderals) have high relative growth rates (e.g. Higgs & James 1969). These have been amply confirmed by Grime and Hunt (see Hunt 1970) who have compared the relative growth rate attained under standardized conditions of 95 species of differing ecological distribution in the Sheffield area. As Dr Grime points out, one cannot rely on relative growth rate alone. A slow-growing species with a large seed may be as successful in a fertile community as a fast-growing plant with a small seed.

Nutrient contents of plants

There is little information on the nutrient contents of naturally occurring grassland species (Brynmor Thomas & Trinder 1947, Jefferies & Willis 1964a) and to clarify the picture in its own area the Unit of Grassland Research collected, during a short period in July 1969, the green leaf material of 53 herbaceous species from 24 sites representing plants of both widespread and restricted distribution and the main soil types, topography and management systems of the Sheffield area. The questions being asked include: do the contents of individual species vary significantly with site, strata and/or with differences in associated species; are the significant variations which occur related to individual elements, to the balance of ions and/or to valency patterns?

A preliminary analysis* shows that:

Table 1. Mineral nutrient contents of green leaf material expressed as mg of element per gm dry wt.

		N	P	K	Ca	Mg	Fe
Acidic sites	Grasses[1]	14·0	1·4	14·4	1·9	0·7	0·13
	Forbs[2]	19·4	1·6	15·6	11·0	2·4	0·29
Calcareous sites	Grasses[3]	15·7	1·5	17·6	4·8	1·3	0·13
	Forbs[4]	24·6	1·4	11·7	22·4	4·3	0·24

Means of three replicates of each of:

1. *Deschampsia flexuosa*
   Nardus stricta
   Festuca ovina
2. *Potentilla erecta*
   Galium saxatile
   Vaccinium myrtillus
3. *Festuca ovina*
   Helictotrichon pratense
   Koeleria cristata
4. *Lotus corniculatus*
   Poterium sanguisorba
   Helianthemum chamaecistus

*Detailed analyses of these results will be published elsewhere.

Herbs in general have higher nutrient concentrations than grasses on both acidic and calcareous soils; grasses have approximately the same concentrations of nutrients whether they grow in acidic or calcareous soils, except for Ca and Mg, and that their ratio of K/Ca tends to be high; the contents of herbs are more variable and the K:Ca ratio from calcareous sites is the reverse of the samples from acidic sites.

It is also interesting to note that Fe concentrations are similar in both acidic and calcareous media.

A species which grows on a range of both acidic and calcareous soils, *Festuca ovina* (Table 2) shows very similar nutrient concentrations in both con-

Table 2. Mineral nutrient contents of green leaf material expressed as mg of element per gm dry wt.

	N	P	K	Ca	Mg	Fe
Deschampsia flexuosa	13·6	1·4	15·9	1·8	0·9	0·13
Fustuca ovina, acidic	14·0	1·5	14·3	2·0	0·7	0·12
Festuca ovina, calcareous	13·6	1·2	13·6	3·3	0·9	0·13
Arrhenatherum elatius	27·8	3·8	19·9	9·4	1·5	0·19

ditions. It is closely paralleled in content in acidic soils by *Deschampsia flexuosa* but most grasses from calcareous soils have higher nutrient levels. An extreme example is *Arrhenatherum elatius* which has a particularly high NPK content. It is also a plant with a high relative growth rate and since the samples were from only moderately fertile soils and even stabilized scree, it presumably has a highly efficient uptake system.

Nutrient additions in the field—effects recorded with time

The experiments which have continued for the longest time are on the hill pastures of mid-Wales and the hay meadows of Rothamsted and they provide a fascinating contrast.

The Welsh hill experiments, reviewed by Jones (1967), were started by Milton in 1930. Infertile grassland dominated by either *Festuca ovina* and *Agrostis tenuis* or *Molinia caerulea* was given various combinations of lime and NPK, and subjected to different grazing regimes (Harper, this volume). In the early years there was a change in the relative contribution of the species originally present while latterly new species (*Lolium perenne, Dactylis glomerata, Phleum pratense*, and forbs) associated with lowland grassland became established, and in the limed plots they became dominant. Controlled grazing accelerated and helped to maintain the floristic changes initiated by nutrient additions. The sward could thus be changed from one dominated by one or two species to a mixed grassland community with twelve or more associated dicotyledonous species.

The Rothamsted plots originated in 1856 (Thurston 1969) and were laid out on a moderately fertile silt-loam soil overlying clay and chalk. The original meadow contained some 60 species of flowering plants and subsequent additions of nutrients led to a great increase in growth and a fall in numbers of species.

The unmanured plot retains its original diversity of over 40 species. *Briza media* and *Primula veris* are noted as characteristic of poor land. The vegetation is very short, the hay crop poor (18 cwt/acre, a 7-year average) and the soil pH *c.* 5·0. The result is a poor, open turf with no dominants and many species surviving. The complete nutrient treatment of NPK, Na, Mg, with nitrogen as $NaNO_3$ gives a soil pH of *c.* 6·0 and a yield of 54 cwt/acre. The nitrate is said to ensure the dominance of the grasses *Alopecurus pratensis*, *Arrhenatherum elatius* and *Dactylis glomerata*.

The Rothamsted results were achieved in the absence of grazing and with only two hay cuts a year. The general trend following nutrient additions has been a maximum response to nitrogen and dominance by a few fast-growing grasses.

A brief comparison between results from the Welsh hill pastures and the Rothamsted meadow shows that:

Fertilizer treatments (particularly of lime $\pm$ phosphorus), together with controlled grazing, brought the hill grassland from a state of impoverishment and dominance by a few species to a state of moderate fertility and species-diversity, such as existed initially at Rothamsted. The move to high fertility at Rothamsted led to dominance by a few species and this trend was helped by the mowing technique employed.

There are at least two equally interesting ecological examples. The first concerns a field on the acid Greensand at Abinger in Surrey which was discovered by Hope Simpson (1938). Part of the area had been limed at least 50 years before and this had led to the invasion of many plants, including calcicoles. At the time of the discovery a comparison of the treated and untreated areas revealed 15 species restricted to the original acidic soil and 41 species restricted to the now calcareous soil. The overall fertility of the treated site was not raised appreciably and the turf remained stunted and open but the shift in pH from *c.* 4·8 to 7·4 and slight change in nutritional state had markedly affected the floristic composition.

In contrast, the work of Willis & Yemm (1961) and Willis (1963) on the sand dunes of Braunton Burrows, N.Devon, showed what drastic effects additions of NPK can have on the floristic composition of pioneer communities. Response was particularly marked to N and P. Slow-growing prostrate species like *Thymus drucei*, which survive without additions, are squeezed out. Some like *Phleum arenarium* and *Arenaria serpyllifolia* benefit initially but are eventually eliminated by the densely-growing *Festuca rubra*.

A few larger dicotyledonous plants, e.g. *Crepis capillaris* and *Senecio jacobaea*, thrived temporarily but within 2 years were completely dominated by the grasses. He also showed a very interesting example of how the presence of leguminous species can help the nitrogen nutrition of grasses in an unfertilized pioneer community.

Lotus corniculatus was seen to occur in circular patches which were in-creasing in diameter through areas of *Festuca rubra*. Some of the larger circles were decaying at the centre as the older parts of the *L.corniculatus* colony died out. Outside the rings *F.rubra* was not very vigorous, but at the decaying centres where *F.rubra* began to take over it grew much more vigorously.

Evidence pointed to the nitrogen released by decaying *L.corniculatus* causing increased vigour of the invading *F.rubra* which then became dominant.

The basic message of these investigations is that large additions of nutrients lead to drastic changes which, under conditions of competition, only a few species can survive. To maintain the *status quo* of floristic composition relatively small additions of nutrients may suffice and their effects can be even more carefully regulated by controlled grazing. However small the nutrient additions, some form of management is necessary to ensure that grass-land below 300 m (1,000ft) OD does not revert to scrub. It is equally important to remember that over-grazing will cancel out beneficial effects of nutrient additions (Milton 1947).

Effects of nutrients on individual species

Nutrient additions to soils

It is of particular interest that many of the infertile acidic (see below) and calcareous (Jeffrey, this volume) soils examined in this country are primarily deficient in phosphorus, as the following examples show.

(1) Limestone grasslands. You will see on the post-conference tour species-rich, open sites at the Avon Gorge (Carboniferous Limestone) which are now dominated by *Bromus erectus* and *Festuca ovina*, primarily as a result of phosphorus additions (Willis, unpublished).

(2) Acidic moorland soils dominated by *Deschampsia flexuosa* or *Festuca ovina* are often deficient primarily in phosphorus in so far as the dominant species respond to the addition of phosphorus and increased phosphorus supply allows the establishment of species which are slightly less calcifuge than the original dominants.

Raising pH by degrees also allows the entry of less strictly calcifuge plants, partly by the repression of soil acidity factors including aluminium toxicity, but also by the increased availability of essential nutrients. This is well illustrated by the growth of *Rumex acetosa* in a very acidic soil from the

Millstone Grit of N.Derbyshire to which different inorganic salts had been added (Table 3).

Table 3. The dry weight (mg) of *Rumex acetosa* grown for six weeks in an acidic mineral soil ± the addition of chemicals.

Control	47		
+ NaNO₃	50	+ Ca(H₂PO₄)₂	90
+ K₂SO₄	49	+ NaOH	91
+ CaSO₄	32	+ CaCO₃	157

It is of particular interest that response was to phosphorus and not to nitrogen or potassium and that in plants grown in soils in which the pH was raised (+ NaOH and + CaCO₃) the amount of phosphorus removed by each plant was greater than in the + P treatment (μg phosphorus/plant: Control 110, + P 288, + CaCO₃ 670).

The interest again in these results is that a shift in pH has improved the nutrient availability to one species without the addition of sufficient nutrients to increase productivity excessively.

The overriding requirement for phosphorus in infertile soil may well be due in part to its relative immobility in the soil (Sutton & Gunary 1969).

Nutrient levels in solution culture

Although solution cultures cannot be directly related to soils where nutrient availability is affected by a number of other rate-limiting physico–chemical steps they do indicate differential response to nutrients by individual species.

Thus it has been shown by a number of workers for both phosphorus (Bradshaw *et al.* 1960, Clarkson 1967, Rorison 1968) and calcium (Jefferies & Willis 1964*b*, Snaydon & Bradshaw 1961) that species vary widely in their requirement for, and their ability to take up and utilize, the elements.

Nitrogen supply

Recent work on nitrogen is less extensive but it is of ecological interest that the form of nitrogen (linked with pH) utilized by plant species may differ (Bogner 1968).

We have grown a range of species, including *Scabiosa columbaria*, *Deschampsia flexuosa* and *Rumex acetosa*, to test the hypothesis that calcifuge species grow better when nitrogen is supplied in the ammonium form; that calcicoles grow better when supplied with nitrate and that widely tolerant species respond equally well to either form. We did this in solution culture at pH's 4·2, 5·8 and 7·2 (Gigon & Rorison in press).

The experimental results (Table 4) showed that species generally responded as predicted. The strictly calcifuge *D. flexuosa* grew very poorly when supplied with nitrate at high pH. The strictly calcicole *S. columbaria* (Lathkilldale) failed completely at low pH when supplied with ammonium nitrogen.

Table 4. The dry weights in mg of plants grown for six weeks in nutrient solutions containing nitrogen in either the ammonium or nitrate form.

Rumex acetosa				Deschampsia flexuosa			
pH	4·2	5·8	7·2	pH	4·2	5·8	7·2
NH₄	239	390	655	NH₄	94	78	117
NO₃	922	887	996	NO₃	80	73	13

Scabiosa columbaria Zurich				Scabiosa columbaria Lathkilldale			
pH	4·2	5·8	7·2	pH	4·2	5·8	7·2
NH₄	—	63	160	NH₄	—	—	123
NO₃	226	598	484	NO₃	145	153	198

There was no shortage of nitrogen in affected plants. In *R. acetosa* and *S. columbaria* supplied with ammonium nitrogen there was a build-up in concentration of nitrogen in both roots and shoots. In acidic soils where nitrification is slow, or doesn't occur, the failure of strictly calcicole species to become established should be considered in terms of nitrogen nutrition as well as in terms of polyvalent cation toxicity and this is particularly true in the pH range 4·5 to 5·5, where polyvalent ions become increasingly insoluble.

The role of silica

Normally the amelioration of soil acidity factors is brought about by liming. This not only raises soil pH but also tends to improve soil texture and increase fertility for some time. NaOH alone (see p. 72) will raise pH enough to remove toxicities but improves nutrient availability only slightly. It tends not to improve soil texture.

A third method of removing toxicities which only minimally affects nutrient conditions concerns the addition to acid soils of soluble silica. The ameliorating effect of silica on manganese toxicity of grasses was recorded by Vlamis and Williams (1967). The effect was examined further by Peaslee and Frink (1969) who added silicic acid H_2SiO_3 to a fine sandy loam of pH 4·2 and found that yield of tomato was not greatly increased but the concentrations and total uptake of both aluminium and manganese into the tops was significantly reduced.

With these results in mind we have recently studied the effects of a range of levels of both manganese and silica on the growth of both calcicole and calcifuge species. Solution cultures containing manganese from $5 \times 10^{-4}M$

down to $5 \times 10^{-6}M$ ($27\cdot5 - 0\cdot275$ mg/L Mn) and silica at $1\cdot5 \times 10^{-3}M$ to $0\cdot3 \times 10^{-3}M$ ($c.$ 40—8 mg/L Si) were maintained at pH $4\cdot2$.

The results for the calcifuge *Deschampsia flexuosa* and the calcicole *Scabiosa columbaria* are given in Tables 5 and 6.

Table 5. Dry weight of whole plant in mg after six weeks in nutrient solutions containing manganese and silica in mg/L as indicated.

Deschampsia flexuosa

	Si_0	Si_8	Si_{40}
$Mn_{0.275}$	64·1	68·2	67·7
$Mn_{5.5}$	60·3	67·6	79·7
$Mn_{27.5}$	62·3	79·0	90·0

Table 6. Dry weight of whole plant in mg after six weeks in nutrient solutions containing manganese and silica in mg/L as indicated.

Scabiosa columbaria

	Si_0	Si_8	Si_{40}
$Mn_{0.275}$	191·7	140·0	122·2
$Mn_{5.5}$	118·6	127·1	97·6
$Mn_{27.5}$	26·2	53·2	26·2

In *D.flexuosa* there is no detectable toxicity due to manganese but there is some stimulation of growth by silica and a stimulation significant at the 5 per cent level when levels of manganese and silica are both increased. The overall effect of silica on *S.columbaria* is to reduce growth but it is not toxic to the same degree as manganese. Some amelioration of the manganese toxicity occurs with the middle level of silica only, but this has yet to be explained. The widespread species *Rumex acetosa* responds in a manner intermediate between *D.flexuosa* and *S.columbaria*. There is some depression on growth due to both manganese and silica singly, but a stimulation when they are supplied together at the highest levels.

These results are ecologically interesting. They suggest that calcicoles such as *S.columbaria* could not become established in an acid soil to which only soluble silica had been added, but that it might encourage some less strictly restricted species to survive.

Conclusions

There is ample evidence that additions of nutrients can lead to drastic changes in the floristic composition of grassland and that these changes can be maintained by careful management. Low levels of nutrients allow many species to survive, both those with low requirements for growth and those with a wide tolerance, e.g. *Festuca ovina* and *Agrostis tenuis*. Results from the Rothamsted meadows suggest that an infertile soil to which phosphorus was added would favour the growth of *Anthoxanthum odoratum* and that nitrogen levels need to be high for *Holcus lanatus* to thrive. High overall levels of nutrients encourage the survival of productive species which, unless the area is heavily grazed, are virtually all grasses, such as *Alopecurus pratensis* and *Dactylis glomerata*. *Arrhenatherum elatius* flourishes in fertile soils and even in moderately fertile soils, since its ability to take up major nutrients is high, but it is unlikely to survive heavy grazing.

There is thus some evidence to suggest how the survival of individual species may be encouraged in a plant community. Each case must be considered according to the soils' current fertility and the species most in need of conservation.

In the British Isles, where precipitation exceeds evaporation for most of the year, surface leaching is common on all but steep calcareous slopes. In cases of leaching, light dressings of lime and major nutrients are needed to maintain the *status quo*, or, as in the Abinger plots, lime alone will encourage a community of calcicolous species which are either slow-growing or which survive low nutrient levels.

If acidity needs encouraging, the addition of sulphates, in some cases ammonium sulphates, would help maintain the required condition. If acidity without undue activity of polyvalent cations is required, it may be practicable to add silicic acid. Some plants, e.g. *Deschampsia flexuosa*, tend to develop acid conditions around them (Grime 1963; see also Grubb & Suter, this volume)— a condition which can be checked by liming or burning. This is an interesting contrast to the influence of legumes which can benefit adjacent species in soils with a very low nitrogen content.

In semi-natural as opposed to cultivated grassland, it is undesirable to produce uniform conditions. Natural situations are full of local pockets which vary in their mineral nutrient content (Hallsworth 1965) as evidenced by the micro-distribution of *Trifolium repens* (Snaydon 1962). Every community tends to have its own combinations and it is this variety, together with the ability of some species to become adapted, which can help the survival of a wide range of species.

One final question should be asked—need we consider 'competition between plants for nutrients' as a major factor? Laboratory experiments often beg the question of competition but it is not necessarily a vital factor especially during seedling establishment. If each species can become established in a gap which is fertile or infertile it may survive there for its whole lifespan. Competition may be avoided or minimized by plants having different rooting zones, deep or shallow. They may have differing nutrient requirements for growth. They may vary in their efficiency of uptake and recycling of certain nutrients. Their time of maximum activity may vary from early spring to late summer (Woodhead 1915). If we know enough of the autecology of species we wish to conserve we should be able to provide the right niches to use as a basis for studies of competition during later phases of survival. The extent of intra- and interspecific competition which follows will be influenced by the degree of openness of each site and its fertility.

The subject is a good example of how field observations in an area showing various stages of development can lead to a combination of field and laboratory experiments. The culmination should be confirmatory field tests of specific problems and there is still much experimental work to be done.

Acknowledgements

Data used in Fig. 1 and in Tables 1 and 2 were collected by members of the Nature Conservancy Unit of Grassland Research, Sheffield University, as part of a programme financed by NERC. The chemical analyses were carried out by the Nature Conservancy Chemical Service, Grange-over-Sands.

References

BOGNER W. (1968) Experimentelle Prufung von Waldbodenpflanzen auf ihre Anspruche an die Form der Sticksoff-Ernahrung. *Mitt. Vereins forstl. Stand u. Forstpfl.* 18, 1–45.

BRADSHAW A.D., CHADWICK M.J., JOWETT D., LODGE R.W., & SNAYDON R.W. (1960) Experimental investigations into the mineral nutrition of several grass species III. Phosphate level. *J. Ecol.* 48, 631–7.

CLARKSON D.T. (1967) Phosphorus supply and growth rate in species of *Agrostis* L. *J. Ecol.* 55, 111–18.

ELLENBERG H. (1963) *Vegetation Mitteleuropas mit der Alpen, in kausaler, dynamischer und historischer Sicht.* Stuttgart.

GIGON A. & RORISON I.H. (in press) The response of some ecologically distinct plant species to nitrate- and to ammonium-nitrogen. *J. Ecol.*

GRIME J.P. (1963) An ecological investigation at a junction between two plant communities in Coombsdale on the Derbyshire limestone. *J. Ecol.* 51, 391–402.

HALLSWORTH E.G. (1965) The relationship between experimental pedology and soil classification. In *Experimental Pedology* (Ed. E.G.Hallsworth & D.V.Crawford), pp. 354–74 London.

HARLEY J.L. (1969) A physiologist's viewpoint. In *Ecological Aspects of the Mineral Nutrition of Plants* (Ed. I.H.Rorison), pp. 437–47 Oxford.

HIGGS D.E.B. & JAMES D.B. (1969) Comparative studies on the biology of upland grasses I. Rate of dry matter production and its control in four grass species. *J. Ecol.* 57, 553–65.

HOPE SIMPSON J.F. (1938) A chalk flora on the Lower Greensand. Its use in interpreting the calcicole habit. *J. Ecol.* 26, 218–35.

HUNDT R. (1966) *Ökologisch-Geobotanische Untersuchungen an Pflanzen der Mitteleuropäischen Wiesenvegetation.* Jena.

HUNT R. (1970) *Relative growth-rate; its range and adaptive significance in a local flora.* Ph.D. thesis, University of Sheffield.

JEFFERIES R.L. & WILLIS A.J. (1964*a*) Studies on the calcicole-calcifuge habit. I. Methods of analysis of soil and plant tissues and some results of investigations on four species. *J. Ecol.* **52**, 121–38.

JEFFERIES R.L. & WILLIS A.J. (1964*b*) Studies on the calcicole-calcifuge habit. II. The influence of calcium on the growth and establishment of four species in soil and sand cultures. *J. Ecol.* **52**, 691–707.

JONES Ll.I. (1967) *Studies on Hill Land in Wales.* Tech. Bull. Welsh Plant Breed. Sta. No. 2.

LLOYD P.S., GRIME J.P. & RORISON I.H. (1971) Grassland vegetation of the Sheffield region. I. General features. *J. Ecol.* **59**.

MILTON W.E.J. (1947) The yield, botanical and chemical composition of natural hill herbage under manuring, controlled grazing and hay conditions. 1. Yield and botanical section. *J. Ecol.* **35**, 65–89.

OLSEN C. (1923) Studies on the hydrogen ion concentration of soil and its significance to vegetation especially to the natural distribution of plants. *C.r.Trav.Lab.Carlsberg*, **15**, 1–166.

PEASLEE D.E. & FRINK C.R. (1969) Influence of silicic acid on uptake of Mn, Al, Zn and Cu by tomatoes (*Lycopersicum esculentum*) grown on an acid soil. *Proc. Soil Sci. Soc. Am.* **33**, 569–71.

RORISON I.H. (1967) A seedling bioassay on some soils in the Sheffield area. *J. Ecol.* **55** 725–41.

RORISON I.H. (1968) The response to phosphorus of some ecologically distinct plant species. I. Growth rates and phosphorus absorption. *New Phytol.* **67**, 913–23.

SNAYDON R.W. (1962) Micro-distribution of *Trifolium repens* L. and its relation to soil factors. *J. Ecol.* **50**, 133–43.

SNAYDON R.W. & BRADSHAW A.D. (1961) Differential response to calcium within the species *Festuca ovina* L. *New Phytol.* **60**, 219–34.

SUTTON C.D. & GUNARY D. (1969) Phosphate equilibria in soil. In *Ecological Aspects of the Mineral Nutrition of Plants* (Ed. I.H.Rorison), pp. 127–34. Oxford.

THOMAS, BRYNMOR & TRINDER N. (1947) The Ash Components of some Moorland Plants. *Emp. J. exp. Agric.* **15**, 237–48.

THURSTON J.M. (1969) The effect of liming and fertilizers on the botanical composition of permanent grassland, and on the yield of hay. In *Ecological Aspects of the Mineral Nutrition of Plants* (Ed. I.H.Rorison), pp. 1–10 Oxford.

VLAMIS J. & WILLIAMS D.E. (1967) Manganese and Silicon interaction in the Gramineae. *Pl. Soil* **27**, 131–40.

WILLIS A.J. & YEMM E.W. (1961) Braunton Burrows: mineral nutrient status of the dune soils. *J. Ecol.* **49**, 377–90.

WILLIS A.J. (1963) Braunton Burrows: the effects on the vegetation of the addition of mineral nutrients to the dune soils. *J. Ecol.* **51**, 353–74.

WOODHEAD T.W. (1915) *The Study of Plants. Introduction to Botany and Plant Ecology* pp. 350 Oxford.

The experimental alteration of a *Kobresia*-rich sward in Upper Teesdale

D.W. JEFFREY, *Department of Biological Sciences, University of Lancaster*
Present address: *School of Botany, Trinity College, Dublin*

Introduction

It is not often that the opportunity arises to investigate the ecology of a rare plant in the field. In consequence the conservation of rare species, and of uncommon and often fragile plant communities, may have to be faced without clear knowledge of their behaviour under management techniques. Whilst not designed with a conservation aim in mind, this study of a community dominated by *Kobresia simpliciuscula* (Wahlenb.) Mackenzie may serve as a contribution towards tackling this sort of problem. The vegetation studied in this work will be largely destroyed by inundation later in 1970, leaving but a few fragments of *Kobresia* sward in the area. It is perhaps ironic that the inevitability of the destruction made the work at all feasible.

A generally accepted view of the arctic-alpine species in the Teesdale area is that they are relict members of a post glacial flora (Böcher 1951, Pigott 1956). A pollen analysis recently carried out by Dr J.Turner, and Miss V.P.Hewitson of the University of Durham (personal communication) has tended to confirm this view. Their evidence demonstrates the presence of arctic-alpine species in the area throughout zones VI and VII of the pollen record. They have also shown that a closed woodland canopy probably did not exist in the area during this period. The ecological problem is therefore a matter of deciding which environmental factors have contributed to the long term survival of arctic-alpine species.

Kobresia simpliciuscula was chosen as the major subject in the investigation for a number of reasons. It is a model arctic-alpine species, occupying moist calcareous sites (Hulten 1942), and is a very rare plant in Britain. Here it occurs in a few sites in Scotland above 760 m and in Teesdale at about 450–500 m. In Teesdale it is the only arctic-alpine actually dominating a plant community. This community was sufficiently extensive to permit replicated field experiments. In the areas most intensively studied, a total of 24 angio-sperm species, one pteridophyte, five bryophytes and one conspicuous blue green alga were recorded. However, more than 90 per cent of the angiosperm cover was contributed by only five species, namely, *Kobresia simpliciuscula* (*c.* 67 per cent), *Carex panicea*, (*c.* 6 per cent), *Carex lepidocarpa* (*c.* 2 per cent). *Festuca ovina* (*c.* 16 per cent) and *Plantago maritima* (*c.* 4 per cent). The vegetation was thus simple and open in structure, a further advantage from the experimental point of view.

In designing experiments relevant to the survival of *Kobresia*, it was assumed that certain stress factors were depressing the performance and competitive ability of other species. Conversely it was also assumed that *Kobresia* tolerated these stresses. This view is implicit in the account of Pigott (1956). Possible stress factors which the investigation takes into account are climate, grazing and trampling, heavy metal toxicity and major nutrient deficiency.

Manley (1942), in his account of the weather records of Great Dun Fell, emphasizes the subarctic climate of the Upper Tees valley, with its prolonged snow cover and relatively short cloudy summer. This seemed an obvious factor which could depress the performance of lowland species.

Grazing of domestic animals has long been a feature of the valley, and even before the coming of man, selective grazing of more palatable grasses could have occurred. This, combined with trampling of unstable substrata, could have maintained open habitats for slower growing species (Pigott 1956).

Many of the rare species, and *Kobresia* in particular, occur on soils associ-ated with carboniferous limestone metamorphosed by contact with the Whin Sill, an igneous intrusion. This remarkable limestone, commonly known as 'sugar limestone', weathers to give fragments of crystalline calcite, and thus soils containing calcareous gravel. Commercially exploited veins of Barytes ($BaSO_4$) with some associated Galena (PbS) cross the limestone and con-tribute variable amounts of lead and barium to the soils. Hence a selective toxicity could also be involved in the ecological system.

Lastly, in view of the demonstrations of major nutrient deficiencies of grasses on calcareous soils (Willis 1963; Lloyd & Pigott 1967), it seemed that nitrogen or phosphorus deficiency could be yet another factor contributing to depressed competition.

In order to obtain information relating to climate, biotic factors, and nutrient deficiency, two fertilizer addition experiments were carried out. The first, a short pilot experiment, was carried out on *Kobresia* turf removed to the University of Lancaster field station which has a lowland maritime climate. A second experiment was carried out over a period of two full seasons in the field. The field site on Widdybank Fell was fenced to exclude grazing animals. For comparison, a further enclosed field experiment was carried out on a drier

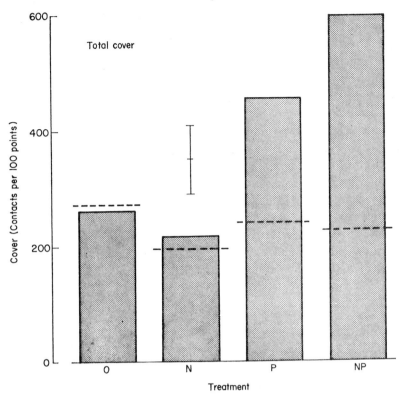

Figure 1. The effect of nutrient addition on vascular plant cover. Total cover 2 years after commencement of treatment is indicated by shaded histograms. The corresponding values at the commencement of treatment is shown by broken crosslines. The 95 per cent confidence limit is indicated.

Sesleria grassland site a few hundred metres away. The experimental design used throughout was a factorial addition of nitrogen and phosphorus. The four experimental treatments were plus nitrogen (N), plus phosphorus (P), plus nitrogen and phosphorus (NP) and control (O). As the structure of the vegetation was simple, consisting of mainly linear-leaved species, vertical point quadrats were used to monitor all experiments. The results of these point analyses are expressed as cover.

The field experiment was laid out in July 1967 on a sward chosen for its uniformly high cover of *Kobresia*. The area of each experimental plot was 1 m². The nitrogen application was at a rate of 10g N per m² as ammonium nitrate, and the phosphorus dressing was 5g P per m² as calcium hydrogen phosphate. Before application of the nutrients, the sward composition was estimated by placing 100 point quadrats in the central 50 × 50 cm portion of each plot. An interim partial recording of cover was made in July 1968 and in consequence all the nitrogen addition treatments were re-applied. A final recording, the results presented in this paper, was made in July 1969.

In both the pilot and field experiments a large increase in plant cover occurred in response to the P and NP addition treatments. Since the overall results of both experiments are essentially similar, only those of the prolonged field experiment will be discussed. The magnitude of this response is indicated in Fig. 1. Changes in cover in either the O or N treatments were very slight, and were probably random.

The increased growth of grass species was the main reason for the almost doubled cover. Figure 2 makes this clear, and indicates the contribution of two species to the response. In the P treated plots, *Festuca ovina* was the species contributing most to cover. This is not unexpected since *F.ovina* was the co-dominant species in the original *Kobresia* dominated sward. *Festuca rubra*, which made up less than one per cent of the original cover, experienced a ninetyfold increase under the P treatment, and almost equalled the cover of *F.ovina* in the NP plots, an increase of nearly 200 times. The general appearance of the P and NP treated plots was similar to a dune slack or saltmarsh

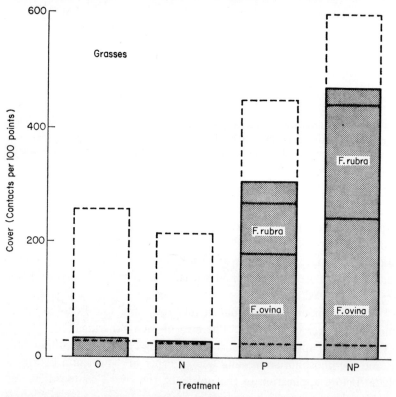

Figure 2. The effect of nutrient addition on grass cover. Total cover is also indicated. In P and NP treatments contributions of *Festuca ovina*, *F. rubra* and other grass species are distinguished. The values for grass cover at the commencement of treatment are shown by broken crosslines.

sward, similarity with the latter being accentuated by the presence of *Plantago maritima*.

The cover of *Kobresia* decreased under both P and NP treatments to 30 per cent and 10 per cent of the original value respectively (Fig. 3). Individual plants became etiolated in the increased depth of sward, and died. This was clearly observable within the first season of treatment. Failure was probably due to a metabolic and morphological inability of *Kobresia* to respond to additional phosphate, the plants finally succumbing to competition for light from the faster growing grasses. The diagram in Fig. 4. which is compiled from all the point analyses carried out in this work, gives some indication of the reaction of *Kobresia* to increased cover. In the natural situation it seems clear that *Kobresia* can compete successfully in sward densities up to a total cover of 300 contacts per 100 points, and contributing some two-thirds of this cover. If total cover is raised to about 400 contacts/100 points, in this case by the phosphate addition, *Kobresia* collapses, and its contribution to cover is halved. This gives some indication of the narrow margin between dominance

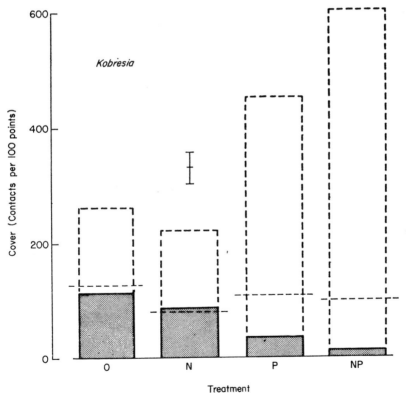

Figure 3. The effects of nutrient addition on *Kobresia* cover. Total cover is also indicated. The 95 per cent confidence limit for final *Kobresia* cover is shown and cover before treatment is indicated by the broken crosslines.

and near elimination. Under the cover finally achieved by the NP treatment, nearly 600 contacts per 100 points, *Kobresia* all but disappeared. *Kobresia* has not yet been completely eliminated, however, from any of the treated plots, and it would have been interesting to know if its long term survival at low frequency is possible. This mode of survival would be facilitated by gaps in the vegetation generated by senescence of other species.

The main conclusion to be drawn from the field experiment is that phosphate supply is the major factor depressing growth of grasses, which can otherwise compete to the detriment of *Kobresia* in the Teesdale environment. This response to phosphate is in surprising contrast to the results of Lloyd and Pigott (1967) and Willis (1963) who recorded responses of *Festuca rubra* to added nitrogen in two differing calcareous soils. The absence of a primary nitrogen response is not due to insufficient nitrogen application, since there is a clear nitrogen response in the presence of added phosphate.

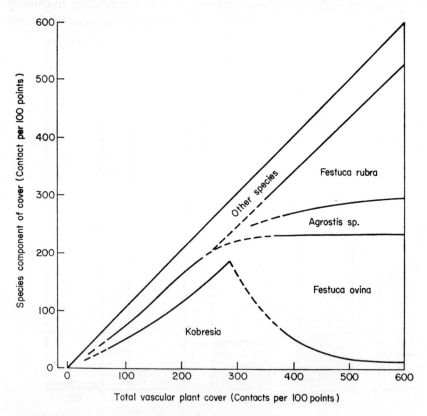

Figure 4. Species components of cover plotted against total cover. All the point analyses undertaken in the study have been used in compiling this curve which is drawn freehand. The range of total cover includes that occurring naturally in the field, and that generated by the addition treatments over two seasons.

Because of this ecologically important response to nutrient addition in face of the Teesdale climate it must also be concluded that climatic factors alone are not sufficient to depress the vegetative growth of competitor species. However, climate may well reinforce the effects of low nutrient supply in depressing overall plant production. This could well be significant in marginal edaphic situations. There may also be important climatic requirements involved in the reproductive biology of several arctic-alpine species. The lack of a response to the removal of grazing was in contrast to the results obtained from the *Sesleria* grassland experiment. Cover of *Sesleria* in particular did increase when grazing ceased. One casual observation common to both experiments, and not readily detected by point analysis, was the increase in frequency of flowers obvious generally in the enclosed areas, and particularly in the P and NP treated plots. Grazing could thus exert long-term selection against those species able to reproduce successfully from seed. It is unlikely that this is of great importance in the case of *Kobresia*. It is also probable that selective grazing would minimize the effects of local nutrient accumulation.

Since it seemed clear that a powerful edaphic factor was operating in favour of *Kobresia*, an investigation was carried out of the soils on which it occurred. Twenty-seven soil samples collected from all the relevant sites on Widdybank Fell were analysed. The results are presented in Table 1. Because of the variation of soil density encountered, the results are expressed in terms of soil volume.

Table 1. Analytical results from soils associated with *Kobresia simplicisucula*. In most cases the soil bulk density was calculated from the estimated ignition loss by the method of Jeffrey (1970). Where both bulk density and ignition loss were measured, however, good agreement with this method was observed.

	Mean	S.D. Mean	Range
pH	6·69	0·5	5·2 – 7·6
Total nitrogen	777mg/dm³	120	188 – 190
Total phosphorus	168mg/dm³	18	45 – 292
Inorganic P	93mg/dm³	29	28 – 236
Organic P	75mg/dm³	9	0 – 128
Total lead	889mg/dm³	135	106 – 2787
Ignition loss (% dry weight)	33·3%	9·0	6·4 – 67·1%
Bulk density (g per ml)	0·45		0·15 – 0·98

This analysis indicates nitrogen and phosphorus concentrations which are low by agricultural standards, but which are comparable with figures for dune slack (Willis *et al.* 1959) or the *Festuca* zone of a west coast salt marsh (unpublished data). The levels of lead are quite high when compared with the 50–100 p.p.m. lead encountered in 'normal' soils. When tabulating these results, it was observed that the phosphate concentration of the soils, in particular the inorganic phosphate concentration, was positively correlated with the lead concentration. This is demonstrated in Fig. 5. The question of lead acting as a factor depressing the availability or utilization of soil phosphate thus arises.

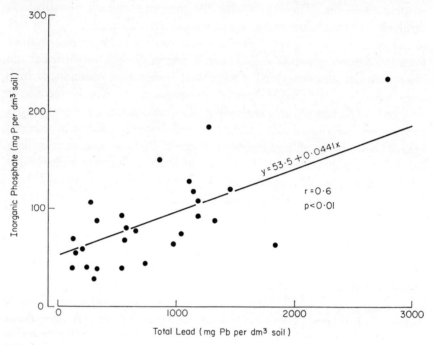

Figure 5. Inorganic phosphate and total lead content of 27 soil samples from *Kobresia* sites on Widdybank Fell.

As low phosphate supply is critical in ensuring the survival of *Kobresia*, factors must be postulated which control phosphate availability throughout the range of observed soil phosphate concentrations. Statistical correlation with phosphate concentration is a likely property of any such mechanism. Work is in progress at the present time to assess the effects of solid phase lead as galena, on the utilization by a range of plants of solid phase calcium phosphates.

As the ecological problem of *Kobresia* survival depends on the performance of grasses, results are presented of an early experiment with *Festuca ovina*. Two sources of material were used, clonally propagated tillers from Teesdale, and commercial seed. The plants were grown in a sand culture system comprising silica sand with 5 per cent calcium carbonate as the basic medium. The four experimental treatments were suggested by the correlation demonstration in Fig. 4. The treatments were 50 mgP/dm³, zero lead; 50 mgP/dm³,

1000 mgPb/dm³; 100 mgP/dm³, zero Pb; and 100 mgP/dm³, 1000 mgPb/dm³. Nitrogen, potassium, magnesium, and trace elements were supplied as a culture solution. According to the hypothesis, if the system is operating in the same manner as in the field, performance of plants in the P 100–Pb 1000 treatment should be similar to those at P 50–Pb zero. Performance at the other treatments should be relatively elevated (P 100–Pb zero) or depressed (P 50–Pb 1000). The results (Fig. 6), which are statistically reliable, appear to

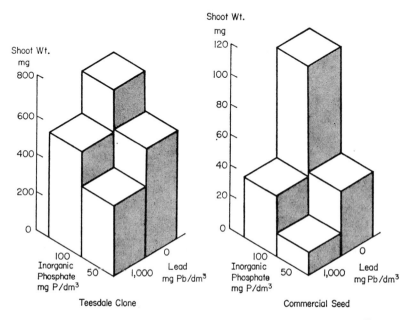

Figure 6. Shoot weights of two *Festuca ovina* populations grown experimentally on substrate modelled on the data shown in Fig. 5. Note difference in order of weight between clonal and seed material.

bear this out. Experiments carried out so far with *Kobresia* and sedges have not been a success because of the difficulty of obtaining uniform material, and because of their rather slow growth in any type of medium. The overall impression given of these species is of a lack of response to phosphate, and an overall depression of growth by the lead treatments. This impression is, however, not out of keeping with the hypothesis.

In similar experiments carried out with barium as barium sulphate no inhibitory effects have been detected. It is considered that the direct ecological effect of barytes in calcareous soils is probably negligible.

In any discussion of this work, it is important to realize that it is based mainly on an experimental examination of 12 m² of turf. The experiment carried out in the field indicates how closely, from a competition point of view, *Kobresia* is to its tolerance limit. Thus the amelioration of the main limiting factor to plant growth, phosphate supply, combined with the presence of two potentially fast-growing grass species, has produced conditions causing the virtual elimination of the slower-growing *Kobresia*. Since the soil phosphate concentrations of the *Kobresia* sites are not measurably low, it is inferred that a particular availability control is in operation. There is analytical and experimental evidence which supports the view that this factor could be the concentration of lead in the soils. This may be an ecological situation similar to that described for *Arenaria humifusa* by Rune (1955). This plant appears on calcareous rocks in the far north of Scandanavia, but as a relic in the south is confined to serpentine.

From a conservation viewpoint, it is clear that the nutritional *status quo* in Teesdale should be guarded. Microclimatic changes will probably not have much effect on the vegetative persistence of *Kobresia*. It would be unwise however, to extend the findings of this work to other situations or species without a check on their validity, but it is clear that eutrophication is a possible danger to this vegetation. Dr D.T.Streeter (this volume) has documented how public pressure, eutrophication, and radical changes in chalk downland vegetation are linked. It thus seems likely that yet other vegetation types on calcareous soils are susceptible to this type of pollution, and that management aimed particularly towards the conservation of rarer calcicole species should bear this in mind.

Acknowledgements

Professor C.D.Pigott has been very closely associated with all phases of this work, in particular the planning and execution of the field experiments. I wish to thank him for his very generous help and advice. The whole financial cost of this investigation was borne by the Teesdale Trust of Imperial Chemical Industries, and thanks are due to the trustees for their consideration.

In carrying out the field work, many people have helped in many ways. In particular Mr Tom Buffey, Site Research Officer, must be thanked for his constant supervision of the sites and generally invaluable work in facilitating research in the field.

Summary

A fertilizer addition experiment has been carried out on a sward dominated by the arctic-alpine relict, *Kobresia simpliciuscula*. Survival of species such as *Kobresia* has previously been attributed to the maintenance of an essentially open habitat by climatic or biotic factors. Phosphate addition, however, stimulated the growth of grasses, including species present in the original sward at low frequency and cover, with resultant closure of the sward. *Kobresia* was virtually eliminated by this treatment. The addition of nitrogen alone had no such effect.

The hypothesis is thus advanced that survival of *Kobresia* in Upper Teesdale has been dependent on the occurrence of low nutrient sites. Further evidence towards this view is presented.

References

BOCHER T.W. (1951) Distributions of plants in the circumpolar area in relation to ecological and historical factors. *J. Ecol.* **39**, 376–95.

HULTEN E. (1942) Flora of Alaska and Yukon. Vol. II. *K. fysiogr. Sällsk. Lund Förh.* N.F. **53** Nr. 1.

JEFFREY D.W. (1970) A note on the use of ignition loss as a means for the approximate estimation of soil bulk density. *J. Ecol.* **58**, 297–313.

LLOYD P.S. & PIGOTT C.D. (1967) The influence of soil conditions on the course of succession on the chalk of southern England. *J. Ecol.* **55**, 137–46.

MANLEY G. (1942) Meteorological observations on Dun Fell, a mountain station in northern England. *Q. Jl R. met. Soc.* **68**, 151–62.

PIGOTT C.D. (1956) The vegetation of Upper Teesdale in the North Pennines. *J. Ecol.* **44**, 545–85.

RUNE O. (1955) *Arenaria humifusa* i Sverige. *Svensk bot. Tidskr.* **49**, 197–216.

WILLIS A.J., FOLKES B.F., HOPE-SIMPSON J.F. & YEMM E.W. (1959) Braunton Burrows: The dune system and its vegetation. Part 1. *J. Ecol.* **47**, 1–24.

WILLIS A.J. (1963) Braunton Burrows: The effects on the vegetation of the addition of mineral nutrients to the dune soils. *J. Ecol.* **51**, 353–74.

Calluna heathlands: use and conservation in the light of some ecological effects of management

C.H.GIMINGHAM, *Department of Botany, University of Aberdeen*

Introduction

As recently as 100 years ago *Calluna* heathlands were extensive in western Europe, from southern Scandinavia to north-western France. Since then in many parts of this region their areas have become greatly reduced. Scotland and northern England, however, constitute an exception, retaining wide expanses of heath, mainly in upland districts, from which much of the character of the landscape is derived as well as some economic return to owners and occupiers of the land.

Heath vegetation is of interest from several standpoints: in addition to a certain value (particularly in harsh climates and on poor soils) as grazing for domestic and game animals or birds and suitability for recreational purposes, it is of great ecological importance both for research purposes and as a reservoir of wild life. However, because much of it occupies land of marginal agricultural value, heath has generally been exploited by minimum-input systems of herbivore production, based on management by burning which involves little labour. Conservation, therefore, implies on the one hand the action necessary to maintain viable examples of this vegetation in regions where it is fast disappearing, and on the other a broadly-based ecological approach to land use and management throughout whole districts in which heaths are still extensive, with habitat improvement and rehabilitation as the aim. While a continuing role for heathland in such regions should be envisaged, improved management and changing patterns of land use may further reduce its area, by introducing a greater variety of ecosystems.

Extensive research has recently been focused on heath ecosystems and the effects upon them of management by burning and grazing. Their responses to a variety of influences are now well understood. However, the use and conservation of heathlands may be approached with one or more of a number of different objectives in view. It is therefore the purpose of this paper to show how the results of research may be applied in determining the type of management which will achieve a specific objective.

Origins of heaths

Except at the higher altitudes (with which this paper is not concerned) there is ample evidence that, over the greater part of their area, heaths have been derived from former forest vegetation. Heathlands are now largely or entirely treeless, and while in some examples scattered tall shrubs (*Juniperus communis*) occur, these too are often lacking. The canopy-forming stratum is that of the ericoid dwarf-shrubs, and attention is here confined to communities in which *Calluna vulgaris* is dominant. Associated dwarf-shrubs and herbaceous species may form discontinuous strata below; there is frequently a ground stratum composed of mosses or lichens (or both). Such vegetation belongs to the oceanic and sub-oceanic regions of western Europe, and is best developed on relatively freely-drained soils or partially dried peat. On substrata liable to prolonged saturation it is replaced by moist heath or bog.

The northern part of the range of *Calluna* heathlands lies in the northern needle-leaved forest zone. Southwards, heaths extend well into the zone of the west European broad-leaved deciduous forest. Hence, in the past both these forest types must in various localities have given place to heath. While there has been considerable controversy about the influences which led to this replacement, accumulating palynological evidence lends strong support to the view that, in many parts of the region, the activities of man in destroying forest have played a major part. However, interference with the original ecosystem has generally been restricted to the removal of trees by burning or felling and the subsequent prevention of their return. The latter followed from use of the resulting vegetation as grazing for domestic animals, backed up by a system of management based on haphazard or, more recently, periodic burning. Hence, the communities are composed of species which, in the natural course of events, have survived or colonized after the disappearance of trees, many of them components of the lower strata of former forest vegetation. Since subsequent management has usually been confined to grazing and occasional burning, the species which remain as prominent components of heath communities are those which are tolerant of this treatment. Hence valuable opportunities are provided for investigating the effects of these factors upon an ecosystem composed of naturally-occurring species.

History of management

Where heaths replaced forest, they were often relatively intensively grazed at first, either by cattle or, as in the case of the Scottish uplands from the mid-eighteenth century, by sheep. At first rather infrequent burning was probably adequate to maintain production, but following upon some decline in the number of animals, periodic burning became necessary and by about 1800 was the rule among shepherds (Lovat 1911). Later, when on many estates the emphasis shifted from sheep rearing to game birds (grouse, *Lagopus l. scoticus*), it became evident, after some interruption in the sequence, that regular burning was just as necessary if not more so. The generally recommended frequency with which any stand should be burnt is once in every 10 to 12 years; hence, burning and subsequent regeneration may have occurred up to about 15 times in some heaths in the course of nearly two centuries, in addition to any spasmodic burning which may have taken place earlier.

Experience showed that this system was effective in preventing the return of trees and tall shrubs, and in maintaining relatively pure, dense, even-aged stands of *Calluna*. Further, a reasonable level of production of edible material by *Calluna* was sustained. This supplies almost the whole of the food requirements of grouse and, on acid soils low in calcium and other soil nutrients, also a valuable proportion of the diet of hill sheep. Hence, apart from some of the pasture grasses, *Calluna* is one of the few naturally occurring species in Britain to be managed for a sustained yield.

Rotational burning, supplemented by grazing, is in fact a system of management well suited to achieve these aims. During its life-span (normally limited to between 30 and 40 years) the individual *Calluna* plant if undisturbed by burning or grazing passes through a series of relatively well-defined growth-phases (Watt 1955; Gimingham 1960; Barclay-Estrup & Gimingham 1969). During the period of establishment (pioneer phase) plants are small, rather pyramidal in shape, and cover is incomplete. Later, after about 6 years, plants pass into the building phase in which production per unit area becomes maximal (Barclay-Estrup 1970) and the characteristic branching pattern produces a dense canopy. From an age of about 15 years there is a decline in the rate of growth of peripheral shoots and a tendency for the canopy to thin out near the centre of the dwarf-shrub. This is described as the mature phase, and is followed by the degenerate phase in which the central branches tend to collapse and die, forming an expanding gap in the centre of the plant. Cover declines to about 40 per cent.

Determinations of productivity and of the concentrations of nutrients in the edible portions of the plant show that by the time a stand has reached an age of about 10 years its grazing value has already deteriorated. This decline may be postponed indefinitely on an experimental scale by regimes of persistent defoliation (clipping or heavy grazing; Grant & Hunter 1966), but not in the field at normal rates of stocking. Hence, burning is indispensable, but at least in northern Britain the capacity for effective vegetative regeneration after fire is reduced with increasing age (Mohamed & Gimingham 1970). Furthermore, as additional fuel is continually accumulating in the woody parts of the plant there is a tendency for higher temperatures to be generated in older stands (Kenworthy 1963), increasing the probability of damage or destruction of the stem base. From all points of view, therefore, burning should be carried out while the plant is still in the building phase, preferably before it reaches the age of about 15.

Effects of management

The most obvious results are that the great majority of heath stands are even-aged, and that they are prevented from reaching the mature and degenerate phases. Since cover and quantity of edible material are both limite din the pioneer phase, management aims to minimize the duration of this phase. Burning is carried out, as far as possible, under conditions favouring rapid and uniform regeneration and the re-establishment of closed cover within 3 to 4 years. Although the hillsides generally show a patchwork of stands* of differing age, most of the patches consist of *Calluna* in the building phase. Hence, some of the ecological consequences of this system of management can be assessed by comparing the habitat and associated species characteristic of *Calluna* in its building phase with those typical of the other phases. This is best done in an area where all phases are represented; that is, in a stand having an uneven-aged population of *Calluna*. Except for fragments in rough or inaccessible terrain such stands are scarce, for they must have been free from burning (and heavy grazing) for considerably longer than a single life-span of *Calluna*, probably for at least 60–100 years, to reach this condition. However, examples can be found, on one of which, a few miles south of Aberdeen, detailed observations have recently been made (Barclay–Estrup & Gimingham 1969).

Such an area displays a mosaic of individuals of *Calluna* at all stages of the life-history. Analysis of the micro-habitat and associated species shows that the greatest contrasts are between the building and mature phases on the one hand, and the pioneer and degenerate on the other. It has already been noted that production of new shoots per unit area and density of canopy are maximal during the building phase. Correspondingly, illumination and air-movement close to the ground surface are minimal (illumination reduced to 2 per cent or less of that above the canopy; air-movement generally negligible). Temperatures fluctuate less in the building than in any other phase, and the atmosphere below the canopy remains moist throughout the whole

---

* Relatively small patches are recommended for grouse-moors: larger blocks usually satisfy the requirements of sheep farming. But in both cases the objective is to burn as much as possible of the *Calluna* heath on a 10–12 year rotation.

year (Barclay-Estrup 1971). However, a significant proportion of the rainfall is interpreted by the canopy of building or mature plants, and re-evaporated into the atmosphere. The contribution of litter to the soil surface increases with age until plants are about 20 years old and thereafter remains fairly steady (Chapman 1967), so that there is marked accumulation during the building and mature phases. The effects on the dispersion of associated species are striking. In 1955 Watt demonstrated a reduced frequency and performance of *Pteridium aquilinum* fronds in patches of building *Calluna*. Similarly, the cover of all other vascular plant species in the community is least in the areas occupied by building *Calluna*, and the same applies to bryophytes and lichens (Barclay-Estrup & Gimingham 1969). No associated species of any kind can survive in the period during which the *Calluna* canopy is at its densest, and throughout the building phase the accompanying flora may be restricted largely to a weak understorey of shade-tolerant species such as *Erica cinerea*, *Vaccinium vitis-idaea*, and *Festuca ovina*, a few scrambling plants such as *Potentilla erecta* which can bring their leaves to canopy level each year, and scattered mosses such as *Hypnum cupressiforme* or *Dicranum scoparium*.

The invertebrate fauna of the patches occupied by building and mature *Calluna* is also clearly distinguished from that of the other phases, consisting mainly of species requiring the shade, shelter and other characteristics of the microclimate mentioned above, particularly centipedes (Chilopoda) and millipedes (Diplopoda) (Barclay-Estrup, personal communication).

However, the communities of uneven-aged stands of *Calluna* are often rich in species both of animals and plants. It follows that, apart from the animals just mentioned, they tend to a great extent to arrange themselves amongst pioneer *Calluna* or in the gaps in the centres of degenerate individuals, where illumination reaches about 75 per cent of that above canopy level and temperatures rise in sunlight (although greater extremes of cold, wind-exposure and saturation deficit also occur). Here, in the quadrats investigated, the maximum cover was given by the 10 species of vascular plants (other than *Calluna*), 10 bryophytes and 1 lichen; while the occurrence of other invertebrates such as spiders, phalangids and ants (Arachnida: Araneae and Opilionida; Hymenoptera, Formicoidea) was most frequent.

The purpose of establishing this contrast is to demonstrate that heath management, ensuring as it does that the greatest possible area is occupied by building *Calluna*, has a profound influence on the communities, quite apart from the direct impact of fire and grazing on the ecosystem. This influence is in the direction of reducing both variety and quantity (biomass and cover) of plant species other than *Calluna*, and reducing the variety of invertebrate animals.

The direct effects of fire and grazing must next be considered, but can be reviewed briefly since these have been the subject of numerous recent publications (Allen 1964; Gimingham 1964; Grant & Hunter 1966; Kayll & Gimingham 1965; McVean 1960; McVean & Lockie 1969; Miller 1964; Miller & Miles 1970; Mohamed & Gimingham 1970; Nicholson 1964; Robertson & Davies 1965; Whittaker 1961; Whittaker & Gimingham 1962). While the sequence of events through one or two burning rotations can sometimes be followed, the long-term consequences are more difficult to assess. Attempts have been made to compare heath ecosystems with adjacent unburnt woodland (Elliott 1953), but it is impossible to test the original comparability of the habitat, or the effects of subsequent modifications of the woodland. Often the best that is possible is to compare heaths which are known to have been burnt many times with others much less frequently burnt, allowing for differences in soil and climate. It is seldom possible to distinguish clearly between the immediate effects of repeated burning, and those produced by the additional impact of grazing and by the encouragement of rapid uniform regeneration of *Calluna*. However, certain species stand out as susceptible to the regime in general, where it is practised systematically: these include, for example, *Juniperus communis*, *Polypodium vulgare*, *Vaccinium vitis-idaea*, *Empetrum nigrum*, etc. In general, species lacking the power of rapid vegetative regeneration from the stem base or underground parts are the most susceptible.

Despite the progressive elimination of some species, the effect of fire is to maintain at all times, in some part of the heath, areas in the pioneer phase. These ensure the continuation of a considerable pool of plant species (depending on the nature of the soil surface), which may include a variety of herbs and numerous mosses and lichens. The effects of fire in directly reducing floristic diversity may be more apparent than real, although the result is to reduce greatly the quantitative contribution of species other than *Calluna*. Where grazing closely follows upon burning, this may lead more rapidly to the elimination of palatable grasses and herbs.

A fire causes extensive temporary changes in the structure of the ecosystem. Some of the nutrients formerly contained in the vegetation are lost in smoke (or by volatilization). Kenworthy (1964) and Allen (1964) have shown that at about 600°C, over 60 per cent of the total nitrogen contained in the vegetation is lost in this way. Quantities lost increase with temperature, and above about 800°C the loss of the other elements including phosphorus and potassium may become significant. The remainder are deposited on the soil surface in the form of ash. Hence, for a time the total fund of nutrients in the ecosystem is located in the soil and, as some of the contents of ash are water-soluble, the concentration of available nutrients in the surface is temporarily increased. Other changes at the surface include the spread of algae and lichens: at Kerloch in Aberdeenshire, for example, Scott (personal communication) found that *Lecidia uliginosa* spreads like a film over the raw humus and old *Calluna* litter, covering about 67 per cent of the surface in 2 years, later declining. This skin perhaps both reduces rain penetration and aeration of the surface.

These effects are short-lived, and *Calluna* regeneration is probably encouraged by the flush of available minerals. However, the possibility has been raised (Elliott 1953) that every fire results in some loss of nutrients, not only in smoke, but also in solution in rainwater draining through the soil or running off the surface. More recently, estimations have indicated that this is likely to be important only in the case of N and P, since for the rest the losses over the period between fires are more than equated by input of ions contained in rainwater, assuming that these are largely retained in the rooting region (Allen 1964; Robertson & Davies 1965). The cycle of repeated burning, therefore, does not appear seriously to deplete the nutrient fund, but may make worse the deficiencies of N and P which have probably characterized heath soils ever since forest clearance. Some types of heath community, however, may be protected against depletion of N by the presence of *Ulex minor* or *Ulex gallii* in strong admixture with *Calluna*.

Properly carried out, the traditional system of management seems therefore to achieve the desired aims without serious degradation of the habitat. However, certain long-term changes are inherent in the treatment, and others may be initiated if it is wrongly applied. As McVean & Lockie (1969) point out, the species which regenerate freely after burning are, in the main, shallow-rooted and produce an acid, raw humus. Humic acids promote leaching of the upper horizons, resulting in downward passage of nutrients to levels which are below the rooting region, where they are lost to the system.

Podsolization is promoted, often to the extent of the formation of hardpan. The exact effects of a monoculture of *Calluna* in hastening this development have never been quantified, but observation suggests that they are significant. This is a progressive change which is inherent in the pattern of management, as is the slow removal of nutrients by cropping the herbivores, sheep, cattle, grouse, hares or deer. That this is not a heavy cropping is shown by Miller (1964), but over a period of time it may be a contributory factor. The grazing animal may also cause a more rapid uptake of nutrients from the soil by the vegetation during the period between fires.

Poor control or unwise application of burning results in a delay of regeneration. This may have several consequences. Most usual is a tendency for *Calluna* to be replaced by unwanted (weed) species: notably *Pteridium aquilinum*, or in wetter habitats *Nardus stricta*, *Scirpus caespitosus*, *Molinia caerulea* or *Juncus squarrosus*. When the bare or pioneer phases are unduly prolonged 'sheet washing' occurs, causing the loss of much of the surface humus and even some of the mineral soil; on steeper slopes gully erosion takes place (McVean & Lockie 1969). In unsuitable weather conditions, a fire may generate too great a heat and burn off the surface organic matter, greatly delaying regeneration and increasing the dangers of erosion. McVean & Lockie also suggest that wet heaths and peat areas are more vulnerable to all the above dangers than those on the more freely drained, mineral soils. According to McVean(1960), there has been a decline in the amount of heather in the wetter, western parts of northern Scotland as a result of burning, whereas to the east fire continues to maintain the pure stands of *Calluna* which it originally created.

Conservation

As indicated by the foregoing discussion, enough is now known of the eco-logical effects of the various treatments to which heathlands have been sub-ject to devise appropriate systems of management to serve the needs of conservation. However, conservation in heathland districts may be approached with any one of several different objectives in view and it is essential to define these precisely, for management will differ accordingly. In some instances re-habilitation and improved production from a large area will be the aim of con-servation in its widest sense, in others the continued existence of quite large tracts of heath for their aesthetic, sporting or recreational value may be re-quired, while small areas may be set aside as nature reserves on account of their wildlife and scientific interest.

The application of principles of conservation to regional planning and development is still in its infancy, but its importance is becoming widely accepted. Where a countryside containing extensive heathland is concerned, account must be taken of the effects of past systems of management. Where burning and grazing have been applied carefully, at the right intensity and at suitable intervals in appropriate habitats, depletion of resources is minimal. None the less, the system promotes the formation of raw humus and podsoli-zation, reduces the variety of herbs and of animal species, and involves a slow extraction accompanied by little or no input of nutrients. Further, there can be few instances in which a high standard of management has been main-tained throughout the history of burning. Almost everywhere some deteriora-tion is possible when, for one of several reasons, regeneration is slow after burning, while in some areas nutrient deficiency, especially of N and P, and erosion have become pronounced. Except in a few areas conservation, to be effective, requires measures to counteract these processes. One approach might be the application of fertilizers to eliminate nutrient deficiency and to improve the feeding value of heather. In remote or exposed localities, or where soils are very poor, some consideration is being given to this means of achieving a modest improvement of the traditional system. Since, however, so small a proportion of the biomass of *Calluna* is actually used by herbivores this may be a wasteful method, involving expense where it can least be afforded and will provide only a small return.

In all the more favourable environments, rehabilitation will generally involve greater change, for the processes inherent in a monoculture of *Calluna* can only be counteracted fully by fundamentally altering the ecosystem. In the main, heathland has developed in habitats unusable for cultivation, although in Denmark notably successful conversion of heaths to arable land has been achieved in the course of just over 100 years. More generally, heaths have given place on the one hand to forestry, and on the other to improved herbage for grazing. Afforestation has eliminated almost all heathland in Sweden, and is taking increasing acreages in Scotland. There has been a tendency to assume that return of a forest community to land which formerly carried it would restore ecological health. Certainly the ecosystem benefits by the use of fertilizers, by improvements effected in the soil hydrology, and by amelioration of the microclimate both within and around the plantation. However, under trees of commercial value the raw humus layer will continue to increase in thickness and acidity (Rennie 1961), and the long-term effects of commercial afforestation on the habitat have not been fully investigated.

Improvement of the herbage for sheep or cattle, to be effective, requires rather massive injection of nutrients into the system, and close control of grazing: under these circumstances grassland replaces heath either by natural invasion, encouraged by grazing, or as a result of re-seeding with grass and clover species. Small areas have been upgraded in this way in many parts of northern Britain; they have increased the carrying capacity of the ground and to some extent improvement in soil and herbage has extended outwards from the area treated. Little is known, however, of the degree of permanence of these effects or the best ways to secure lasting changes in the soil and vegetation. These are not likely to be very significant without a departure from the 'free-range' type of grazing management towards the more intensive use of chosen areas.

Applying a wide definition of conservation, these developments in the use of land now largely heath-covered satisfy some of its requirements. They are not necessarily the best that can be devised, and are certainly not the only ones which will be attempted. For example, the possibilities of using native trees (e.g. *Alnus glutinosa*, *Betula* spp.) to effect some soil improvement and a better cycling of nutrients has been raised by McVean & Lockie (1969), and have hitherto been little explored. It is therefore of the first importance that extensive developments should be preceded by research which will establish in full their impacts on the ecosystem, so that the end results can be shown to improve on the heathland system.

This approach to conservation implies that, on a large scale, improved production from these areas will involve greater diversity of vegetation and perhaps considerable contraction of the heath communities. *Calluna* stands are unlikely to disappear because of their value for winter-feed, and because they provide grazing under conditions unsuitable for other herbage. There is a strong argument, however, for the retention of at least some extensive tracts of heath because of their scenic, recreational and sporting value. To achieve this would require little more than a continuation of present management practices. None the less, both conservation policy and the interests of sport would require close attention to the recommendations, already well established, for a burning regime which achieves its ends with minimal habitat deterioration. Picozzi (1968) has shown that, more than any other factor, burning management is responsible for the maintenance of good stocks of grouse on *Calluna* heaths. As far as possible, heather should always be burnt before it exceeds 10–12 years of age, but individual fires, though numerous, should be limited to small areas (less than 2 ha). Not only does this provide a suitable pattern of young and older *Calluna* for a high density of grouse territories, but it also ensures that fires will be burnt only in weather conditions permitting close control. The danger of excessive heat will be minimized, so encouraging rapid regeneration; while the small size of each burnt patch reduces the incidence of excessive run-off or erosion. In this way management can be brought into line with the results of research reviewed earlier in this paper.

The recreational and sporting value of heathland may ensure its survival in Britain, but unfortunately the necessary management, however well controlled, does not serve the purpose of maintaining diversity of wild-life. Areas managed for sports cannot therefore at the same time adequately fill the role of nature reserves. Heathland is a man-made landscape, but it is one which has become an integral and characteristic feature of parts of western Europe. The habitats and communities, although maintained only by continuance of human activity, have developed into well-defined ecosystems which must therefore be included in any representative series of habitats and vegetation types selected as nature reserves. Some heaths, as a result of nearly 200 years of the management described, have become biologically uniform, perhaps monotonous; but, ecologically, vegetational pattern and diversity of species (both plant and animal) are more characteristic.

Where the aim is a wild-life reserve, the conservation of heathland therefore requires not only the prevention of tree and shrub invasion, but also the encouragement of small-scale pattern. As shown above, this results when the *Calluna* population is uneven-aged, having the effect of creating corresponding variations in the micro-environment which permit numerous species of differing ecological requirements, both plants and animals, to occur in a restricted area. This type of community is of great scientific value and of interest to a wide range of naturalists. To encourage its development may require freedom from burning for a considerable period, although in most areas occasional recourse to fire will always be essential to prevent succession to scrub and woodland (and may, in some localities, require to be supplemented by other control measures). Moore (1962) has suggested, for example, that the survival of the Dartford warbler (*Sylvia undata*) on Dorset heaths depends on the maintenance of an adequate supply of old *Calluna* with *Ulex europaeus*, as produced by a mosaic of not-too-frequent fires. Unfortunately, just as uneven-aged stands provide opportunities, in the patches of pioneer or degenerate *Calluna*, for a variety of other species of interest, so there are opportunities for unwanted species to invade. Continued management must therefore be directed towards elimination of species which can reduce the dominance of *Calluna*, such as *Pteridium aquilinum* or tree species. If this is successful, small-scale pattern in the vegetation will be perpetuated, for the changes associated with the life history of *Calluna* are cyclical (Watt 1955; Barclay-Estrup & Gimingham 1969), owing to the eventual return of pioneer *Calluna* in the gaps left by degenerate plants, even though these may temporarily be occupied by other species. In an uneven-aged stand different stages of the cycle will be represented in adjacent patches.

For purposes of reserve management, it is also important to know what minimum area it is necessary to control in order to maintain a typical example of this type of community structure. Much more research on this problem is necessary, along the lines established by Moore (1962) with special reference to the Dorset heaths. By comparative and experimental investigation, the area required by any species to maintain a viable population can be estimated. For any particular community the key species can be taken as those characteristic of the community-type and those of greatest interest in regard to wildlife conservation. The minimal size for a reserve is reached only at an area in which populations of all the key species can survive; in most cases this has yet to be determined. However, the loss of key species consequent upon fragmentation of the habitat, and isolation of the fragments, has been demonstrated.

Summary

Heathland possesses unique scientific interest, both in virtue of its distinctive flora and fauna and of the opportunity it affords for examining a managed ecosystem composed of naturally established species. The areas it occupies are rapidly being claimed for afforestation, cultivation, reseeding and other purposes. In some western European countries almost the only surviving examples are those now protected in reserves established to safeguard their scenic, scientific or historical interest (the latter, for example, in northern Germany where in certain reserves traditional forms of management are perpetuated because of their historical and cultural significance). In parts of southern England contraction and fragmentation of types of heathland of great ecological interest has proceeded so far that there must be some doubt of the viability of even those samples rescued and declared as reserves. While a similar fate may threaten many types of so-called natural vegetation, these can survive if rescued in time, whereas a type such as heath which owes its origin to human activity is especially vulnerable when cultures and patterns of land use evolve and change. In northern Britain it may appear that time is on the side of those who recognize the interest of *Calluna* heaths, but when change comes it may be far-reaching and it is wise to be prepared. Already some examples of different types of heath are included in National Nature Reserves, but conservation of the heath areas should be approached more systematically, bearing in mind the three requirements:

first, for the up-grading of the habitats generally, with reduction of the total area of heath;

second, for the maintenance of some large tracts of heath for sport, recreation and landscape; and

third, for the adequate representation of heaths in nature reserves.

The intention of this paper has been to show that one form of management will not serve all three purposes. The function of each area must be precisely determined and management planned to secure definite objectives.

References

ALLEN S.E. (1964) Chemical aspects of heather burning. *J. appl. Ecol.* 1, 347–67.

BARCLAY-ESTRUP P. (1970) The description and interpretation of cyclical processes in a heath community. II. Changes in biomass and shoot production during the *Calluna* cycle. *J. Ecol.* 58, 243–9.

BARCLAY-ESTRUP P. (1971) The description and interpretation of cyclical processes in a heath community. III. Microclimate in relation to the *Calluna* cycle. *J. Ecol.* 59, 143–66.

BARCLAY-ESTRUP P. & GIMINGHAM C.H. (1969) The description and interpretation of cyclical changes in a heath community. I. Vegetational change in relation to the *Calluna* cycle. *J. Ecol.* 57, 737–58.

CHAPMAN S.B. (1967) Nutrient budgets for a dry heath ecosystem in the south of England. *J. Ecol.* 55, 677–89.

ELLIOTT R.J. (1953) *Heather burning.* Ph.D. Thesis, Sheffield University.

GIMINGHAM C.H. (1960) Biological flora of the British Isles: *Calluna vulgaris* (L.) Hull. *J. Ecol.* 52, 285–97.

GIMINGHAM C.H. (1964) Land use in the Scottish Highlands. III. The composition of the vegetation and its balance with environment. *Advmt Sci., Lond.* 21, 8–13.

GRANT S. & HUNTER R.F. (1966) The effects of frequency and season of clipping on the morphology, productivity and chemical composition of *Calluna vulgaris* (L.) Hull. *New Phytol.* 65, 125–33.

KAYLL A.J. & GIMINGHAM C.H. (1965) Vegetative regeneration of *Calluna vulgaris* after fire. *J. Ecol.* 53, 729–34.

KENWORTHY J.B. (1963) Temperatures in heather burning. *Nature, Lond.* **200**, 1226.

KENWORTHY J.B. (1964) *A study of the changes in plant and soil nutrients associated with moor burning and grazing.* Ph.D. Thesis, University of St Andrews.

LOVAT, LORD (1911) Heather burning. In *The Grouse in Health and Disease* (Ed. A.S. Leslie), pp. 392–412. London.

MCVEAN D.N. (1960) Muir burning and conservation. *Scott. Agric.* **39**, 78–82.

MCVEAN D.N. & LOCKIE J.S. (1969) *Ecology and Land Use in Upland Scotland.* Edinburgh.

MILLER G.R. (1964) Land use in the Scottish Highlands. VII. The management of heather moors. *Advmt Sci., Lond.* **21**, 23–9.

MILLER G.R. & MILES J. (1970) Regeneration of heather (*Calluna vulgaris* (L.) Hull) at different ages and seasons in north-east Scotland. *J. appl. Ecol.* **7**, 51–60.

MOHAMED B.F. & GIMINGHAM C.H. (1970) The morphology of vegetative regeneration in *Calluna vulgaris*. *New Phytol.* **69**, 743–50.

MOORE N.W. (1962) The heaths of Dorset and their conservation. *J. Ecol.* **50**, 369–91.

NICHOLSON I.A. (1964) Land use in the Scottish Highlands. VI. The influence of management practices on the present day vegetational pattern, and developmental trends. *Advmt Sci., Lond.* **21**, 18–23.

PICOZZI N. (1968) Grouse bags in relation to the management and geology of heather moors. *J. appl. Ecol.* **5**, 483–8.

ROBERTSON R.A. & DAVIES G.E. (1965) Quantities of plant nutrients in heather ecosystems. *J. appl. Ecol.* **2**, 211–19.

RENNIE P.J. (1961) Some long-term effects of tree growth on soil productivity. In: *Recent Advances in Botany*, pp. 1636–40. Toronto.

WATT A.S. (1955) Bracken versus heather, a study in plant sociology. *J. Ecol.* **43**, 490–506.

WHITTAKER E. (1961) Temperatures in heath fires. *J. Ecol.* **49**, 709–15.

WHITTAKER E. & GIMINGHAM C.H. (1962) The effects of fire on the regeneration of *Calluna vulgaris* (L.) Hull from seed. *J. Ecol.* **50**, 815–22.

Importance of soil toxicity in relation to the stability of plant communities

R.K.ROBINSON *Department of Forestry, University of Oxford*

Introduction

It is unusual to find in a mesophytic environment any one factor able to dictate completely the pattern of plant associations, and in this respect soil toxicity is no exception. Nevertheless, in some communities there is little doubt that toxic compounds in the soil do exert a marked differential effect on the growth of competing higher plants. The origin of these compounds is usually a higher plant, either as a growing entity or as a source of material for decomposition, and the toxins produced may be either fungitoxic or phytotoxic in action. Many species have been reported as providing sources of metabolites which are toxic to other plants (Bonner 1950; Woods 1960), and for this reason the material in this paper refers only to situations where the stability and species composition of an entire community is, at least in part, determined by toxic factors in the soil. In particular the influence of such factors in relation to the dominance of *Calluna vulgaris* (Hull) over certain heathland areas is considered.

Evidence suggesting the presence of toxic compounds in heathland soils

It has long been known that heathlands are inhospitable sites for afforestation, and Muller (1903) was perhaps the first to observe the 'checking' of growth of Norway spruce and silver fir on *Calluna* heathlands in western Jutland. Satisfactory growth of the spruce took place only for as long as re-invasion of the sites by *Calluna* did not occur. It has been suggested that competition for available nutrients or soil moisture are responsible for this 'checking' of spruce by *Calluna*, but Braathe (1950) sees these factors as subsidiary to a biological effect on spruce by *Calluna* itself. Changes in the root systems of 'checked' Sitka spruce following the killing of *Calluna* around their bases have been described by Yeatman (1955). Where the *Calluna* was killed by mulching, the first reaction of the spruce was to produce a crop of adventitious roots between the mulch and the original peat. Then, over the next three years, the original root system formed in the nursery began to develop and a normal overall growth rate for spruce was resumed. The same author was of the opinion that an increased availability of nutrients was not responsible for the resumed growth. The obvious conclusion remains, therefore, that the inhibition of root extension was due to some antagonistic factor in the *Calluna* peat, a view which has been confirmed in this laboratory.

The idea that the superficial organic layer of heathland soils contains substances inimical to root growth and the formation of ectotrophic mycorrhizas had already been suggested by Rayner & Neilson-Jones (1944). However, in the absence of concrete evidence as to the nature of this inhibitory material or its origin their conclusions met with some scepticism. Brian, Hemming & McGowan (1945) carried the investigation a stage further by suggesting that antibiotics from the normal saprophytic microflora might be implicated, at least in suppressing the formation of mycorrhizas. However, further study soon established that antibiotics are unlikely to occur in significant amounts in the soil. In this present investigation the toxicity of *Calluna* peat to the growth of certain plant species was assumed to be due to two discrete types of toxic metabolite; one, phytotoxic in nature and derived from decaying litter, the other, fungitoxic and having its origin in the living *Calluna* plant. It was further postulated that both could be equally effective in relation to the stability and species composition of *Calluna* heathlands.

Phytotoxic activity of *Calluna* raw humus

The work of Yeatman, already mentioned, and that of Laing (1932) indicates an almost total absence of root development by spruce in the organic layer of heathland soils. The same is true where the colonization of heathland has been attempted by seedlings of indigenous species, for example, birch. Available field evidence indicates that this condition could be due to some phytotoxic component within *Calluna* raw humus. This conclusion was supported by a factorial experiment designed to determine the extent to which factors, such as acid pH, low availability of nutrients or unsuitable soil moisture content, influenced the growth of wheat (var Koga II) in pots containing a mixture of non-calcareous grit and *Calluna* peat. The results of this experiment and other preliminary trials with different test species, e.g. peas, and tomatoes, clearly showed that some material from *Calluna* raw humus was capable of preventing root development, irrespective of how other factors were manipulated.

To be ecologically active it is probable that a factor of the type proposed would have to be water-soluble, and the validity of this surmise was tested by growing seedlings in sand culture; the nutrient solution of Hoagland & Arnon (1938) was used amended by water extracts of *Calluna* peat. Seedlings of horticultural crops were employed simply to facilitate experimentation but, where possible, specific aspects of the basic hypothesis were examined further using species which might be expected to compete with *Calluna* under field conditions. To obtain an aqueous extract containing the toxic factor, raw humus (500 g) was fragmented into a 2 litre flask together with 500 ml of distilled water. It was then left to stand for 12 hours. After this time the liquid was removed from the organic matter by means of a press, followed by filtration through two layers of muslin. The product was a brown, opalescent fluid, and one such preparation was used to amend the nutrient solutions for the sand culture experiment referred to above; in each case (see Table I) the final concentration of nutrients was the same.

The roots of the test plants showed a restriction of growth correlated with increasing concentration of peat extract, but in no case could any sign of fungal invasion be discerned. It is clear, therefore, that *Calluna* peat does contain

Table 1. Effect of water extract of *Calluna* peat on root growth of the test seedlings indicated.

Test material	Mean root length in cm (average of 20 plants sampled at 14 days)				
	% extract present in 35 ml of solution				
	0	25	50	75	100
Wheat	7·5	5·4	1·5	0·6	0·5
Barley	8·3	4·8	2·2	0·4	0·5
Pea	5·2	2·4	1·2	0·2	0·0
Sweet pea	6·1	2·8	0·9	0·3	0·0
Tomato	4·8	3·1	1·2	0·8	0·4

a water-soluble factor capable of inhibiting the growth of roots of certain higher plants.

It was further possible to inhibit the growth of isolated pea roots with water-extracts of *Calluna* peat under aseptic conditions employing the technique of Torrey (1959), and to correlate this restricted growth with an inhibition of oxygen uptake by similar root material. Comparable results were obtained employing seedlings of tomato. The diminished oxygen uptake induced by these water-extracts formed a useful assay for the presence of the phytotoxic factor, and the following procedure was adopted as a standard means of screening samples of *Calluna* raw humus for phytotoxicity.

Tomato seeds (Moneymaker) were surface sterilized with hypochlorite solution and incubated on moist filter paper (sterile) in the dark for 4 days. Batches of 50 germinated seeds with radicles approximately 5–10 mm in length were selected and placed in 100 ml of a water-extract of *Calluna* peat for 12 hours. After this time the seedlings were washed in distilled water and transferred to 3·0 ml of phosphate buffer ($M/15$ Na_2HPO_4/KH_2PO_4, pH 4·5) in Warburg flasks; carbon dioxide was absorbed by 20 per cent KOH. Four flasks were used with each test treatment, and each experiment was repeated at least three times. The control treatment was similar except that the soil extract was prepared from a grassland loam soil (pH 4·2); the influence of peat extracts on oxygen uptake by the test roots was referred to this standard.

This procedure gave a simple and reproducible means of detection of the phytotoxin, and Fig. 1 shows the results of a typical series of assays carried out during August 1968. Similar results were obtained using roots from both wheat (var. Koga) and peas (var. Onward) and with roots of *Picea abies*. Although one cannot, on the basis of laboratory results, directly suggest an ecological significance for an occurrence, it is reasonable to propose that the phytotoxicity displayed, *in vitro*, by water-extracts of *Calluna* peat may also be operative under field conditions.

Evidence to date suggests that the phytotoxin is a small, water-soluble

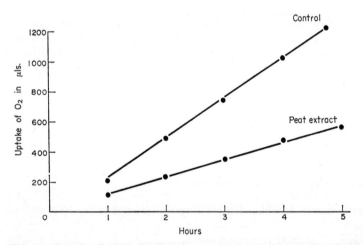

Figure 1. Uptake of oxygen in μlitres by tomato roots in the presence of water-extracts of *Calluna* peat.

molecule which is easily degraded even at the pH at which it normally occurs. It is derived from the decomposition of the *Calluna* litter, for incubation of freshly fallen leaf material gives rise to a phytotoxin in all respects identical to that present in water-extracts of naturally occurring peat. One last feature of the phytotoxic phenomenon which is of interest in relation to its role in the field is that the level of detectable activity fluctuates markedly with season (see Fig. 2). This variation suggests that it is of biological origin, being produced in easily detectable amounts only when the summer rise in soil temperature stimulates the microflora into activity. This effect of temperature has been

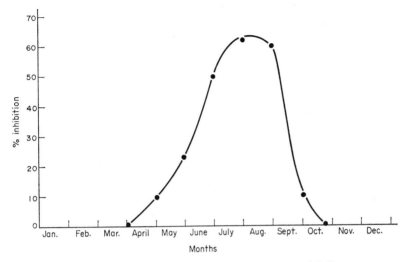

Figure 2. Seasonal variation in phytotoxicity of water-extracts of *Calluna* peat—percentage inhibition of oxygen uptake by tomato roots.

verified in the laboratory, and it is feasible to suppose that under environmental conditions suitable for the germination of seedlings, there is also a steadily increasing level of phytotoxicity. The role of this factor, therefore, in relation to the firing of heathland sites could well be important in terms of decreasing competition pressures during the re-establishment phase of *Calluna*, an effect enhanced later by the presence of a fungitoxic compound in the raw humus derived apparently from living *Calluna* plants.

Relation of the fungitoxic component to heathland ecology

It has been clearly established by Handley (1963) that water-extracts of peat from beneath healthy plants of *Calluna* do contain a substance inhibitory to the growth of certain mycorrhizal fungi in culture; moreover, this factor is barely detectable in peat samples under poorly developed plants, e.g. subject to shading. This evidence, together with the fact that the fungitoxin cannot be detected during the decomposition of *Calluna* litter, strongly suggests that the source of the mycorrhizal inhibitor is the roots of living *Calluna*, possibly as a secretion from the fine roots. It is true that evidence for the secretion of organic materials from the roots of a mature living plant is notable for its scarcity. However, there is one significant difference between most of the plant species examined in this way and *Calluna*, namely that the latter has a very definite form of endotrophic mycorrhiza. This means that the fungitoxin need not be a normal metabolite of the *Calluna* itself, but rather the result of a combined fungus/host interaction.

It has already been shown (Condon & Kuc 1959; Martin 1958) that exposure of plant material to culture filtrates of specific fungi, or infection by the organism itself, can cause the host tissue to produce organic chemicals at levels far in excess of those normally present. It is reasonable to suggest, therefore, that the presence of the endophyte within the fine roots of *Calluna* could be associated with a similar effect. Indeed it is possible that the balance between host and endophyte in *Calluna* involves a chemical control system of the type found in orchids (Gaumann & Kern 1959). If this is so, then the secretion of a fungitoxin by the roots of *Calluna* becomes a feasible hypothesis, and in this context the findings of Stalder & Schutz (1957) working with *Erica gracilis* are of some interest. They found that when mycorrhizal associations of this species were eradicated by the application of nitrogenous fertilizers, then the roots succumbed to a heavy infection by a species of *Olpidium*. Plants with normal endotrophic mycorrhizas growing in the same soil showed no disease symptoms, and *Ericaceae* from natural habitats were never found to be infected by this pathogen. From their experiments they deduced that the mycorrhizal associate of *E. gracilis* exerted an antagonistic effect on *Olpidium*. A similar influence arising from the roots of *Calluna* could well explain the failure of certain ectotrophic mycorrhizal fungi to form associations with tree roots intertwined with those of heather.

Such a suggestion is not without parallel, for Munro (1966) has found that a dominant grass from the savanna in Southern Rhodesia secretes a toxin from its roots which differentially suppresses nitrifying bacteria. The secretion of this bacteriocidal material, when viewed in relation to the lowered competitive ability of *Hyparrhenia filipendula* in the presence of inorganic nitrogen, endows this species with a selective advantage for maintaining a dominant position in the grassland. A fungicidal secretion from the roots of *Calluna* could have a similarly selective effect, in that competing tree species would be prevented from reaching sufficient maturity to shade out the *Calluna*. Experimental evidence of the secretion of a fungicidal compound by the roots of *Calluna* has yet to be obtained, but circumstantial evidence strongly supports its existence.

Discussion

It is clear that on certain heathlands in this country dominated by *Calluna vulgaris*, the floristic stability of the community is, in part, maintained by compounds in the raw humus toxic to other plant species. One of these components exerts a strong phytotoxic effect by inhibiting the growth of roots, while the other factor suppresses the formation of ectotrophic mycorrhizas on the roots of competing tree species.

The operation of these factors can best be envisaged by considering what happens when a section of heathland is cleared of living *Calluna* by fire, for at this point in time both groups of toxic factors will be reduced to a low level. It is in this situation, as was found by McPherson & Muller (1969) in considering the vegetation of the Chaparral, that plant species incapable of competing with the dominant flora on allelopathic grounds make an appearance. On heathland areas, tree seedlings, e.g. birch, as well as some herbaceous plants, such as *Holcus mollis*, become established, but after 4–5 years the flora is usually again Ericaceous with only a few stunted birches providing evidence of their former invasion. It is a reasonable hypothesis to suggest that this decline of competing species is due to the build-up of toxic factors in the raw humus. These toxic metabolites, localized in the raw humus layer, are well placed for their proposed role in suppressing root growth—an effect enhanced by the fact that, even if these toxins are unable to kill potential invaders, they may render them more susceptible to the ravages of other factors, for example, grazing. Support for such an idea comes from field observations that many unmanaged heaths are, since the decline of the rabbit, being colonised by woody species.

However, the very fact that birch may ultimately become established is of interest, for it implies a declining fungitoxic activity on the part of *Calluna*. It has been shown by Handley (1963) that any factor, e.g. shading, which adversely affects the heather leads to a lower level of fungitoxic activity in the raw humus beneath the plant. It is, therefore, clearly pertinent to ask whether the diminishing fungitoxic activity observed on unmanaged heaths is not due to the fact that the *Calluna* is approaching senescence, and further whether this senescence is not a manifestation of autotoxicity. For it has been shown on a number of occasions (cf. Miller & Miles 1970) that the ability of *Calluna* to regenerate after firing or cutting declines with age. One possible explanation of this phenomenon could be that the roots of *Calluna* are, to some extent, susceptible to the toxic metabolites building up in the raw humus, and that exposure to these factors over a number of years has a debilitating effect on the whole plant. Support for such an hypothesis is provided by the work of Muller (1966), who showed that an allelopathic influence from *Salvia leucophylla*, which restricted the growth of annual herbs, also caused a deterioration of the shrub itself. Whether or not auto-intoxication in this form exerts a real influence on the ecology of *Calluna* heaths remains to be established, but the fact that two distinct types of inhibitory material can be obtained in some quantity from heathland soils clearly indicates that such an hypothesis may not be without foundation.

The overall conclusion which may be drawn from our studies to date is that the presence of toxic compounds in heathland soils, whether providing stability to the community through antagonism to competing species or eventually opening the way to succession through auto-intoxication, is an ecological factor of almost unrealized potential. Obviously, there are many details of the general hypothesis which require critical examination before the role of soil toxicity in the ecology of heathlands can be assessed with authority, but the evidence is accumulating. If it can be shown that chemical antagonism between species is involved in maintaining the stability of *Calluna* heaths, then it is obviously pertinent to speculate upon the question of just how widespread this type of phenomenon may be. Certainly Muller (1966) has demonstrated one extremely clear-cut example of where the ecology of an area is dominated by the influence of toxic metabolites. Surely it is unreasonable to suppose that this is just an isolated occurrence. More likely his results form the tip of an uncharted 'ice-berg', the true dimensions of which will become apparent only when more plant associations have been examined along similar lines.

Acknowledgements

The author gratefully acknowledges the helpful advice and criticism offered by Dr. W.R.C.Handley during the course of this work, and the conscientious technical assistance provided by Mrs Christine Simpson.

Financial assistance was provided by the Natural Environment Research Council.

Summary

The exposed nature of heathlands, together with the low mineral status of the soil and the susceptibility of the vegetation to burning, are all factors instrumental in ensuring the dominance of *Calluna vulgaris* over certain areas. Nevertheless, these factors may be subsidiary in importance to an allelopathic effect from the shrub itself. Thus, after the vegetation of some lowland heaths has been fired, trees, such as birch, can rapidly become established, only to fail some 4–5 years later. The apparent reason for this growth failure is the presence of phyto- and fungitoxic compounds in the raw humus; so that not only is growth of the birch roots restricted, but also the formation of efficient mycorrhizal associations.

Experiments have shown that a water-soluble factor is present in raw humus from beneath living *Calluna* which can inhibit root growth of a number of plant species, possibly through interfering with the respiration of the root tissue. Such a compound, absorbed on to the organic matrix of the peat, could well form a formidable barrier to the establishment of seedlings; an inhibition reinforced, in certain instances, by fungitoxic components. The chemical characteristics of the phytotoxic compound as examined in vitro support the view that it is ecologically significant in the role suggested. It is further speculated that this compound may be operative in dictating the growth pattern of *Calluna* itself, so that the eventual senescence of an individual bush may well be due, in part, to autotoxicity; the changing competitive ability of *Calluna* with observed growth phase, may also be correlated with the production of toxic metabolites.

References

BONNER J. (1950) The role of toxic substances in the interaction of higher plants. *Bot. Rev.* 16, 51–65.

BRAATHE P. (1950) Granas veksthemning pa lyngmark. *Tidsskr. Skogbr.* 58, 42–5.

BRIAN P.W., HEMMING H.G. & McGOWAN J.C. (1945) Origin of a toxicity to Mycorrhiza in Wareham Heath soil. *Nature, Lond.* 155, 637–8.

CONDON P. & KUC J. (1959) A biochemical mechanism for the resistance of carrot root tissue to attack by *Ceratostomella fimbriata. Phytopathology* 49, 536.

GAUMANN E. & KERN H. (1959) Über chemische Abwehrreaktionen bei Orchideen. *Phytopath. Z.* 36, 1–26.

HANDLEY W.R.C. (1963) *Mycorrhizal associations and Calluna heathland afforestation.* Bull. For. Commn, Lond., No. 36.

HOAGLAND D.R. & ARNON D.I. (1938) *The water-culture method of growing plants without soil.* Circ. Calif. agric. Exp. Stn. 347.

LAING E.V. (1932) *Studies on tree roots.* Bull. For. Commn, Lond. No. 13.

MARTIN P. (1958) Einfluss der Kulturfiltrate von Mikroorganismen auf die Abgabe van Scopoletin aus den Keimwurzeln des Hafers (*Avena sativa* L). *Arch. Mikrobiol.* 29, 154–68.

McPHERSON J.K. & MULLER C.H. (1969) Allelopathic effects of *Adenostoma fasciculatum*, 'Chamise', in the California Chaparral. *Ecol. Monogr.*, 39, 177–98.

MILLER G.R. & MILES J. (1970) Regeneration of heather (*Calluna vulgaris*) at different ages and seasons in north-east Scotland. *J. Appl. Ecol.* 7, 51–61.

MULLER C.H. (1966) The role of chemical inhibition (allelopathy) in vegetational composition. *Bull. Torrey bot. Club* 93, 332–51.

MULLER P.E. (1903) Über das Verhältnis der Bergkiefer zur Fichte im den Jutlandischen Heidekulturen. *Naturw. Z. Land- u. Forstw.* 1, 289–306.

MUNRO P.E. (1966) Inhibition of nitrifiers by grass root extracts. *J. appl. Ecol.* 3, 231–8.

RAYNER M.C. & NEILSON-JONES W. (1944) *Problems in tree nutrition.* Faber and Faber.

STALDER L. & SCHUTZ F. (1957) Untersuchungen über die kausalen Zusammenhange des Erikawurzelsterbens. *Phytopath. Z.* 30, 117–48.

TORREY J.G. (1959) A chemical inhibitor of auxin-induced lateral root initiation of *Pisum. Physiologia* Pl. 12, 873–87.

WOODS F.W. (1960) Biological antagonisms due to phytotoxic root exudates. *Bot. Rev.* 26, 546–69.

YEATMAN C.W. (1955) *Tree root development on upland heaths.* Bull. For. Commn, Lond. No. 21.

The mechanism of acidification of soil by *Calluna* and *Ulex* and the significance for conservation

P.J.GRUBB and M.B.SUTER *Botany School, Cambridge University*

Introduction

The work reported here has been carried out in relation to a specific problem of management in a particular community, chalk heath, but we believe that it has implications for the conservation of a variety of plant communities with a topsoil pH in the range 5–6. Chalk heath is an intimate mixture of the usual chalk grassland plants with heather (*Calluna vulgaris*) or bell heather (*Erica cinerea*). It is found on shallow loam soils over flints over chalk (Fig. 1). Depending on parent materials the loam may be a clay loam, silty loam or sandy clay loam; the organic matter content is *c*. 10–50 per cent. At the site we have studied in detail (Lullington Heath National Nature Reserve, National Grid Reference 51/544017) the loam is a silty loam (largely loess-derived), generally about 10–15 cm deep and with an organic matter content of 20–50 per cent.

The intimate mixture of calcicoles and calcifuges in chalk heath is stable so long as the topsoil pH remains in the range 5–6 and is thus of particular scientific interest in demonstrating that the constituent species have over-lapping pH tolerances (Grubb *et al.* 1969). Historically the intimate mixture has been maintained for centuries under grazing by sheep and rabbits. Grazing by sheep on most of the chalk in England came to an end early this century and grazing by rabbits virtually stopped as a result of myxomatosis in 1954; there have been only minor recoveries by rabbits at Lullington Heath since 1954.

The consequences for chalk heath of a cessation of grazing are shown in outline in Fig. 1 (for a fuller account see Grubb *et al.* 1969). Bushes of *Calluna*, *Erica* and *Ulex* rapidly acidify the soil and, if they are cleared, a new mixture of calcifuges and indifferent species is established—the original chalk heath mixture is lost.

At Lullington most of the chalk heath has changed into *Ulex* scrub.

Clearance of more *Ulex* scrub cannot by itself be regarded as a policy of value in conserving chalk heath. It is highly desirable that we try to obtain a full understanding of the mechanism of soil acidification so that we have a sound theoretical basis for developing some practical means of reversing the process.

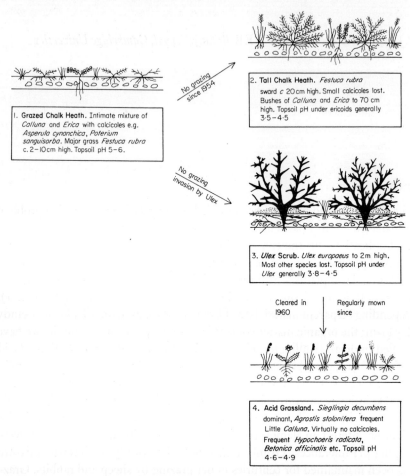

1. Grazed Chalk Heath. Intimate mixture of *Calluna* and *Erica* with calcicoles e.g. *Asperula cynanchica, Poterium sanguisorba*. Major grass *Festuca rubra* c. 2–10 cm high. Topsoil pH 5–6.

No grazing since 1954

2. Tall Chalk Heath. *Festuca rubra* sward c 20 cm high. Small calcicoles lost. Bushes of *Calluna* and *Erica* to 70 cm high. Topsoil pH under ericoids generally 3.5–4.5

No grazing invasion by Ulex

3. *Ulex* Scrub. *Ulex europaeus* to 2 m high. Most other species lost. Topsoil pH under *Ulex* generally 3.8–4.5

Cleared in 1960 | Regularly mown since

4. Acid Grassland. *Sieglingia decumbens* dominant, *Agrostis stolonifera* frequent Little *Calluna*. Virtually no calcicoles. Frequent *Hypochoeris radicata, Betonica officinalis* etc. Topsoil pH 4.6–4.9

Figure 1. A summary of the effects on chalk heath of a cessation of grazing and of the effects of clearance of gorse scrub derived from chalk heath.

There appear to have been very few studies aimed at determining precisely the mechanism of acidification of soil by plants. We shall discuss the limited information in the literature when we have given an account of our own work.

Our approach has been to ask the following questions.

1   Is any of the acidification due to addition of mineral acids, e.g. sulphuric or nitric, released perhaps by microbial processes?

2   Is any of the acidification due to addition of organic acids, e.g. citric or oxalic, derived perhaps from the litter.

3   Is any of the acidification due to addition of new exchange sites for cations, provided by humic acid *sensu lato* ?
4   Is any of the acidification due to removal of bases and, if so, what parts of the cycle of bases in the community are affected ?

Methods

All analyses of soil (except those for nitrate and titratable acidity) have been made on material passing a 2 mm sieve; extracts have been made of fresh soils within a few days of collection. All analyses of plants have been made on digests prepared with a mixture of concentrated nitric and perchloric acids (5:1). Roots have been washed repeatedly in demineralized water. Results of various analyses are expressed on a dry weight basis; subsamples of all material were dried at 105°C for 24 hours.

pH has been determined electrometrically on samples brought to a paste with demineralized water. Nitrate has been extracted with a dilute copper sulphate solution from unsieved soils dried for 24 hours at 50°C 2 days after collection and determined spectrophotometrically after reaction with phenol 2,4-disulphonic acid (Jackson 1958). Sulphate has been extracted with cold water and determined by back titration of barium chloride with versene and Eriochrome Black T indicator (Jackson 1958). Soluble acids have been extracted with cold water (50 ml per 15 g of dry soil for 14 hours) and determined with barium hydroxide (phenolphthalein indicator). Cation exchange capacity (C.E.C.) at pH 7 has been determined by a modification of the method of Jackson (1958, p. 61). C.E.C. at field pH has been determined similarly but with all solutions (other than the 80 per cent acetone) brought to the required pH with acetic acid or hydrochloric acid beforehand. Exchangeable cations have been extracted with N ammonium acetate at pH 7. Potassium and sodium have been determined by emission flame photometry; calcium and magnesium by atomic absorption flame photometry after addition of lanthanum chloride to suppress interference. Organic matter in the soil has been determined by ignition at 375°C (Ball 1964); the calcium carbonate content is <0·002 per cent in loamy topsoil (Grubb *et al.* 1969).

The nomenclature follows Clapham *et al.* (1962).

Results

Nature of increased acidity

Mineral acids

Some analyses of nitrate are shown in Table 1. There is no marked increase under either *Calluna* or *Ulex*. Lehr (1950) found that 40 µg/g NO₃-N were needed to reduce the pH of a sandy soil with little buffering power from 5·5 to 4·5.The values for NO₃-N that we have obtained are much smaller (*c.* 0·5–5·0 µg/g). Furthermore, our soil is better buffered; an addition of 40 µg/g of NO₃-N as nitric acid reduces the pH from 5·2 to 5·0 only. The values we have obtained for sulphate (soils sampled 16 January 1970) are also low and show no evidence of an increase with fall in pH.

Table 1. Concentrations of nitrate-nitrogen and titratable acidity in extracts of topsoil (0–2 cm) under tall *Festuca rubra*, under *Calluna* and under *Ulex*. Soils sampled 22 June 1970.

	Festuca	Calluna	Ulex
(a)*Nitrate-N* (µg/g D.W.)			
Mean	2·84	0·97	3·05
Range	0·67–9·34	0·40–1·47	0·67–5·69
Number of samples	4	6	3
pH range	5·1 –5·6	3·7 –4·2	3·6 –3·8
(b) *Titratable acidity* (m.equiv./100 g D.W.)			
Mean	0·12	0·54	0·33
Range	0·10–0·13	0·52–0·57	0·30–0·35
Number of samples	2	2	2
pH range	5·1 –5·3	3·7 –4·2	3·6 –3·8

Organic acids of low molecular weight

These have been estimated indirectly as titratable acidity in water extracts (Table 1). If all the nitrate and sulphate that we have measured is present as nitric and sulphuric acids, they will account for 0·04 and 0·11 m equiv./100 g dry soil at most. Together they may therefore account for the acidity of extracts of soil under *Festuca*. They cannot, however, account for the acidity of extracts of soil under *Calluna* and *Ulex*. We have no values for water-soluble phosphoric acid but it seems unlikely that it will be present in greater quantity at low pH. We conclude that there probably is a small increase in the organic acids in the soil under *Calluna* and *Ulex*. The increase amounts to 0·5 m equiv./100 g at most and is unlikely to contribute much directly to the soil's acidity. However, the acids concerned may be active in the process causing acidification (see p. 130).

Cation exchange sites

The cation exchange capacity (C.E.C.) at pH 7 is found to decrease rather than increase as a part of the acidification process under *Calluna* and *Ulex*. Some data for *Calluna* are set out in Fig. 2. The points in Fig. 2a suggest a

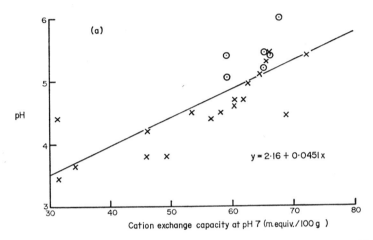

Figure 2a. The relationship between pH and cation exchange capacity at pH 7: samples at 0–2 cm taken from under turf of *Festuca rubra* (⊙) and from under bushes of *Calluna vulgaris* of a range of sizes (x).

curved relationship but other sets of determinations we have made, e.g. those

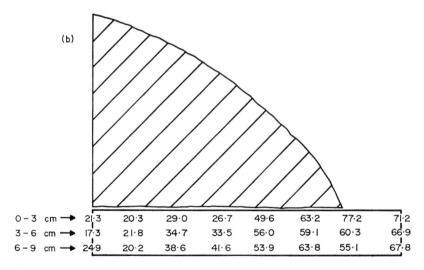

0 – 3 cm ➜	21·3	20·3	29·0	26·7	49·6	63·2	77·2	71·2
3 – 6 cm ➜	17·3	21·8	34·7	33·5	56·0	59·1	60·3	66·9
6 – 9 cm ➜	24·9	20·2	38·6	41·6	53·9	63·8	55·1	67·8

Figure 2b. The relationship between cation exchange capacity and position in the soil underneath and outside a *Calluna* bush: readings taken 15 cm apart, bush 65 cm high.

for Fig. 2b, all fit linear plots. C.E.C. at field pH is likely to fall even more as a function of pH than C.E.C. at pH 7 because of blocking of exchange sites by polymers of the hydrated aluminium ion (Black 1968). The few data we have on C.E.C. at field pH are consistent with this expectation. In a highly organic loam like that at Lullington most of the exchange sites are likely to reside in the organic matter. It is therefore interesting that the loss on ignition at 375°C is not significantly related to pH. Eighty-nine determinations at pH 3·5–6·0 in the top 2–3 cm of 'mineral' soil have given a mean 36·80 per cent $\pm$0·72

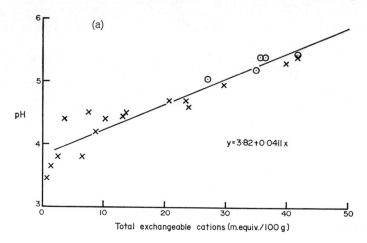

Figure 3a. The relationship between pH and total exchangeable cations: samples as for Fig. 2a.

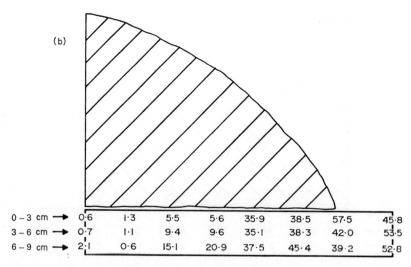

0 – 3 cm ➜	0·6	1·3	5·5	5·6	35·9	38·5	57·5	45·8
3 – 6 cm ➜	0·7	1·1	9·4	9·6	35·1	38·3	42·0	53·5
6 – 9 cm ➜	2·1	0·6	15·1	20·9	37·5	45·4	39·2	52·8

Figure 3b. The relationship between total exchangeable cations and position in the soil underneath and outside a *Calluna* bush: samples as for Fig. 2b.

per cent (S.E. of the mean). The values for 3–6 cm and 6–9 cm are 26·91 per cent±0·63 per cent and 25·5 per cent±0·74 per cent respectively (16 determinations at each level).

Exchangeable cations

The content of total exchangeable cations, as conventionally defined (Ca, Mg, K, Na), falls very markedly with decrease in pH under both *Calluna* and *Ulex*. Some data for *Calluna* are shown in Fig. 3. The decrease in total exchangeable cations is relatively greater than that in cation exchange capacity so that base saturation falls from *c*. 80 per cent at pH 6 to *c*. 10 per cent at pH 4 (Fig. 4). Calcium is the dominant cation at pH 6 and loss of calcium accounts for most of the decrease in total exchangeable cations (*c*. 20 m equiv./100 g per 1·0 pH

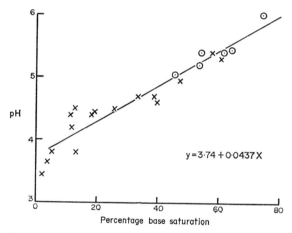

Figure 4. The relationship between pH and percentage base saturation: samples as for Fig. 2a.

unit). The changes in exchangeable magnesium, potassium and sodium are more complex and less regular; where they do show a decrease, this amounts to only *c*. 1·0, *c*. 0·7 and *c*. 0·5 m equiv./100 g per 1·0 pH unit). It is planned to discuss these changes in more detail elsewhere.

Summary

There is no evidence that acidification is due to an increase in mineral acids, in organic acids of low molecular weight or in humic acid *sensu lato*. Loss of cations seems to be the chief cause of increased acidity.

Changes in the cycling of bases

A summary of the movements of bases through a generalized plant is set out in Fig. 5. There are at least four situations which can lead to a net loss from the topsoil.

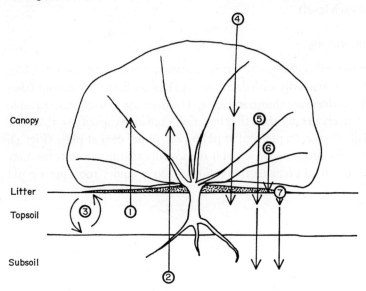

Figure 5. A summary of the major movements of bases through and under a generalized plant: 1. Uptake from the topsoil; 2. Uptake from the subsoil; 3. Mixing of soil by animals especially earthworms; 4. Supply via rain and dust; 5. Leaching of canopy; 6. Shedding of litter; 7. Leaching of litter.

1   A plant may immobilize the bases that it has taken up into its shoots; it may shed very little litter, form a litter that decays very slowly or suffer negligible leaching.
2   A plant may have very few or no deep roots exploiting the subsoil.
3   A plant may inhibit the activities of animals that mix up the soil profile, particularly the surface-casting earthworms.
4   A plant may produce from its shoots or its litter organic compounds that form complexes with bases and accelerate leaching down the profile.
  We can consider briefly each of these possibilities.

Immobilization of calcium in the plant

The major base lost is calcium and we present here only the data for calcium. In assessing the present position we have made an allowance for the calcium immobilized in the plants of the short chalk heath which occupied the soil before the development of a given bush of *Calluna* or *Ulex*. We estimated this amount by sampling the short chalk heath at Lullington maintained by mowing (cf. Grubb *et al.* 1969, p. 191). This closely resembles the grazed chalk heath of pre-1954 days but is rather taller. Unfortunately the determinations were not made at the same time as those of other fractions but in July 1970. The way in which we have subdivided bushes for sampling and analysis is shown in Table 2; one fraction included is that of suppressed and dying chalk heath plants included within the area of the bush.

Table 2. *The weights of the different fractions of selected* Calluna *and* Ulex *bushes and of short chalk heath plants on an equivalent area, together with calcium concentrations and contents.*

Fraction	Calluna bush 2			Ulex bush 2		
	Dry weight (g)	Calcium concentration (m.equiv./g.)	Calcium content (m.equiv.)	Dry weight (g)	Calcium concentration (m.equiv./g)	Calcium content (m.equiv.)
Green small shoots	874	0·199	174	9621	0·189	1819
Old small shoots	918	0·073	67	7569	0·180	1364
Larger branches	715	0·069	49	7739	0·056	436
Roots	576	0·165	95	2252	0·161	363
L Litter	626	0·126	79	2004	0·154	309
F Litter	771	0·208	160	340	0·412	140
Grass etc under bush	418	0·267	111	2633	0·356	938
Total	4898	—	735	32158	—	5369
Short chalk heath on an equivalent area						
Shoots	643	0·3014	194	3312	0·3014	998
Roots	1619	0·4674	758	8340	0·4674	3906
Total	2262	—	952	11652	—	4904

The calculation of the amount of calcium lost from the soil beneath a bush is made relatively easy by the linear relationship between pH and concentration of exchangeable calcium. The collected data for *Ulex* are given in Fig. 6. The comparable regression for *Calluna* is $y = 3·79 + 0·0451x$ (40 determinations). We have made transects of the soil beneath the bushes, measuring the pH at three levels, generally 0–3 cm, 3–6 cm and 6–9 cm. We have used the results at each level to make maps of pH, isolating arbitrarily areas with a reasonably narrow pH range (Fig. 7). Arithmetic mean values of pH have been calculated for each area at each level. It is assumed that the mean pH of the unacidified area is approximately the same as the mean pH was in the area now acidified before the bush grew up. Then it is possible to calculate the calcium lost for each segment showing acidification, using the regressions given in Fig. 6 and above, together with values for bulk density determined on blocks of soil 15×15 cm in area and corrections for flints in the 6–9 cm layer.

The results of comparing calcium lost and calcium immobilized are shown for four bushes in Table 3. It appears that in the case of *Calluna* the

Table 3. Amounts of calcium immobilized in, and lost from beneath, four bushes, together with other relevant data.

Bush	Time of sampling	Mean pH outside bush	Lowest recorded pH at 0–3 cm	Dry weight of bush and litter (g)	Calcium immobilized (m.equiv.)	Calcium lost (m.equiv.)
Calluna 1	Oct. 69	5·2	3·5	8136	− 548[1]	3350
Calluna 2	May 70	5·2	3·4	4898	− 217[1]	1512
Ulex 1	Mar. 70	5·7	4·3	39056	806	1793
Ulex 2	Apr. 70	5·2	4·0	32158	465	3261

[1] Minus sign indicates that there is less calcium in the *Calluna* than in an equivalent area of short chalk heath.

calcium lost far exceeds that immobilized. Indeed there has been no immobilization by the bushes but rather a net loss from the system; calcium lost under *Ulex* considerably exceeds that immobilized. The possible errors in our comparison are many and hard to evaluate. We cannot discuss them in detail here, but we believe that they are unlikely to be so large as to change the conclusion for *Calluna*. In the case of *Ulex* we cannot yet reach any firm conclusion, but the position is similar to that for *Calluna*. Further, *Ulex* has many roots running through the calcareous, flinty loam–chalk boundary (Fig. 1) and these presumably take up an appreciable amount of calcium without causing any acidification—the pH of calcareous soil being so effectively buffered against loss of calcium. Therefore we should expect immobilization in the plant to exceed apparent loss from the soil by a wide margin, if acidification is effected solely by immobilization.

Occurrence of deep rooting

As indicated above, failure of deep rooting certainly cannot be considered a means of changing the cycling of the bases through *Ulex*. On the other hand *Calluna* develops very few, very small roots in the calcareous subsoil. It is hard to assess the contribution to acidification of this failure to form deep roots. The unacidified chalk heath had only a certain proportion of species with marked deep-rooting, e.g. *Poterium sanguisorba* (Fig. 1). Other calcicoles that were common develop most of their roots in the loam top soil, e.g. *Filipendula vulgaris* and *Scabiosa columbaria* (Figs, 4 and 5 in Grubb *et al.* 1969). We hope to be able to present figures on the importance of this issue in a later publication.

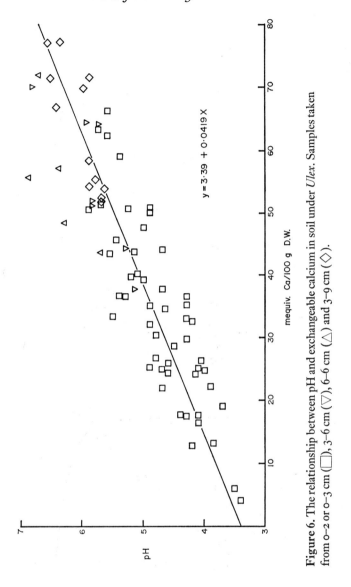

Figure 6. The relationship between pH and exchangeable calcium in soil under *Ulex*. Samples taken from 0–2 or 0–3 cm (□), 3–6 cm (▽), 6–6 cm (△) and 3–9 cm (◇).

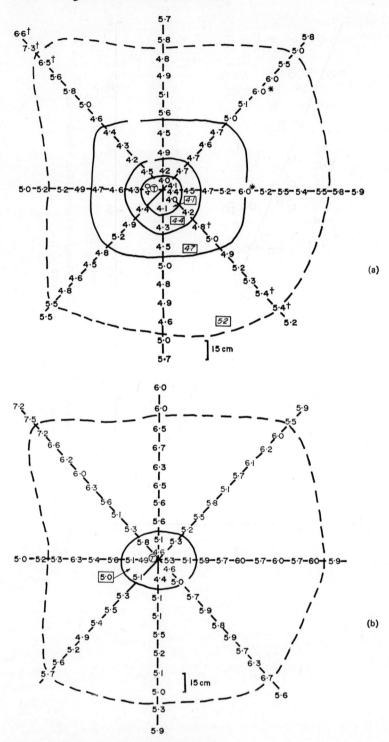

Figure 7a, b. For explanation see next page.

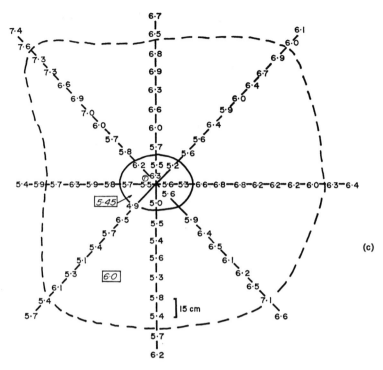

Figure 7. Transects of pH under a *Ulex* bush at three levels (a) 0–3 cm, (b) 3–6 cm, (c) 6–9 cm. The main samples were 15 cm apart. * signifies that a high density of worm casts was noted at this point. † signifies that flints were present at depth < 6 cm. The 'contours' separate areas with the mean pH's indicated in italics. The pecked lines indicate the outline of the bush.

Activities of surface-casting earthworms

Some values for the amounts of recognizable worm casts in tall chalk heath, under *Calluna* and under *Ulex* are given in Table 4 and some values for numbers and weights of earthworms in these three situations in Table 5. It is

Table 4. Dry weights of recognizable worm casts in tall chalk, under *Calluna* and under *Ulex*. Five plots of 50 × 50 cm sampled in each situation on 22–23 June 1970.

	Tall chalk heath	Under *Calluna*	Under *Ulex*
Mean weight per 2500 cm² (± S.D.)	13·8 ± 11·7	3·8 ± 1·7	20·9 ± 10·0
pH range	(4·6*–) 5·0–6·4	3·7 – 4·6	3·8 – 4·2

* The site of this sample might have been under *Ulex* for some years in the period 1954–64.

seen that *Calluna* inhibits earthworm activity. However, relatively large numbers of earthworms can be found under some *Calluna* bushes. One might suppose that this is because of the presence of a calcareous subsoil but many of the worms found under *Calluna* 2 in Table 5 were well up among the *Calluna* roots in soil of about pH 4.5. Unfortunately most of the worms we found were immature so that they could not be identified to species level. The majority of the mature worms under *Festuca* and *Ulex* have been identified by Dr T.D. Piearce as *Allolobophora chlorotica* (Savigny); a few *A. caliginosa* (Savigny)

Table 5. Numbers and dry weights of earthworms in soil under tall chalk heath, under *Calluna* and under *Ulex*. Plots of 50 × 50 cm, dug out to *c.* 25 cm depth and sorted by hand, 15–18 April 1970.

		Number of earthworms	Dry weight of earthworms (g)
Tall chalk heath	1	29	1·26
	2	35	3·36
Calluna	1	2	0·60
	2	31	2·40
Ulex	1	51	5·02
	2	17	2·56

were also present. *Ulex* seems to stimulate earthworm activity, perhaps because it forms nitrogen-rich roots which are particularly attractive, when either alive or dead. The pH of most of the casts under *Ulex* is remarkably low (Table 4). Presumably the worms ingest earth mostly while they are in the uppermost few cm of soil and that is why the abundant casting does not generally reverse the acidification process. The species responsible for the surface-casting is not yet known. We have sometimes found casts of higher pH (5·5–6·1) under tall *Ulex* so that deeper soil is sometimes ingested; where earthworm activity is particularly intense, acidification may indeed be reversed (starred values in Fig. 7).

Acceleration of leaching

We can summarize the findings so far as follows. Immobilization does not appear to be a major factor in the case of *Ulex*; failure of deep-rooting and inhibition of earthworms do not apply. In contrast both these latter factors may be important for *Calluna* and go some way to explaining the difference between bases immobilized and bases lost. We do not think that these two factors are likely to account for most of the acidification by *Calluna* because they would be unlikely to produce the regular pattern of acidification that is found (cf. Figs. 2, 3 and 7; also Fig. 8 in Grubb *et al.* 1969). Deep-rooted calcicoles were scattered irregularly in the original sward and earthworm activity is well known to be patchy at any one time. In contrast acidification shows a rather regular diminution in intensity from the centre of a bush outwards, with occasional outstanding values of pH where earthworms have recently been active (Fig. 7). The regular pattern could readily be produced by removal of bases either by uptake into roots or by accelerated leaching.

Discussion

We have shown that rapid acidification of chalk heath soil beneath bushes of *Calluna* and *Ulex* is effected by a removal of bases, particularly calcium, rather than by an addition of acid. It appears impossible to account for removal of calcium by *Calluna* and *Ulex* as due wholly to immobilization in the bushes and their litter; the position regarding *Ulex* is not yet clear. Inhibition of earthworms that bring up subsoil and failure to form deep roots probably play a part in acidification by *Calluna*, but there is possibly also an accelerated leaching of calcium down the profile.

   Of the plant-induced soil changes described in the literature, that most closely resembling the acidification of a chalk heath soil seems to be the 'degradation' of a chernozem or prairie soil. Chernozems resemble chalk heath soils in their large store of exchangeable calcium; most are derived chiefly from loess and this makes the similarity to certain chalk heath soils, like the one at Lullington, especially close. Chernozems, like the chalk heath soils, are developed under a grass cover and, when they are invaded by trees, whether broad-leaved or coniferous, 'degraded chernozems' or leached grood soils begin to develop (Levchenko 1930; Tiurin 1930; Wilde 1958). The first stage seems to be acidification of the top soil, effected by leaching of bases, but we have not been able to trace any critical work on the mechanism of this leaching. When the pH of the top soil falls, some of the incorporated organic matter is mobilized and leached away. Oxides of iron and aluminium are also translocated. Eventually a strongly leached A_2 horizon and a spodic B horizon may develop (Wilde 1958). As yet we have no indisputable evidence that the development of the chalk heath soils is proceeding into the podsolization stage even under *Calluna* but it is notable that the humic substances do seem to be more readily leached from the acidified soils; this is readily seen when various soil extractions are made.

   Acidification of soils initially very low in humus seems to proceed quite differently from acidification of soils rich in humus. The case investigated in most detail is that of podsolic soils in southern Australia being acidified under crops of *Trifolium subterraneum* fertilized with superphosphate; Williams & Donald (1957) found a marked increase in cation exchange capacity but a much smaller increase in exchangeable calcium and so explained the drop in pH from 5·6–6·0 to 5·1–5·8. The nearest parallel under semi-natural vegetation concerns the succession on sand dunes; Salisbury (1952) found a parallel between a general increase in humus content and a general fall in pH. Salisbury (1925) and Wilson (1960) found substantial increases in humus content correlated with a rapid fall in pH under *Calluna*. Unfortunately no analyses of exchangeable calcium were given by these authors.

The forest soils, in which acidification by various trees has been studied, have generally been of moderate to low humus content. The chemical basis of acidification at most sites is quite unclear but the data given by Ovington (1953, 1956, 1958) for the top 5 cm of a brown forest soil at Bedgebury show evidence of both an increase in organic matter and a decrease in exchangeable calcium. It is notable that the amount of calcium lost from the top 50 cm of soil examined by Ovington was appreciably less than that immobilized in the crop and its litter. Many tree crops, including conifers, can, in fact, increase the amounts of exchangeable nutrients in the topsoil by the agency of their roots and litter, provided there is a suitable reservoir of unweathered minerals in the topsoil and/or an accessible subsoil (see Dimbleby 1952 and papers cited there). Much more critical information is needed on nutrient cycles under crops of trees that acidify the soil. The few relevant studies (e.g. Livens & Vanstellen 1956, 1957; Smirnova & Suhanova 1964) yield no conclusive evidence that accelerated leaching of calcium, of the type which seems to occur under *Calluna* on chalk heath soil, has any part in the acidification process in a forest soil. However, nobody yet seems to have compared the mineral contents of water draining from under, say, intact oak forest and planted pine, on a brown forest soil (*sol brun* or *sol brun lessivé*); accelerated leaching may indeed be very important in such situations.

If there is indeed an accelerated leaching of calcium, then great interest attaches to the mechanism concerned. Much may be learnt from the large volume of work done in the last 20 years on the complexing of iron and aluminium by organic molecules as a part of the podsolization process. A view widely favoured at present is that organic acids such as citric are chiefly responsible and that an essential feature of the podsolization process is an inhibition of the destruction of aliphatic acids under mor humus (see Bruckert & Jacquin 1969a and papers cited there). It is thought that phenolic materials may be responsible for the inhibition of microbial processes under mor (see Beck, Dommergues & van den Driessche 1969 and papers cited there) and that also they may play some part directly in translocation of iron and aluminium as organic complexes (see Bruckert & Jacquin 1969b and papers cited there). Little work has been done on translocation in the soil of calcium, magnesium or potassium. However, aliphatic acids such as citric certainly can leach these ions from the soil (Bruckert & Jacquin 1969a) and it may be that the acidification of chalk heath soil by loss of bases under *Calluna* is effected by essentially the same mechanism as outlined above for podsolization (cf. increase in titratable acids in soil extracts, Table 1). According to this view the microbial population of the soil is likely to have a key role in acidification by *Calluna*. Rapid acidification of soils by increase in humus content, as under *Calluna* on sand dunes, is probably chiefly due to inhibition of the breakdown of humus by bacteria (cf. Beck *et al.* 1969), though it may be partly because the plant residues are richer in humus precursors, i.e. various polyphenols as well as lignin (cf. Hurst & Burges 1967). Any inhibition of the microbial population is likely to affect the supply of such key nutrients as nitrogen and phosphorus (cf. Beck *et al.* 1969) and it is highly desirable that our present study should be extended to investigate this aspect.

Ultimately we are concerned, in the context of management, to discover how best to prevent and reverse acidification of soils initially in the pH range 5–6. This work has only just begun to uncover the complex changes in soil chemistry and biology that are involved. However, it should be plain that certain types of management are unlikely to succeed in regenerating chalk heath soil. Addition of nitrogen, which can apparently reverse podsolization by stimulating a re-activation of the profile (Romell in Harley 1954) is unlikely to be effective in regenerating chalk heath soil because such a massive loss of calcium from the above-flints layer has taken place. Clearly ploughing is not admissible because the calcifuges would then be unable to recolonize the calcareous topsoil just as the calcicoles are lost under acidification. Possibly a carefully controlled addition of powdered chalk or lime water ($Ca(OH)_2$) could be effective. We hope to try out this technique with the co-operation of the Nature Conservancy in the next year.

Acknowledgements

This work has been supported by a research grant from the Natural Environment Research Council. We are indebted to various members of the Nature Conservancy for their continuing co-operation.

Summary

Acidification is considered in the context of a specific problem in the management of a particular community (chalk heath). Chalk heath is an intimate mixture of calcicoles and calcifuges growing in a shallow loam over chalk (top soil pH 5–6). Since the virtual cessation of rabbit-grazing with myxomatosis in 1954, bushes of *Calluna* and *Ulex* have grown up and acidified the soil below them (top soil pH 3·5–5·0). When the *Ulex* scrub is cleared a mixture of calcifuges and indifferent species becomes established; the calcicoles cannot return (Grubb *et al.* 1969). We have investigated first the mechanism of acidification. It seems that removal of bases is more important than addition of acids. We have investigated next certain functions of the cycling of bases in the community. It seems that the removal of bases by *Ulex* may be accounted for wholly by immobilization in the bushes and their litter whereas the removal by *Calluna* involves also a failure of deep rooting, an inhibition of earthworm activity and possibly an accelerated leaching. The results are discussed in relation to the few data in the literature on acidification of other soils and in relation to practical management.

References

BALL D.F. (1964) Loss-on-ignition as an estimate of organic matter and organic carbon in non calcareous soils. *J. Soil Sci.* **15**, 84–92.

BECK G., DOMMERGUES Y. & VAN DEN DRIESSCHE R. (1969) L'effet litière. II. Etude expérimentale du pouvoir inhibiteur des composés hydrosolubles des feuilles et des litières forestières vis-a-vis de la microflora tellurique. *Œcologia Pl.* **4**, 237–66.

BLACK C.A. (1968) *Soil-Plant Relationships.* 2nd edn. J. Wiley, New York.

BRUCKERT S. & JACQUIN F. (1969a) Interaction entre la mobilité de plusieurs acides organiques et de divers cations dans un sol à mull et dans un sol à mor. *Soil Biol. Biochem.* **1**, 275–94.

BRUCKERT S. & JACQUIN F. (1969b) Complexation du fer (III) par les fractions organiques d'un extrait naturel de mor. *C.r. hebd. Séanc. Acad. Sci., Paris* **269**, 1625–8.

CLAPHAM A.R., TUTIN T.G. & WARBURG E.F. (1962) *Flora of the British Isles.* 2nd edn. Cambridge University Press.

DIMBLEBY G.W. (1952) Soil regeneration on the north-east Yorkshire moors. *J. Ecol.* **40**, 331–41.

GRUBB P.J., GREEN H.E. & MERRIFIELD R.C.J. (1969) The ecology of chalk heath: its relevance to the calcicole-calcifuge and soil acidification problems. *J. Ecol.* **57**, 175–212.

HARLEY J.L. (1954) Tree growth on acid soil. *Nature, Lond.* **174**, 855–6.

HURST H.M. & BURGES N.A. (1967) Lignin and humic acids. In *Soil Biochemistry* (Eds A.D.McLaren & G.H.Peterson). E.Arnold, London.

JACKSON M.L. (1958) *Soil Chemical Analysis.* Constable, London.

LEHR J.J. (1950) Seasonal variations in the pH value of the soil, as influenced by nitrification. *Trans. Fourth Int. Congr. Soil Sci.* **2**, 155–7.

LEVCHENKO F.I. (1930) Grey soils of the forest steppe in the European part of the U.S.S.R. *Pochvovedenie* **25**, 49–72.

LIVENS J. & VANSTELLEN R. (1956) Recherches sur le rôle de la litière dans la desaturation en bases des sols forestiers sur limon loessique. *Agricultura, Louvain* **4**, 103–32.

LIVENS J. & VANSTELLEN R. (1957) Extraits aqueux de litières en decomposition: leur reaction et teneur en bases. *Agricultura, Louvain* **5**, 99–119.

OVINGTON J.D. (1953) Studies of the development of woodland conditions under different trees. I. Soil pH. *J. Ecol.* **41**, 13–34.

OVINGTON J.D. (1956) *Idem.* IV. The ignition loss, water, carbon and nitrogen content of the mineral soil. *J. Ecol.* **44**, 171–9.

OVINGTON J.D. (1958) *Idem.* VII. Soil calcium and magnesium. *J. Ecol.* **46**, 391–405.

SALISBURY E.J. (1925) Note on the edaphic succession in some dune soils with special reference to the time factor. *J. Ecol.* 13, 322–8.

SALISBURY E.J. (1952) *Downs and Dunes.* Bell, London.

SMIRNOVA K.M. & SUHANOVA N.P. (1964) Effect of pure and mixed Scots pine stands on the changes on the composition of lysimeter water with time. *Soviet Soil Sci.* 10, 1053–62.

TIURIN I.V. (1930) Genesis and classification of forest steppe and forest soils. *Poch-vovedenie* 25, 104–41.

WILDE S.A. (1958) *Forest Soils.* Ronald Press, New York.

WILLIAMS C.H. & DONALD C.M. (1957) Changes in organic matter and pH in a podzolic soil as influenced by subterranean clover and superphosphate. *Aust. J. Agric. Res.* 8, 179–89.

WILSON K. (1960) The time factor in the development of dune soils at South Haven Peninsula, Dorset. *J. Ecol.* 48, 341–59.

Part 2
Factors regulating the Numbers of Individuals in a Community

Part 2

Factors controlling the floristic composition of some plant communities in Breckland

A.S.WATT *Botany School, Cambridge University*

Introduction

To name a species is one thing: to know how to grow it is another, and the description or diagnosis of a plant community must not be taken as knowing how to control its floristic composition (defined here as numerical representation of the species as well as species content). Intelligent as distinct from empirical control involves an understanding of what is happening and the factors involved in affecting the presence or absence of species and the relationships between them.

The following four examples from recent work on some Breckland communities represent contributions towards what I regard as one of the most fascinating as well as urgent problems confronting the plant ecologist, namely, the identification of factors controlling floristic composition with the object in view of discovering our limitations as well as indicating possibilities and potentialities—the creation, through understanding what is happening, of something in addition to our existing heritage.

Bracken v. heather

The study (Watt, 1955) on the relationship between bracken and heather on a well-developed podsol on Lakenheath Warren showing heather as the physiological dominant is experimentally confirmed by the graphs in Fig. 1 based on the data from a plot from which the uneven-aged heather was cut at ground level and removed, compared with those from a similarly uneven-aged control.

The cutting of the heather is followed within a few years by a fivefold increase in the number of fronds. In the dry year of 1959 both plots show a decrease, strikingly so in the cut plot, as the heather by then has reproduced vegetatively to form a more or less even-aged cover in the pioneer phase. From

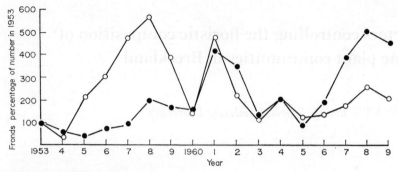

Figure 1. Comparison between the change in the number of fronds (expressed as a percentage of the initial number) in two plots, each 10 ft × 10 ft (3 m × 3 m) from one of which the heather had been cut and removed. Cut plot (o–o): control (●–●).

1958 to 1965 there are fluctuations, but a general fall in the cut plot. From then on when the heather in the cut plot is in the late building to early mature phase there is an increasingly wide divergence with the numbers in the control high and in the cut plot relatively low. Incidentally both are higher than the initial numbers.

Factors at work are revealed in the analysis of data from a permanent plot (100 ft × 4 ft : 33 m × 1·2 m) established in 1954 and recorded until 1969 with an interruption from 1959 to 1963 inclusive. The data (Table 1) show an increase in the number of fronds from 60 in 1954 to a maximum in 1967 of 787. It is not to be supposed that the increase has been uniform, as the data in Fig. 1 confirm fluctuations during the unrecorded years 1959–63.

Table 1. Calluna v. Pteridium in plot, 100 × 4 ft (33 m × 1·2 m)

Year	No. of fronds	No. of fronds per 10 ft² (0.92m²) of each phase				Percentage area of phase in Callunetum			
		Pioneer	Building	Mature	De-generate	Pioneer	Building	Mature	De-generate
1954	60	5·5	1·9	0·6	4·7	3·6	24·4	62·4	9·6
1955	70	[9·0	2·4	0·8	3·9	—	—	—	—
1956	136	8·3	1·9	2·1	13·8	—	—	—	—
1957	164	11·0	1·6	1·4	24·9*]	—	—	—	—
1958	264	9·8	5·3	1·8	14·0	5·9	10·8	50·9	32·4
1964	298	17·9	3·3	2·7	7·2	7·0	1·5	10·1	81·4
1965	445	27·4	9·0	2·8	10·2	10·1	2·5	10·6	76·8
1966	350	17·6	4·4	5·1	7·8	13·4	2·2	11·4	73·0
1967	787	34·8	8·8	4·0	18·9	17·4	3·7	11·2	67·7
1968	681	20·0	10·0	7·3	18·2	—	—	—	—
1969	717	25·4	10·9	11·0	17·6	19·6	4·8	13·2	62·4

* The figures in brackets are based on the assumption that during 1955–7 there was no material change in the relative areas of the phases.

Two factor complexes emerge as important, the weather and the total competitive power of the heather.

The data in Table 1 confirm that the competitive power of the heather varies with the phase: with a few minor exceptions the data show a fall in the number of fronds per unit area of the phase from a relatively high number in the pioneer to a minimum in the mature followed by a rise in the degenerate.

Eliminating competition as a factor and comparing phase with phase and the data for 1954 with those of the maximum (1967) we get a four- to six-fold increase: and taking all four phases together 12·7 fronds per 40 ft² (3·7 m²) in 1954 against 66·5 in 1967, i.e. roughly a fivefold increase. In this increase weather factors are involved (spring rainfall, frost (Watt, 1950, 1964)).

The other major factor is the total competitive power of the heather. In 1954 this is high for the combined building and mature phases have a percentage area of 86·8: in 1964 this combination is only 11·6 per cent and in 1967 is 14·9 per cent. An estimate of this fall in competitive power of the heather on the number of fronds is given first by calculating the number of fronds that would have been present at the rate of stocking per phase in 1967 and the relative areas of the phases in 1954: this comes to 309·5 fronds, i.e. just over five times the actual number. Second, the difference between 787 and 309·5 is 477·5, i.e. roughly eight times the original number, due to causes other than weather including the most important, namely the reduction in total competitive power of the heather.

A complete picture demands data for the whole period. From the 1958 data it is clear that some change in the relative areas of the phases has taken place, but that a major change took place following the severe winter in the early months of 1963 is supported by the reports sent me, when abroad, about the wholesale death of the heather in Breckland and confirmed by my observations and records in 1964. Thus this catastrophic event allowed bracken to increase after the death of *Calluna*, of which bracken was not the cause.

Since 1964 there has been a gradual fall in the area of the degenerate phase and an increase in the other phases, but the qualitative implications of the quantitative change in bracken make predictions as to the future relationships between bracken and heather difficult, especially since the start of the experiment coincided with the extinction of rabbits by myxomatosis and the uninhibited growth of grass (*Festuca ovina* and *Agrostis canina* and *A. tenuis*) and the shade cast by the greater number of fronds militate against the establishment of seedling *Calluna*. In other words there is the possibility, and under the continuance of the present regime even the probability, of the entry of a grass phase. On the other hand, the much-diminished *Calluna* in its small patches in the building and mature phase extends outwards vegetatively, but at an absolute rate less than the change from the degenerate to the pioneer phase. Even if the weather emerged from the trough in which it now is (Lamb,

1967) and differentially favoured the *Calluna*, the continued absence of rabbits would still place obstacles in the way of *Calluna* regeneration by seed. Also the long-term relationships between *Calluna* and *Festuca ovina* in the continued absence of rabbits have still to be elucidated.

To get rid of bracken, at least cost, from a mixed heather and bracken community in the situation described, the aid of heather is enlisted by converting it first to an even-aged community and then burning it in the mature phase when bracken is at a minimum. Burning will be followed by an increase in bracken, but also by a speeding up of the return of heather, because establishment by seedling on mineral soil is more rapid than on mor in Breckland conditions. Doubtless bracken would persist for many years, but repetition of the treatment when bracken is minimal will at least help to keep the number of fronds small. Burnings of the heather at shorter intervals would prevent it exercising its full competitive power and result in an increase in bracken.

Senescence in Festuca ovina

The exclusion of rabbits from a floristically poor acidiphilous grassland resulted after 11–13 years in the dominance of *Festuca ovina*, the complete elimination of the accompanying species, *Aira praecox, Galium hercynicum, Luzula campestris, Rumex tenuifolius* and the near extinction of *Agrostis tenuis* (Fig. 22, Watt, 1960). The records covered the years 1936–57.

From the same plot annual records (made in the beginning of July) have been continued until 1969 and refer almost exclusively to the behaviour of the fescue since the attainment of dominance. The data for cover, over the whole period 1936–69 (Fig. 2), show the rise to a maximum followed by the fluctuating fall which is the subject of the present note. Incidentally *Agrostis*

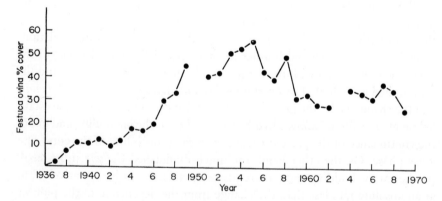

Figure 2. Change in the cover % of *Festuca ovina* in the enclosure 1936–69.

tenuis survived until 1965 (2 shoots) but in the enclosure as a whole and apart from the zinc-affected margin, there were about 6 shoots only in 1969.

A selection from the annual charts (Fig. 3) shows (especially in the part to the right) the scattered population of young (small) fescue plants which by 1964 have formed a complete cover, but by 1969 the old fescue has died

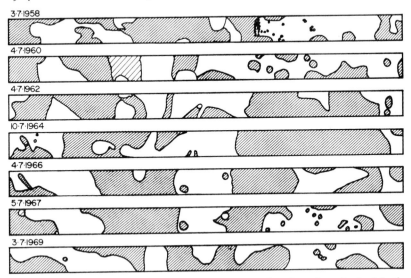

Figure 3. A selection from the series of annual charts (based on data obtained in the beginning of July) between 1958 and 1969 showing the cycle of change in the cover of *Festuca ovina*.

leaving a small population of plants (some from surviving shoots of old plants) set in a background of fescue litter. The cycle of change runs to about 10 years.

The end, however, has not returned to the point of departure. Since fescue became dominant three changes of significance have taken place: patchiness as between young and old, patchiness as between live and dead and an increase in the thickness of the litter (Fig. 4).

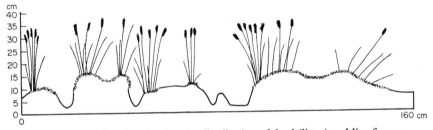

Figure 4. Profile of the plot showing the distribution of dead (litter) and live fescue, young fescue with abundant inflorescences and old with few, and the thick litter, in places becoming matted with lichen thalli as it becomes consolidated.

While fescue never showed 100 per cent cover nor ever was 100 per cent even-aged, yet the vigorous freely flowering fescue in the earlier years of the enclosure contrasts sharply with the later, in which, with increasing age and death of the old fescue plants, the cover is differentiated into patches of dead (litter) and live, and young with abundant leaves and inflorescences and old with few of both. In 1969 there were 115·8 inflorescences per 100 cm² as against 12·7, based on 10 samples of each: S.E. ± 10·92. Further, out of the total live cover, young plants in 1958 contributed 21·5 per cent: in 1969, only 8·3 per cent. The community has become old.

The third point of significance is the increase in the thickness of the litter whereby fescue 'fouls its own nest'. This bulky litter is hostile to the establishment of seedlings and with increasing thickness becomes increasingly so, while during the same period fescue regenerates freely in the mat of *Cladonia arbuscula* outside the enclosure. That this is the explanation of the failure is supported by Fig. 5 in which the plotted points of spring rainfall (May and

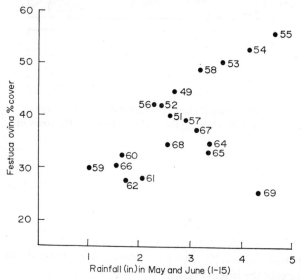

Figure 5. The relationship between the rainfall for May and the first half of June and the cover of fescue (recorded in early July) for the years 1949–69 (except 1950 and 1963).

the first half of June) against fescue cover for 1948–60 fall almost on a straight line. Since 1960 all points (except 1966) fall below this line, suggesting a reduction in the efficiency of the high and relatively high spring rainfall. It is possible also that the accumulated litter shortens the life or depresses the vigour of the fescue plant.

To restore the diversity of species content the accumulation of litter must be prevented or if accumulated then got rid of, e.g. by burning or grazing. On the other hand, the changed habitat may be expected to invite invasion by other more competitive species, yet, though *Deschampsia flexuosa* and *Calluna* —both freely spreading outside the enclosure and successful competitors of *Festuca*—are in the near neighbourhood of the enclosure, both have so far failed to gain a footing in it. It is possible that the thick litter has a differential effect on seedling establishment.

Relationships between species in the restricted presence of the potential dominant (*Festuca ovina*)

Where the potential dominant is prevented (e.g. by grazing) from exercising control over the accompanying species, then fluctuations in their populations are due to factors other than competition with the dominant.

The future of the control plot to the enclosure mentioned in the previous section was predictable: after the incidence of myxomatosis in 1954 the whole plot would eventually have been dominated by *Festuca ovina* which by 1958 had occupied about 18 per cent. The relationships of the accompanying species could then be investigated by maintaining the fescue cover at a more or less constant level (actually it fluctuated between 12 per cent and 25 per cent) by clipping the tussocks and removing the seedlings.

The experience previously gained pointed to the significance of weather on the populations of some. To identify the factors involved and pin-point their incidence the plot was charted frequently from April to October and infrequently in winter. Absence abroad interrupted the continuity of the record in 1963 and again in the winter of 1965–6.

The methods of assessment of the populations were those previously used (Watt, 1960). The data are not yet fully analysed, but those available (Figs. 6 and 7) show the influence of the rainfall (Fig. 8).

Galium hercynicum. The graph (Fig. 6) shows two catastrophic drops in the spring of 1959 and 1967 and recoveries therefrom with minor fluctuations. Both major and minor drops are related to spring drought (Fig. 8). In most years there is also a drop in winter, part of which is explained by the swelling of the lichen mat of *Cladonia arbuscula* obscuring leaves visible in drier periods.

Luzula campestris is less sensitive (Fig. 6). A fairly uniform ceiling of between 100 and 150 rosettes is interrupted by drought with depressions in June–July (1960, 1961, 1962), July–August (1959, 1964), with humps (1965, 1968, 1969), a hump followed by a hollow (July–August 1967) and with little change in 1958, and 1966. Drought dries up the old leaves, retards the emergence of new rosettes: hence the depressions. With continuously wet weather there is an overlap of old and young: hence the hump. There is no appreciable fall in winter except in the severe winter of 1962–3.

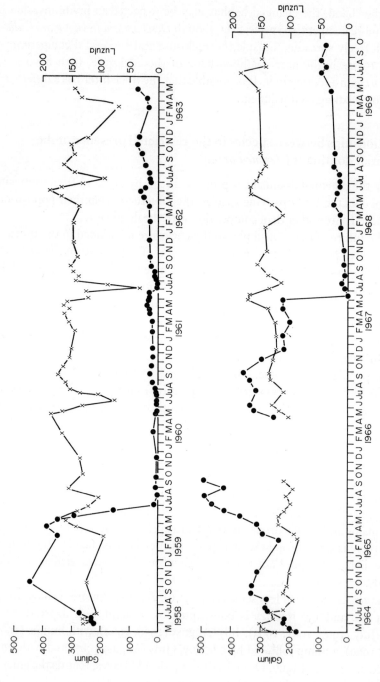

Figure 6. Occurrences (out of a possible 1024) of *Galium hercynicum* (●) and number of rosettes of *Luzula campestris* (X) for 1958–69.

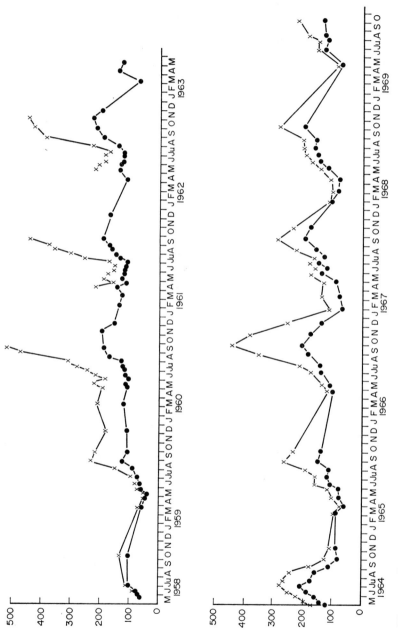

Figure 7. Occurrences (●) out of a possible 1024 and number of shoots (X) of *Agrostis canina* for 1958–69.

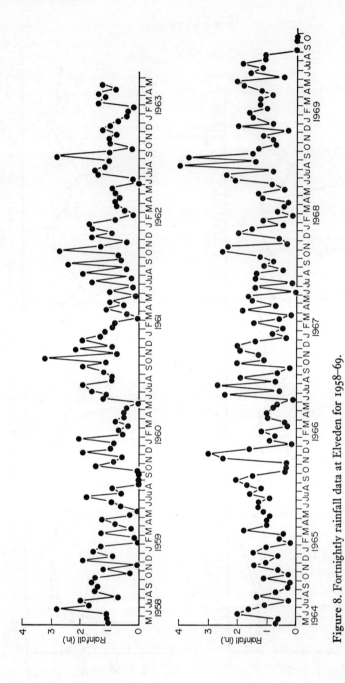

Figure 8. Fortnightly rainfall data at Elveden for 1958–69.

Agrostis canina was assessed in two ways: by occurrences (i.e. the number of small squares of side 1·25 cm in which the shoot is present) and less accurately by a count of the number of shoots (Fig. 7). There is a marked seasonal rhythm, a fall in winter (related to winter frost) which may continue as late as July, but in most is checked by the appearance of live shoots from April onwards. Flowering takes place usually towards the end of June and the beginning of July, after which there is normally a big increase in the number of shoots the incidence of whose maximum varies, however, from July (1964) to November (1962). In a general way these fluctuations are related respectively to winter frost, spring, summer and early autumn rainfall with the possibility that spring temperature is a significant factor, e.g. in the early increase in the population in spring 1964 with its high temperature in May (515°F (186°C) cumulative degrees over 40°F (4·4°C) compared with the mean for the 12 years of 403·4°F (224°C)).

The possible effect of *Agrostis canina* on *Galium hercynicum* and *Luzula campestris* is indicated in Figs. 9 and 10. The data in both are based on sections of the plot where the presence of *Festuca ovina* is minimal. Fig. 9 shows that factors other than competition with *Agrostis* influence the numbers of *Galium*, but there is an indication that at the higher levels competition with *Agrostis* may take place. Similarly in Fig. 10 both *Luzula* and *Agrostis* increase until a further increase in *Agrostis* sets a limit to the increase of *Luzula*.

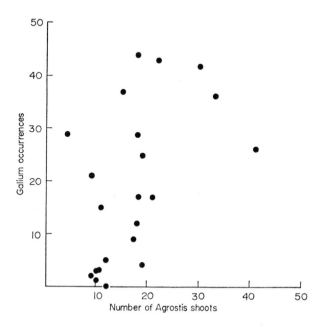

Figure 9. Relationship between *Agrostis canina* and *Galium hercynicum* from a section of the plot containing no *Festuca ovina*.

During the period 1958–69 one *Calluna* seedling appeared in the plot and was removed, one plant of *Deschampsia flexuosa* entered late and has been left. *Rumex tenuifolius*, the only other higher plant in the plot, shows from small beginnings a general increase from 1958 to 1961 after which there is a close parallelism to the fluctuations in the occurrences of *Agrostis* with, however, local increase following local disturbance of the *Cladonia* mat by birds.

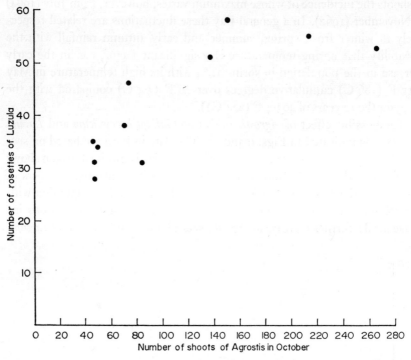

Figure 10. Relationship between *Agrostis canina* and *Luzula campestris* in sections containing a minimum amount of *Festuca ovina*.

Moles and the floristic composition of ungrazed chalk grassland

The ungrazed chalk pasture of Foxhole Heath (grassland B in Watt, 1957) showed four kinds of patches interpreted on a brief scrutiny as the 'pioneer', 'building', 'mature' and 'degenerate' phases in a cycle of change (Fig. 11). Further examination, however, shows them to be stages in a succession initiated on eroded mole-hills and differentiated by rate of establishment and maturation (annuals before perennials, and perennial herbs before perennial grasses) and by competition (annuals eliminated by perennials and most perennial herbs by perennial grasses) leaving a mature phase with relatively few species mainly grasses and a few perennial herbs. The degenerate litter-covered phase of dead grasses is colonized, not by annuals of the pioneer phase but mostly from neighbouring plants, grasses and some perennial herbs, leaving the probability in an unbroken turf of a cycle of change without the 'pioneer' phase. Thus, the flora of the ungrazed grassland of Foxhole Heath is enriched by the activity of moles and the proportional representation of the component species would be affected by the relative areas under the different 'phases'.

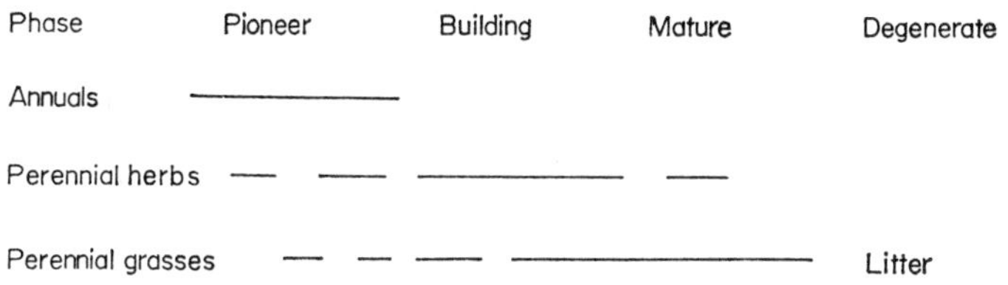

Phase	Pioneer	Building	Mature	Degenerate
Annuals	————————			
Perennial herbs	—	——	————————	——
Perennial grasses	— — ——		—————————	Litter

Figure 11. Diagrammatic representation of the effect of moles on the floristic composition of the ungrazed chalk grassland on Foxhole Heath.

At present this type of community includes five of the rarer Breckland species, *Silene otites* and *Veronica spicata* subsp. *spicata*, characteristic of the building phase, and *Carex ericetorum*, *Medicago falcata*, and *Phleum phleoides*, characteristic of the mature phase. There are, however, no rare annuals.

The potentialities of this area for supporting and maintaining a richly diversified flora, including some of the rare annuals as well, is suggested from a comparison with the communities of the secondary succession on abandoned arable land of similar soil type. In the absence of grazing and of invasion by woody plants the initial community rich in annuals, including several of the Breckland rarities, develops eventually into a grassland similar to that on Foxhole. Thus we may say that on Foxhole we have an integration of the attenuated representatives of communities of the secondary succession differing, however, in detail and particularly in the comparative floristic poverty of the pioneer phase believed traceable to the non-availability of a sufficient supply of seed and to the difference in total area of the pioneer phase, represented as it is by small patches variously distributed in space and transient in time, and separated from each other by the ungrazed intervening vegetation acting as a differentiating screen to the dispersal of the species. For a species to spread from one bare patch to another, the patches must lie within its effective dispersal range and to survive, the availability for colonization of these patches must overlap in time.

A consideration of this interpretation of the dynamic structure of this ungrazed chalk pasture and the relationships between its component species forms the background to what could be a most interesting series of experiments whose detail would depend on the declared objective, but whose management as a repository of the continental contingent in Breckland and as a self-maintaining community rich in species and independent of a continuous external source of seed supply involves decisions on the total minimum area of bare soil, the size of the individual patch and the distribution of the patches in space and in time.

Discussion

All four examples may be viewed against the background of the effect of the dominant or potential dominant, itself like other species subject to environmental influence including that of itself: the catastrophic death of *Calluna*, the interruption of continuity in ungrazed chalk grassland by moles, the effect of *Festuca ovina* on its own dominance, and the artificial check to it by clipping and removal of seedlings, have repercussions on the accompanying species.

Three of the examples emphasize the part played by climatic factors in causing fluctuations in number, as indeed one might expect in the stop-go, Atlantic–Continental climate of Breckland. They also question the validity of observations, subjectively or objectively made once only in particular years or at particular times of the year to be representative of the community as a whole. Further they make us aware of our limitations, for while local control of the climate may be exercised in various ways (shelter-belts, hedges, brushwood, accumulation of litter, etc.) management in general is planned within the framework of the given climate.

One of the important issues emphasized is the need for understanding what is happening in a plant community and the correct interpretation of the relationships between the various species. The chance visitor seeing dead *Calluna* under bracken would as the historical record shows be wrong to deduce that bracken killed the heather. Similarly from the relative cover of heather and bracken he would be wrong to identify physiognomic dominance with physiological dominance: for while heather by its spread actively reduces the number of bracken fronds, bracken increases mainly by occupying areas vacated by live *Calluna*. Also because in 1969 the number of fronds in the cut plot exceeds that at the beginning in 1954, he would be wrong to conclude that the heather had no effect on the bracken, for there has in the meantime been a change in the spring rainfall.

It will be many years before the mixed *Pteridium-Calluna* returns to a norm—and a hypothetical or statistical norm at that—but neither in the cyclic pattern in this community, nor in the sequential pattern in the ungrazed chalk grassland with mole hills do the processes at work differ essentially from those in the gross pattern as illustrated by the effects of fire on the conifer forest of western north America, on the prairies of the mid-west of the United States, or the heaths of South Australia, by the hurricanes on the deciduous forest of eastern North America, or by the avalanches of the Rockies leaving in their wake ribbands of aspen transgressing several altitudinal zones. Each event, whether death from old age or prematurely from other causes, induces a fresh beginning, the outcome of which is a matter of scale and the available biota.

The extension in area of the mole hill may be visualized in the abandoned arable field where a secondary succession is initiated. At the other extreme the dispersion of the bare soil in tiny pieces and/or the reduction in competitive power of species following mowing or grazing leads to a telescoping of phases, whether cyclic or sequential, and a relatively rich admixture of species (cf. Alpine mown meadows).

The maintenance of floristic wealth in such mown or grazed pastures is dependent on the removal of effects harmful to themselves including the accumulated litter. The classical example of the change of one grassland community to another by the use of fertilizers is the Park grass plots at Rothamsted whereby the floristically rich unmanured plot is converted to a highly productive one of relatively few and different species. What is not generally appreciated is that if the manured plot were left unmown the natural agencies of decay would be unable to cope with the litter at the rate of its production. While there is no unmown manured plot to prove the point, it is safe to predict that because of the accumulation of litter the floristic composition would change and production fall.

Similarly among natural communities, Willis (1963) has shown how by the use of fertilizers one community may be changed to another—as indeed has just been confirmed by the use of phosphate in Teesdale (Jeffrey, this volume). Yet these are short-term results. In the present context of community management, the chief interest of these experiments lies not so much in transforming one community into another but in the possible use of nutrients as edaphic tools to change the balance of species within the community.

The management of plant communities begun by Neolithic man and continued ever since primarily for utilitarian ends now embraces the field of 'natural' communities which present a challenge to ecologists first to understand them, then to control them for defined objectives.

Finally the Nature Conservancy was founded on the twin pillars of the Society for the Promotion of Nature Reserves and the British Ecological Society, the former representative of the naturalist who lives with his plants (or animals), sees them change from day to day, season to season, and year to year, the latter representative of people whose primary interest is in scientific generalization. For the practical business of management, knowledge from both sources is needed whether provided from the person of a single individual or of two or more, but the opportunity is there for massive and creative co-operation.

152   *A.S.Watt*

Acknowledgements

I am much indebted to Miss S. Bishop, for drawing the Figures.

Plant names follow *Flora of the British Isles*, Clapham A.R., Tutin T.G., and Warburg, E.F. (1962), 2nd ed., Cambridge. Lichen nomenclature follows 'New Check List of British Lichens', P.W.James (1965), *Lichenologist* 3, 95–153.

References

HEADY H.F. (1956) Changes in a California annual plant community induced by manipulation of natural mulch. *Ecology* 37, 798–812.

LAMB H.H. (1967) Britain's changing climate. *Geogrl J.* 133, 445–68.

WATT A.S. (1950) Contributions to the ecology of bracken (*Pteridium aquilinum*). V. Bracken and frost. *New Phytol.*, 49, 308–27.

WATT A.S. (1955) Bracken versus heather, a study in plant sociology. *J. Ecol.* 43, 490–506.

WATT A.S. (1957) The effect of excluding rabbits from grassland B (Mesobrometum) in Breckland. *J. Ecol.* 45, 861–78.

WATT A.S. (1960) Population changes in acidiphilous grass-heath in Breckland, 1936–57. *J. Ecol.* 48, 605–29.

WATT A.S. (1964) Some factors affecting bracken in Breckland. *J. Ecol.* 52, 63–77.

WILLIS A.J. (1963) Braunton Burrows: the effects on the vegetation of the addition of mineral nutrients to dune soils. *J. Ecol.* 51, 353–74.

The influence of burning and grazing on the growth and development of *Rubus chamaemorus* L. in *Calluna-Eriophorum* bog

K. TAYLOR and T. C. MARKS *Department of Botany and Microbiology, University College London*

Introduction

The distribution of *Rubus chamaemorus* (Cloudberry) is boreal-circumpolar, which corresponds to the arctic-subarctic climatic belt (Hultén 1950, Hare 1954). The plant is exclusively northern and montane in Europe. In the British Isles it is most characteristic and abundant in floristically poor, acid bog in which *Calluna vulgaris* and *Eriophorum vaginatum* are co-dominant. This association, described as Calluneto-Eriophoretum by McVean and Ratcliffe (1962), is remarkably constant in composition and is widespread in the uplands. On Dartmoor and in south Wales, however, *R. chamaemorus* is absent from the community. The plant has a local distribution in the Berwyn mountains in north Wales (Tallis 1969), but is not found in Snowdonia proper (Ratcliffe 1959). It is a common plant on blanket peat throughout the Pennines, the Cheviots, the east Southern Uplands and in the Scottish Highlands.

The distribution map of cloudberry in Britain (Perring & Walters 1962) corresponds closely with a map of the annual average potential water deficit (Green 1964); it is associated with areas of low potential water deficit with the exception of the western Highlands and Islands of Scotland. *R. chamaemorus* is more or less confined to blanket peat and to this extent it is limited, both climatically and topographically, to areas of low potential water deficit and to level or gently sloping ground which is suitable for the formation of blanket-bog. It is found on the hummocks or in well-drained areas of these ombrogenous mires. The geographical distribution and altitudinal restriction at the southern limits to the range correlate well with the 60°F (15·6°C) July mean isotherm and a short growing season.

In the Late-glacial and early Post-glacial periods (Bartley 1962, 1966, Birks 1965) the species occurred in the lowlands of northern England, but with the amelioration of the climate retreated to higher ground where peat formation became extensive from Atlantic times onward. There is no available evidence to suggest that *R. chamaemorus* has ever occurred beyond the southern limit of its present range in the British Isles.

From the discussion above, it can be seen that climate is a factor of primary importance in the ecology of *R. chamaemorus*. One particular aspect of this relationship has quite understandably attracted attention, namely the frequency and amount of fruit production. There is evidence that cloudberry fruits have been sufficiently numerous, locally in Britain, to make it worth while gathering them in some years. Dallman (1932) cites evidence of good and bad years for fruiting in the seventeenth, eighteenth and nineteenth centuries. More recently 1940, 1951, 1960 and 1968 stand out as being years in which fruits were produced in abundance throughout the range. There are no records which suggest that the harvest has ever reached the marketable proportions which it frequently attains in northern Europe. In Norway there is a good deal of variation in yield from year to year although fruits can always be found (Resvoll 1929). This fluctuation in the harvest is considered to be due to a sensitivity to frost during the flowering period particularly in northern regions.

Evidence from place names indicates that in the past fruits were produced in abundance in certain areas of the British uplands. Recently fruit has been found in most years on Carter Fell, Roxburgh; White Coomb, Dumfries; and Cairnwell, East Grampians. During a period of observation from 1965 to 1968 on the Moor House National Nature Reserve, Westmorland, large numbers of cloudberry fruits were seen each year, but only in areas where the bog had been fenced to exclude hill-sheep. This observation indicated that the intensity of grazing was also important in controlling the abundance and reproductive capacity of *R. chamaemorus*. Furthermore, the Reserve provided a unique opportunity for investigating the interaction between grazing and climate and their separate effects on the behaviour of the species.

The vegetation, climate and sheep-grazing regime at Moor House have been described recently by Eddy, Welch and Rawes (1969), Rawes and Welch (1969). Prior to the purchase of the Reserve in 1952 the area was managed as a grouse moor and the heather (*Calluna vulgaris*) was burnt in patches on a rotation system in spring. It is common land which may well have been grazed by sheep for the last thousand years. About half of the 3850 ha Reserve is covered by ombrogenous peat which mainly supports Calluneto-Eriophoretum, the typical blanket-bog of the Pennines. Most of this vegetation has not been burnt in the last 25 years.

A trial was established by the Nature Conservancy at Moor House in 1954, so that the long-term effects of rotational burning and sheep grazing on *Calluna-Eriophorum* bog could be studied (details are documented in volumes of the Moor House Reserve Record). We are carrying out a detailed investigation of these effects with particular reference to the ecology of *R. chamaemorus*. The results presented in this paper concern only the general responses of the plant to the experimental treatments.

Description of experiment

An area of Calluneto-Eriophoretum situated on the east flank of Hard Hill around 2000 ft (610 m) was burned in the spring of 1954. Four blocks (A, B, C and D) were laid out within this area in a series with increasing altitude, in 1957. Each contained the same burning and grazing treatments in a restricted random 2 × 3 factorial arrangement in which the three ungrazed plots (30 m²) were included beside each other within a single fenced area (30 m × 90 m), with the unfenced treatments similarly arranged immediately adjacent.

Preliminary observations made on the experiment in 1967 to 1968 showed a similar pattern of response in each of the four blocks. Therefore one block (C) only was selected for a full investigation and details of the treatments and their designations are as follows:

	No further treatment	Short rotation (Burnt in 1965, to be burnt again in 1976)	Long rotation (To be burnt in 1976)
Unfenced	C/N	C/S	C/L
Fenced	C/NF	C/SF	C/LF

At the time of sampling, treatments C/N and C/NF were the same as C/L and C/LF respectively. In order not to violate the long term aims of the experiment, attention was therefore confined to treatments C/S, C/L, C/SF and C/LF.

Methods

Sampling of plant material

The most obvious feature of *R. chamaemorus* during the growing season is the annual aerial shoot with foliage leaves and sometimes a terminal flower, which develop from a resting bud. At seasonal maturity, however, the above-ground parts represent only approximately one-third of the total dry weight of the plant per unit area. Below-ground is an extensive much branched perennial rhizome system with slender adventitious roots. The individual may be described as consisting of a single shoot together with its supporting rhizome and root system, although such a unit has to be defined arbitrarily. Measurements have been made therefore on a unit area basis as well as in terms of shoot numbers.

In each treatment plot an area 25 m² was marked out and ten samples were taken using co-ordinates selected from random number tables. At each sampling point all shoots of *R. chamaemorus* were collected from within a 1 m² quadrat. Sample points devoid of shoots were included in the final analysis. The number of samples taken and the size of the sampling unit were calculated to be adequate to allow the detection of between treatment differences at the 5 per cent level of probability, based on the preliminary observations made in 1967 to 1968. Plant samples were taken at intervals during the growing season, from May to August 1969. For each sample the number of shoots was counted and the material separated into leaf lamina, stem plus petioles plus flowers, and fruits when present. At the same time the numbers of male and female flowers were noted. Leaf area determinations were made, but are not presented here. Then the various fractions of the shoot were dried separately at 80°C to constant weight and their dry weight determined. Bulking of fresh leaf samples was necessary for some treatments in order to obtain reasonable estimates of leaf area.

A single 8 in (20·3 cm) diameter core was taken to a depth of 50 cm from each treatment on 5 August 1969. Rhizome and root material of *R. chamaemorus* was washed out of the peat, separated, dried at 80°C and the dry weight determined.

Chemical analysis

Chemical determinations were made on the oven-dried fractions previously ground in a Christy and Norris mill to pass a 0·4 mm sieve. A single digestion procedure, involving the use of sulphuric acid with selenium as catalyst, lithium sulphate as accelerator and hydrogen peroxide as an oxidizing agent, was employed to bring mineral elements into solution (S.E.Allen pers. com.). Total nitrogen was then determined by steam distillation. Total calcium, total magnesium and total potassium were determined using a Unicam SP90 atomic absorption/emission spectrophotometer. Finally total phosphorus was estimated colorimetrically using a molybdenum blue method.

Results

Shoot density

The progress curves of the mean number of shoots per square metre together with the standard error of the means for each treatment are presented in Fig. 1. Shoot distribution shows a marked contagion which is mostly due to the perennial sympodial system of annual shoots produced from the terminal

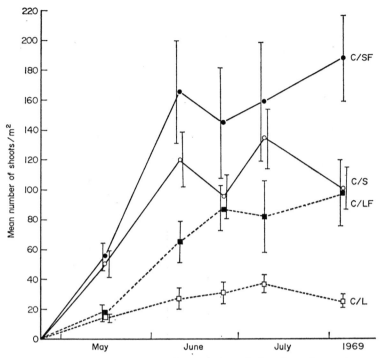

Figure 1. The treatment effect on shoot numbers during the 1969 growing season. The limits shown represent ± standard error of the means.

rhizome buds. This morphological pattern is accentuated in the treatment having the highest shoot density (C/SF) and is reflected in the large standard error values. The treatment last burnt in 1965 and from which sheep have been excluded (C/SF) has been the most effective in promoting the growth of *R. chamaemorus*, resulting in a fivefold increase in mean shoot number.

Comparing the plots which have not been burnt since the start of the experiment (C/L and C/LF), the prevention of sheep grazing has led to an increase in mean shoot density (C/LF). Similarly the additional burning treatment applied in 1965 to a grazed plot has been effective in bringing about an increase in shoot number.

There is a suggestion in the data of a sustained slight increase in shoot density throughout the growing season in the fenced treatments (C/SF and C/LF), whilst both unfenced treatments show a small decline towards the end of the season probably due to defoliation by sheep.

Aerial dry matter yield

The treatment differences indicated by shoot densities are even more strikingly displayed by the mean total dry weight values for the above-ground standing crop (Fig. 2). Burning in the absence of grazing has resulted in a twelvefold increase at maturity in mean dry matter per square metre (C/SF). Exclusion of sheep (C/LF) and the combined effects of grazing and burning (C/S) have both resulted in a similar fivefold increase in mean total dry weight as compared with the grazed plot which has not been burnt since the beginning of the experiment (C/L). The data support the contention put forward above of a continued increase in mean dry weight in the C/SF treatment and a decline towards the end of the season in the grazed areas (C/S and C/L).

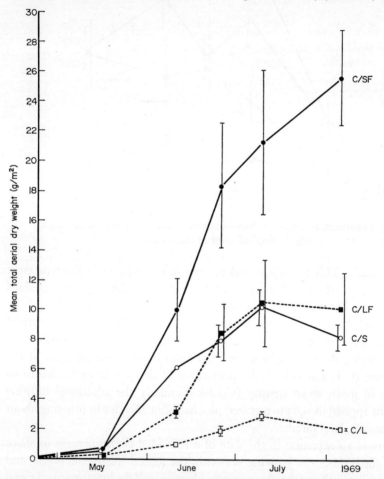

Figure 2. The treatment effect on total aerial dry matter during the 1969 growing season. The limits shown represent ± standard error of the means.

Individual shoot dry weight

The effect of burning in the absence of grazing (C/SF) has led to the production of a shoot population which has a mean dry weight per shoot almost twice that of the grazed areas (C/S and C/L), whilst prevention of grazing alone (C/LF) appears to produce shoots intermediate in weight (Fig. 3).

Rhizome and root dry matter

The dry weight of rhizome and root material obtained from a single core in each treatment is shown in Table 1, together with the numbers and dry weights of shoots associated with these cores. Ratios of rhizome dry weight

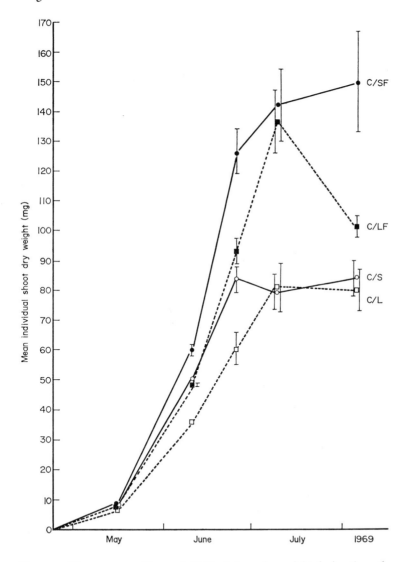

Figure 3. The treament effect on individual shoot dry weight during the 1969 growing season. The limits shown represent ± standard error of the means.

Table 1. Above-ground and below-ground parts of *Rubus chamaemorus* obtained from a single core in each treatment.

Treatment	Number of shoots	Oven-dry weight (g)			Rhizome dry weight ÷ root dry weight	Estimated dry weight/m² (g)	
		Shoot	Rhizome	Root		Rhizome	Root
C/SF	15	2·64	3·29	3·85	1·2	102	119
C/LF	8	0·68	0·08	0·43	1·2	25	13
C/S	17	1·38	0·98	0·91	0·7	30	28
C/L	10	0·82	1·18	0·51	1·4	37	16

to shoot dry weight are approximately unity in each case. Estimated rhizome and root dry matter per square metre shows a large increase in the recently burnt and fenced plot (C/SF) corresponding to the effects described above for the aerial parts.

Numbers of flowers and fruits

Larger numbers of flowers of both sexes developed inside fenced plots than outside them (Table 2). The effect of grazing pressure can be clearly seen in

Table 2. Total numbers of flowers and fruits in 10 × 1 m² samples in each treatment.

Treatment		1969	10 June	25 June	9 July	5 August
C/SF	♂ flowers	} 126		46	24	44
	♀ flowers			30	32*	21*
	Fruits		0	0	29 (2·77)†	19 (2·47)†
C/LF	♂ flowers	} 42		13	2	2
	♀ flowers			14	11*	23*
	Fruits		0	0	15 (1·85)†	4 (0·33)†
C/S	♂ flowers	} 13		7	6	1
	♀ flowers			4	1*	1
	Fruits		0	0	0 (0)†	0 (0)†
	♂ flowers	} 1		0	0	1
	♀ flowers			0	0	1
	Fruits		0	0	1 (0·08)†	0 (0)†

* Female flowers which failed to set fruit.
† Fruit yield (oven-dry weight g).

the rapid decline in flower numbers at each harvest. Fruit production was virtually confined to the fenced plots, with the biggest yield being in the treatment burnt in 1965 (C/SF).

Mineral nutrient concentrations

The levels of nitrogen, phosphorus and potassium percentage oven-dry weight of the above-ground parts were similar in all treatments and showed the same downward trend as the growing season progressed (Fig. 4). In

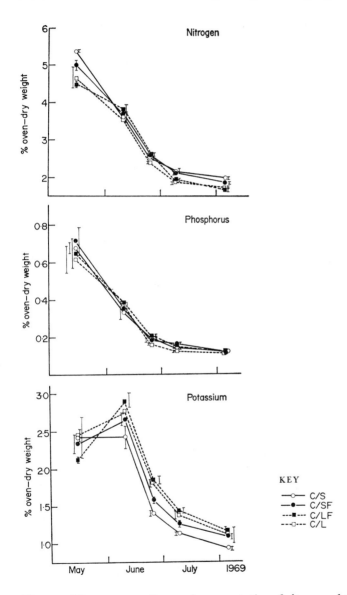

Figure 4. The treatment effect on the concentration of nitrogen, phosphorus and potassium in the total aerial dry matter during the 1969 growing season. The limits shown represent ± standard error of the means.

contrast the concentrations of calcium and magnesium, although they were similar for all treatments, increased at each harvest (Fig. 5).

With the single exception of calcium the concentrations of the mineral elements in the rhizomes and roots are also essentially the same in all treatments (Table 3).

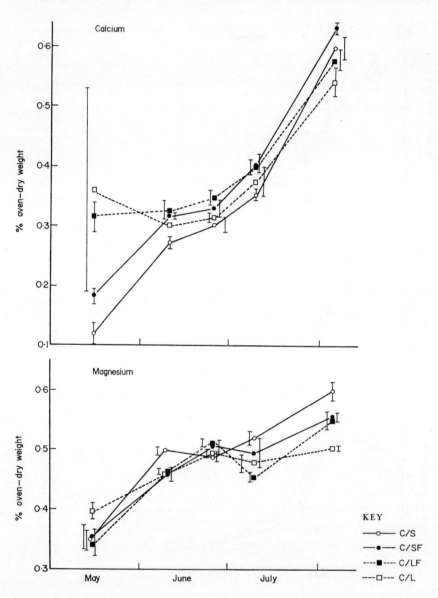

Figure 5. The treatment effect on the concentration of calcium and magnesium in the total aerial dry matter during the 1969 growing season. The limits shown represent ± standard error of the means.

Table 3. Mineral nutrient concentrations of below-ground parts of *Rubus chamaemorus* obtained from a single core taken in each treatment on 5 August 1969.

Treatment		% oven-dry weight				
		N	P	Ca	Mg	K
C/SF	Root	1·36	0·12	0·89	0·45	0·59
	Rhizome	1·10	0·09	0·43	0·18	0·42
C/LF	Root	1·47	0·13	0·44	0·36	0·49
	Rhizome	1·39	0·10	0·40	0·13	0·36
C/S	Root	1·34	0·09	0·81	0·22	0·41
	Rhizome	1·35	0·11	0·32	0·15	0·42
C/L	Root	1·23	0·08	0·41	0·34	0·49
	Rhizome	1·24	0·10	0·27	0·15	0·35

Discussion

Effects of sheep grazing

In the absence of recent burning, the exclusion of sheep has resulted in an increase in the mean total dry weight of the above-ground standing crop of *R. chamaemorus*. There was a doubling of the mean shoot density and the establishment of a population of larger shoots. The numbers of flowers and fruits also showed a marked increase. As a result of burning one of the grazed plots in 1965, there was a similar increase in the mean dry matter of the aerial parts but there was no corresponding increase in the mean shoot weight. It would seem that the grazing factor had prevented the establishment of a population of large shoots during the growing season and led to the production of a number of small new shoots, which has the effect of reducing the mean individual dry weight of the population. The number of flowers was also much reduced and no fruits were produced in this plot.

The effects produced by hill-sheep are all the more remarkable, considering that they graze grassland in preference to blanket-bog vegetation on the Reserve. The grazing pressure on the blanket-bog about a mile to the northeast of the experiment, on the same ridge, reached a peak value of less than 1 sheep/100 acre (40 ha) in June to July 1964, during a grazing season which extended from April to November (Welch & Rawes 1966). Although the intensity is extremely low, the maximum grazing pressure corresponds closely with the main period of vegetative growth and flowering of cloudberry. Hill-sheep seek out and closely graze the young shoots and flowers of *Eriophorum vaginatum* and *Rubus chamaemorus*.

Effects of burning

When the blanket-bog is burnt in the spring the resting buds of cloudberry are not materially damaged and produce normal shoot systems later in the same year. *Eriophorum vaginatum* recovers rapidly and is dominant for several years. When regeneration of *Calluna vulgaris* is good, complete recovery to maturity takes about 20 years (Eddy *et al.* 1969). Typical Calluneto-Erio-phoretum returns with the onset of the senescent phase of the life cycle of *Calluna* (Watt 1955, Gimingham 1960).

In the absence of sheep grazing the effect of burning the vegetation in 1965 has resulted in a doubling of the mean total aerial dry matter of *R. chamaemorus*, the production of twice the mean number of shoots and the establishment of a population of large shoots by 1969. There is a suggestion in the data presented in Figs. 1–3 that the plant is still responding to this treat-ment. Presumably the response will diminish when *Calluna* enters the building phase of growth and eventually there will be a decrease in dry matter production of cloudberry as the vegetation reverts to typical *Calluna-Eriophorum* bog.

The response of *R. chamaemorus* to the burning treatment is not a direct response to the fertilizing effect of the mineral nutrient-rich ash which is added to the peat surface (Allen 1964). Additional nutrients were taken up, but the concentration of nutrients in the various parts of the plant are similar in all treatments in spite of the differences in growth response.

The removal of the dwarf-shrub canopy by fire also brings about changes in the micro-climate which may be correlated with the increased growth and development of cloudberry.

Separation of the effects of the addition of mineral ash and removal of the plant canopy is being carried out in a field experiment. Preliminary results, in terms of shoot numbers, suggest that the availability of nutrients is not a limiting factor. Full details will be presented in a further paper. Gore (1961) found a similar lack of response, particularly to phosphate and nitrogen, in attempting to establish *Molinia caerulea* on blanket-peat on the Reserve. There appeared to be a very strong climatic suppression of growth in this species at the high altitude. Climate appears also to be the factor limiting growth of cloudberry.

Implications for management for conservation

The rotational burning of the fenced plot of Calluneto-Eriophoretum has produced a most impressive increase in the vegetative and reproductive vigour of *R. chamaemorus*. The mean fruit yield of 0·2 g per square metre per year is, however, very much lower than the value given by Østgård (1964) as low productivity characteristic of a bog of medium fertility in north Norway. Annual fruit production in very fertile bogs may reach 8 to 12 g per square metre. It would be pointless to add fertilizer to increase the crop of cloudberry fruits at Moor House because of the limitations of climate, apart from the costs involved.

The fact that the Reserve is common land means that sheep grazing cannot be prevented on a large scale. Combined with burning, the low sheep density on the blanket-bog permits the vegetative spread of *R. chamaemorus*, but discourages flower and seed production. In a few areas on the Reserve, which appear to escape the attentions of sheep, flowers and fruits are produced in abundance. These areas together with the small areas of blanket-bog which have been fenced for experimental purposes, provide a source of viable seed which is dispersed by the red grouse (*Lagopus scoticus*).

It would appear that the presence of a few permanently fenced plots, burnt on a rotation system, is desirable to allow the potential spread of *R. chamaemorus*, which is one of the more attractive mountain plants in the northern Pennines, especially if sheep density on the Reserve was to increase. Even these measures may not prove adequate if sheep density exceeded a value of between 1 sheep per 10 acre (4 ha) and 1 sheep per 2 acre (0·8 ha) suggested by Welch & Rawes (1966) as being compatible with normal bog growth on the Reserve.

In the wider context of factors regulating the abundance and reproductive capacity of *R. chamaemorus* in Calluneto-Eriophoretum in the British Isles, sheep grazing and moor burning which are widespread are likely to be important factors within the limitations of the climate. It would be unwise, however, to attempt to extrapolate the results of the present investigation to other situations in the absence of information about the proportions of different vegetation types and the numbers of sheep grazing in summer in a particular locality.

Acknowledgements

We should like to thank Miss Joan Salmon for carrying out the chemical analyses and for skilled technical assistance. Dr H.Frankland, Regional Officer (North) the Nature Conservancy, kindly gave permission for the research to be carried out and Mr M.Rawes, Officer-in-Charge, Moor House Field Station, provided facilities. One of us (T.C.M.) was in receipt of a N.E.R.C. Research Studentship throughout this work.

References

ALLEN S.E. (1964) Chemical aspects of heather burning. *J. appl. Ecol.* **1**, 347–67.
BARTLEY D.D. (1962) The stratigraphy and pollen analysis of lake deposits near Tadcaster, Yorkshire. *New Phytol.* **61**, 277–87.
BARTLEY D.D. (1966) Pollen analysis of some lake deposits near Bamburgh in Northumberland. *New Phytol.* **65**, 141–56.
BIRKS H.J.B. (1965) Late-glacial deposits at Bagmere, Cheshire, and Chat Moss, Lancashire. *New Phytol.* **64**, 270–81.

DALLMAN A.A. (1932) The pollination of the Cloudberry, *Rubus chamaemorus* L. *N.West. Nat.* 7, 209–13.

EDDY A., WELCH D. & RAWES M. (1969) The vegetation of the Moor House National Nature Reserve in the Northern Pennines, England. *Vegetatio* 16, 239–84.

GIMINGHAM C.H. (1960) Biological Flora of the British Isles: *Calluna vulgaris* (L.) Hull. *J. Ecol.* 48, 455–83.

GORE A.J.P. (1961) Factors limiting plant growth on high-level blanket peat. II. Nitrogen and phosphate in the first year of growth. *J. Ecol.* 49, 605–16.

GREEN F.H.W. (1964) A map of annual average potential water deficit in the British Isles. *J. appl. Ecol.* 1, 151–8.

HARE F.K. (1954) The Boreal conifer zone. *Geogrl Stud.* 1, 4–18.

HULTÉN E. (1950) *Atlas of the distribution of vascular plants in N.W. Europe.* Stockholm.

McVEAN D.N. & RATCLIFFE D.A. (1962) *Plant communities of the Scottish Highlands.* London.

ØSTGÅRD O. (1964) Investigations on Cloudberries (*Rubus chamaemorus* L.) in North Norway. *Forsk. Fors. Landbr.* 15, 409–44.

PERRING F. & WALTERS S.M. (1962) *Atlas of the British Flora.* London.

RATCLIFFE, D.A. (1959) The vegetation of the Carneddau, North Wales. I. Grasslands, heaths and bogs. *J. Ecol.* 47, 371–413.

RAWES M. & WELCH D. (1969) Upland productivity of vegetation and sheep at Moor House, National Nature Reserve, Westmorland, England. *Oikos* Suppl. 11, 7–72.

RESVOLL T.R. (1929) *Rubus chamaemorus* L. A morphological-biological study. *Nyt Mag. Naturvid.* 67, 55–129.

TALLIS J.H. (1969) The blanket bog vegetation of the Berwyn Mountains, North Wales. *J. Ecol.* 57, 765–88.

WATT A.S. (1955) Bracken versus heather, a study in plant sociology. *J. Ecol.* 43, 490–506.

WELCH D. & RAWES M. (1966) The intensity of sheep grazing on high level blanket bog in Upper Teesdale. *Ir. J. agric. Res.* 5, 185–96.

Comparative autecology as a guide to plant distribution

F.H.WHITEHEAD *Imperial College, London*

Introduction

When attempts have been made to account for the distribution of plants, it has often been the practice to look for correlations between the factors of the environment and these distributions. Less often have these correlations been tested by experiment. Good correlations can be obtained between either one or a set of fairly clear-cut environmental factors and some distributions. Correlations between factors and distribution for other plants are frequently far less clear, or appear to be clear over the main part of the distribution, but fail completely to account for the anomalous parts of the distribution pattern. The reason for these differences can be found if certain premises are accepted. That is, during the phases of growth of an individual there are continuous changes in physiology, morphology and anatomy. Further that the majority of these physiological differences are dependent on morphological and/or anatomical changes. It would appear then that where the correlation between a factor and a distribution is more or less complete, this is because that factor is operative in a limiting manner at all stages of a particular plant's development. The other case is where a factor may be important at one stage of development but is relatively unimportant at others. For example, absence of light may be necessary to germination of some seeds, but presence of light will be necessary at other phases of development of the plant. From such considerations it is proposed that studies of distributions within and between communities of plants (also equally applicable to animals) will require a very extensive knowledge of their autecology. With the assistance of a number of colleagues, over several years, investigations of the comparative autecology of a number of species have been carried out. These species were chosen because of some definite feature of their distribution, either within a community or, frequently, within a number of communities. These investigations of particular cases have already proceeded far enough for it to be possible to formulate, as hypotheses, certain general requisites for successful competition and survival in different situations.

Epilobium hirsutum and *Lythrum salicaria*

As a first example I would like to refer to work carried out with Dr Shamsi of the University of the Punjab, Lahore. In outline, the problem is that in certain situations in this country *Epilobium hirsutum* and *Lythrum salicaria* for a time appeared fairly equal competitors, even though, later, *Epilobium* frequently replaces *Lythrum*. Other *Lythrum* monospecific stands are taken over by other species, such as *Juncus*, etc. On the other hand, *Lythrum* has a very much wider edaphic range than *Epilobium*.

Lythrum is found on the margins of quite acid bogs, by the side of streams, lakes, fens, irrespective of whether these are of high or low pH, whether they contain large amounts of calcium or not. *Epilobium*, on the other hand, appears to be more restricted to calcicole situations. Both require a fairly moist habitat at some stages of their growth, but, on the whole *Epilobium* appears to be more tolerant of drying out than *Lythrum*. In general, in this country, *Epilobium* frequently forms large, more or less monospecific stands and less frequently, occurs as small clumps or individuals amongst the other vegetation. In contrast, *Lythrum* seldom forms large monospecific stands, though these do occur, and is more often found as scattered individuals in communities, though they may form a very prominent component of such communities. In southern Yugoslavia the picture is quite different. For instance, in the large fens around Metkovic, on the estuary of the Neretva river, *Lythrum* frequently forms rather small monospecific stands and is a more or less constant and frequent component of the communities. *Epilobium hirsutum*, on the other hand, does not form, or only very occasionally, any monospecific stands. It occurs as scattered individuals in the *Phragmites* beds, but in general, it is a much less important component than *Lythrum*. Quite a different type of distribution is found in parts of Czechoslovakia and northern Yugoslavia. Here, monospecific stands are seldom, if ever, formed. Both species, *Epilobium* and *Lythrum* occur as scattered individuals throughout the communities, but *Lythrum* is in much greater abundance than *Epilobium*.

These problems of distribution can be stated as follows: (1) to account for the general overall wider distribution of *Lythrum* on soils varying from pH 4·5 to well above neutrality and a wide range of soils of varied nutrient status, from the fertile soils of the calcareous fens to soils of low nutrient availability at the margins of acid bogs. In contrast, *Epilobium* is found only on soils of fairly high pH and high nutrient status. (2) The apparent anomalies in distribution in the British Isles, the southern Adriatic and in central Europe.

From Dr Shamsi's experiments, which are at present in course of preparation for publication, the whole physiology of these two species emerges in full detail. I will extract from these data only a few of the more significant points. Firstly, the question of tolerance of low mineral status shown by *Lythrum* in contrast to the high nutrient requirements of *Epilobium*. Experiments were carried out by growing both of these plants at various dilutions of a standard Long Ashton water culture solution. Later, further experiments were carried out in which one nutrient at a time was made progressively limiting. The results of these experiments showed clearly that *Lythrum* was much more successful in reacting to nutrient stress than *Epilobium*. It was important to know the details of this reaction. They are the clues to important mechanisms of survival and the more successful ability of one of these species to compete. It was found that a new form of growth analysis was of great use in interpreting these experiments. It consists of plotting over a series of harvests the dry weights of the main morphological categories of leaf, stem and root as percentages of the total dry weight of an individual of the average of the harvest. This type of analysis enables us to determine the progressive change of balance in morphological development independently of size. There appears to be a characteristic pattern common to species, irrespective of variation of experimental conditions. This I propose to call 'the genetic pattern of development'. Superimposed upon this pattern is another pattern which I call 'the response to the environment pattern'. Mathematically it can be envisaged that the former pattern is in accordance with a specific formula and that the second pattern is due to the alteration of the value of a constant in this formula.

With *Epilobium*, at a tenfold and a twentyfold dilution, the increasing dilution of the solution is accompanied by a large increase in the proportion of root material and a corresponding decrease of stem with leaf material more or less constant. With time these differences are accentuated. This may be considered a compensating mechanism in the sense this term was first used by me. This ability to compensate for an adverse feature in the environment is not unlimited. Already at a fiftyfold dilution it is clear that the *Epilobium* plants (Plate 1), though they might under protected non-competitive conditions continue to survive, would not flower or form stolons. In other words, under natural conditions of competition they would not contribute to future populations.

Lythrum salicaria behaves differently: it was still compensating for the lowered nutrient status of the solution in a 200-fold dilution. Though tiny, the plants were robust and flowered at a greatly reduced rate compared to the control plants. They were still making some contribution to future population numbers, whereas the *Epilobium*, at a fiftyfold dilution, had ceased to do so. This situation was found in a number of species. Nearly always there was some effect on either vegetative reproduction or reproduction by seed. Whilst the plant continues to compensate, the reproduction rate, both vegetative and/or by seed, becomes progressively less. It was interesting to note that every species investigated showed a different critical level of dilution, either of the complete solution or of a single element where failure to compensate occurred. Nitrogen in most species appeared to be the limiting nutrient in respect of ability to compensate. This shows how the morphological, anatomical and physiological response to the environment compensating mechanism accounts for the wider distribution of *Lythrum* in respect of nutrient status.

With regard to the other anomalous distributions, monospecific stands, etc., in the three European regions, the situation is more complex. Both species are sensitive to day length (Plate 2) although *Epilobium hirsutum* is more so. Both species, under the influence of short days, produce a plagiogeo-tropic shoot, with short internodes and with a slow growth rate. The *Epilobium* shoot branches and under a prolonged spell of short days at temperatures when growth can occur, the growing plant can form a more or less V-shaped, flat plate over the ground. This shoot system has short internodes, a pair of small, more or less glabrous, leaves at each node. It roots strongly, not at the nodes, but between the nodes. This is a truly short day response in that if such a plant is put in to long days and allowed to form an upright shoot and is then replaced by short days, the shoot turns parallel to the ground, small, more or less glabrous leaves are formed, and profuse rooting between the nodes occurs although this is in completely dry air. As might be expected, the degree of development in length of these adventitious roots is greater when they are in contact with moist soil, but the number produced is unaffected. When the critical day length period is reached, *Epilobium* produces large rosettes of about fourteen big, hairy leaves, from which an upright shoot fairly quickly develops. The initial development is such that over the whole area pre-empted by the short day shoot, there is a complete dense shading, sufficient sometimes to suppress the growth of established *Phragmites*. With the further development of the upright shoot, the degree of shading does not significantly fall off until the shoot has reached 45–60 cm above the ground. In other words, from the initiation of long day response up to a height of 45–60 cm, the shading of the ground is almost complete. *Lythrum*, with a growth rate of half that of *Epilobium* in a period of short day growth, branches less frequently so that less territory is occupied in any given period of time. Secondly, germination experiments showed that 3–5 per cent germination of *Epilobium hirsutum* can occur down to as low as 3°C, but quite significant (over 20 per cent) occurs at temperature of 4 or 5°C and almost complete germination at temperatures of 7 or 8°C. In contrast, virtually no germination of *Lythrum salicaria* occurs until temperatures of about 12 to 14°C. In some experiments 1 per cent ger-

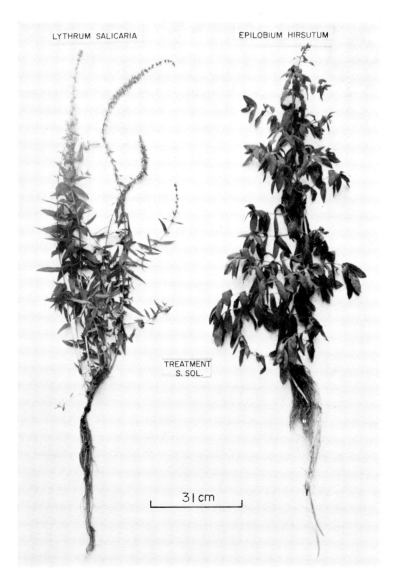

LYTHRUM SALICARIA   EPILOBIUM HIRSUTUM

TREATMENT
S. SOL.

31 cm

Plate 1. Effect of lack of mineral nutrient on growth and development of *Lythrum salicaria* and *Epilobium hirsutum*. Plants grown for 75 days. Dilutions: S = standard Long Ashton solution, s/10 = tenfold dilution, etc.
See also overleaf.

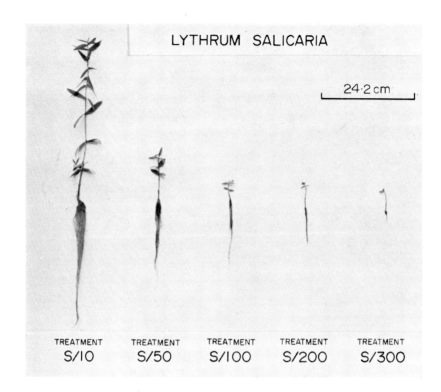

LYTHRUM SALICARIA

24·2 cm

TREATMENT S/10   TREATMENT S/50   TREATMENT S/100   TREATMENT S/200   TREATMENT S/300

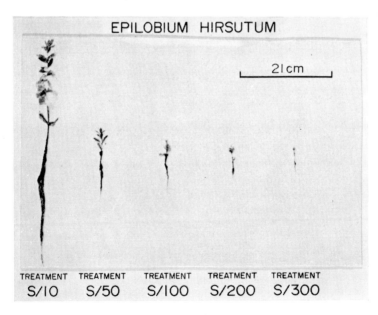

EPILOBIUM HIRSUTUM

21 cm

TREATMENT S/10   TREATMENT S/50   TREATMENT S/100   TREATMENT S/200   TREATMENT S/300

Plate 1 (continued)

Plate 2. Effect of day length on growth and development of (a) *Lythrum salicaria* and (b) *Epilobium hirsutum*. The scale shown (a) also applies to (b).

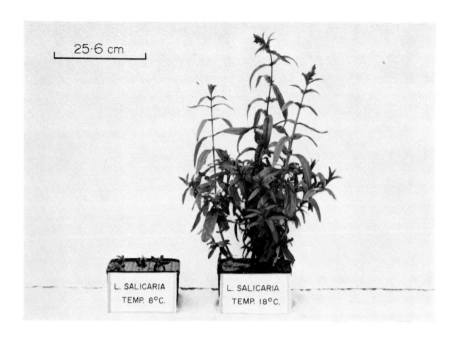

25·6 cm

L. SALICARIA
TEMP. 8°C.

L. SALICARIA
TEMP. 18°C.

16 cm

E. HIRSUTUM
TEMP. 8°C.

E. HIRSUTUM
TEMP. 18°C.

Plate 3. Effect of different temperature regimes on growth and development (after 60 days' treatment).

mination was found at 11°C. Once germinated some growth can occur at slightly lower temperatures. For instance in *Lythrum* a minute amount of growth can occur at 8–10°C. At these temperatures a considerable amount of growth is shown by *Epilobium* which continues adding to its dry weight down to temperatures of 4 or 5°C, although at a slow rate (Plate 3). When the plants were grown in constant environment chambers, at carefully regulated regimes, it was found that over a considerable range of temperatures, from about 14 to 15°C up to 30°C, the growth rate in terms of dry weight-increment-time for *Lythrum* is almost double that of *Epilobium*. It can be seen that in short days the growth rate of *Epilobium* is twice that of *Lythrum*, but in long days the situation is reversed. We have now the essential main facts required to account for the anomalous distribution. In the British Isles autumn temperatures are quite high and some germination of both *Lythrum* and *Epilobium* can occur. *Lythrum* has a poorly developed cold requirement for germination so that only a proportion of the seeds will germinate in the autumn. *Lythrum*, having germinated with the approach of cold weather, may form a shoot of about 3–10 cm in length. It makes little or no growth during the rest of the winter and early spring. In contrast, *Epilobium* with relatively clement English winters has many periods of time when temperatures are above 5°C and growth can occur. A piece of newly bared mud, if it is available in the autumn, will be heavily seeded by *Epilobium* and *Lythrum*. The *Epilobium* will overgrow the *Lythrum* and pre-empt the ground to such an extent that when the long day period starts in March, it has already formed its first rosette of leaves in many parts of Britain. The *Lythrum* is shaded out together with any other seedlings which have either germinated or are starting to germinate. Hence, the bared patch develops as a large monospecific stand of *Epilobium hirsutum* in Britain. Occasionally large areas are bared during the winter. There were many examples of this in Wheat Fen Broad, Norfolk, according to information from E.A.Ellis during the high Coypu population years where they completely ate out *Typha* or *Phragmites* rhizomes, etc., and these areas tended to be occupied by monospecific stands of *Lythrum* the following summer. This, of course, is because the *Epilobium* had no chance to become established during the winter, or very little chance to pre-empt ground. The *Lythrum* seeds once a reasonable temperature has been reached developed at a much faster rate than those of *Epilobium* due to its faster growth rate in long days. In these cases the spring bared soil patches developed as monospecific stands of *Lythrum salicaria*. In following springs owing to the rather late start of *Lythrum salicaria*, such monospecific patches are gradually taken over by other species, particularly by *Phragmites* or *Typha* species, and after a fairly short period of years the monospecific stands of *Lythrum* disappear. In contrast, once the *Epilobium* monospecific stands are established they can persist for a very long time since invasion of their territory is so much more difficult because it occurs at a time when most plants are either just germinating or starting into growth. How is it then that in parts of eastern Europe we have few or no monospecific stands at all and a predominance of *Lythrum* in the vegetation? The answer lies in this question of susceptibility to temperature by the plants. In these regions temperatures can be as low as −20°C, so that any seedlings developed in the autumn are usually killed and all germination occurs in the spring. Although *Epilobium* will be quicker to germinate it will not have much opportunity to pre-empt ground before *Lythrum* germinates and with its much faster growth rate overtops the *Epilobium* and excludes it. However, this occurs in competition with established vegetation which has already started into growth. The *Phragmites* will already be up to 15 or 30 cm in height before competition between *Lythrum* and *Epilobium* really starts. No monospecific stands can be formed and in this spring germination *Lythrum* will have advantages over *Epilobium*. This accounts for the greater proportion of *Lythrum* compared to *Epilobium*. The situation in the southern Adriatic regions, is, of course, virtually the complete opposite of the British conditions. Here we have a relatively mild winter, one in which both *Epilobium* and *Lythrum* have no limits on either germination or growth. From the autumn onwards, despite its slower short day growth rate, because the temperature is high *Lythrum* will be growing at a reasonably fast rate. There is no chance of the *Epilobium* pre-empting ground unopposed by any other species. Although in the short day form *Lythrum* has a relatively slower growth rate than *Epilobium*, at higher temperatures it is fast enough to overtake *Epilobium*. *Lythrum* never shows the vigorous growth that *Epilobium* shows in short days in the British Isles. Such monospecific stands of *Lythrum* as do become established are usually much smaller than their British *Epilobium* counterparts. The faster growth rate of *Lythrum* is in every way significant in favouring *Lythrum* against *Epilobium*. The final result is that in these rich fens the monospecific stands, though relatively small, are of *Lythrum* and there is a greater proportion of *Lythrum* compared to *Epilobium* found as scattered plants amongst the rest of the marsh vegetation.

Filipendula ulmaria and *Iris pseudacorus*

The work of Mr Faheemudin deals with two rather different species, *Filipendula ulmaria* and *Iris pseudacorus*. Without going into this work in great detail one significant contribution was yielded by the type of proportionality analysis described above. Here are the results of experiments with respect to light intensity using these two species and looking particularly at the degrees of xeromorphy. From the graph (Fig. 1) it can be seen clearly that the genetic developmental pattern of *Filipendula* is one which starts off with a high proportion of leaf and a relatively low proportion of root. With time this genetic pattern shifts to give a plant increasingly xerophytic and where the balance of leaf to root is greatly reduced. If we look at the 'response to environment' development pattern it can be seen that what has occurred is a shifting of the curve rather than a change in its shape, that is the end proportionality comes to different arithmetical figures but the general trends are unchanged. Even in the lowest light intensity the more adult plant is less leafy and more rooty than at earlier stages. In full light intensity the degree of rootiness relative to leafiness of the plant is even greater. Now in relation to the main habitat of *Filipendula*, that is wet water meadows and suchlike situations, it can be seen how this pattern is ideally suited for the type of environment which this plant is able to exploit. In the spring, when it starts into growth, either as a seedling or as renewed growth from the root-stock, its leaves are usually either amongst last year's detritus or more frequently amongst other growing plants. It is relatively shaded and at the same time these meadows are usually very wet so that a relatively large amount of leaf is produced relative to the root. Water relations present no problem to this plant at that time of the year, but sufficient light for assimilation purposes is of importance. During the development and growth of this plant as the season advances the meadows tend to dry out and the whole habitat becomes increasingly more xerophytic. This switching, or diversion, of nutrients to greater root production at the expense of leaf production serves a twofold purpose. It increases the areas of uptake for water and it decreases the area of loss. It should be mentioned, of course, that these later leaves are much more xeromorphic. They are more pubescent, covered with hair all over and the stomatal number and size are parallel to those of wind-exposed plants. *Filipendula* can be relatively successful in the shade and it does possess a relatively reasonable compensating mechanism with regard to light, that is the production or diversion of assimilates to the production of more leaf material frequently spread over a larger area.

Iris to some extent has a similar compensating mechanism in relation to low light intensity. The *Iris* pattern of development is very fixed after the first few weeks of growth, but there are some significant points about its early seedling growth (Fig. 1). At the beginning, there is a very high proportion of root relative to shoot, in fact practically all the seed store is utilized in producing this considerable root system with little development of new tissue in the first leaf. That is, there is cell elongation and enlargement but not a great amount of cell division in the plumule at this stage. D.Bolton, currently working in my section on this species, has found that, in the situations where there are water movements, particularly the slight ebb and flow found on many of the Norfolk Broads, this early 'rootiness' may have considerable survival value. In the early spring and in the autumn, *Iris* seeds are

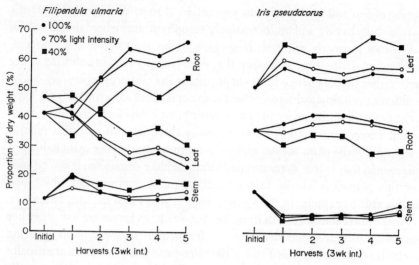

Figure 1. Effect of varying levels of light intensity on the distribution of gross production into various morphological categories of the plant at successive harvests.

found floating in large number on the surface and in the spring a large number germinate and put out roots. A very simple experiment was carried out. A number of these seedlings were taken and their root systems left intact. A replicate sample had approximately half the root system removed. Both sets were then planted or pushed into the soft mud on the side of a dyke in Wheat Fen Broad so that they were in completely exposed bare mud. The tidal ebb and flow is a matter of only a few feet at this point. The seedlings were left for a complete tidal cycle. At the end of the period more than half of the untreated seedlings still remained anchored in the mud. On the other hand, less than 10 per cent of the treated seedlings still remained. This early rootiness can be regarded as a growth modification increasing the chances of establishment in many habitats. It is interesting to compare this with the situation of the main growths. After a relatively short period of time, some three to four weeks, the genetic pattern of development switches over and attains a fairly constant proportionality which, providing the environmental conditions are not altered, remains relatively unchanged over the rest of the growing season. With a lowering of light intensity there are large displacements of the actual values of these curves.

There is a large decrease in root material and in rhizome material with a concomitant increase in leaf material. This leaf material does not appear to lead to any great increase in the breadth of the leaf which is usually narrower but longer. There is a small effect on the thickness since the shade leaves are thinner. The length of the leaves is profoundly affected so that between full day light and 40 per cent day light the leaf length is frequently doubled in the shade. The flowers, when produced, are terminal, and further growth is taken up usually by a pair of buds behind the apex. This affects the vegetative spread. In the conditions of the wet fen, particularly in the fen carr, the *Iris* rhizomes are preserved for many years, so that it is possible to trace back some 30 to 40 years the extent of flowering, branching and the annual increment size. A compensating mechanism for light intensity exists in this species but it is not adequate in the deepest shade to compensate for the great reduction in the light intensity. There appears to be a critical amount of material needed before flowering takes place. It has been possible to relate the size of the annual increment to the overall photosynthetic conditions during that particular year. From this it was possible to deduce that the half phase duration of the cycle of opening and closing canopy in these carrs is approximately 14 to 15 years, on average.

In Mr Groom's work on the comparative biology of *Ranunculus sceleratus* it was observed that although seeds were being shed as early as May relatively few of these germinated immediately though conditions appeared to be ideal. From observations made it appeared that only a very small proportion of fresh seeds germinate (*c.* 3 per cent). In the following season, however, the remaining seeds germinate rapidly in the early spring and are capable of forming a dense mass of small plants if no competition for light is made by other species. This can be seen very clearly in newly drained carp ponds in Czechoslovakia and was demonstrated in a marvellous manner on the draining of the last polder in Holland, where there were literally square miles of dense *Ranunculus* 0·6 to 0·9 m in height and all blooming vigorously in May and June, but few or no seedlings. There appeared to be some dormancy mechanism which is not absolute because of the immediate 3 per cent germination. It was very effective on the remainder of the seeds. This was investigated and it was found that in the first year about 97 per cent of seeds require a set of rather precise thermo-periodic conditions before germination can occur. The day and night difference must be of about 8–10°C and the night temperature preferably should be about 5°C. This mechanism, appears gradually to decrease in effectiveness with time, so that after 6 or 7 years all seeds will germinate immediately without any thermo-periodic requirement. These temperature conditions are those found in early spring throughout its range. Obviously, this mechanism must have considerable survival value. Although the first germinated seeds of the new crop will complete their life cycle in that season, the later germinated seed will not. In this country some may overwinter provided that they are not too deeply flooded, but in other parts of their range this does not occur because of the extremely low winter temperatures.

These few examples show that it is possible to predict necessary qualities in a species if it is to play any part in a community. For instance if soil nutrient conditions are low it must possess a compensating mechanism of increasing root at the expense of stem. In shade conditions it must be able to increase its leaf proportionality so that maintenance of carbon accumulation /time, etc., can be achieved. All these compensating mechanisms must pay the price of reduced reproductive capacity. In a paper in preparation it is shown that these shifts in employment of assimilates is brought about by endogenous morpho-regulating substances. This kind of knowledge, both particular and general, is basic to many problems of conservation and land use.

Finally I would like to thank my colleagues for their assistance and N.E.R.C. for the scholarships of Mr Groom and Mr Bolton.

Summary

By examining in a comparative manner the autecology and physiological ecology of a number of species, it is found that such diverse physiological attributes as thermo-periodicity, photo-periodicity, temperature, light and mineral nutrition play important parts in determining distributions. It is further shown that these attributes become important at various stages in the life cycle of the plant. It is suggested that the morpho-anatomical changes which result in physiological adaptation to environment are mainly controlled by morpho-regulatory substances.

It is suggested that the ecological requirements of a species and its suitability for a particular role in conservation and land use can be predicted from such studies.

Conservation aspects of the genetical constitution of populations

R.J.BERRY *Royal Free Hospital School of Medicine, London*

Conservation is the 'management or guidance by Man . . . of the complex natural processes which sustain life on earth' (Nicholson 1964). Since the genetical constitution of any species is determined by the sum of past environments experienced by that species, it follows inevitably that conservation practices are potentially capable of producing genetical changes. This is somewhat ironical since the purpose of conservation is usually to minimize environmental changes produced by pollution or technology. Consequently it is of some importance to recognize this possibility of inadvertent genetical change, and attempt to assess its importance. I propose to do this by seeking the answers to four questions:

1   Can genetical change take place through any man-made manipulation of the environment?

2   Conservation in practice involves the establishment of nature reserves and the use of management procedures: do these create or involve genetical forces?

3   Are there any particular problems to be faced with preservational measures (i.e. 'rescuing' species from extinction)?

4   Can one make practical rules regarding conservation practice and genetical change?

Genetical change through man-made environmental changes

The effects of man in producing genetical change are well documented. They can be considered under three headings.

1   *Direct effects of pollution*

Perhaps the best-known example of any recent evolutionary change is the spread of melanic forms in over 100 species of trunk-sitting, cryptically-coloured moths over the last 120 years in Britain alone. This has happened only in the areas where the fall-out from smoke pollution has drastically changed the background upon which the moths sit (Kettlewell 1961a). However, industrial melanics occur also in other groups. For example, melanic forms are rare in spiders, but they have been reported in four species: one form (*Salticus scenicus* (Clerck)) apparently being confined to the area of Stockport Gasworks, while another (*Arctosa perita* (Latr.)) occurs on colliery spoil heaps in Warwickshire and Leicestershire (Mackie 1964, Arnold & Crocker 1967). Melanic lady-birds (*Adalia bipunctata* L.) are also largely confined to industrial areas (Creed 1966).

2   *Incidental results of man's activities*

Technological advances can change local environments on such a large scale that adaptation to new conditions may follow. For example, the rise in water temperature as a consequence of industrial cooling procedures (particularly in the neighbourhood of large power stations) may have profound ecological effects (e.g. Naylor 1965) and local ecotype establishment has been recorded in at least one case (in the serpulid worm *Hydroides norvegica* (Gunnerus): Gee 1963). Other examples of differentiation from a parent stock following introduction into a new environment by man are legion (Baker & Stebbins 1965): e.g. in the house sparrow (*Passer domesticus* L.) in North America after its deliberate introduction from Europe in 1852 (Johnston & Selander 1964); and in the long-tailed field mouse (*Apodemus sylvaticus* (L.)) on the islands of the North Atlantic whither it was inadvertently brought by the Vikings on their colonizing voyages (Berry 1969a).

We can also include under this heading the new selection pressures set up by the release of unusual or new chemical substances into the environment. This is a growing problem with the increased introduction of new drugs, some of which may be toxic to particular people (e.g. sensitivity to the anti-malarial drug primaquine in persons lacking the enzyme glucose-6-phosphate dehydrogenase; to barbiturates in sufferers from some sorts of porphyria), or which may cause potentially dangerous side-effects such as interfering with steroid metabolism (as do chlorinated hydrocarbons in birds: Risebrough, Rieche, Peakall, Herman & Kinen 1968; since genetic variation exists in adrenal metabolism, the effects of DDT, etc., on vertebrates will be subject to natural selection: Spickett, Shire & Stewart 1967) or chromosome stability. (Fishing is now banned in parts of Sweden because of mercury in the water. This is concentrated by fish to the extent where it acts as a breaker of chromosomes: Ramel 1969, Ackefors 1971).

3   *Consequences of pesticide application*

We are becoming increasingly aware of 'pest' species that develop an inherited resistance to chemical poisons: house-flies in different parts of the world have independently become less susceptible to DDT control, as have at least eight species of mosquitoes, including the more important carriers of malaria (W.H.O. 1964); reports have appeared of organophosphorus resistance in the house-fly, in several mosquito species, in blow-flies and aphids (Dunn & Kempton 1966); strains of mice and rats resistant to warfarin are known from both Britain and continental Europe (Drummond 1970); penicillin resistant staphylococci can be a major problem in hospitals, while resistant gonococci are creating growing social problems; and inherited resistance to myxomatosis in rabbits is believed to occur (Sobey, Connolly, Haycock & Edmunds 1970). This list could be extended considerably. The point to be made is that in all cases resistance appears to have arisen as a chance mutation which has been able to spread rapidly under conditions where there is strong selection against the normal susceptible forms.

The answer to the question as to whether genetical change *can* arise through man-made manipulation of the environment is, therefore, a very definite 'yes'. Hence we must face up to the question as to whether conservation practice is likely to be genetically important. The answer to this question involves an understanding of the factors affecting the amount of variation existing in a population. In turn, this means a digression to summarize modern ideas on population genetical structure.

The genetical structure of populations

Theory teaches us that there are a small number of factors which determine the frequency of an allele and a genotype in a population. This is the meaning of the Hardy-Weinberg equilibrium, which shows that the frequency of any allele will remain constant from generation to generation unless affected by one of four disturbing agencies: mutation, selection, 'drift', or differential migration of particular genotypes. The algebraic consequences of this simple situation were worked out by mathematical geneticists in the 1930s—principally by R.A.Fisher, J.B.S.Haldane, L.Hogben and Sewall Wright. Their results stand. However ecological and experimental studies have now overtaken these simple bases, and as a consequence we have to make some important modifications to the predictions of the theoreticians. These involve us in both qualitative and quantitative reassessments.

The strength of natural selection

Fisher (1930) and Haldane (1932) calculated what would happen in nature if selective intensities of 0·1 to 1·0 per cent was acting (even though Haldane himself had shown as early as 1924 that the spread of the dark form of the peppered moth, *Biston betularia* L., in the Manchester area between 1848 and 1895 could only be accounted for by a 30 per cent disadvantage of the typical pale form over the melanic). This has turned out to be far too low in almost every ecological situation studied (Table 1). Indeed, Waddington (1957) was probably not unfair when he commented that 'the outcome of the mathematical theory was, in the main, to inspire confidence in the efficiency of the process of natural selection'.

Table 1. Selection under natural conditions

Selection for:	% strength of selection	Data of
A. Directed selection (i.e. extreme phenotype favoured) (after Antonovics 1969)		
Heavy metal tolerance of grasses on mine soil:		
(a) *Agrostis tenuis* on a copper mine	54–65	McNeilly (1968)
(b) *Holcus lanatus* on a lead/zinc mine	46	Antonovics (unpublished)
Heavy metal susceptibility on pasture:		
Agrostis tenuis downwind from a copper mine	27–62	McNeilly (1968)
Non-banded *Cepaea nemoralis* in woodlands	19	Cain & Sheppard (1954)
Light-coloured *C. nemoralis* on dunes (*v* brown)	6+	Clarke & Murray (1962)
Single-banded *C. nemoralis* on dunes	5+	Clarke & Murray (1962)
Female *Maniola jurtina* with low hind wing spot numbers	69–74	Dowdeswell (1961)
Melanic (*carbonaria*) form of *Biston betularia* in various regions of Great Britain	5–35	Kettlewell (1958)
Spotted form in overwintered Leopard frog, *Rana pipiens* (*v* unspotted)	23–28	Merrell & Rodell (1968)
Unbanded water snakes (*Natrix sipedon*) (*v* heavily banded)	77	Ehrlich & Camin (1960)
Tooth-size in a fossil horse (*Merychippus primus*)	27–61	Van Valen (1965*a*)
Normality in man (*v* many biochemical and chromosomal disorders giving low-grade mental defect)	100	—
B. Stabilizing selection (i.e. intermediate phenotype favoured)		
Selection for:	% strength of selection	Data of
Survivors among sparrows (*Passer domesticus*) stunned in a storm	—	Bumpus (1899)
Coiling in snails (*Clausilia laminata*)	8	Weldon (1901)
Variation in over-wintering wasps (*Vespa vulgaris*)	10	Thompson, Bell & Pearson (1911)
Size and hatchability in duck eggs	10	Rendel (1943)
Birth weight and survival in human babies	2·7	Karn & Penrose (1951)

Clutch size in swifts		Lack & Lack (1951)
Inversion heterokaryosis in *Drosophila pseudoobscura*	up to 50	Dobzhansky (1961, etc.)
Mating efficiency and morphological variation in the beetle *Tetraopes tetraophthalmus*	—	Mason (1964)
Tooth variability (i.e. *de*-stabilizing selection) in *Mus musculus*	21–26	Van Valen (1965*b*)
Tooth size in *Rattus rattus*	4	Van Valen & Weiss (1966)
Non-metrical skeletal variation in over-wintered *Mus musculus*	0–27	Berry (1965)
Shell variability in *Nucella lapillus* on shores exposed to different strengths of wave action	0–91	Berry & Crothers (1968)
Colour morphs in *Sphaeroma rugicauda*	50+	D. Heath (pers. comm.) (see also Bishop 1969)

Genetical studies on populations date, with very few exceptions, from after 1945. For example, Ford and his co-workers (summarized Ford 1964) have studied the geographical distribution of spot numbers on the posterior margin of the hind wings in meadow brown butterflies (*Maniola jurtina* (L.)) over a 20-year period. This is an inherited character (McWhirter 1969) which has apparently been constant for over 50 years throughout southern Britain (and western Europe: Dowdeswell & McWhirter 1967). In Cornwall and on different islands in the Scilly group, other expressions of the character are present, which are constant in successive generations if ecological conditions do not change (Fig. 1). Largely from this geographical evidence, Ford and his colleagues concluded that the character was controlled by natural selection. A more direct connection between phenotype and survival was discovered by Dowdeswell (1961). He found that caterpillars collected near Winchester soon after hibernation gave rise to butterflies with a spot pattern very similar to that in butterflies raised from eggs in the laboratory, but very different to that found in the field. On the other hand, caterpillars collected late in the season were heavily parasitized with the hymenopteran *Apanteles tetricus* Reinhard and suffered a high mortality rate. But the few butterflies that hatched were identical to those flying in nature. Selection acts *via* differential elimination of different phenotypes by the parasite, and can be calculated to have a strength of about 70 per cent. Other populations of the butterfly are subjected to even higher selection pressures as a result of bacterially determined mortality (McWhirter & Scali 1965).

The common dog-whelk (*Nucella lapillus* (L.)) experiences stabilizing selection of up to 90 per cent on wave-exposed shores during life (as measured by the reduction in variance of a shell character between young and old members of the same population), although whelks living on sheltered shores

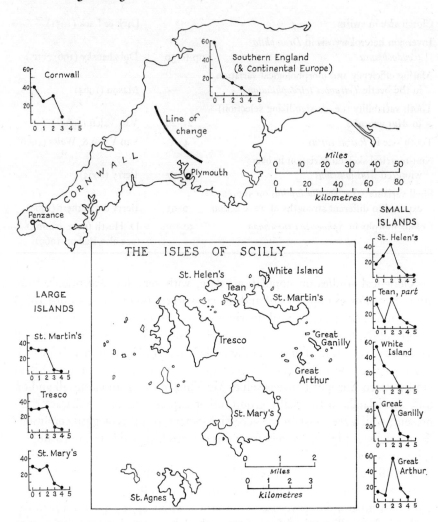

Figure 1. Distribution of spots on the hind wings of female *Maniola jurtina* in Devon, Cornwall and different Scilly Isles. The vertical axis of the graphs represent percentage of moths with spot numbers 0–5 (horizontal axis). After Ford (1955, 1964); Creed, Dowdeswell, Ford & McWhirter (1970).

undergo no selection of this nature (Fig. 2) (Berry & Crothers 1968). Not surprisingly there is a high correlation (about 70 per cent) between the amount of environmental stress (wave action) and the intensity of selection.

Instances of strong selection acting in nature could be multiplied considerably. The point to be made here is that observed selection pressures are sufficiently strong to override the much weaker non-adaptive forces which may change gene frequencies (Fig. 3). For example, wind-pollinated heavy metal tolerant grasses have evolved on the spoil heaps of mines despite the

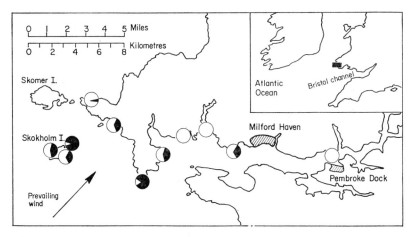

Figure 2. Stabilizing selection in *Nucella lapillus*. The proportion of black in each circle represents the difference in variance in a shell character between young and old members of the same population. Variance loss (= amount of selection) is highest in populations exposed to high wave action. Based on Berry & Crothers (1968).

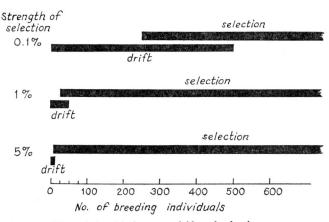

Figure 3. The relationship between drift and selection.

high rate of 'immigration' of pollen from non-tolerant plants outside the mine area (Bradshaw, McNeilly & Gregory 1965, Jain & Bradshaw 1966). The change from 'tolerant' to 'non-tolerant' plants is very abrupt (Fig. 4), showing the selective disadvantage of the characters producing tolerance under conditions of normal growth.

Now the effectiveness of selection as shown by examples like these is important because of the number of times in which random factors have been used to 'explain' population differentiation. In fact no unequivocal example of true genetic drift (i.e. sampling fluctuation of gene frequencies from generation to generation in a small population) has ever been proved (Cain 1951).

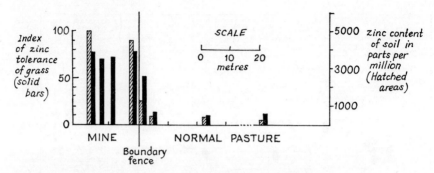

Figure 4. Zinc tolerance in *Anthoxanthum odoratum* on, and adjacent to, Trelogan mine, Flintshire. After Gregory & Bradshaw (1965); Jain & Bradshaw (1966).

For example, two of the 'best' examples of drift—the speciation of the land-snail *Partula* Férussac on Moorea in the Society islands (Crampton 1932), and the distribution of banding and colour patterns in the field snail *Cepaea nemoralis* (L.) (Taylor 1907–14, Diver 1940, Lamotte 1951) have been shown to be determined by selection, even though selection may not be operating on any particularly obvious adaptive character (Cain & Sheppard 1954, Cain

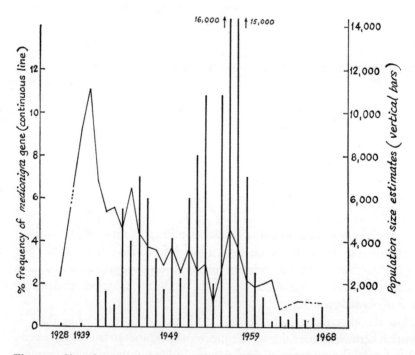

Figure 5. Size of a colony of *Panaxia dominula* at Cothill, Berkshire in different years, and the frequency of the *medionigra* gene in the colony. Based on Fisher & Ford (1947); Ford (1964); Ford & Sheppard (1969)

& Currey 1963, Clarke 1966, 1968, Clarke & Murray 1969). Equally, in the theoretically most favourable situation for drift to occur—in isolated small colonies—selection has been shown in one case at least (the *medionigra* form of the scarlet tiger moth *Panaxia dominula* (L.)) to override any random changes (Fig. 5) (Fisher & Ford 1947, Williamson 1960, Ford & Sheppard 1969).

It is, of course, impossible to prove that drift never occurs. Clearly there are occasions when a rare catastrophe reduces the size of a local population so drastically that drift may occur. Elton (1930) used this as a major explanation for evolutionary change. It almost certainly happened in the *Cepaea nemoralis* population studied by Goodhart (1962) on the Hundred Foot Bank near Ely. In 1952 he found marked differences in gene frequencies along a linear and apparently uniform bank alongside a canal, with frequencies in the snails along the ecologically more varied verge below a road running along the foot of the bank paralleling those on the bank proper (Fig. 6). Goodhart concluded that the snail population had been reduced to small pockets of survivors during the floods of 1947, when the bank was virtually submerged for

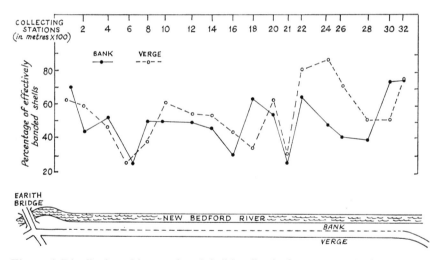

Figure 6. Distribution of frequencies of shell banding in *Cepaea nemoralis* along a section of the Hundred Foot Bank. After Berry (1967), based on Goodhart (1962).

three weeks, and that the gene frequencies in these isolates would necessarily fluctuate around the overall frequencies along the bank before the flood. In a second sample, collected eight years after his first, Goodhart (pers. comm.) found that the extremes of fluctuations were less than previously. This meant that the first sample represented a genetically unstable situation, and hence a new distribution of gene frequencies appeared as gene flow took place and new equilibria were approached.

In general, it seems that if a population of organisms is regularly of so small a size that drift changes can occur, it will be close to the point where it may be unable to survive for ecological reasons. This is important for the conservationist, because he is often faced with situations where a nature reserve has become an isolate in a developed or polluted area, and in which the population size of any organisms living therein will be correspondingly restricted.

The organization of the genotype

A more profound change in our way of thinking about populations has come about with the realization that they have a genetical *structure* as well as a genetical *content*. In other words, both organism and population are more than the sum of their genes. This was recognized first by the early geneticists with the discovery of linkage, followed by their realization of the complicated genetic and epigenetic interactions that take place during development. However we are still a long way from a full understanding of the mechanism of 'genetical architecture' (Clausen & Hiesey 1958, Grant 1964).

Perhaps the easiest sort of genetical architecture to comprehend is that involved in the modification and evolution of dominance and recessivity. The fact that dominance is a property of a character rather than a gene was argued in detail by Fisher (1922, 1930; see also Goodrich 1924). The first experimental test of the theory was made by Fisher himself (1935), followed by E.B.Ford (1940). Ford selected for greater and less expression of the variable yellow *semilutea* form of the currant moth, *Abraxas grossulariata* L. In four generations, he had 'made' the character almost completely recessive (with the heterozygotes indistinguishable from the homozygous *lutea* form). Ford then crossed his selected heterozygotes back to wild-caught moths and obtained offspring of the normal variable heterozygous type. In other words, the modifiers of dominance which were accumulated by the selection experiment were dispersed again—dominance was broken down by changing the modifying genes, not the *lutea* gene itself.

Kettlewell has gone a stage further with *Biston betularia* (L.). The earliest industrial melanics (presumed heterozygotes) preserved in museum collections all show patches of white on the wings which are rarely present in modern heterozygotes (Kettlewell 1958). Kettlewell argued that complete dominance only evolved when selection for crypsis placed it at an advantage, and went on to show that there is no mechanism for producing melanic dominance in the Canadian species *Amphidasys cognataria* Gn. (which is conspecific with European *B. betularia*) (Kettlewell 1965). Melanism is not known in the area from which Kettlewell's Canadian moths came, and the British melanic gene, *carbonaria*, shows no dominance when introduced into the Canadian species: F₂ heterozygotes from a cross between British *car-bonaria* and Canadian typical *cognataria* range in appearance from *carbonaria* to typical. However, even the lightest heterozygote produced completely distinct black and light moths in the first generation when crossed back to British typical *betularia* (Plate 1, facing p. 194). The genome of the Canadian moths has not evolved the alternative developmental pathways which produce a clear-cut switch between typical and melanic; the British genome—although sufficiently similar to the Canadian one to permit crossing with full fertility and undisturbed sex-ratio among the offspring—is organized in a way to make the two distinct phenotypes available. This very radical difference in the potentiality for survival is brought about by genetic organization (or architecture) and *not* by gene substitution (Berry, 1968).

We can now return to the more general case of genetic architecture. Firstly we have to take into account two facts:

1   the enormous amount of variation found in every species studied in nature (Table 2) (Lush 1970, Selander 1970), and

2   the commonness with which intermediate values of a metrical character give higher fitness than extreme values (Table 1*b*) (Penrose 1955).

Table 2. Amount of protein (genic) variation in some animal species (based on Selander 1970)

Species	No. of populations sampled	No. of proteins studied	% of loci variable per population	% of loci heterozygous per individual	Reference
Limulus polyphemus	4	24	25	5·7	Selander *et al.* (1970)
Acris crepitans	3	16	14–23	—	Dessauer & Nevo (1969)
Drosophila persimilis	1	24	25	10·5	Prakash (1969)
D. pseudoobscura	3	24	42	12·3	Prakash, Lewontin & Hubby (1969)
Mus musculus	7	36	26	8·5	Selander, Hunt & Yang (1969); Selander & Yang (1969)
Homo sapiens	1	20	30	7·4	Harris (1969)

We must then add the theoretical desirability of a population combining short-term phenotypic uniformity in a stable environment with long term flexibility.

The easiest genetical way of achieving this situation is for the character in question to be controlled by alleles at different loci, some alleles acting to increase the expression of the character, others acting to decrease it. In such a case Fisher (1930) showed that selection will favour linkage between responsible loci, and also the accumulation of 'balanced' chromosomes with 'positive' and 'negative' alleles. Thus the simplest case will involve two segregating loci *A, a* and *B, b* with *A, B* acting in one direction and *a, b* in the other (i.e. normal additive genes). Here the intermediate type can be either the attraction or the repulsion heterozygote, *AB/ab* or *Ab/aB*. However, Fisher pointed out that the repulsion heterozygote (*Ab/aB*) will be favoured since it will be less likely (than *AB/ab*) to produce zygotes giving the extreme phenotypes (Fig. 7). For the same reason, any mechanisms bringing about tighter linkage

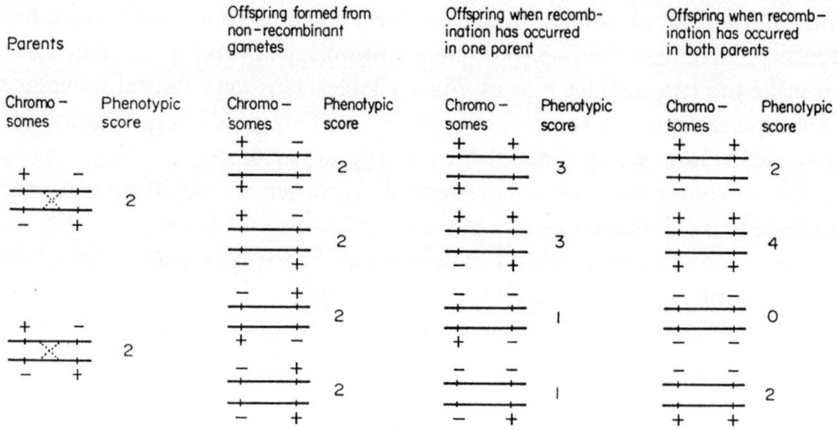

Figure 7. Effect of linkage on the incidence of the extremes of manifestation of a continuously-distributed variable. If + produces a phenotypic effect of 1, and — an effect of 0, then the repulsion heterozygote yields a minimum of extreme phenotypes (i.e. ones of 0 or 4).

between the loci concerned (such as a chromosomal inversion) will tend to spread.

This theoretical argument has been subjected to experimental analysis (mainly through selection experiments in *Drosophila*) by a number of workers (notably Mather and Thoday) (reviewed Mather 1943, Bodmer & Parsons 1962, Lee & Parsons 1968). As far as the facts go, they confirm the expectation.

Now the reason for setting out this theory is to underline the complexity of the genetical relationships expected within any particular organism, and to provide a basis for understanding a whole range of observed facts. This scheme accounts for:

1 selection (natural or artificial) for any character almost invariably produces correlated responses in other, developmentally-independent, characters (Wigan & Mather 1942, Haskell 1954, Cooper 1960);

2 gene-loci affecting viability traits and other characters are intermingled along many of the chromosomes (Mather & Harrison 1949, Breese & Mather 1957, Thoday 1961, Spickett & Thoday 1966);

3 the highest rate of artificial induction of new variation (e.g. by ionizing radiation) is many times less than that arising spontaneously (i.e. through recombination) (Scossiroli 1959);

4 the fact that inversions are so often found in nature, particularly in highly polymorphic forms (Fisher 1930, 1939, Cain & Sheppard 1954, White 1958, Levitan 1958, Searle, Berry & Beechey 1970);

5 deleterious gene combinations (even to the point of lethality) may arise solely as a result of recombination (Dobzhansky 1946, 1950, Wallace 1956, Batten & Thoday 1969).

It is worth noting in passing that in a particular population selection for one trait will be accompanied by a spread of unrelated traits by virtue of linkage. In time advantageous and unwanted effects may be separated as recombinants occur. However, before this happens and as the primary trait becomes more common, it could be that all members of the *group* carrying the trait could be favoured over the *group* not carrying the trait. This would lead to an accelerated spread of the original trait and its associated characters. This, in turn, could give rise to the inheritance of social systems in the way suggested by Wynne-Edwards (1963; see also Smith 1964, Lack 1966, Anderson 1970): the genetically and evolutionarily respectable idea of preadaptation thus may produce the commonly disbelieved effect of group selection (Napier 1970).

Coadaptation in natural populations

If the foregoing presentation has any relationship to the situation existing in nature, we should expect to find that any genetical state of affairs is likely to be highly complex (Berry 1970). This proves to be true. Even such an apparently simple example as the maintenance of the industrial melanic form of *Biston betularia* which Kettlewell (1955a) showed was subject to heavy predation by birds in non-polluted areas, is complicated. I have already referred to dominance modifiers in this species: Kettlewell (1955b, 1961a) has shown that there may be growth rate and behavioural differences between the dark and light morphs; while Clarke & Sheppard (1966) have suggested that the homozygous melanic *carbonaria* form may have a 15 per cent disadvantage as compared to the heterozygote, although the wing coloration in both is identical.

Occasionally it is possible to identify the action of different genes contributing to natural variation. This has been done for determinants of the pin-thrum polymorphism in *Primula vulgaris* L., where different members of a linked group of loci control anther-height, style-length, pollen size, rate of pollen-tube growth, and length of the papillae on the stigma (Ernst 1933, Dowrick 1956, Bodmer 1958, 1960); for the mimetic patterns in the African swallow-tail butterflies *Papilio dardanus* (Clarke & Sheppard 1960); and (less completely) for colour and banding patterns in *Cepaea nemoralis* (Cain, King & Sheppard 1960, Ford 1964). More often it is only possible to conclude that different components of a character complex are inherited as a unit (whether linked or not), i.e. that the gene-complex is *coadapted* (Cook 1961).

There are two apparently paradoxical properties of such a coadapted state: conservatism or resistance to change, and flexibility or ability to change.

Conservative nature of the coadapted system

Selander, Hunt & Yang (1969; Selander 1970) have described a particularly vivid example of coadaptation in house-mice (*Mus musculus*, L.). They measured the amount of protein variation (by means of starch gel electrophoresis) in population samples from different parts of Denmark on both sides of a line where a dark-bellied form (*M.m. domesticus*) and a light-bellied form (*M.m. musculus*) meet with a narrow zone of intergradation (which has been apparently constant for at least 30 years: Degerbøl 1935, Ursin 1952). Although the two forms are infertile in the laboratory, the gene frequencies on the two sides of the hybrid zone were very different to each other (Fig. 8). Even more remarkable is the fact that the frequencies in light-

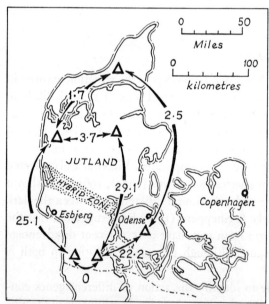

Figure 8. Genetical differentiation between populations of *Mus musculus domesticus* and *M.m. musculus* in Denmark, showing the effect of coadaptation in producing relative homogeneity within each sub-species but distinction between them. The figures are multivariate measures of divergence × 100 (Berry, 1964, 1967), calculated from data of Selander, Hunt & Yang (1969)

bellied mice from California (*M.m. brevirostris*), which are derived from the same stock as the light-bellied European mice, were more similar to the light-bellied southern Danish mice than the southern Danish were to the northern Danish ones. Californian mice are fairly characteristic of mice from the southern U.S.A. (Selander, Yang and Hunt 1969). Despite the greatly different conditions in California to those in Europe, the genotype of these mice has remained surprisingly constant.

Once a population has become established, it will not be subject to change by new individuals entering it. How persistent any particular gene co-adaptation remains in face of continuing or resumed gene flow, is not certain (Ford 1964), nor is the question of how much restriction of gene flow is necessary before a coadapted genotype can form (Thoday & Boam 1959, Mayr 1963, Smith 1966). These questions are only important from the practical conservation point of view if an attempt is being made to perpetuate a local form. However what *is* important is that the characteristics of any local race of animals or plants are dependent upon the alleles present, and the presence and frequencies of these alleles are affected more by the *prevention of immigration* allowing local adaptation and coadaptation than by continued influx from some genetically different part of the species range (Mayr 1954, Kettlewell & Berry 1961). In the absence of a high rate of immigration, adaptation is almost bound to occur in any form able to successfully establish itself (Berry & Crothers 1970).

Availability of genetical variation. Associated with this stability of the population genotype is the fact that selection—and adaptation—is opportunistic and functional rather than perfectionist. For example, the moth *Procus literosa* L. became extinct in Sheffield in its typical form early in the industrial revolution, and only recolonized the area many years later when a melanic mutation occurred and spread (Kettlewell 1957).

The functional nature of selection arises if the genetical variation available to a species in two separate but ecologically similar areas is different (as it will be if the population in one area is founded by a small number of colonizers, which are almost bound to possess different gene frequencies from their ancestral population: Berry 1967). In this case adaptation to the same environment by the two forms will necessarily use different gene systems and hence physiological mechanisms. For example, in the house-mouse population on the small Pembrokeshire island of Skokholm, there are two alleles at a locus which affects the physical characteristics of the haemoglobin molecule. During the summer, which is a time of rapid population increase but high juvenile mortality, the proportion of heterozygotes increases to about 60 per cent above the expectation on the Hardy-Weinberg equilibrium; whilst during the winter, when there is negligible breeding and considerable adult mortality, the proportion of heterozygotes decreases so that there is approximately the expected number of heterozygotes in the spring (Berry & Murphy 1970). The different phenotypes seasonally change in frequency to maximize the number of better adapted animals present in the population at any one time, and hence buffer the population against climatic fluctuations. (This temporal change is directly analogous to the geographical changes in gene frequencies in relation to air pollution in a species such as the peppered moth.) Now in direct contrast to the situation on Skokholm, the mouse population on the Forth island of May, which is faced with exactly similar ecological problems to the Skokholm one, is monomorphic at the haemoglobin locus. The May animals have adapted to their environment, but they have had to do it by means other than those used by the Skokholm animals (Berry 1964, and Table 3).

Table 3. % gene frequencies in two island populations of *Mus musculus* exposed to similar environmental conditions

Allele	Skokholm (Berry & Murphy, 1970)	May (Berry & Murphy, unpublished)
Hbb^a	58·7	0
$Pep\text{-}B1$	99·1	100
$Pep\text{-}C1$	4·7	0
$Pep\text{-}C2$	79·5	87·3
Trf^A	0·9	
$Es\text{-}2^a$	68·9	
$Es\text{-}5^a$	99·6	

Another example of different genetical means producing the same phenotypic result is in the lesser yellow under-wing moth (*Triphaena comes* Huebner). This species has a dominantly-inherited dark form in central and north-west Scotland. Dominance at the two extremes of its range (at Barra in the Outer Hebrides, and in Orkney) is effected through different modifiers (Ford 1955). Presumably selection has had to use different loci in different parts of the range because of their non-uniform distribution (cf. Van Valen 1965).

Evolutionary convergence to produce more and more similar phenotypes will take place as new genetical variation arises—as witnessed by the successive spread of different and more efficient alleles in situations as different as industrial melanism in moths (Kettlewell 1965, Lees 1968) and malaria protection in man (Livingstone 1965.)

An adapted—and coadapted—population may be very limited in its extent. It may occupy a minute or a major part of the range of a species. The house-mice of Skokholm and the Isle of May almost certainly possess a co-adapted genotype, and here the population size varies between about two hundred and five thousand. Equally, the mice of the entire area of Great Britain are genetically very homogeneous (Berry 1963, 1964), and probably represent another coadapted genotype. The number of coadapted genotypes in a species will depend on the extent to which there is free gene flow throughout the species range. There are several coadapted genotypes of the meadow brown butterfly in the British Isles: one for much of Great Britain, one for west Cornwall, and one (or more) on each of the smaller Scilly Isles (Dowdeswell & Ford 1953, Ford 1964) (Fig. 1). The so-called 'area effects' in *Cepaea nemoralis* where certain phenotypes occur at a high frequency over large and diverse regions (such as the Marlborough Downs of Wiltshire) can be explained in the same way (Goodhart 1963, Clarke 1968).

Flexibility and response in a coadapted system

Despite the internal cohesion of a coadapted genotype, there is so much variation being released in each generation (i.e. becoming manifest in the phenotype and hence available for selection) that it is highly probable that any non-fleeting environmental change will affect the fitness of certain genotypes, and therefore produce adaptive change. *Endocyclic selection* (i.e. different phenotypes favoured at different stages of the life history) has already been mentioned in *Maniola jurtina*, but the most elegant examples come from Dobzhansky's work on *Drosophila* species (particularly *D. pseudoobscura*). This is another form in which the distribution of genetical variants (inversions in the third chromosome) seemed at first to be entirely haphazard and hence due to drift. Breeding flies in the laboratory showed this to be false: the frequency of different variants varied with the temperature, food, competition and degree of crowding. From this it was shown that the frequencies of different variants in wild populations changed with the season, altitude, degree of urbanization, etc.—in other words that the genetical constitution of the populations studied was extremely sensitive to selective pressures produced by environmental changes (Dobzhansky 1947, 1961, etc.).

Another example on the same theme is in house-mouse populations where the territorial organization and frequent production of small isolates would seem to favour random changes (Anderson 1970), but where adaptation during the breeding and overwintering periods may produce significantly different genomes at different times of the year (Berry & Jakobson 1971).

I have dealt with the stability of a coadapted system at greater length than its property of flexibility and adaptation because it is less familiar to most people. In practice the two properties are equally important in determining the characteristics and range of response of a population.

An example: the moth *Amathes glareosa* in Shetland

These points are illustrated by the autumnal rustic moth, *Amathes glareosa*

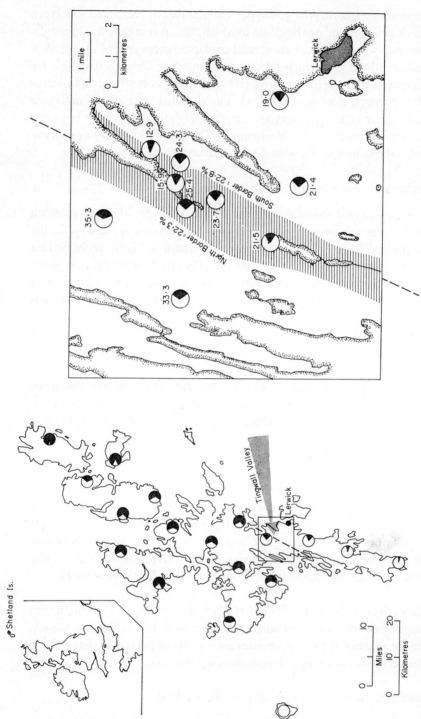

Figure 9. Distribution of the melanic form (*f. edda*) of *Amathes glareosa* in Shetland: the proportion of black in each circle represents the frequency of *f. edda* in the sample. The enlarged section on the right shows frequencies in part of the Tingwall Valley (numbers = % of *f. edda*) where frequency differences are maintained despite virtually no movement of moths across the Valley. Based on Kettlewell & Berry (1961, 1969).

Plate 1. Effects of genes modifying dominance. *F. carbonaria* of *Biston betularia* (top row) crossed with:
LEFT: *f. typica* from Birmingham, produces clear-cut distinction between *f. typica* (normal homozygote) and *f. carbonaria* (heterozygote).
RIGHT: *f. typica* of Canadian origin for four generations, produces a range of forms of varying darkness.
(Specimens of H.B.D. Kettlewell, based on Kettlewell 1965).

Plate 2. Looking north across the cultivated Tingwall Valley in Shetland. Few moths move across the valley, but local differences in frequency of the melanic *f. edda* persist from year to year (after Kettlewell & Berry 1969). Photograph by the author.

Esp., in Shetland where it occurs in very large numbers (Kettlewell & Berry 1969, Kettlewell, Berry, Cadbury & Phillips 1969) (Fig. 9). This is a grey moth which has a very distinct dominantly-inherited melanic morph (*edda*) (Kettlewell 1961*b*, 1961*c*). The frequency of melanics decreases from 97 per cent in the north of Shetland to less than 2 per cent in the south, a net distance of about 70 miles. The simplest explanation for a cline like this is that the melanic is favoured in north Shetland, where it occurs at very high densities on the short and varied flora of serpentine soils, but disfavoured in the south, and that the change of frequency is like a leaking oil tanker—a flow of genes pours out of the north and becomes ever more diluted away from its source. However, this is not so: although individual moths may fly a net distance of a mile or more, they rarely leave heather, but the frequencies of melanic morphs on opposite sides of sounds between islands are similar. Furthermore there is virtually no movement of moths across a fertile cultivated valley which runs across the centre of the Shetland mainland (even though it is only a quarter of a mile wide in parts), yet here again the frequencies of melanics on the two sides of the valley are exactly the same. Even more striking, there are genetical differences between samples caught in different parts of the islands unrelated to the *edda* melanism: dominance is more complete in the north than in the south, and moths from the northern part of the island group have an unusual behaviour pattern, probably related to a reduced tendency to fly. But most significant are signs of local adaptation:

1 moths released at sites away from their place of capture have a lower chance of survival (as measured by probability of recapture) than the native moths at that place, and

2 marked differences in *edda* frequency over a short distance persist from year to year despite being unrelated to the main frequency cline (Fig. 9 and Plate 2, facing this page).

There is selection against the typical form by birds in north Shetland, but this can only be part of the story of the genetical forces acting, particularly since there are no large continuous differences in either climate or vegetation throughout Shetland which can explain the main cline.

The point about this example is that in *A. glareosa* in Shetland we have local adaptation, partly related to environmental discontinuity, partly apparently not; habitat choice; great differences in population density; areas of free and restricted gene flow; observed and inferred evidence of natural selection; and considerable genetical heterogeneity. These are all factors which have ecological relevance and which also directly describe or affect the genetical constitution(s) of *A. glareosa*.

Nature reserves

This discussion of the genetical constitution of populations gives an answer to the question as to whether any genetical consequences are likely to occur as a consequence of the establishment of nature reserves. There are two points.

1   Observed selection pressures are so strong that any limitations on population size due to a reserve of finite size becoming an ecological isolate, are extremely unlikely to produce random and possibly deleterious genetical changes due to drift.

2   The ecological isolation of many reserves will produce a profound effect by limiting immigration and allowing local adaptation and coadaptation to take place.

Genetical adjustment and conservation practice

Any change in the environment is likely to produce an adaptive genetical adjustment in animal or plant populations affected by that environment (Table 4). This is not to imply that phenotypic plasticity is unimportant for survival, nor that a genetic response is commoner than a phenotypic one (Birch 1960, Bradshaw 1965, Slobodkin 1968). The point is that genetical change is far from being the rare and upsetting phenomenon that might be inferred from the work of many ecologists and palaeontologists. Although the concept of an invariable 'type' is officially dead, it is far easier to use than the idea of an adjustable reaction system. It may be that geneticists have failed properly to educate their colleagues in this respect.

The examples of genetical change set out in Table 4 are far from complete: they are merely intended to illustrate the conditions which have produced genetical change in natural populations. Once it is recognized that any population of animals or plants is existing in a dynamic genetical equilibrium with its environment, it is necessary to conclude that the genetical constitution of that population is subject to—indeed, is very sensitive to—change in the environment. Put another way, this means that only a highly adapted form in the centre of a stable environment is likely to remain genetically constant.

From here, we can now return to the last two questions about the genetical consequence of conservation procedures asked at the beginning of this essay. As is clear, the answers must depend on the principle of the equilibrium which exists between the genetical constitution of any population and its environment.

Rescue from extinction

It may be held that special genetical considerations apply when the numbers of a species fall so low that special 'rescue' operations have to be undertaken

Table 4. Examples of genetical change.

Species	Change	Environmental conditions	Reference
Apodemus sylvaticus hirtensis Barrett-Hamilton (on St Kilda)	Non-metrical skeletal characteristics	During period when human population was evacuated, and *Mus musculus muralis* Barrett-Hamilton became extinct	Berry & Tricker (1969); Berry (1970)
Stercorarius parasiticus (L.)	Frequency of dark morph (the mates of which are less aggressive than those of the pale morph, and thus pair more readily and breed earlier)	Differences in times of maximum food availability in different parts of the species range	Berry & Davis (1970)
Aedes aegypti (L.)	Slower in feeding after several generations of breeding in captivity	No danger of retaliation by host, and hence selection for fast feeding	Gillett (1967)
Mosquitoes and aphids (various species)	Loss of inherited resistance to insecticide poisoning	Removal from conditions of exposure to insecticide	Abedi & Brown (1960); Dunn & Kempton (1966) (cf. Bradshaw, McNeilly & Greogory (1965))
Drosophila pseudoobscura	Spread of a chromosomal inversion from extreme rarity to 8 per cent in California over a 15-year period	Correlated in time and space with an increase in DDT residues	Dobzhansky (1961, 1963) Cory, Fjeld & Serat (1971)
Panaxia dominula (L.)	Reduction in expression of *medionigra* gene in both heterozygous and homozygous condition in colonies where it has been artificially introduced	Passage of time (and 'normal' selective pressures) since introduction	Ford & Sheppard (1969)

Table 4. Examples of genetical change—*continued*

Species	Change	Environmental conditions	Reference
Melitaea (Euphydras) aurinia von Rott	Changes in wing pattern	Following a few years in which the butterfly was exceptionally abundant (when, presumably, selection was relaxed allowing new gene combinations to be tried out in a large number of animals)	Ford & Ford (1930)
Maniola jurtina (L.)	Change in hind wing spotting number in southern England in 1956, followed by reversion to the previous pattern by 1958	Relaxation of selection pressure followed by reimposition of stringent selection (?)	Ford (1964)
Maniola jurtina (L.)	Hind wing spotting number of females on the Scillonian island of Tean	Removal of a herd of cattle, with a consequent change of vegetation	Ford (1964)

(as with Père David's deer, or the Hawaian né-né), since so much variation will have disappeared when numbers decrease that the species may be so genetically rigid as to be effectively inviable. Leaving aside the question as to why the species has become so rare (which would in many cases seem to suggest some adaptive inflexibility) there is no reason to expect that any particular genetical problems will arise.

1   The position of a species reduced to a few pairs of breeding animals is in principle the same as a group of animals or plants colonizing a new and isolated habitat. Many such groups survive and flourish (Baker & Stebbins 1965, Berry 1969*a*, 1969*b*).

2   Since intraspecific selection is likely to be small in a species being subjected to 'rescue', the internal structure of the genotype is less important than under normal circumstances.

Guidelines for conservation

Finally we are able to arrive at a series of conclusions which can serve as genetical rules for conservationists.

1   Any environmental change (be it natural or part of 'management') within the normal tolerance of a species will result in genetical adaptation in the affected population; if the changes exceed the species tolerance, the population will, of course, become extinct (as happened to both the British and introduced Dutch forms of the large copper butterfly, *Lycaena dispar* Haw, in the fens Duffey 1968). There is a slight paradox here, because 'tolerance' is, of course, a genetical property (Berry & Crothers 1970). However, this should not be a serious problem in practice, since management is effectively directed towards maintaining or restoring a *status quo*.

2   Adaptation is rapid and precise, and is normally based on variation existing within a population. The chance of random—and potentially deleterious—changes taking place are very slight and can probably be neglected.

3   The amount of variation (at least in a normally outbred, diploid species) is extremely large and resistant to loss. Even in a population subjected to rigorous and long-continued directional selection, considerable variation remains unused (e.g. Lerner 1954, Carson 1967, Wallace 1968). Moreover a population with a primary poverty of variability seems to acquire more: the Skokholm house-mouse population, isolated since it was founded by a few individuals 70 years ago, nevertheless contains the same amount of variation as British mainland mouse populations (Berry & Murphy 1970). (Forms subject to a varying environment at the edge of their range may lose genetical markers such as inversions—which reduce crossing-over, and hence appear to suffer a poverty of variation: Carson 1958, Zohary & Imber 1963, Prakash, Lewontin & Hubby 1969.) It is extremely unlikely that any natural manage-

ment procedures could significantly affect the amount of variation in a local population to the extent of making that population unable to respond to environmental change.

4   Intermittent drift could lead to a change in a local form—but so could straightforward natural selection as in the examples quoted above. Local forms have ecological interest and taxonomic kudos, but no eternal value. Attempts at preservation (as in the 'gene-bank' at Whipsnade: Rowlands 1964) may provide some alleles available for study or possible introduction into a wild stock, but will certainly not preserve the whole genotype of the form in question. The attempt to improve the native turkey stock in Missouri by releasing commercially bred hybrid birds is a cautionary tale here: the released birds proved inferior to the wild birds in every aspect of viability studied—brain, pituitary and adrenal size, and breeding success (Leopold 1944).

Acknowledgements

My thanks are especially due to Dr H.B.D.Kettlewell of Oxford University for providing the photograph of dominance breakdown in *Biston betularia* (Plate 1), and to Mr A.J.Lee for drawing the figures.

References

ABEDI Z.H. & BROWN A.W.A. (1960) Development and reversion of DDT-resistance in *Aedes aegypti*. *Can. J. Genet. Cytol.* 2, 252–61.

ACKEFORS H. (1971) Mercury pollution in Sweden with special reference to conditions in the water habitat. *Proc. R. Soc. B.* 177, 365–87.

ANDERSON P.K. (1970) Ecological structure and gene flow in small mammals. *Symp. zool. Soc. Lond.* 26, 299–325.

ANTONOVICS J. (1969) The heterogenous environment: its effect on the genetics of natural populations. Paper read at the meeting of the British Association for the Advancement of Science in Exeter, September 1969.

ARNOLD G.A. & CROCKER J. (1967) *Arctosa perita* (Latr.) from colliery spoil heaps in Warwickshire and Leicestershire. *Bull. Br. Spider Study Group*, no. 35, 7–8.

BAKER H.G. & STEBBINS G.L. (1965) *Genetics of Colonizing Species*. Academic, New York and London.

BATTEN J.L. & THODAY J.M. (1969) Identifying recombinational lethals in *Drosophila melanogaster*. *Heredity, Lond.* 24, 445–55.

BERRY R.J. (1963) Epigenetic polymorphism in wild populations of *Mus musculus*. *Genet. Res.* 4, 193–220.

BERRY R.J. (1964) The evolution of an island population of the house mouse. *Evolution, Lancaster, Pa.* 18, 478–83.

BERRY R.J. (1965) Genetical change in an island mouse population. *Ann. hum. Genet.* 29, 110.

BERRY R.J. (1967) Genetical changes in mice and men. *Eugen. Rev.* 59, 78–96.

BERRY R.J. (1968) The biology of non-metrical variation in mice and men. In *The Skeletal Biology of Earlier Human Populations*: 103–33. (Ed.) Brothwell D.R. Pergamon, London.

BERRY R.J. (1969*a*) History in the evolution of *Apodemus sylvaticus* (Mammalia) at one edge of its range. *J. Zool., Lond.* **159**, 311–28.

BERRY R.J. (1969*b*) The genetical implications of domestication in animals. In *The Domestication and Exploitation of Plants and Animals*: 207–17. (Eds. Ucko P.J. & Dimbleby G.W.) Duckworth, London.

BERRY R.J. (1970) Covert and overt variation, as exemplified by British mouse populations. *Symp. zool. Soc. Lond.* **26**, 3–26.

BERRY R.J. & CROTHERS J.H. (1968) Stabilizing selection in the Dog whelk (*Nucella lapillus*). *J. Zool., Lond.* **155**, 5–17.

BERRY R.J. & CROTHERS J.H. (1970) Genotypic stability and physiological tolerance in the Dog whelk (*Nucella lapillus* (L.)). *J. Zool., Lond.* **162**, 293–302.

BERRY R.J. & DAVIS P.E. (1970) Polymorphism and behaviour in the Arctic Skua (*Stercorarius parasiticus* (L.)). *Proc. R. Soc. B.* **175**, 255–67.

BERRY R.J. & MURPHY H.M. (1970) Biochemical genetics of an island population of the house mouse. *Proc. R. Soc. B.* **176**, 87–103.

BERRY R.J. & JAKOBSON M.E. (1971) Life and death in an island population of the house mouse. *Exp. Geront.* **6**, 187–97.

BERRY R.J. & TRICKER B.J.K. (1969) Competition and extinction: the mice of Foula, with notes on those of Fair Isle and St. Kilda. *J. Zool., Lond.* **158**, 247–65.

BIRCH L.C. (1960) The genetic factor in population ecology. *Am. Nat.* **94**, 5–24.

BISHOP J.A. (1969) Changes in genetic constitution of a population of *Sphaeroma rugicauda* (Crustacea: Isopoda). *Evolution, Lancaster, Pa.* **23**, 589–601.

BODMER W.F. (1958) Natural crossing between homostyle plants of *Primula vulgaris*. *Heredity, Lond.* **12**, 363–70.

BODMER W.F. (1960) The genetics of homostyly in populations of *Primula vulgaris*. *Phil. Trans. R.Soc. Ser. B.* **242**, 517–49.

BODMER W.F. & PARSONS P.A. (1962) Linkage and recombination in evolution. *Adv. Genet.* **11**, 1–100.

BRADSHAW A.D. (1965) Evolutionary significance of phenotypic plasticity in plants. *Adv. Genet.* **31**, 115–55.

BRADSHAW A.D., McNEILLY T.S. & GREGORY R.P.G. (1965) Industrialization, evolution and the development of heavy metal tolerance in plants. *Symp. Brit. ecol. Soc.* **5**, 327–43.

BREESE E.L. & MATHER K. (1957) The organization of polygenic activity within a chromosome in *Drosophila*. I. Hair characters. *Heredity, Lond.* **11**, 373–95.

BUMPUS H.C. (1899) The variations and mutations of the introduced sparrow, *Passer domesticus*. *Biol. Lectures, mar. biol. Lab., Woods Hole* (1896–7), 1–15.

CAIN A.J. (1951) So-called non-adaptive or neutral characters in evolution. *Nature, Lond.* **168**, 424, 1049.

CAIN A.J. & CURREY J.D. (1963) Area effects in *Cepaea. Phil. Trans. R. Soc. Ser. B.* **246**, 1–81.

CAIN A.J. & SHEPPARD P.M. (1954) Natural selection in *Cepaea. Genetics, Princeton*, **39**, 89–116.

CAIN A.J., KING J.M.B. & SHEPPARD P.M. (1960) New data on the genetics of polymorphism in the snail *Cepaea nemoralis*, L. *Genetics, Princeton*, **45**, 393–411.

CARSON H.L. (1958) Response to selection under different conditions of recombination in *Drosophila. Cold Spring Harb. Symp. quant. Biol.* **23**, 291–306.

CARSON H.L. (1967) Permanent heterozygosity. *Evol. Biol.* **1**, 143–68.

CLARKE B.C. (1966) The evolution of morph-ratio clines. *Am. Nat.* **100**, 389–402.

CLARKE B.C. (1968) Balanced polymorphism and regional differentiation in land snails.

In *Evolution and Environment*, 351–68. (Ed. Drake E.T.) Yale University Press, New Haven and London.

CLARKE B.C. & MURRAY J.J. (1962) Changes of gene frequency in *Cepaea nemoralis*: the estimation of selective values. *Heredity, Lond.* 17, 467–76.

CLARKE B.C. & MURRAY J.J. (1969) Ecological genetics and speciation in land snails of the genus *Partula*. *Biol. J. Linn. Soc.* 1, 31–42.

CLARKE C.A. & SHEPPARD P.M. (1960) Super-genes and mimicry. *Heredity, Lond.* 14, 175–85.

CLARKE C.A. & SHEPPARD P.M. (1966) A local survey of the distribution of industrial melanic forms in the moth *Biston betularia* and estimates of the selective values of these in an industrial environment. *Proc. R. Soc. B.* 165, 424–39.

CLAUSEN J. & HIESEY W.M. (1958) Experimental studies on the nature of species. *Publs Carnegie Instn*, no. 615, 1–312.

COOK L.M. (1961) The edge effect in population genetics. *Am. Nat.* 95, 295–307.

COOPER J.P. (1960) Selection and population structure in *Lolium*. IV. Correlated response to selection. *Heredity, Lond.* 14, 229–46.

CORY L., FJELD P. & SERAT W. (1971) Evironmental DDT and the genetics of natural populations. *Nature, Lond.* 229, 128–30.

CRAMPTON H.E. (1932) Studies on the variation, distribution, and evolution of the genus *Partula*: the species inhabiting Moorea. *Publs Carnegie Instn*, no. 410, 1–335.

CREED E.R. (1966) Geographic variation in the two-spot ladybird in England and Wales. *Heredity, Lond.* 21, 57–72.

CREED E.R. DOWDESWELL W.H., FORD E.B. & McWHIRTER K.G. (1970) Evolutionary studies on *Maniola jurtina* (Lepidoptera, Satyridae): The 'boundary phenomenon' in southern England 1961 to 1968. In *Essays in Evolution and Genetics in honor of Theodosius Dobzhansky*, 263–87. (Eds Hecht M.K. & Steere W.C.) North-Holland, Amsterdam.

DEGERBØL M. (1935) On *Mus musculus spicilegus* Pet. in Denmark. *Vidensk. Meddr. dansk naturh. Foren.* 99, 233–8.

DESSAUER H.C. & NEVO E. (1969) Geographic variation of blood and liver proteins in cricket frogs. *Biochem. Genet.* 3, 171–88.

DIVER C. (1940) The problem of closely related species living together in the same area. In *The New Systematics*: 303–28. (Ed. Huxley J.S.) Clarendon Press, Oxford.

DOBZHANSKY TH. (1946) Genetics of natural populations. XIII. Recombination and variability in populations of *Drosophila pseudoobscura*. *Genetics, Princeton.* 31, 269–390.

DOBZHANSKY TH. (1947) Adaptive changes induced by natural selection in wild populations of *Drosophila*. *Evolution, Lancaster, Pa.* 1, 1–16.

DOBZHANSKY TH. (1950) Genetics of natural populations. XIX. Origin of heterosis through natural selection in populations of *Drosophila pseudoobscura*. *Genetics, Princeton*, 35, 288–302.

DOBZHANSKY TH. (1958) Genetics of natural populations. XXVII. The genetic changes in populations of *Drosophila pseudoobscura* in the American Southwest. *Evolution, Lancaster, Pa.* 12, 385–401.

DOBZHANSKY TH. (1961) On the dynamics of chromosomal polymorphism in *Drosophila*. *Symp. R. ent. Soc. Lond.* 1, 30–42.

DOBZHANSKY TH. (1963) Genetics of natural populations. XXXIII. A progress report on genetic changes in populations of *Drosophila pseudoobscura* and *Drosophila persimilis* in a locality in California. *Evolution, Lancaster, Pa.* 17, 333–9.

DOWDESWELL W.H. (1961) Experimental studies on natural selection in the butterfly, *Maniola jurtina*. *Heredity, Lond.* 16, 39–52.

DOWDESWELL W.H. & FORD E.B. (1953) The influence of isolation on variability in the butterfly *Maniola jurtina* L. *Symp. Soc. exp. Biol.* 7, 254–73.

DOWDESWELL W.H. & McWHIRTER K.G. (1967) Stability of spot-distribution in *Maniola jurtina* throughout its range. *Heredity, Lond.* 22, 187–210.

DOWRICK V.P.J. (1956) Heterostyly and homostyly in *Primula obconica. Heredity, Lond.* 10, 219–36.

DRUMMOND D.C. (1970) Variation in rodent populations in response to control measures. *Symp. zool. Soc. Lond.* 26, 351–67.

DUFFEY E. (1968) Ecological studies on the large copper butterfly *Lycaena dispar* Haw *batavus* Obth. at Woodwalton Fen National Nature Reserve, Huntingdonshire. *J. appl. Ecol.* 5, 69–96.

DUNN J.A. & KEMPTON D.P. (1966) Non-stable resistance to demeton-methyl in a strain of *Myzus persicae. Ent. exp. & appl.* 9, 67–73.

EHRLICH P.R. & CAMIN J.H. (1960) Natural selection in middle island water snakes (*Natrix sipedon* L.). *Evolution, Lancaster, Pa.* 14, 136.

ELTON C. (1930) *Animal Ecology and Evolution.* Clarendon Press, Oxford.

ERNST A. (1933) Weitere untersuchungen zur phänalyse zum fertilitäts problem und zur genetik heterosyler Primeln, I. *Primula viscosa. Arch. Julius Klaus-Stift. VererbForsch.* 8, 1–215.

FISHER R.A. (1922) On the dominance ratio. *Proc. R. Soc. Edinb.* 42, 321–41.

FISHER R.A. (1930) *Genetical Theory of Natural Selection.* Clarendon Press, Oxford.

FISHER R.A. (1935) Dominance in poultry. *Phil. Trans. R. Soc. Ser. B.* 225, 197–226.

FISHER R.A. (1939) Selective forces in wild populations of *Paratettix texanus. Ann. Eugen.* 9, 109–122.

FISHER R.A. & FORD E.B. (1947) The spread of a gene in natural conditions in a colony of the moth *Panaxia dominula* L. *Heredity, Lond.* 1, 143–74.

FORD E.B. (1940) Genetic research in the Lepidoptera. *Ann. Eugen.* 10, 227–52.

FORD E.B. (1955) Polymorphism and taxonomy. *Heredity, Lond.* 9, 255–64.

FORD E.B. (1964) *Ecological Genetics.* Methuen, London.

FORD E.B. & SHEPPARD P.M. (1969) The *medionigra* polymorphism of *Panaxia dominula. Heredity, Lond.* 24, 561–9.

FORD H.D. & FORD E.B. (1930) Fluctuation in numbers and its influence on variation in *Melitaea aurinia. Trans. R. ent. Soc. Lond.* 78, 345–51.

GEE J.M. (1963) On the taxonomy and distribution in South Wales of *Filograna, Hydroides* and *Mercierella* (Polychaeta: Serpulidae). *Ann. Mag. nat. Hist.* (13). 6, 705–15.

GILLETT J.D. (1967) Natural selection and feeding speed in a blood-sucking insect. *Proc. R. Soc. B.* 167, 316–29.

GOODHART C.B. (1962) Variation in a colony of the snail (*Cepaea nemoralis* (L.)). *J. Anim. Ecol.* 31, 207–37.

GOODHART C.B. (1963) 'Area effects' and non-adaptive variation between populations of *Cepaea* (Mollusca). *Heredity, Lond.* 18, 459–65.

GOODRICH E.S. (1924) *Living Organisms.* Oxford.

GRANT V. (1964) *The Architecture of the Germplasm.* Wiley, New York.

GREGORY R.P.G. & BRADSHAW A.D. (1965) Heavy metal tolerance in populations of *Agrostis tenuis* Sibth. and other grasses. *New Phytol.* 64, 131–43.

HALDANE J.B.S. (1924) A mathematical theory of natural and artificial selection. *Trans. Camb. phil. Soc.* 23, 19–41.

HALDANE J.B.S. (1932) *Causes of Evolution.* Longmans, Green, London.

HARRIS H. (1969) Enzyme and protein polymorphism in human populations. *Br. med. Bull.* 25, 5–13.

HASKELL G. (1954) Correlated responses to polygenic selection in animals and plants. *Am. Nat.* 88, 5–20.

JAIN S.K. & BRADSHAW A.D. (1966) Evolutionary divergence among adjacent plant populations. *Heredity, Lond.* 21, 407–41.

JOHNSTON R.F. & SELANDER R.K. (1964) House sparrows: rapid evolution of races in North America. *Science, N.Y.* 144, 548–50.

KARN M.N. & PENROSE L.S. (1951) Birth weight and gestation time in relation to maternal age, parity and infant survival. *Ann. Eugen.* 16, 147–64.

KETTLEWELL H.B.D. (1955*a*) Selection experiments on industrial melanism in the Lepidoptera. *Heredity, Lond.* 9, 323–42.

KETTLEWELL H.B.D. (1955*b*) Recognition of appropriate backgrounds by the pale and dark phase of Lepidoptera. *Nature, Lond.* 175, 934.

KETTLEWELL H.B.D. (1957) Industrial melanism in moths and its contribution to our knowledge of evolution. *Proc. R. Instn Gt Br.* 36, 1–14.

KETTLEWELL H.B.D. (1958) A survey of the frequencies of *Biston betularia* (L.) (Lep.) and its melanic forms in Great Britain. *Heredity, Lond.* 12, 51–72.

KETTLEWELL H.B.D. (1961*a*) The phenomenon of industrial melanism in the Lepidoptera. *A. Rev. Ent.* 6, 245–62.

KETTLEWELL H.B.D. (1961*b*) Geographical melanism in the Lepidoptera of Shetland. *Heredity, Lond.* 16, 393–402.

KETTLEWELL H.B.D. (1961*c*) Selection experiments on melanism in *Amathes glareosa* Esp. *Heredity, Lond.* 16, 415–34.

KETTLEWELL H.B.D. (1965) Insect survival and selection for pattern. *Science, N.Y.* 148, 1290–6.

KETTLEWELL H.B.D. & BERRY R.J. (1961) The study of a cline. *Heredity, Lond.* 16, 403–14.

KETTLEWELL H.B.D. & BERRY R.J. (1969) Gene flow in a cline. *Heredity, Lond.* 24, 1–14.

KETTLEWELL H.B.D., BERRY R.J., CADBURY C.J. & PHILLIPS G.C. (1969) Differences in behaviour, dominance and survival within a cline. *Heredity, Lond.* 24, 15–25.

LACK D. (1966) *Population Studies of Birds.* Clarendon Press, Oxford.

LACK D. & LACK E. (1951) The breeding biology of the Swift *Apus apus. Ibis,* 93, 501–46.

LAMOTTE M. (1951) Recherches sur la structure génétique des populations naturelles de *Cepaea nemoralis,* L. *Bull. biol. Fr. Belg. Suppl.* 35, 1–239.

LEE B.T.O. & PARSONS P.A. (1968) Selection, prediction and response. *Biol. Rev.* 43, 139–74.

LEES D.R. (1968) Genetic control of the melanic form *insularia* of the peppered moth *Biston begularia* (L.). *Nature, Lond.* 220, 1249–50.

LEOPOLD A.S. (1944) The nature of heritable wildness in turkeys. *Condor,* 46, 133–97.

LERNER I.M. (1954) *Genetic Homeostasis.* Oliver & Boyd, Edinburgh.

LEVITAN M. (1958) Non-random associations of inversions. *Cold Spring Harb. Symp. quant. Biol.* 23, 251–68.

LIVINGSTONE F.B. (1965) The distribution of the abnormal haemoglobin genes and their significance for human evolution. *Evolution, Lancaster, Pa.* 18, 685–99.

LUSH I.E. (1970) Biochemical variation in mammalian populations. *Symp. zool. Soc. Lond.* 26, 43–71.

MACKIE D.W. (1964) A melanic form of *Salticus scenicus* (Clerck). *Bull. Br. Spider Study Group,* no. 24, 4.

MCNEILLY T. (1968) Evolution in closely adjacent plant populations. III. *Agrostis tenuis* on a small copper mine. *Heredity, Lond.* 23, 99–108.

MCWHIRTER K.G. (1969) Heritability of spot-number in Scillonian strains of the meadow brown butterfly (*Maniola jurtina.*) *Heredity, Lond.* **24**, 314–18.

McWHIRTER K.G. & SCALI V. (1965) Ecological bacteriology of the meadow brown butterfly. *Heredity, Lond.* **21**, 517–21.

MASON L.G. (1964) Stabilizing selection for mating fitness in natural populations of *Tetraopes. Evolution, Lancaster, Pa.* **18**, 492–7.

MATHER K. (1943) Polygenic inheritance and natural selection. *Biol. Rev.* **18**, 32–64.

MATHER K. & HARRISON B.J. (1949) The manifold effect of selection. *Heredity, Lond.* **3**, 1–52, 131–62.

MAYR E. (1954) Change of genetic environment and evolution. In *Evolution as a Process*: 157–80. (Eds Huxley J., Hardy A.C., Ford E.B.). Allen & Unwin, London.

MAYR E. (1963) *Animal Species and Evolution.* Harvard Univ. Press, Cambridge, Mass.

MERRELL D.J. & RODELL C.F. (1968) Seasonal variation in the leopard frog, *Rana pipiens. Evolution, Lancaster, Pa.* **22**, 284–8.

NAPIER J.R. (1970) *Roots of Mankind.* Smithsonian Institute, Washington.

NAYLOR E. (1965) Biological effects of a heated effluent in docks at Swansea, South Wales. *Proc. zool. Soc. Lond.* **144**, 253–68.

NICHOLSON E.M. (1964) Nature conservation in perspective. In *The Countryside in 1970*, 203–5. H.M.S.O., London.

PENROSE L.S. (1955) Evidence of heterosis in man. *Proc. R. Soc. B.* **144**, 203–13.

PRAKASH S. (1969) Genic variation in a natural population of *Drosophila persimilis. Proc. natn. Acad. Sci. U.S.A.* **62**, 778–84.

PRAKASH S., LEWONTIN R.C. & HUBBY J.L. (1969) A molecular approach to the study of genic heterozygosity in natural populations. IV. Patterns of genic variation in central, marginal and isolated populations of *Drosophila pseudoobscura. Genetics, Princeton*, **61**, 841–58.

RAMEL C. (1969) Genetic effects of mercury compounds. *Hereditas*, **61**, 208–54.

RENDEL J.M. (1943) Variations in the weights of hatched and unhatched ducks' eggs. *Biometrika*, **33**, 48–58.

RISEBROUGH R.W., RIECHE P., PEAKALL D.B., HERMAN S.G. & KIRVEN M.N. (1968) Polychlorinated biphenyls in the global ecosystem. *Nature, Lond.* **220**, 1098–1102.

ROWLANDS I.W. (1964) Rare breeds of domesticated animals being preserved by the Zoological Society of London. *Nature, Lond.* **202**, 131–2.

SCOSSIROLI R.E. (1959) On the relative role of mutation and recombination in responses to selection for polygenic traits in irradiated populations of *D. melanogaster. Int. J. Radiat. Biol.* **1**, 61–9.

SEARLE A.G., BERRY R.J. & BEECHEY C.V. (1970) Cytogenetic radio-sensitivity and chiasma frequency in wild-living male mice. *Mutat. Res.* **9**, 137–40.

SELANDER R.K. (1970) Biochemical polymorphism in populations of the House mouse and Old-field mouse. *Symp. zool. Soc. Lond.* **26**, 73–91.

SELANDER R.K., HUNT W.G. & YANG S.Y. (1969) Protein polymorphism and genic heterozygosity in two European subspecies of the house mouse. *Evolution, Lancaster, Pa.* **23**, 379–90.

SELANDER R.K. & YANG S.Y. (1969) Protein polymorphism and genic heterozygosity in a wild population of the house mouse (*Mus musculus*). *Genetics, Princeton*, **63**, 653–67.

SELANDER R.K., YANG S.Y. & HUNT W.G. (1969) Polymorphism in esterases and hemoglobin in wild populations of the house mouse (*Mus musculus*). Stud. Genet. 5, *Univ. Texas Publn* no. 6918, 271–338.

SELANDER R.K., YANG S.Y., LEWONTIN R.C. & JOHNSON W.E. (1970) Genetic variation in the horseshoe crab (*Limulus polyphemus*), a phylogenetic 'relic'. *Evolution, Lancaster, Pa.* **24**, 402–14.

SLOBODKIN L.B. (1968) Toward a predictive theory of evolution. In *Population Biology and Evolution*: 187–205. (Ed. Lewontin, R.C.). Syracuse, New York.

SMITH J.M. (1964) Group selection and kin selection. *Nature, Lond.* **201**, 1145–7.

SMITH J.M. (1966) Sympatric speciation. *Am. Nat.* **100**, 637–50.

SOBEY W.R., CONNOLLY D., HAYCOCK P. & EDMONDS J.W. (1970) Myxomatosis: the effect of age upon survival of wild and domestic rabbits with a degree of genetic resistance and unselected domestic rabbits infected with myxoma virus. *J. Hyg., Camb.* **68**, 137–49.

SPICKETT S.G., SHIRE J.G.M. & STEWART J. (1967) Genetic variation in adrenal and renal structure and function. *Mem. Soc. Endocr.* **15**, 271–88.

SPICKETT S.G. & THODAY J.M. (1966) Regular responses to selection. 3. Interaction between linked polygenes. *Genet. Res.* **7**, 96–121.

TAYLOR J.W. (1907–14) *Monograph of the Land and Freshwater Mollusca of the British Isles*. Taylor, Leeds.

THODAY J.M. (1961) The location of polygenes. *Nature, Lond.* **191**, 368–70.

THODAY J.M. & BOAM T.B. (1959) Effects of disruptive selection. II. Polymorphism and divergence without isolation. *Heredity, Lond.* **13**, 205–18.

THOMPSON E.Y., BELL J. & PEARSON K. (1911) A third cooperative study of *Vespa vulgaris*. Comparison of queens of a single nest with queens of the general autumn population. *Biometrika*, 8, 1–12.

URSIN E. (1952) Occurrence of voles, mice and rats (Muridae) in Denmark, with a special note on a zone of intergradation between two subspecies of the house mouse (*Mus musculus* L.). *Vidensk. Meddr dansk naturh. Foren.* **114**, 217–44.

VAN VALEN L. (1965a) Selection in natural populations. III. Measurement and estimation. *Evolution, Lancaster, Pa.* **19**, 514–28.

VAN VALEN L. (1965b) Selection in natural populations. IV. British house mice (*Mus musculus*). *Genetica*, **36**, 119–34.

VAN VALEN L. (1965c) Morphological variation and width of ecological niche. *Am. Nat.* **99**, 377–90.

VAN VALEN L. & WEISS R.A. (1966) Selection in natural populations. V. Indian rats (*Rattus rattus*). *Genet. Res.* 8, 261–7.

WADDINGTON C.H. (1957) *Strategy of the Genes*. Allen & Unwin, London.

WALLACE B. (1956) Studies on irradiated populations of *Drosophila melanogaster*. *J. Genet.* **54**, 280–93.

WALLACE B. (1968) *Topics in Population Genetics*. Norton, New York.

WELDON W.F.R. (1901) A first study of natural selection in *Clausilia faminata* (Montagu). *Biol. Metrica*, **1**, 109–24.

WHITE M.J.D. (1958) Restrictions on recombination in grasshopper populations and species. *Cold Spring Harb. Symp. quant. Biol.* **23**, 307–17.

W.H.O. (1964) Genetics of Vectors and Insecticide Resistance. *Wld Hlth Org. Tech. Rep. Ser.* **268**, 1–40.

WIGAN L.G. & MATHER K. (1942) Correlated response to the selection of polygenic characters. *Ann. Eugen.* **11**, 354–64.

WILLIAMSON M.H. (1960) On the polymorphism of the moth *Panaxia dominula* (L.). *Heredity, Lond.* **15**, 139–51.

WYNNE-EDWARDS V.C. (1963) Inter-group selection in the evolution of social systems. *Nature, Lond.* **200**, 623–6.

ZOHARY D. & IMBER D. (1963) Genetic dimorphism in fruit types in *Aegilops speltoides*. *Heredity, Lond.* **18**, 223–31.

A self-regulation to density-independent continuum in Australian parrots, and its implication for ecological management

JOHN LE GAY BRERETON *Department of Zoology,*
University of New England, Armidale, New South Wales, Australia

The purpose of this paper is to review the social system and population regulatory mechanisms of species of Australian parrots occurring along a gradient from wet to increasingly arid habitats, and from this to draw general conclusions about the scientific management of animals and plants.

Flock size

The studies summarized in this paper were made from the wet eastern scarplands (rainfall up to 2,032 mm/year), to the arid western plains (down to 254 mm/year) of northern New South Wales. The habitats change along this gradient from subtropical rainforest to sclerophyll forest, then to woodland, and finally to grassland with scattered trees and shrubs. The broad relationship of selected parrot species to these habitats is set out in Table 1 and it will be seen there that flock size increases as habitats become more arid-adapted.

More information about social organization emerges if the frequency distribution for groups is plotted. This has been done for four parrot species representative of increasingly arid habitats, Table 2, Fig. 1. For each activity (flying, perching, and feeding) there is a clear-cut trend towards increase in flock size as the habitats become more dry. This is not only evident in the reduction in the frequency of groups of 1–5 individuals as the habitats become more arid, but it is also evident in an increase in groups greater than 26 individuals. In other words the trend to increasing group size is coming about not through a shift in the mean towards the right, but through a developing bi-modality. In the case of the budgerigar the process has gone so far that the left hand mode has virtually disappeared and the distribution is mono-modal for large groups, in contrast to the eastern rosella which is mono-modal for small groups. Another important trend evident in these data is the

Table 1. Showing the broad relationship of flock size in selected parrots to habitat.

Species of Parrot	Habitat	Food	Flock size
Alisterus scapularis (king parrot)	Rainforest, sclerophyll	Canopy and shrub seed and fruit	4
Platycercus elegans (crimson rosella)	Sclerophyll forest	Canopy and shrub seed and fruit	3–4
Platycercus eximius (eastern rosella)	Savannah woodland	Herb seed, with some canopy feeding	4
Barnardius barnardi (buln buln)	Open savannah woodland	Herb seed, with some canopy feeding	5
Kakatoe roseicapilla (galah)	Open savannah woodland	Herb seed, some roots	15
Nymphicus hollandicus (quarrion)	Grassland with clumps of trees	Herb seed	20
Melopsittacus undulatus (budgerigar)	Grassland with clumps of trees and shrubs	Herb seed	Most commonly 15+

Table 2. The relative frequency of groups in flying, perching and feeding activities.

	Group sizes						Total individuals counted	Total number of groups
	1–5	6–10	11–15	16–20	21–26	26+		
Flying								
P. eximius	0·92	0·06	0·01	—	—	—	1366	511
K. roseicapilla	0·82	0·08	0·04	0·03	0·01	0·02	2768	353
N. hollandicus	0·47	0·28	0·07	0·04	0·01	0·13	5598	401
M. undulatus	0·12	0·20	0·15	0·12	0·15	0·26	5849	157
Perching								
P. eximius	0·82	0·15	0·03	—	—	—	391	103
K. roseicapilla	0·47	0·21	0·09	0·02	0·02	0·18	1866	129
N. hollandicus	0·26	0·14	0·08	0·14	0·06	0·33	1319	66
M. undulatus	0·06	0·12	0·05	0·06	0·08	0·62	6143	114
Feeding								
P. eximius	0·62	0·35	0·03	—	—	—	1489	297
K. roseicapilla	0·36	0·26	0·12	0·05	0·03	0·19	6950	298
N. hollandicus	0·11	0·16	0·18	0·16	0·05	0·33	2168	79
M. undulatus	—	0·03	0·03	0·05	0·02	0·87	5863	63

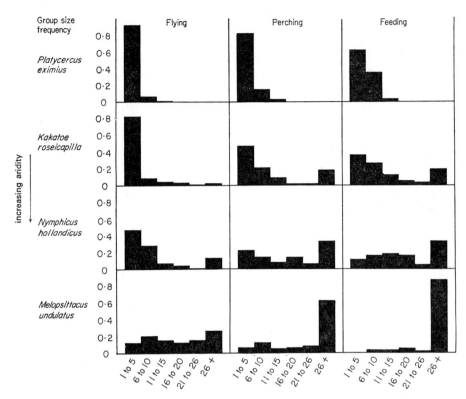

Figure 1. Showing how number of individuals become greater as aridity increases and resources become more sparse. Note the bi-modality of intermediate forms.

increase in group size in each species for feeding over perching, and for perching over flying. This will be considered more closely in later sections.

It is intended in the following sections to consider other results which explain how the changes in modality occur and which give some insight into the adaptive significance of these changes.

The population of life-history of the eastern rosella (*P. eximius*) and the galah (*Kakatoe roseicapilla*)

By means of permanent feeding and trapping sites at Armidale a population of the eastern rosella has been studied closely for a number of years. This work will be summarized here in order to show how this population has an incipient flocking component as well as a stable array of small groups.

The salient events in the annual cycle are summarized in Fig. 2. The system is best presented as a core (*C pop.*) and a subsidiary (*S pop.*) population. The core is composed of entirely sedentary hierarchially arranged high status pairs, while the subsidiary population is composed of less stable groups of about 4–6 individuals. These groups range more widely than the pairs of the core, and the individual composition is changeable. The status of the groups is ranked and the individuals within the groups are also ranked. As spring develops the permanent pairs and the groups begin to search for nest holes and to show more intense agonistic behaviour to other pairs or groups who come within range. The larger groups show more intra-group agonistic behaviour now and tend to break up. As a consequence of this general increase in agonistic behaviour the groups are more widely spaced, but interspersion continues to occur, Fig. 2(*a*, *e*). Gradually the senior status pairs select trees for nesting, then lay, incubate, and care for the nestlings, Fig. 2(*b*). After about four weeks owing largely to the antagonism on the part of the female the juveniles are found less and less in the presence of the parents. This break occurs in stages so that the younger juveniles stay longer with the parents. At this time groups of juveniles are seen but they are composed of birds from different nests. Ultimately in autumn loose flocks are encountered in which incipient or loose and changeable groups may be detected, Fig. 2(*c*). As the autumn advances the loose flock gradually fragments into groups led by young adults and composed largely of juveniles. These groups scatter and intersperse through the area of the sedentary adult pairs, Fig. 2(*d*).

It needs to be pointed out here that the foregoing summary is based on a large number of flagged birds studied in an 800 acre area and making up an estimated population of about 100 individuals in which up to 20 per cent were unflagged. The data were obtained by watching flagged individuals, studying the communication system, and from data obtained by trapping and releasing birds at monthly or fortnightly intervals. These results will be treated in detail in subsequent papers.

The pattern of the eastern rosella is thus seen to be one of groups arranged according to status, with individuals ranked within groups. Territoriality in the sense of a boundary which is patrolled and defended is totally lacking. For a short period in the autumn a loose flock of low status individuals is formed, composed of the young of the year and of the previous year. This flock fragments into small groups composed of the young of the year bonded with one or a few young of the previous year. These groups intersperse with the high status sedentary pairs. This pattern may now be compared with that of the galah.

The population life cycle of the galah has been studied by R. Pidgeon over a period of four years (Pidgeon 1970). Again it is found that the adult pairs are sedentary. However, in contrast to the eastern rosella the immatures and the adults roost in the same area, occasionally in the same tree, whereas this type of roosting occurs only in the short-lived phase of flocking by the immatures in the eastern rosella. Normally groups, and pairs also, of the eastern

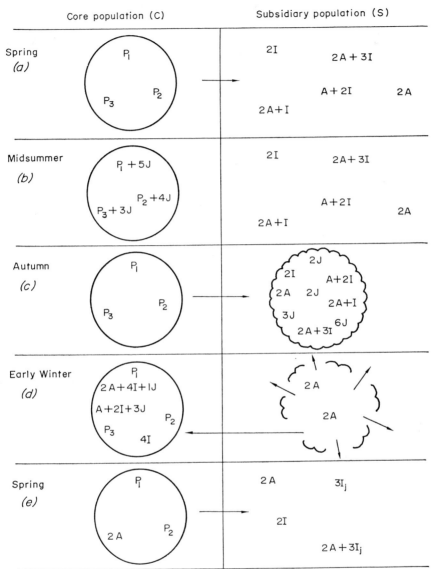

Figure 2. The inferred dynamics of the Eastern Rosella population system.

rosella, are well separated, and individuals are frequently in different trees. At daybreak the galah frequently flies out of the roost in a large flock and perches as many groups in dead trees. From here small groups and pairs fly out to feed. The small groups join larger and larger feeding groups and by the midday roosting time flocks have formed. These break down to small groups as the birds go out to the evening feeding session and coalesce into even larger flocks for roosting. Thus flocking develops through groups joining feeding flocks which persist through resting and roosting, but break up with dispersal flights out to feeding areas.

The galah system appears to be one of large feeding and roosting flocks which are dispersed as the birds fly out to feed. Closer study, however, reveals that the galah organization also contains a core and a subsidiary population. This is shown by ringing and by tagging studies. Recovery distance of adult birds averages 3·7 km, while that of immatures is 110 km. Flagged adult pairs watched over a period of three years have not changed partners or localities. At the same time young birds have appeared at the roosting and feeding sites of the adult pairs. They are thus flocks in numbers too great to be accounted for by the breeding of the adult pairs which have arrived from elsewhere. Aggression at feeding is very rare and at all times it is less conspicuous and less frequent than aggression in the eastern rosella. Nevertheless the sedentary adult pairs can be categorized as the core and the immatures as the subsidiary population. As the breeding season develops most of the S population disappears, but a few remain though they do not breed. The mechanism leading to the departure of the greater part of the S population and the non-breeding of those that remain is not as yet clear.

To summarize, the flocking phase of the galah also involves the S population and is more highly developed and more permanent than that of the eastern rosella. The galah is more tolerant of other groups and other individuals than the eastern rosella. The core and subsidiary populations tend to coalesce into an amorphous feeding flock, and close proximity is maintained at roosting.

Communication system

The vocal, visual and tactile communication system of the eastern rosella and the galah have been studied closely. The vocal communication system of other forms has also been investigated. A thorough knowledge of communication systems would be no doubt the most efficient means of describing and comparing social systems of different species. For this reason a summary of what is at present known of Australian species is given here, but throughout emphasis will be placed on understanding the change in the social system from small groups to large flocks as habitats become more arid.

Although the eastern rosella has an extensive array of conspicuous visual and vocal signals it is clear from a study of the known co-ordinated behaviour that the obvious signals are not sufficient to account for this co-ordination. Closer study has shown that some co-ordination is the result of leadership. In the permanent pairs most activities which are not alarm or escape actions are initiated by the male. Once this is known the observer himself is able to anticipate frequently what will happen next, provided he understands the context in which he is observing the birds' behaviour. It follows from this that a limited number of signals can provide the basis for a high degree of co-ordination. Reliance is placed on general co-ordination of mood, appreciation of the environment at the time, accepted leadership, and experience under that leadership. Restless individuals and groups, responsive to environmental change will provide a rich source of information to other members of the species. The potentiality for varied and complex co-ordinated behaviour exists in such forms. This suggests that the most suitable measure of social complexity may lie in scoring all visible, acoustic, and tactile behaviour in suitable samples, and analysing these data in terms of information theory. A preliminary test of this method using caged red-back parrots (*Psephotus haematonotus*) and the budgerigar (*Melopsittacus undulatus*) shows promise. However, so far extensive and satisfactory data of this kind is not available, and as visual signals are frequently associated with calls and tactile signals and grade often imperceptibly with movements whose function is not necessarily to do with signalling, the acoustic communication system alone will be reported on now. In doing this the tentative assumption are made that the vocal communication is linearly related to the total communication system.

If we list the vocal inventory for known species from the wet to the arid regions we have: *Alisterus scapularis*, 4; *Platycercus elegans*, 21; *P. eximius*, 25; *Barnardius barnardi*, 16; *Kakatoe roseicapilla*, 11; *Nymphicus hollandicus*, 8; *Melopsittacus undulatus*, 8. This array suggests that the social system first becomes more complex as the habitat becomes more arid, and then with still greater aridity the social system decreases in complexity. (This pattern parallels the shift from mono-modality around small groups, to bi-modality, to mono-modality around large groups.)

Other factors which change in an orderly way as habitats become more arid are sex and age differences in plumage, frequency of agonistic behaviour, and the amount of concerted and unspecific calling. So far these aspects of social behaviour have not been satisfactorily quantified, but a convenient ranking comparison as set out in Table 3 summarizes these characteristics. These trends are complicated and require more rigorous treatment, but nevertheless they are sufficient to indicate changes in the communication system which are related to changes in habitat.

These trends can be considered in more detail. Pidgeon (1970) has shown that the number of signals concerned with agonistic behaviour generally decrease as the habitat becomes more arid from savannah woodland. Thus *P. eximius* has 8–10, *K. roseicapilla* 4, *N. hollandicus* 5, and *M. undulatus* 7 signals. This last reading is anomalous, and may result from the assessment being based wholly on cage studies.

Table 3. Ranking in plumage difference, amount of agonistic behaviour and lack of concerted calling.

	Adults different from young	Adults different by sexes	Young different by sexes	Agonistic behaviour	Lack of concerted calling	Total
A. scapularis	5	10	0	6	10	31
P. elegans	10	5	0	8	10	33
P. eximius	5	5	0	8	8	26
B. barnardi	3	3	0	6	7	19
K. roseicapilla	3	2	0	3	2	10
N. hollandicus	5	5	0	3	2	15
M. undulatus	2	2	0	3	2	7

Calling in flight changes as the flock size increases. The calls become diffuse and cover a wider frequency band. They appear to have more noise. Moreover, there is a very obvious trend towards many individuals calling at once which adds to the noise and diffuseness.

In *P. eximius* only two calls (*c.* 8 per cent) occur in a flocked context while in *K. roseicapilla* four (*c.* 4 per cent) are flock calls. The percentage is still higher in *N. hollandicus* and *M. undulatus*. The information content of vocalization has been assessed for the *P. eximius* population over a two-year period. Using the occurrence rate on an annual basis acoustic information amounts to about 3·2 bits. Of this 0·64 bits (*c.* 21 per cent) are used in flocking contexts. The galah, *K. roseicapilla* has not been so closely studied in this way but it is estimated that vocal communication amounts to about 2·5 bits of which 1·6 (*c.* 62 per cent) are concerned with flocking.

The distribution of frequencies of various group sizes itself is a store of information which can easily be assessed. These results are set out in Table 4. In this series *K. roseicapilla* contains the greatest amount of information by virtue of its flocking configuration. Against this should be considered the estimate of information content based on occurrence rate of calls and on the total inventory (Table 4). This suggests that the eastern rosella has the more complex social system.

To summarize this section on communication, it can be said that the results although scattered and incomplete, suggest a pattern of social

Table 4. Information content resulting from distribution of flocks of different size and from calling for four species of parrots on a gradient to more arid habitats.

Information content (bits)		*P. eximius*	*K. roseicapilla*	*N. hollandicus*	*M. undulatus*
	(i) Flying	2·4	2·9	3·8	3·5
Group size	Perching	2·8	4·5	2·9	2·7
	Feeding	3·8	3·7	3·6	—
	Total	9·0	11·1	10·3	6·2
Vocalizations (ii)	Based on inventory	4·5	3·3	3·0	3·0
Total	(i) + (ii)	13·5	14·4	13·3	9·2

complexity which is relatively simple where resources are abundant, which is most complex where resources are intermediate, and which becomes simple again as resources continue to decrease. This pattern correlates with the changes in the distribution of the groups. For populations where the major effects are determined by the C population and which are thus mono-modal for pairs and small groups, the social and communication systems are simple. Where the C and S populations are equally influential and the grouping system is bi-modal the social and the communication systems are complex. As the dominance passes from the C population to the S population the distribution becomes mono-modal for large groups and the social and communication systems become simple again. The simplicity of the two mono-modal systems is quite different. The small-group mono-modal system has a small number of clear-cut signals directed to individuals or small groups. They are based heavily on agonistic behaviour. The large-group mono-modal system has also few signals but these are diffuse and directed to large relatively amorphous groups. The signals are much more to do with mood co-ordination than with aggression.

Population regulation

In the previous sections the type of social structure has been described, and compared to the degree of aridity of the habitat. In this section the aim is to relate the social system to the type of population regulatory system and to the type of ecosystem.

Broadly speaking ecosystems may be either 'stop-go' systems or 'steady-state' systems. Stop-go systems typically occur where conditions are only sporadically favourable. Steady-state systems occur in favourable areas where resources are steadily available. Stop-go ecosystems are characterized by plant, animal, and microbiological species which increase very quickly and with little or no self-imposed restraint, while steady-state systems are closely regulated by self-imposed mechanisms which are dependent on the state of resources in the environment. With these viewpoints in mind, the regulation of some Australian species of parrots from various habitats will be examined.

The rainforest and surrounding sclerophyll forest are rich in resources. *Alisterus scapularis* occurs in these habitats. Unfortunately the population dynamics of this species has not been studied but even so it is well known that this species does not ever reach plague numbers, nor does the population ever drop to very low levels. The social system is one of many small groups from 2 to 15 individuals. Individuals, especially males, appear to be aggressive.

At the other extreme is *Melopsittacus undulatus*. It occurs on the Mitchell grass plains most commonly in the 608 mm per year region. There is no doubt that this species becomes extremely abundant in favourable times, and in bad times its range is decreased and it becomes few in numbers. It is known to breed several nests to a tree, and there appears to be no social restriction to nesting. It flies and perches in larger flocks than other parrots, and feeds in even larger ones. The eastern budgerigars range well south during the summer when seasons are good and will breed in the south. They do not remain through the winter. In Queensland they are always present breeding when seasons are good, and dying in great numbers when seasons are bad. The quarrion (*N. hollandicus*) appears to be similar.

Only *Platycercus eximius* and to a lesser extent *K. roseicapilla* have been investigated closely. In *P. eximius* a core population of sedentary adults exists. For most of the year small groups intersperse through this area, giving way to the dominant pairs. This system is under tension. On two occasions birds were trapped from an area supporting about 100 birds. From both areas about 300 individuals were removed without any obvious diminution of the population. Tension is also seen in the agonistic behaviour between groups. Various forms of spacing behaviour are seen at feeding sites. This is most notable as roosting time approaches, when it seems concentration on feeding lowers the aggressive tendency somewhat and increases the tendency of subordinate groups to feed with higher status groups. At these times 15–18 individuals will try to feed in a radius of 3 m at a feeding station. At such times agonistic behaviour is continuous. By contrast galahs will feed shoulder to shoulder and new groups are not inhibited from joining existing feeding groups, nor do the feeding groups react to the arrival of the new groups. Thus there is far greater social tension at feeding time in the eastern rosella than there is in the galah, and this may serve to regulate numbers to resources. However, it is in the breeding season that obvious adjustment occurs.

As the tendency to breed rises in C and S populations competition for nest holes occurs. The S pairs are slower to develop reproductive behaviour and the high status C pairs drive off any pairs undertaking nest hole exploration within a radius of 45–90 m. However, this does not prevent low status birds feeding in the vicinity, or even feeding in the presence of high status individuals. This strongly developed reproductive aggression reduces the breeding potential of the area, for many available nest holes are not used owing to their proximity to the nest site of dominant pairs. This mechanism appears to be lacking or to have very high thresholds in the budgerigar. In the galah, however, some similar phenomenon occurs which causes the dispersal of the S population and the non-breeding of accepted low status individuals. Breeding tolerance is also far greater in galahs as they will allow breeding pairs in adjacent and even the same tree.

The existing evidence suggests that in the Australian psittaciformes species which have a well-marked C population there is a high degree of endogenous population regulation. As resources become more scattered and sporadic, the C population merges with the S population and regulation becomes more exogenous. The S population is more far ranging and more socially tolerant. It has less structure and therefore has a lower information content. One large amorphous mass contains less information than the same mass divided into a number of constituent entities. The species dominated by the S population component are gregarious, relatively structureless, far ranging forms. The habitat which is proper to them is also low in information content (species diversity). These habitats are identified as 'stop-go' ecosystems. The strategy for survival depends on capturing resources rapidly during their ephemeral existence and minimizing local resource utilization by moving or by reducing demand, or both, until a new input occurs.

Budgerigar survival is postulated to be dependent on large groups increasing by breeding without restraint when resources are abundant, by maximizing social tolerance where food is abundant, and by dispersing widely in large groups when resources are locally sparse. The greater tolerance and mobility of the S population has emphasized this side of the system in the adaptation of the budgerigar to arid Australia. Where resources are more abundant and more regular and the ecosystems are more nearly steady-state ones endogenous population regulation is favoured and as a consequence the C population is separate and determinative.

Territorial, interspersing, and gregarious species

Based on what has been outlined so far, it is convenient to identify three types of social system; territorial, interspersing, and gregarious.

Territorial systems are unknown in parrots. These are the systems where a boundary is patrolled and no intrusion is tolerated. Some species of animals are territorial in the breeding season and interspersing in the non-breeding season (e.g. feral domestic fowls, McBride *et al.* (1969)). Others are seemingly gregarious in the non-breeding season. Some such as the Australian magpie

(*Gymnorhina tibicen*) are territorial permanently in the C population (Carrick 1963). Some species may have permanent territories held by single individuals, others by pairs (Australian peewee, *Grallina cyaneoleuca*) (Robinson 1947), while in some a group of two to a few individuals hold a territory permanently whose size is a function of the number of individuals in the territory-holding group (Kookaburra, *Dacelo gigas* (Parry 1968)). These variations make the concept of territory in the context used here complex and overlapping. However, it should be pointed out that there are no clear-cut divisions between the categories from territory to interspersing to gregarious species. The postulate presented here is that the social system gradually changes from territoriality to gregariousness as resources become more sparse in space and time. In order to resolve these difficulties about territory for the time being it is suggested that species be labelled according to their system during the breeding season. Endogenous population regulation is well developed in territorial species.

The characteristics of interspersing species are well represented in the eastern rosella (*Platycercus eximius*). Interspersing species are arranged in hierarchical groups, with the individuals within the groups also arranged hierarchially. These are very complex societies and are thus typified by a rich communication system. As with territorial species there is a gradation to the gregarious forms and it seems that endogenous population regulation becomes less effective along the gradient to gregariousness.

Gregarious species are also distributed along a gradient. The limit is a totally flocking, herding or schooling species which has no social structure and only one signal; to home on the largest group. There are probably no such species. Undiscerningly social species have very little agonistic behaviour and breed with little or no restraint when conditions improve. Numbers are seldom related to resources, but when they are the limitation or regulation is exogenous, i.e. it is a direct effect of the environment on the population, there being no evolved behavioural or physiological mechanism to provide negative feed-back or to prevent overcorrection.

It needs to be stressed that the foregoing interpretation rests first on direct evidence from quite insufficient studies of Australian parrots. In the second place there is much evidence in the literature which partially supports the hypothesis, but which cannot be marshalled here. Nor can the evidence which runs counter to the hypothesis be considered here. Further, acknowledgement is not possible here to authors who have put forward similar views.

Social systems of man and his domestic and semi-domestic animals and the implications for management

The purpose of this section is to consider man and the animals with which he is closely associated in the light of comparative social systems. The setting of man among the other primates will be considered first. Both the useful and the pest aspects will be considered.

Early man (say Australopithecus) was a hunter and gatherer in savannah woodland. He lived in small groups, probably of six or a dozen. The habitat, the group size, the method of hunting, and the camp sites, all suggest an interspersing species. Studies of contemporary hunters and gatherers support this contention. For example Berndt and Berndt (1964) describe the various groupings of a typical Australian aboriginal tribe showing that the hunting and everyday living unit was a family party. No effort is made to patrol the boundaries of tribal areas, and encroachment into the home range by nearby tribes occurred. In Centralian tribes boundaries were vague and almost ritual behaviour patterns occurred for meeting intruder groups. On the lower Murray and on the coast where resources were richer more animosity between tribes occurred. It seems that New Guinea tribes also living in habitats rich in resources show more signs of territoriality and antagonism. Modern man also shows very little sign of true territoriality. He is still an interspersing species heavily dependent for social structure on ranking, and to a great degree making use of symbols to signify status. Wars of modern man concern symbols, often conceptual abstractions, rather than geographically defined space. The capture of a queen, a flag, or a fort, is much more important than completely excluding the enemy from a defined area.

In view of the very great size and density of aggregations of man in urban areas, and of the very high threshold to social stress, it can be said that man is on the gregarious side of the interspersing species. Nevertheless there is some evidence of physiological disturbance. For example studies we have made of death-rate for common causes of death (without respect to age distribution) show significantly higher values where the level of urbanization is higher in New South Wales.

The exceptional communication system of man, and his very high intelligence, stamp him an interspersing species. While interspersing species tend to have imperfect population regulatory systems, that of man is even less developed, suggesting a gregarious species. Population regulation appears to occur in primitive people but it is not innate, as is shown by the great variation in methods adopted. It depends on his ability to anticipate events and to make plans. Only very cohesive, closely disciplined societies are able to regulate according to some generally arbitrarily chosen level of natural resources. Most societies are multiplying their numbers with abandon under the impression that they live in a prosperous society which is rapidly growing more prosperous. This lack of restraint suggests a gregarious species more limited by exogenous catastrophy than endogenous regulatory mechanism. It is concluded that man is an interspersing species tending to a gregarious form.

It now becomes of interest to consider differences in social system in other primates than man. This can be summarized briefly by noting that gibbons and orang-utan which live in rainforest are territorial and have permanent pair bonds, while gorillas which range from lowland rainforest to montane rainforest and savannah, and chimpanzees which occur often in fringing rainforest, are also interspersing species. Three striking but not easily interpreted facts stand out; (1) the massive intellectual capacity of man, (2) the near permanent parental pair bonds, contrasted with the promiscuous system of chimpanzees and gorillas, and (3) the tendency for the amalgamation of groups in man, (4) man's origin in savannah woodland.

In the ungulates there appears to exist a pattern ranging from territoriality to gregariousness. This cannot be dealt with in detail but attention should be drawn to the great herds of pronghorn (*Antilocapra americana*) migrating caribou (*Rangifer* spp.) and elk (*Cervus canadensis*), bison (*Bison bison*) and cattle (*Bos* sp.) as examples of gregarious species, while mule and white-tail deer (*Odocoilens hemionus, O. virginianus*) appear to live in woodland as interspersing species, and moose (*Alces americana*) live in a richer and more stable habitat still, and are territorial. Similar trends can be detected in carnivores, rodents, and bats. A similar trend appears to exist also in the macropods. All of these groups need to be analysed in detail. Suffice it to say here that a preliminary examination suggests strongly that this trend is a phenomenon which is very widespread in the animal kingdom and is not unique to the vertebrates.

In the event of this hypothesis proving to be substantially correct, the implications for management can be stated broadly. The principle, in contrast to the practice, for managing gregarious species lies in changing the environment. If resources are increased the population will increase, while it will decrease if resources are reduced. This is not readily so with territorial species. Their range can be managed by managing resources, but not their density. Being discerning agonistic species they do not domesticate easily and cannot be controlled easily. These general deductions apply equally well to the management of pests, as well as to present and future domestic animals, and also to considerations of harvesting big game and managing animals in national parks. Support or overthrowal of the hypothesis will depend (*a*) on close analysis of the literature, (*b*) detailed and wide-ranging field studies, (*c*) laboratory experiments, and (*d*) on its success or failure in its application directly to management.

References

BERNDT R.M. & BERNDT C.H. (1964) *The world of the first Australians*. Ure Smith, Sydney.

CARRICK R. (1963) Ecological significance of territory in the Australian magpie, *Gymnorhina tibicen*. *Proc. Int. Orn. Congr.*, 13th, 740–53.

MCBRIDE G., PARER I.P., FOENANDER F. (1969) The social organization and behaviour of the feral domestic fowl. *Anim. Behav. Monogr.* 2, 127–81.

PARRY R. (1968) *Sociality, territoriality and breeding biology of the kookaburra, Dacelo gigas (Dobbaert)*. M.Sc. Thesis, Monash University, Victoria.

PIDGEON R. (1970) *Ecology and behaviour of the galah, Cacatua roseicapilla*. M.Sc. Thesis, University of New England, Armidale, N.S.W.

ROBINSON A. (1947) Magpie larks: a study in behaviour. *Emu* 46, 265–81; 47, 11–28, 382–91.

Part 3
Conservation Problems
in Freshwater

Eutrophication

J.W.G.LUND *Freshwater Biological Association, Ambleside*

Introduction

In this paper it is the chemical and botanical aspects of the eutrophication of lakes which are emphasized. Apart from the fishery aspect, which is mentioned, these are the features of eutrophication which are most often discussed and which have lead to public and political pressure for action to protect waters from overenrichment.

Hasler (1947) used the word eutrophication in the sense of 'lake enrichment owing to any and all nutritive substances'. In the paper, Hasler describes the results of the excessive inflow of nutrients into lakes, leading in turn to the excessive growth of some organisms and to the decreased growth or disappearance of others. Since that time the word eutrophication has been used more and more generally in the sense of something undesirable. The word is overloaded with prejudice, just as the lakes suffering from eutrophication are overloaded with nutrients. With the present awakening of the general public to the harm man is doing to his environment and is likely to do unless he mends his ways, some prejudice may be forgiven. However prejudice has no place in science. Therefore it is well to remember that eutrophication is derived from two Greek words, one meaning good, brave or noble and the other, nourishment, food or rearing. This noun is also derived from the adjective eutrophic, which, with its opposite oligotrophic, was first used to characterize layers in peat bogs (Weber 1907) or waters of lakes (Naumann 1919) which were rich or poor in nutrients, notably nitrogen and phosphorus. Therefore, in its original meaning, eutrophication represented something desirable rather than, as now, undesirable. If this is remembered, the error will not be made of thinking eutrophication is always a bad thing from the point of view of conservation; it can be a good thing (e.g. Lund 1967). If a lake becomes less eutrophic, as indeed has happened during the history of the

English Lakes (Mackereth 1966), this may lead to losses or impoverishment of the fauna and flora. On the other hand, if a lake becomes more eutrophic this too can also lead to losses or impoverishment. In the first case total production is less; in the second case it is greater. Both changes may be decried by conservationists, depending on what it is that they wish to preserve. The quantitative and qualitative aspects of eutrophication have to be borne in mind. It is not enough to demand universal protection of areas of special scientific interest. Disaster does not threaten the waters of Britain because it threatens Lake Erie or Lake Ontario. It is not necessarily true that what is good for increasing the production of carp in Czechoslovakia or eels in Ireland must be good for coarse fish in general. What is needed is a scientific survey of the problem in any aquatic area worthy of conservation, that is the normal procedure applied to terrestrial areas.

Waters can become more eutrophic as they age irrespective of man's influence, though the common statement that they do become more eutrophic is not always true (Mackereth 1966, e.g. p. 183). Natural eutrophication and its causes are not considered here, only eutrophication through man's activities, that is artificial eutrophication. In most of the recent literature on the subject, especially that in semi-scientific journals or the press, the word eutrophication means artificial enrichment. It is also true that the meaning of the words eutrophication and pollution overlap. The entry of raw sewage into a lake is called pollution by everyone; it is also eutrophication, because raw or treated sewage is rich in actual or potential plant nutrients. However, in general, pollution is the addition of malodorous, harmful or directly toxic materials. The entry of treated organic sewage, that is well-mineralized and oxygenated sewage, can scarcely be called pollution, since the water is of good hygienic quality and appearamce, and is not known to be directly toxic to plants or animals. It is also normally so diluted in the watercourse into which it flows that the nitrate concentration falls below the toxic level for babies.

Sources of enrichment

The chief causes of eutrophication are sewage and agricultural fertilizers. The importance of sewage in causing eutrophication is undoubted (Vollenweider 1968, Weibel 1969). The effect of agricultural fertilizers is less easy to evaluate (Vollenweider 1968, Bigger & Corey 1969, Cooke & Williams 1970, Tomlinson 1970). The great increase in the use of nitrogenous fertilizers (Fig. 1) is not a direct indication of the likely addition to rivers shortly afterwards. The nitrogen is utilized, transformed into plant and animal matter, and partly re-cycled through the soil system. It is a gradual addition to rivers and, since part ends up in sewage, the fertilizer may enter more than one river. Therefore no dramatic increases in the concentration in rivers are to be expected. On the other hand the added nitrogen does not disappear into thin air. The end product of pollution by raw sewage is the same as that of treated sewage, though a portion, usually not a large one, is removed in the sludge of the treatment plant. In the so-called recovery zone (Hynes 1960) downstream of a source of such organic pollution the same type of process of mineralization has taken place as inside a modern sewage works. The course of the improvement of a bad sewage effluent can be followed in a river by

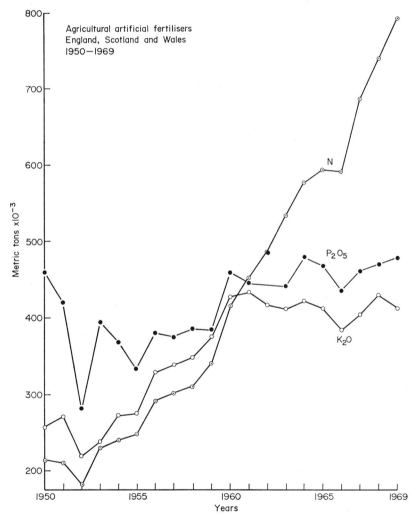

Figure 1. Use of artificial fertilizers in the United Kingdom. Fertilizer figures from 1950 to 1965 are for years ending on 30 June; that is 1966 represents 1 July 1965 to 30 June 1966. Subsequent years end on 31 May; that is 1969 represents 1 June 1968 to 31 May 1969. The figures are obtained from the official statistics of fertilizers delivered under the various Governmental schemes.

changes which illustrate this fact. Plants and animals which were found far
downstream of the sewage outfall, move up towards the sewage works as the
hygienic state of the effluent improves. For example, growths of *Cladophora*,
an alga much disliked by some fishermen, which were downstream of the zone
dominated by sewage fungus, move upstream to the outfall itself (Hynes 1960,
pp. 106–7; 116–17).

It is generally, but not universally, agreed that nitrogen and phosphorus
are the main nutrients from sewage (Vollenweider 1968) and these, in a good
sewage effluent, are present predominately as nitrate and phosphate. A large
proportion of the nitrate content of rivers can come from land drainage. Since
phosphate is not easily leached from soil, large increases in the phosphate
content of rivers usually can be ascribed to sewage. So far as London's river
supplies are concerned, there is no doubt that the dramatic rise in phosphate
comes overwhelmingly from sewage (Fig. 2). The amounts of both elements

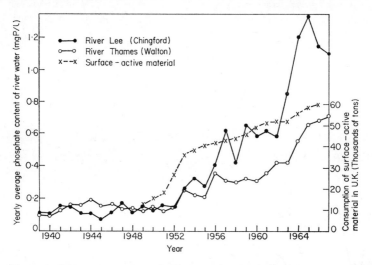

Figure 2. The concentrations of phosphate in two of the main sources of supply for
the reservoirs of the Metropolitan Water Board, London, England, and the use of
surface active materials (e.g. detergents) in the United Kingdom (Anon. 1968).

can be drastically reduced in sewage effluents. The question is how much of
which element ought to be removed and what the cost of the additional treatment needed will be. In practice the determining factor is whether the cost is
acceptable. The amount of phosphorus entering a sewage works could be
reduced by about 30–50 per cent if the polyphosphates were removed from
detergents. There is considerable support for getting detergent manufacturers
to reformulate their products by agreement or compulsion. An acceptable
alternative to the phosphate in detergents is said to be nitrilotriacetic acid

(NTA), and tests of detergents with most of their phosphorus replaced by NTA are being made. NTA, like ethylenediaminetetraacetic acid (EDTA), forms complexes with metals and, though less popular than EDTA, can be used to supply trace elements to algae in culture (Provasoli *et al.* 1957). Therefore NTA might seem to be an undesirable replacement for phosphorus because there are good grounds for believing that metal chelation is very important in promoting the profuse algal growth in nature. It is reported that NTA is decomposed in sewage treatment (Forsberg & Lindqvist 1967, Forsberg & Wiberg 1968). Nevertheless, sufficient tests on NTA in relation to possible effects on man and the environment have not been carried out at the time of writing this paper.

There must also be some doubt whether removing 50 per cent of the phosphorus in domestic wastes would be enough to solve the eutrophication problem (Lund 1970). As the population increases so will the sewage, and there is some evidence that the amount of sewage, detergents apart, per person is rising. It is in principle desirable that detergent phosphorus should be removed. However, in view of the uncertainty as to how great an effect this would have in reducing the fertility of water, there is not, in my view, a clear justification for imposing such changes on detergent manufacturers and, probably, imposing an increase in the price of detergents on the public. At least 95 per cent of the phosphate can be removed from sewage by tertiary treatment and such treatment has much to recommend it if it is not too expensive (Bayley 1970). It also seems likely that a reduction in phosphorus would be more widely valuable than that of nitrogen in sewage. If removal was by flocculation with lime, alum or ferric chloride, then there would also be a reduction in the trace elements and organic matter in the final effluent. These added benefits may be more valuable than is realized. There is a danger that over-emphasis on the importance of nitrogen and phosphorus may lead to underestimating the diversity of other factors controlling production. There are no agreed solutions yet but so much work is being done that the economics of the various methods of reducing nutrients in sewage and their effectiveness in test regions will soon be known.

If sewage effluents are easy to treat because they are point sources of enrichment, the opposite is true of agricultural fertilizers. It is also impractical to imagine that there will be a marked reduction in their use, an increase is more likely, and virtually certain in many areas. The most that can be expected is that there may be increasing use of less easily leached nitrogenous compounds, though no satisfactory formulations have yet been produced, and some attempt to reduce the flow of agricultural sewage into watercourses. The latter presents a greater potential threat than inorganic fertilizers.

What may be done in the near future will depend largely on the political pressure on governments to reduce everything coming under the umbrella of environmental pollution. In the meantime it is very urgent that ecological investigations should be increased so that there is better information on which to determine which waters should be conserved and how to manage those already in nature reserves.

Eutrophication of waters outside the United Kingdom

Eutrophication is world-wide, but concern about it is expressed more frequently and vociferously in developed than in underdeveloped countries. Political pressure, arising from the general concern about pollution of the environment, has not always aided a sensible approach to the problem. It is especially in relation to amenity that complaints arise. Conservation is mentioned largely in relation to the protection of recreational facilities, though, of course, this often coincides with the protection of the more or less natural ecosystem. The phrase 'more or less' is used because the majority of the waters about which most concern is expressed have been enriched to some extent in the past. Examples are the Swiss lakes (Thomas 1969), the Wisconsin lakes and Lake Washington in the United States (Edmondson 1968, 1969), The Great Lakes of North America (Beeton 1969), Lake Maggiore, Italy (Bonomi et al. 1968), Scandinavian (Willén 1968, Rodhe 1969), eastern European (Straškraba & Straškrabová 1969, Topachevskiǐ 1968) and Japanese lakes (Hori 1969). In the lakes concerned, waterblooms, and slimy and entangling growths of littoral algae have interfered with fishing, swimming, boating and the enjoyment of the beauty of the countryside. In New Zealand (Fish 1963) most concern is expressed about the growth of macrophytes. The changes in the plant populations affect other organisms and the chemistry of the water.

The International Biological Programme includes the project Aqua which is designed to produce a list of waters which are of scientific interest from the nature of their ecosystems or the types of organisms within them, or because of the investigations made upon them. Though it may be too late to save some of the waters listed, the final report should be of great value in showing the extent of the problem and preventing further deterioration of the conditions in a number of famous waters. Even Lake Baikal, which contains about 20 per cent of the freshwater resources of the world and hundreds of endemic organisms, is threatened, though there the chief danger seems to be pollution. In view of its unique flora and fauna, it is welcome news that Russian scientists, through Aqua, meetings and a series of articles, have been able to ensure that there are plans for its protection (Kozhov 1967, Galaziǐ et al. 1968, Anon. 1969). In view of the common emphasis on amenity, the emphasis in the International Biological Programme on conservation for scientific purposes is especially valuable.

The changes in the Great Lakes of America (Beeton 1969) have been caused largely by pollution. Michigan, Ontario and Erie are most affected, the last showing what would be considered as mild eutrophication in a small lake. However, their biology would have been altered without pollution or eutrophication. New fish have been introduced and the entry of the sea lamprey caused drastic changes before it was controlled. The construction of the Welland Canal alone has so altered their biology that it seems unlikely that they can ever be the same. It is the vast size of these lakes that has enabled them to absorb so much pollution and enrichment but equally it is their size which makes the dangers of eutrophication so great, for once changed it must take a long time for any remedial measures to succeed. The Great Lakes have been singled out for special mention because so much of the political pressure and propaganda against eutrophication are based on what has happened in them and what may happen in the future. Because of the size factor alluded to above, it is necessary to point out that their problems are not typical of those of the eutrophication of smaller lakes.

Conservation of British waters

Some consideration can now be given to the situation in the United Kingdom. First a word must be said about lakes and reservoirs used for water supply. Eutrophication of water supplies was very fully considered recently in a Symposium held by the Society for Water Treatment and Examination and the proceedings will be published in the Society's journal in 1971. Biological conservation is likely to take second place to the supply of water of good quality for domestic and industrial purposes. However, there is a number of lakes and reservoirs which are of considerable biological interest and in which there are communities which could be preserved without detriment to the supply of water. There are lakes and reservoirs in upland regions whose maintenance as typical oligotrophic habits is in the interests of both conservation and the water industry, for example the Lakes Thirlmere, Wastwater and Ennerdale in the English Lake District, Stocks Reservoir in Lancashire, Loch Katrine in Scotland and Lake Verney in Wales. The recreational and scientific aspects of eutrophication cannot be kept wholly separate. People can be excluded from a National Nature Reserve, but this is not always the case (e.g. Loch Leven).

On scientific grounds it is desirable to preserve some waters which are very eutrophic, including those which would be objectionable on amenity grounds. The biology of very rich waters is of just as much interest as that of very poor waters. The aim of conservation should be to have as wide a range of aquatic regimes as the climatic and geographical position of our country will permit. Rostherne Mere (Belcher & Storey 1968, Brinkhurst & Walsh

1967) is an example of a National Nature Reserve where extreme eutrophication is acceptable. It has monotonous waterblooms in summer and the
hypolimnion is anaerobic. Indeed it appears that the deeper lying deposits
are toxic to invertebrates at all times of year (Brinkhurst & Walsh 1967). It is
believed that birds are the major cause of this state of affairs. Since the bird
population is the major reason for it being a reserve, we have a combination
of two features of scientific interest.

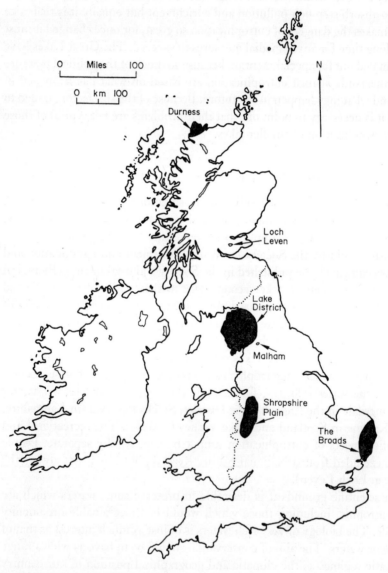

Figure 3. Locations of lakes and lake areas in Britain to which special reference is made.

Apart from waters which are of interest because they represent special hydrobiological types, some of which are uncommon, there are others which are of special value because of the scientific work already done on them. Loch Leven, Scotland, is such a water (Morgan 1970). It is a main site for the International Biological Programme and as a consequence has attracted the attention of some twenty scientists for limnological studies. It will become one of the best known lakes in the United Kingdom. It is a National Nature Reserve but the reserve agreement preserves trout fishing as a major activity and permits a limited amount of bird shooting. In 1905, species of *Chara*, *Nitella*, *Tolypella* and many higher plants were present. There were extensive beds of *Chara*, whose growth between about one and 2·5 m depth was 'prodigious'. In a bay at the east end, *Elodea canadensis* Michx was so abundant that, in summer, 'it is very difficult to row a boat through them'. There were 8 *Potamogeton* spp. (West 1909–10, 1910). Today the *Chara* is very reduced in amount and there are only scattered macrophytes, several species having disappeared. This change has been paralleled by an increase in the phytoplankton to the detriment of fishing (Rosenberg 1937, Brook 1965, Bailey-Watts et al. 1968), though no deaths of fish caused by algae or deoxygenation of the water have been recorded. Two mayflies, *Caenis horaria* (L.) and *Cloëon simile* Etn., have disappeared, dragonflies are absent and the numbers of caddis flies have decreased. It is not yet known what are the major nutrients controlling production. The increasing nitrogen content of the loch is paralleled by the increasing use of nitrogen as an agricultural fertilizer. Figure 4, based on Table III of Morgan (1970) shows how the use of fertilizers in the county of Kinross in which the loch lies, has paralleled the national trend (Fig. 1). Loch Leven poses a test case of how to manage a eutrophic Nature Reserve in which certain sporting rights are retained. In the first place more needs to be known about the exact relationship between the phytoplankton and the valuable trout fishery. This in turn makes necessary a thorough study of the other fish populations and of the invertebrate fauna upon which they feed. It is also necessary to know to what extent these invertebrates utilize the phytoplankton, particularly the predominant diatoms and Cyanophyceae. In the second place, if it is discovered what these interrelationships are, the difficult problem arises of how to manage the loch. Much of the nutrients comes from the land and there is little doubt that the production of crops, especially grass, and cattle are suboptimal because insufficient fertilizers are used. Lastly, whatever conclusions are reached as a result of the present study, detailed biological work will have to continue.

Two examples in the English Lake District are Windermere and Esthwaite Water. The literature on these lakes is large and can be found in the annual reports of the Freshwater Biological Association and Macan (1970). Neither lake is so peculiar that it should be conserved for this reason. The

case for their conservation is that they are the best-known British representatives of their type. There is a complication, namely would a proposal for a
conservation order be successful and if it was would the necessary protection
from further eutrophication be possible? It seems unlikely that either

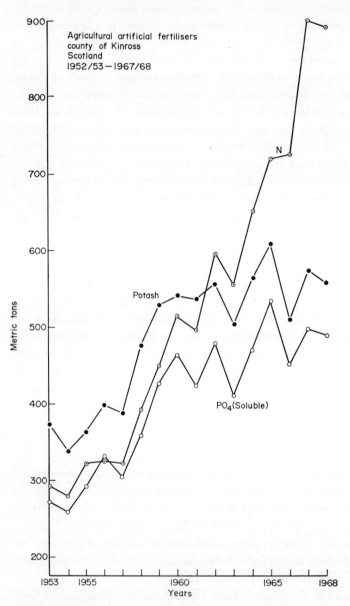

Figure 4. Use of artificial fertilizers in the County of Kinross, Scotland, for the years
1952–3 (1953 on figure) to 1967–8 (1968 on figure). Based on Table III of Morgan
(1970).

possibility could be fulfilled in the case of Windermere but that both are possible in the case of Esthwaite. Further, Esthwaite has a National Nature Reserve at its northern end and is not subject to the same recreational pressures or urban development that Windermere is. A third example in the English Lake District is Blelham Tarn, which illustrates a third variant of the problem. It has undergone relatively mild eutrophication, in part as a consequence of its protection as an area of natural beauty. So far as water chemistry, planktonic algae, parasitic fungi and the invertebrates in its main inflow are concerned its history is especially well documented (Lund 1969, Macan 1949, 1962). Its postglacial history, with special reference to chemistry and diatoms is also known (Mackereth 1966, Evans 1964). It is worthy of conservation as an example of the effects of the enrichment of an oligotrophic lake; a lake in which the consequences of eutrophication can be studied and evaluated historically and in which the full consequences of a recent increase in enrichment are not yet clear. It also has a National Nature Reserve on its shores. Blelham Tarn is near to Esthwaite Water (Lund in press) and much more similar to it than was the case 25 years ago.

There are so many oligotrophic lakes in northern and western Britain that it might be thought that there is no difficulty in selecting sites for conservation. Nevertheless there is a potential threat from agriculture and forestry; a threat which at present is not easy to evaluate, though Blelham Tarn and Esthwaite Water suggest possible dangers. As the best agricultural land decreases, so agricultural production increases on the decreasing amount of land farmed by a decreasing number of people. Agriculture improves in part by the development of more productive strains of plants and animals, and in part by the greater use of fertilizers. The two processes are interconnected since the full potential of new crops is only realized if sufficient nutrients are added to the soil. Present evidence suggests that the upper limit of application of fertilizers to arable land has been reached in some areas and soon will be elsewhere (Tomlinson 1970). We are a long way from this state of affairs in grassland, especially in the areas where the oligotrophic lakes are. If more fertilizer is used, more may be expected to leach into drainage waters directly, or indirectly through farm sewage. In some countries, fertilization of trees from the air is already practised and, efficient though the uptake of nutrients may be, precautions must be taken to avoid contamination of streams (Cooper 1969). As has been mentioned, there is some doubt as to how far agricultural fertilizers influence eutrophication. Nevertheless, there is an immediate need for a selection of oligotrophic waters which, it seems, are unlikely to be enriched significantly or are in areas where the catchments can be included in the reserves.

As an example of a kind of water which is likely to be specially sensitive to enrichment can be mentioned calcareous lakes which show features characteristic both of oligotrophy and eutrophy, such as the Durness lochs in northern Scotland and Malham Tarn in northern England. These lakes generally possess large, dense beds of *Chara* and other macrophytes.

The Durness lochs, Sutherland, are a good example of the problems involved in conservation. They are among the relatively few examples in the United Kingdom of unpolluted calcareous lakes and should be protected. They contain abundant macrophytes, including *Chara* swards, but it is not known whether production is as large as the biomass suggests. On the other hand the water is clear, a sure sign of low production of phytoplankton. The water is not poor in total phosphorus ($30-70$ μg P 1^{-1}) but most of it is likely to be bound in insoluble calcium phosphates. On the other hand soluble nitrogen is very low ($NO_3N + NO_2N$, $3-13$ μg 1^{-1}). Therefore they show features of oligotrophic and eutrophic lakes. They may be very susceptible to changes in the drainage area. For example, from an agricultural viewpoint, the addition of nitrogenous fertilizers to the land might be valuable. This enrichment would in turn lead to an alleviation of the nitrogen shortage in the lochs, either by direct loss of part of the added fertilizers or from the organic nitrogen produced by the greater number of animals per unit area. Additional nitrogen should lead to greater algal production and reduction of the natural macrophytic flora. Sewage would be even more dangerous, adding both nitrogen and phosphorus, and organic matter. The last might be the most dangerous addition. It is well known that many organic compounds chelate metals, and sewage humus (and dung) contains such compounds. Calcareous lakes which are not productive enough to have anaerobic hypolimnia are likely to be extremely poor in available iron. It is almost axiomatic to add iron to algal cultures in the form of an organic chelate. In fertilization experiments on American marl lakes it was shown that the iron complex with ethylenediaminetetra-acetic acid (EDTA) yielded the greatest increase in production (Schelske 1960, Schelske *et al.* 1962, concerning the likelihood of a similar result with NTA, see Forsberg 1968). Such complexes will also chelate calcium and so possibly liberate phosphorus, EDTA being the basis of a standard method of estimating calcium. The reason why such lakes have a predominantly rooted vegetation may be that in the mud more nitrogen is present, phosphorus is available, organic chelates abound and reducing conditions exist. Both the last two features will make iron and other trace metals available.

Malham Tarn is an example of a *Chara* lake which has many of the qualitative characteristics of a eutrophic lake (Lund 1961, Holmes 1965). It has a balance between *Chara* and other macrophytes (e.g. *Potamogeton lucens* L.), planktonic and benthic algae which produces a great diversity of life within it. It also has an old and very acid peat bog on one side which is eroded by the waves. In the lake, *Chara*, a typical calcareous plant, can be seen growing on this eroded peat. It is also one of the very few British lakes which contain *Cladophora* balls (*C. aegagropila* (L.) Rab. (*C. sauteri* auct.)). Fortunately it is situated in wild moorland, but improved grazing could easily be produced by fertilizers. Enrichment would almost certainly lead to increases of non-planktonic algae because the lake is so shallow. Like nearly all calcareous lakes, it has *Cladophora glomerata* L. on its shores and experience suggests that this and other filamentous algae would be a threat to the diversity of the flora, including the *Cladophora* balls, and so to the the fauna.

The encouragement of the growth of filamentous and planktonic algae has been used to control *Chara* and other macrophytes in fish ponds (Smith & Swingle 1941, Surber 1949). The addition of fertilizers early in the year can produce abundant growths of filamentous algae before the macrophytes have attained dominance. The decomposition of the damaged parts of the macro-phytes and of the dying filamentous algae leads to an abundant phytoplank-ton in summer, thus reducing light penetration. This method of controlling macrophytes describes the nutrient conditions produced by the kinds of environmental eutrophication which are considered here. Nutrients are at their maximum in winter when plant growth is least. When the increasing length of day permits increased plant growth, it is the algae which come first, be they planktonic or benthic. It is not uncommon to have large maxima in our lakes when the water temperature is about 5°C. Populations large enough to colour the water ('blooms') can occur under ice.

Among eutrophic lakes, candidates for conservation exist in the Cheshire–Shropshire plain, one of which, Rostherne Mere, has already been mentioned and is already part of a reserve. Crose Mere, Shropshire, is an example of what can be called an agriculturally eutrophic lake. Crose Mere also has a neigh-bour, Sweat Mere, which has a raft of higher plants growing over the water. This is a similar alkaline condition to the acid peaty rafts called Schwingmoor. This area could provide valuable information about different aspects of eutrophication (Phillips 1884, Griffiiths 1925, Reynolds 1967 and pers. comm.), in particular about the effect of adding yet more nitrogen and phos-phorus to already very rich waters.

Another unique set of English lakes, whose history is known, are the Broads. Some are protected, either by the Norfolk Naturalists' Trust or because they are National Nature Reserves. Such waterbodies may illustrate dramatically the effect of protection from the heavy recreational pressure on the neighbouring Broads. A good example is Hoveton Great Broad. Here too there are more or less brackish meres (e.g. Hickling Broad also part of a NNR) in which recently the very toxic alga *Prymnesium parvum* Carter has caused fish deaths. Does conservation include controlling *Prymnesium* or should the intermittent changes it causes in the fish populations and their food be con-sidered to be of special scientific interest?

The examples given underline the need for a review of British waters so that both general problems and those peculiar to each site can be evaluated. We are particularly fortunate that the Nature Conservancy has carried out a review of reserves having aquatic sites in them and of the great majority of other sites which might merit conservation. It is also particularly appropriate that the first part of the review, devoted to standing waters, is under discussion in the European Conservation Year.

Acknowledgements

I am very grateful to Mr N.C.Morgan for commenting on a first draft of the paper and especially for information about the Durness lochs and the invertebrate fauna of Loch Leven. I thank the Director, Commonwealth Bureau of Soils and the Grassland and Crop Improvement Division, Branch B, Ministry of Agriculture, Fisheries and Food, for information on the use of fertilizers. I also thank Mr A.E.Ramsbottom for the final copies of the figures.

References

ANON (1968) [Water Pollution Research Laboratory]. Eutrophication of inland waters. *Notes Wat. Pollut.*, no. 41, 4 pp.

ANON. (1969) Future of Lake Baikal. *Nature, Lond.* **223**, 1091.

BAILEY-WATTS A.E., BINDLOSS M.E., & BELCHER J.H. (1968) Freshwater primary production by a blue-green alga of bacterial size. *Nature, Lond.* **220**, 1344–5.

BAYLEY R.W. (1970) Nitrogen and phosphorus removal—methods and costs. *Wat. Treat. & Exam.* **19**, 259–319.

BEETON A.M. (1969) Changes in the environment and biota of the Great Lakes. In: *Eutrophication: Causes, Consequences, Correctives.* Publ. 1700, Div. Biol. Agric., Natn. Acad. Sci.—Natn. Res. Coun., Wash. 150–87.

BELCHER J.H. & STOREY J.E. (1968) The phytoplankton of Rostherne and Mere meres, Cheshire. *Naturalist, Hull.*, no. 905, 57–61.

BIGGER J.W. & COREY R.B. (1969) Agricultural drainage and eutrophication. In: *Eutrophication: Causes, Consequences, Correctives.* Publ. 1700. Div. Biol. Agric., Natn. Acad. Sci.—Natn. Res. Coun., Wash. 404–45.

BONOMI G., GERLETTI M., INDRI E. & TONOLLI L. (1968) Report on Lake Maggiore. *Symp. on Large Lakes and Impoundments*, Uppsala 1968. O.E.C.D.

BRINKHURST R.O. & WALSH B. (1967) Rostherne Mere, England, a further instance of guanotrophy. *J. Fish. Res. Bd Can.* **24**, 1299–313.

BROOK A.J. (1965) Planktonic algae as indicators of lake types, with special reference to the Desmidiaceae. *Limnol. Oceanogr.* **10**, 403–11.

COOKE G.W. & WILLIAMS R.J.B. (1970) Losses of nitrogen and phosphorus from agricultural land. *Wat. Treat. & Exam.* **19**, 253–76.

COOPER C.F. (1969) Nutrient output from managed forests. In: *Eutrophication: Causes, Consequences, Correctives.* Publ. 1700. Div. Biol. Agric., Natn. Acad. Sci.—Natn. Res. Coun., Wash. 446–63.

EDMONDSON W.T. (1968) Water-quality management and lake eutrophication: the Lake Washington case. In: *Water Resources Management and Public Policy*. Campbell T.H. & Sylvester R.O., Eds. 139–78. Univ. Wash. Press. Seattle.

EDMONDSON W.T. (1969) Eutrophication in North America. In: *Eutrophication: Causes, Consequences, Correctives*. Publ. 1700. Div. Biol. Agric., Natn. Acad. Sci.—Natn. Res. Coun., Wash. 50–64.

EVANS G.H. (1964) *Late-quaternary history of the Blelham Tarn Basin*. Ph.D. Thesis. University of Cambridge

FISH G.R. (1963) Observations on execessive weed growths in two lakes in New Zealand. *N.Z. Jnl Bot.* **1**, 410–18.

FORSBERG C. (1968) Effektes av nitrilotriacetat (NTA) på ^{14}C-assimilation och tillvaxt hos alger. *Vatten* **4**, 339–47.

FORSBERG C. & LINDQVIST G. (1967) Experimental studies on bacterial degradation of nitrilotriacetate, NTA. *Vatten* **4**, 265–77.

FORSBERG C. & WIBERG L. (1968) Om fosforutflockning i avloppsvatten, NTA och algtillväxt. *Vatten* **2**, 142–8.

GALAZIÏ G.I., KUZNETSOV S.I. & SMIRNOV N.N. (1968) Ob okhrane naibolee tsennỹkh vodoemov mira. *Gidrobiol. Zh.* **4**, 89–92.

GRIFFITHS B.M. (1925) Studies on the phytoplankton of the lowland waters of Great Britain. III. The phytoplankton of Shropshire, Cheshire and Staffordshire. *J. Linn. Soc. Bot.* **47**, 75–98.

HASLER A.D. (1947) Eutrophication of lakes by domestic drainage. *Ecology*. **28**, 383–95.

HOLMES P. (1965) The natural history of Malham Tarn. *Fld Stud.* **2**, 199–223.

HORI S. (1969) Asian Lakes. In: *Eutrophication: Causes, Consequences, Correctives*. Publ. 1700. Div. Biol. Agric., Natn. Acad. Sci.—Natn. Res. Coun., Wash. 98–123.

HYNES H.B.N. (1960) *The Biology of Polluted Waters*. Univ. Press, Liverpool.

KOZHOV M.M. (1967) K voprosu o vozmozhnỹkh posledstvykh zagryaznenii vod ozera Baikal promstokami tselluloznoi proỹmshlennosti. In: *Sanitarnaya i Tekhnicheskaya Gidrobiologiya*, 44–9, Nauka, Moscow.

LUND J.W.G. (1961) The algae of the Malham Tarn district. *Fld Stud.* **1**, 85–119.

LUND J.W.G. (1967) Planktonic algae and the ecology of lakes. *Sci. Prog. (Lond.)* **55**, 401–19.

LUND J.W.G. (1969) Phytoplankton. In: *Eutrophication: Causes, Consequences, Correctives*. Publ. 1700. Div. Biol. Agric., Natn. Acad. Sci.—Natn. Res. Coun., Wash. 306–30.

LUND J.W.G. (1970) Primary production. *Wat. Treat. & Exam.* **19**, 332–58.

LUND J.W.G. (in press) Changes in the biomass of Blue-green and other algae in an English lake from 1945–69. In: *Taxonomy and Biology of Blue-Green Algae*. 1st int. Symp. on Blue-green Algae. Madras. 1970.

MACAN T.T. (1949) Corixidae (Hemiptera) of an evolved lake in the English Lake District. *Hydrobiologia* **2**, 1–23.

MACAN T.T. (1962) Biotic factors in running water. *Schweiz. Z. Hydrol.* **24**, 386–407.

MACAN T.T. (1970) *Biological Studies of the English Lakes*. London.

MACKERETH F.J.H. (1966) Some chemical observations on post-glacial lake sediments. *Phil. Trans. R. Soc. B.* **250**, 165–213.

MORGAN N.C. (1970) Changes in the fauna and flora of a nutrient enriched lake. *Hydrobiologia*. **35**, 545–53.

NAUMANN E. (1919) Några synpunkter angående limnoplanktons ökologi med särskied hansyn till fytoplankton. *Svensk bot. Tidskr.* **13**, 129–63.

PHILLIPS W. (1884) The breaking of the Shropshire meres. *Trans. Shrops. archaeol. nat. Hist. Soc.* **7**, 277–300.

PROVASOLI L., McLAUGHLIN J.J.A. & DROOP M.R. (1957) The development of artificial media for marine algae. *Arch. Mikrobiol.* 25, 392–428.

REYNOLDS C.S. (1967) The breaking of the Shropshire meres. *Shrops. Conserv. Trust Bull.* No. 10, 9–14.

RODHE W. (1969) Crystallization of eutrophication concepts in Northern Europe. In: *Eutrophication: Causes, Consequences, Correctives.* Publ. 1700. Div. Biol. Agric., Natn. Acad. Sci.—Natn. Res. Coun., Wash. 50–64.

ROSENBERG M. (1937) Algae and trout. A biological aspect of the poor trout season in 1937. *Salm. Trout Mag.* No. 89, 313–22.

SCHELSKE C.L. (1960) Iron, organic matter and other factors limiting primary productivity in a marl lake. *Science N.Y.* 136, 45–6.

SCHELSKE C.L., HOOPER F.F. & HAERTL E.J. (1962) Responses of a marl lake to chelated iron and fertilizer. *Ecology,* 43, 646–53.

SMITH E.V. & SWINGLE H.S. (1941) The use of fertilizer for controlling several submerged aquatic plants. *Trans. Am. Fish. Soc.* 71, 94–101.

STRAŠKRABA M. & STRAŠKRABOVÁ V. (1969) Eastern European lakes. In: *Eutrophication: Causes, Consequences, Correctives.* Publ. 1700. Div. Biol. Agric., Natn. Acad. Sci.—Natn. Res. Coun., Wash. 65–97.

SURBER E.W. (1949) Control of aquatic plants in ponds and lakes. *Fishery Leafl. Fish Wildl. Serv. U.S.* 344, 20 pp.

THOMAS E.A. (1969) The process of eutrophication concepts in Central European lakes. In: *Eutrophication: Causes, Consequences, Correctives.* Publ. 1700. Div. Biol. Agric., Natn. Acad. Sci.—Natn. Res. Coun., Wash. 29–49.

TOMLINSON T.E. (1970) Trends in nitrate concentrations in English rivers, and fertilizer use. *Wat. Treat. & Exam.* 19, 277–93.

TOPACHEVSKIĬ A.V. (Ed.) (1968) '*Tsvetenie' Vodȳ.* Naukova Dumka, Kiev.

VOLLENWEIDER R.A. (1968) *Scientific fundamentals of the eutrophication of lakes and flowing waters, with particular reference to nitrogen and phosphorus as factors in eutrophication.* OECD. DAS/CSI/68.27.

WEBER C.A. (1908) Aufbau und Vegetation der Moore Norddeutschlands. *Bot. Jb.* 40, Beibl. 90, 19034.

WEIBEL S.R. (1969) Urban drainage as a factor in eutrophication. In: *Eutrophication: Causes, Consequences, Correctives.* Publ. 1700. Div. Biol. Agric., Natn. Acad. Sci.— Natn. Res. Coun., Wash. 383–403.

WEST G. (1909–10) A further contribution to a comparative study of the dominant phanerogamic and higher cryptogamic flora of aquatic habit in Scottish lakes. *Proc. R. Soc. Edinb.* 30, 65–181.

WEST G. (1910) An epitome of a comparative study of the dominant phanerogamic and higher cryptogamic flora of aquatic habit, in seven lake areas of Scotland. In: *Murray, J. & Pullar, L. Bathymetrical Survey of the Scottish Fresh-water Lochs.* 1, 156–260.

WILLÉN T. (1968) Lake Mälaren research. The biological section. *Symp. on Large Lakes and Impoundments,* Uppsala 1968. O.E.C.D. pp. 5.

Dynamic balance between plant species in South Moravian reedswamps

K.FIALA and J.KVĚT *Czechoslovak Academy of Sciences, Institute of Botany, Brno*

Introduction

This paper summarizes certain observations màde during the work on the Czechoslovak IBP/PT Project, no. 1.3.1./Productivity of Wetlands. The reedswamp ecosystems investigated are situated at two sites. First, in the temporarily, from 1960 to 1967, re-flooded part of the former shallow Lake of Kobylí, Kobylské jezero (A in Fig. 1), drained and reclaimed for crop cultivation some 130 years ago. Practically the whole re-flooded area, altogether about 150 ha, had gradually turned into a swamp. The other site, where investigations are continuing, has reedswamps along the shores of the old fishpond of Nesyt near Lednice (B in Fig. 1), which was founded about 1500. About 10 per cent of the whole fishpond area of 322 ha is occupied by different types of ochtohydrophyte reedswamp communities (Hejný 1957, 1970).

The environmental conditions at these two sites are typical of the Pannonian region, which comprises the whole Hungarian basin and its low lying surroundings, including South Moravia. The meteorological data of Lednice, 48°47′N, 16°30′E, altitude 184, m which are presented in Table 1, characterize the climate of South Moravia. The stagnant waters are usually frozen from December to early March, and the mean water temperature in the reedswamps rises above 10°C and 15°C in mid-April and mid-May, respectively, and falls below 15°C and 10°C in late September and October, respectively. In the summer, water temperatures very often exceed 20°C. This is, of course, only a general pattern, and great variation exists in individual years. Relatively wide fluctuations of the water level characterize the hydrological conditions. At the Lake of Kobylí, the fluctuations coincided with those in the adjacent Trkmanka stream while at Nesyt they depend mainly on the current year's balance between precipitation and evaporation, and on the management of the fishpond involving complete drainage every other autumn, when the fish are cropped. Out of Hejný's (1957, 1960) ecophases, the littoral and limosal ecophases prevail (with water level above and at ground level, respectively), while the terrestrial ecophase (with water level below ground level) only covers large areas of the reedswamps in exceptionally dry years; otherwise, it is confined to landward edges of the reedswamp stands. The trophic conditions are, on the whole, favourable for reedswamp at both Lake of Kobylí and Nesyt. Both the waters and the soils can be classified as eutrophic, with a high calcium and carbonate content, showing a tendency towards saline conditions due to an increased content especially of sulphates, but also of chlorides and sodium. Their reaction is mostly neutral to slightly alkaline; pH 6·8 to 8·0. More detailed descriptions of the reedswamp habitats

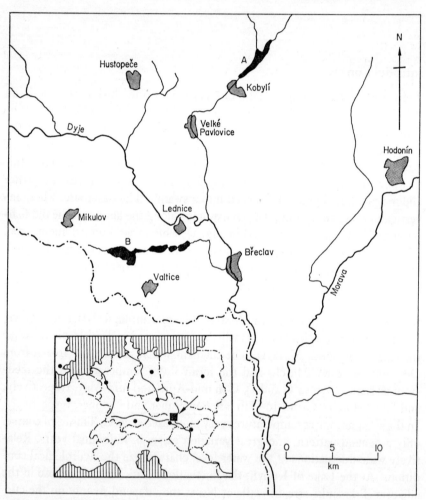

Figure 1. Map showing the location of the two sites investigated in South Moravia: A—Lake of Kobylí. B—Nesyt fishpond.

Table 1. Meteorological data from Lednice (S. Moravia, 48°48'N, 16°48'E, altitude 184 m).

I. Monthly means:

Months:	Jan.	Feb.	March	April	May	June	July	Aug.	Sept.	Oct.	Nov.	Dec.	∅
Temperatures 1901–50 (°C)	−1·7	−0·5	4·1	9·3	14·5	17·3	19·2	18·1	14·2	9·0	3·9	0·0	9·0 total
Rainfall 1901–50 (mm)	28	26	27	37	54	60	70	59	43	44	41	35	524 total
Sunshine duration 1965–9 (hrs)	42	76	124	186	216	228	238	204	163	137	62	38	1714 sum April–Sept.
Sums of total incident radiation 1966–9 (cal/cm²)	—	—	—	11153	14013	14182	14384	11756	8488	(5637)	—	—	73976

II. Lowest or highest monthly means of minimum or maximum temperatures (a) and daily mean temperatures (b) recorded in January and July, respectively of 1965–9:

	1965		1966		1967		1968		1969		mean	
	a	b	a	b	a	b	a	b	a	b	a	b
	−7·0*	23·6	−7·4	23·8	−4·1	27·1	−7·0	25·1	−5·6	26·7	−6·2	25·3
	−3·2	17·7	−4·3	18·1	−1·5	20·8	−3·2	18·6	−2·3	20·0	−2·9	19·0

* February

at both the Lake of Kobylí and Nesyt will be presented in other papers. An outline of the ecology of the Lednice fishponds has been recently written by Losos and Heteša (1967). A brief description and a list of earlier papers dealing with the Lednice fishponds are contained in the Project Aqua list (Luther and Rzóska, ed. 1969).

According to the plant-sociological classification, proper reedswamps belong to alliance Phragmition communis Koch 1926. In this paper, however, we include also communities falling under the alliance Scirpion maritimi Dahl et Hadač 1941, for their occurrence in our area is rather stable, in both space and time (which is not the case, e.g., in South Bohemia), and they characterize certain stages in the development of the reedswamps. A brief description of both Phragmition and Scirpion in Czechoslovakia is given by Holub et al. (1967). Most of the South Moravian Phragmition stands found around larger bodies of stagnant water belong to the association Scirpo-Phragmitetum Koch 1926, dominated in most instances by *Phragmites communis* Trin. or *Typha angustifolia* L., also locally by *Typha latifolia* L., or *Schoenoplectus lacustris* (L.) Palla. Communities belonging to Glycerietum aquaticae Hueck 1931, also falling within Phragmition, are confined to a few highly eutrophicated corners of the Nesyt fishpond. The Scirpion stands are dominated by *Bolboschoenus maritimus* (L.) Palla, mostly in its subspecies *compactus* (Hoffman) Hejný, indicating a somewhat increased salinity. Both the Phragmition and Scirpion stands can exist in all the three ecophases mentioned before.

This paper attempts to explain some of the important factors determining balance within the reedswamp communities in three particular situations typical of the development of Pannonian reedswamps. Some conservation measures applicable to these communities are also suggested.

There are three typical situations.

(*a*)   The early stage of reedswamp development for which the temporary re-flooding of parts of the Lake of Kobylí offered a unique opportunity.

(*b*)   The relatively stabilized reedswamps occurring at sheltered sites. Their stability largely depends on the prevention of further succession in the land-forming sere of communities. These situations have been observed in the shallow bays in the western and south-eastern parts of the Nesyt fishpond.

(*c*)   Unstabilized littoral communities where the combination of wind and wave effects with human activities and animal grazing prevents the formation of larger reedswamp stands. These situations have been observed along the unsheltered eastern shore of Nesyt.

Methods

The methods employed in our investigations were partly those of standard vegetation survey and analysis, as described by Klika *et al.* (1954). Methods of assessing the biomass and growth of underground organs, and of following the vegetative propagation in stands or colonies of reedswamp species, are described by Fiala *et al.* (1968) and Fiala (1970, 1971). The techniques applied to assessing the shoot biomass have been described, e.g. by Květ, Svoboda and Fiala (1969), Květ and Svoboda (1970) and by Husák and Květ (1970). Pelikán, Svoboda and Květ (1970) give details about muskrat activity affecting the reedswamps while Květ (1970) and Květ and Hudec (in press) describe in detail the effects of goose grazing. The chemical analyses of soil and water were made by K.Fiala, L.Rejthar and J.Vacek. Most of the Latin names of higher plant and animal species follow Rothmaler (1962) and Gaevskaya (1966), respectively.

Results of observations

Early stages of reedswamp formation

The zonation and succession of plant communities in the waterlogged and re-flooded parts of the Lake of Kobylí were mainly determined by the hydrological conditions, and are shown in the following schemes.

(*a*) *Alliances*
Agropyro–Rumicion crispi
(Bidention tripartiti)
↓
Scirpion maritimi
↓
Phragmition communis

(*b*) *Dominants in Scirpion and Phragmition*
Bolboschoenus maritimus ssp. *compactus*
↓
Typha latifolia
↙   ↘
Phragmites communis   (*Typha angustifolia*)

Representative vegetation records are presented in Table 2.

The sites which were waterlogged, but which were only rarely flooded, mostly at the beginning of the growing season, were occupied by communities dominated by *Agropyron repens* (L.) P.B., *Agrostis stolonifera* L., *Rumex crispus* L., *Plantago major* L., *Chenopodium* spp. and, locally, also by *Calamagrostis epigeios* (L.) Roth., *Bidens tripartitus* L., *Echinochloa crus-gali* (L.) P.B. or *Alisma plantago-aquatica* L. Most of the species forming these communities were, in fact, the local weeds given favourable conditions when their root systems reached the underground water level.

Table 2. Phytocoenological records of several typical stands at the Lake of Kobylí (Abundance + dominance established according to Braun-Blanquet)

Number of record	1	2	3	4	5	6	7	8	9	10	11
Area in sq. m	100	100	100	100	100	50	25	50	20	25	10
Water depth in cm	50	20-40	40	60	50	0-10	40	L*	L	T**	L
Date	10.11 1967	6.10 1967	10.11 1967	10.11 1967	10.11 1967	21.9 1967	3.11 1967	6.10 1967	3.11 1967	11.9 1967	5.10 1967
Phragmites communis	5	5	–	–	–	–	–	–	–	–	–
Typha latifolia	–	1	1	+	4-5	3	+	–	–	+	–
Typha angustifolia	–	–	4-5	5	–	–	–	–	–	–	–
Bolboschoenus maritimus ssp. *compactus*	–	–	1	–	–	2	4	4	–	2	+
Schoenoplectus tabernaemontani	–	–	1	–	–	–	1	–	–	–	1
Rumex crispus	–	–	–	–	–	–	1	–	1	+	1
Agropyron repens	–	–	–	–	–	–	–	+	4	–	–
Agrostis stolonifera	–	–	–	–	–	2	+	1	4	5	2
Ranunculus repens	–	–	–	–	–	–	–	–	–	+	4
Potentilla anserina	–	–	–	–	–	–	1	–	1	1	1
Epilobium adnatum	–	–	–	–	–	–	–	1	1	–	+
Plantago pauciflora	–	–	–	–	–	–	–	1	2	–	1-2
Cirsium arvense	–	–	–	–	–	–	–	+	–	–	–
Ranunculus sceleratus	–	–	–	–	–	–	–	1	–	+	–
Bidens tripartitus	–	–	–	–	–	–	–	–	–	+	–
Atriplex hastata	–	–	–	–	–	–	–	1	–	–	–

Polygonum amphibium	+	ı	—	3	—	ı	—	—
Echinochloa crus-galli	ı	—	2	—	—	—	2	—
Lemna minor	+	2	—	ı	—	ı	+	2
Lemna gibba	—	—	+	—	—	—	—	—
Lemna trisulca	2	4	2	+	2	—	—	—
Spirodela polyrrhiza	—	—	+	—	—	ı	—	—
Ricciocarpus natans	2	ı	—	ı	4	ı	+	—
Juncus articulatus	—	—	—	—	—	—	+	—
Symphytum officinale	—	—	—	—	—	—	+	+
Calamagrostis epigeios	—	—	—	—	—	ı	+	+
Tripleurospermum maritimum	—	—	—	—	—	—	+	+
Tussilago farfara	—	—	—	—	—	—	2	—
Taraxacum officinale	—	—	—	—	—	—	+	+
Plantago major	—	—	—	—	—	—	—	2
Phalaris arundinacea	+	—	+	—	—	—	—	—

Achillea millefolium no. of record 9 (+), *Alisma plantago-aquatica* 7 (1), *Anagalis arvensis* 9 (1), *Cichorium intybus* 10 (+), *Daucus carota* 10 (+), *Eleocharis palustris* 10 (+), *Euphorbia peplus* 10 (+), *Inula salicina* 11 (+), *Juncus gerardi* 11 (1), *Melilotus dentatus* 11 (1), *Mentha arvensis* 11 (1), *Stachys palustris* 9 (+), *Trifolium fragiferum* 11 (2), *Trifolium pratense* 9 (1), *Trifolium repens* 11 (+), *Triticum* sp. 8 (+), *Veronica anagallis-aquatica* 6 (+).

(*) Limosal ecophase.
(**) Terrestrial ecophase.

The development of these weeds was suppressed at sites remaining in the littoral to limosal ecophases for most of the year, with water level rising to +30 cm above ground level, and where the ground was exposed only occasionally. A community belonging to Scirpion maritimi, with dominant *Bolboschoenus maritimus* ssp. *compactus* (Bolboschoeneto-Schoenoplectetum according to Vicherek, in press) took over at these sites within one year from the onset of waterlogging. Tussocks of *Schoenoplectus tabernaemontani* (C.C.Gmel.) Palla became established locally.

Sites which remained in the littoral ecophase for most of the year, with the limosal ecophase confined only to occasional short periods, were somewhat less favourable for Scirpion maritimi. Such conditions enhanced the invasion by species of Scirpo-Phragmitetum, first by *Typha latifolia*, and later by *Phragmites communis*. The former species spread primarily by seeding while the latter did both vegetatively, mainly from old stands along ditches, and by seeding. Vegetative spreading of *Phragmites* from the established seedlings resulted in a pronounced clonal structure of the *Phragmites*-dominated stands, the boundaries between clones being usually easy to identify (Svoboda, Hradecká and Květ unpublished). *Typha angustifolia* stands formed only small, though dense, patches within the area occupied by Scirpo-Phragmitetum.

Typha latifolia played a key role in the rapid conquest of the area by Scirpo-Phragmitetum within 1 to 2 years from the abandonment of the waterlogged arable land. The easy anemochorous and hydrochorous spreading enabled *T. latifolia* to establish its seedlings over most of the area, and the subsequent expansive vegetative propagation speeded up the colonization of new ground by this species. The rate of its vegetative propagation depends on the rapid growth of the rhizomes and on their typical multiple branching. Fig. 2 documents the expansion of a *T. latifolia* colony recorded during the growing season of 1966 and early in 1967. The initial colony with 10 shoots had presumably arisen from a seedling in late 1965. By the end of the 1966 growing season and by June 1967, the colony diameter increased to 6 m and 8 m, respectively. Our observations at the Lake of Kobylí agreed with those made in other parts of Pannonia by Hejný (1960), who has stressed the ecological importance of the rapidity of both generative and vegetative propagation in *T. latifolia*, as opposed to the prevailing importance of vegetative propagation in *Bolboschoenus* and mostly also in *Phragmites*.

Fig. 3 illustrates the change of a *Bolboschoenus*-dominated into a *Typha*-dominated community. The extensive rhizome systems of *T. latifolia* relatively easily penetrated into stands of *Bolboschoenus*. The *Typha* rhizomes run either close to the ground surface, just below the thin detritus layer, or somewhat deeper, below the bulk of the *Bolboschoenus* tubers. The emerging *Typha* rhizomes gave rise to tall shoots shading off the shorter shoots of

Bolboschoenus. T. latifolia was thus more successful in the competition for solar radiation. The same seems to apply to the competition for soil nutrients, with most roots of both *Typha* and *Bolboschoenus* occupying the same soil layer, from o to −10 cm. The shaded *Bolboschoenus* plants seemed to form progressively smaller and fewer underground organs, especially tubers, giving way to the rhizomes and roots of *T. latifolia*. *Polygonum amphibium* L. was abundant only in the zone of the most intense interference between *Typha* and *Bolboschoenus*. Its presence did not affect the outcome of the succession towards the dominance of *T. latifolia* which severely suppressed and sometimes nearly eliminated *B. maritimus* ssp. *compactus*.

A growth analysis, performed in one of the *T. latifolia* stands by Květ, Svoboda and Fiala (1969), has shown that the mean stand density increased from about 16 shoots/m² at the beginning of the growing season to about 28 shoots/m² at its end, the maximum and final leaf area index being about 3·3. In such relatively loose stands, *Phragmites communis* encounters conditions permitting its existence, and it can spread gradually from both generative and vegetative diaspores that have formed at least one shoot taller than those of *T. latifolia*. The penetration of a *Phragmites* clone into a stand of *T. latifolia* was followed along a transect 8 m long, shown in Fig. 4. The length of the transect corresponds to 4 to 6 years of expansion of the *Phragmites* clone,

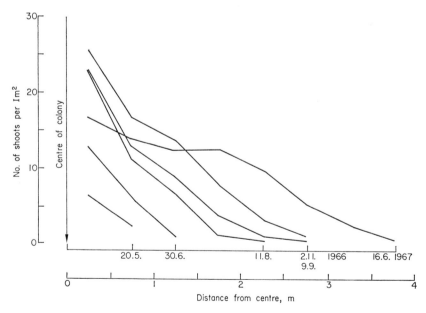

Figure 2. Record of vegetative spreading of a *Typha latifolia* colony at the Lake of Kobylí in 1966–7. Each line shows the stand density (number of shoots per 1 m²– ordinate) in dependence on the distance from the colony centre, on dates indicated along the abscissa below the end of each line.

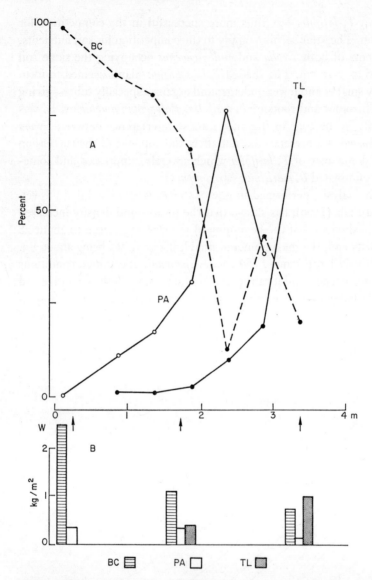

Figure 3. Transect from a stand dominated by *Bolboschoenus maritimus* ssp. *compactus* (BC), with admixed *Polygonum amphibium* (PA) to a stand dominated by *Typha latifolia* (TL), Lake of Kobylí, October 1966. Abscissa: transect length in metres. Ordinate: A—relative abundance of shoots of each species. B—Biomass (W) of underground parts, to a depth of −30 cm, of each species at points of the transect indicated by the arrows.

thus offering an approximate time scale. The horizontal *Phragmites* rhizomes advanced easily into the *Typha* stands at a depth of −20 to −30 cm, i.e. below the bulk of the *Typha* rhizomes. After having branched sympodially, these rhizomes bent upwards to bear vigorous terminal shoots (see Haslam 1969a b) usually taller than those of *Typha*. In *Phragmites*, the growth of most shoots and of the foliage is nearly completed in July whereas a *Typha latifolia* stand tends to grow till autumn (Květ, Svoboda and Fiala 1969), with maximum formation of new shoots in July (Hejný 1960, Fiala in press). Shading by

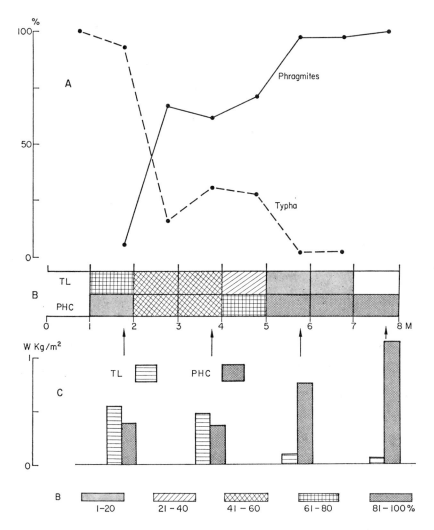

Figure 4. Transect from a *Typha latifolia*-dominated stand to a pure stand of *Phragmites communis*. Lake of Kobylí, October 1966. Abscissa: transect length in metres. Ordinate: A—relative abundance of shoots of each species. B—relative abundance of *Typha latifolia* (TL) and *Phragmites communis* (PHC) rhizomes to the depth of −90 cm. C—Biomass (W) of *Typha latifolia* (TL) and *Phragmites communis* (PHC) rhizomes, recorded to the depth of −100 cm at points of the transect indicated by the arrows.

the taller *Phragmites* shoots depresses the photosynthetic production in *Typha* and, consequently, reduces the growth of its rhizomes and formation of new shoots. At the same time, *Phragmites* appears to grow without limitations, as shown in Fig. 4. It is also evident that most roots of both *T. latifolia* and *Phragmites* occupy the same soil layer from 0 to −20 cm; their fine nutrient-absorbing roots are found in the uppermost soil layer. The density of these roots in *Phragmites* is about twice that found in *Typha*. *Phragmites* thus appears to be more successful in the competition for both solar radiation and soil nutrients.

In this way, stands of *P. communis* had gradually reduced, suppressed or replaced the stands dominated by *T. latifolia* on some 25 ha, i.e. about one-half of that part of the Lake of Kobylí, which had been flooded for approximately 6 years (Svoboda, unpublished).

Table 3 summarizes some of the biomass data recorded at the Lake of Kobylí by Květ, Svoboda and Fiala (1969), and by Svoboda, Květ, Fiala and Hradecká (unpublished). The combination of hydrotope and trophotope (Krotkevich 1966) seems to determine their primary productivity (see also Westlake 1965a b, Björk 1967).

Perhaps the most important animal factor affecting the balance between different types of communities at the Lake of Kobylí were the muskrats, *Ondatra zibethica* L. Their preference for *T. latifolia* as food has been demonstrated by Pelikán, Svoboda and Květ (1970). Fig. 5 shows the degree of damage to *Typha* stands growing around the muskrat houses. *Phragmites* was affected much less; about 90 per cent of the material accumulated in the muskrat houses were pieces of *Typha* shoots and rhizomes, and only some 10 per cent were bits of *Phragmites*. With a mean density of 16 muskrat houses per ha the estimated loss of the net shoot production in a *T. latifolia* community amounted to 100 to 180 kg of dry weight per ha, i.e. up to 10 per cent of the shoot production in an undamaged stand. The selective grazing of muskrats on *Typha* has presumably speeded up the advance of *Phragmites*. The retreat of *Typha* was partly documented by the fact that older muskrat houses were found mostly inside the *Phragmites* stands, with narrow corridors towards the feeding area in the *Typha* stands; relatively new muskrat houses were mostly situated either in the *Typha* stands or near the boundary between *Typha* and *Phragmites*. In the winter, muskrats seem to feed on rhizomes of *Typha* (Smirenskij 1951), thus reducing its capacity to propagate vegetatively. The rate of colonization of new ground through vegetative propagation is appreciably smaller in *Typha angustifolia* than in *T. latifolia*, the colonies of the latter being looser but more extensive (Fiala, unpublished). With no conspicuous preference for either of the two *Typha* species, the muskrats were perhaps partly responsible for the rather limited occurrence of *T. angustifolia* stands at the Lake of Kobylí, though the environmental conditions would have enabled their establishment at a number of sites.

Table 3. Production characteristics of various stands at the Lake of Kobylí. (From data acquired by J.Květ, J.Svoboda, K.Fiala and D.Hradecká).

Type of stand	Area stand (ha)	Area sampled	Date	Shoot no. per 1 m²	Shoot length (cm) mean	Shoot length (cm) max.	Leaf area index	Biomass (g/m²) Shoots	Biomass (g/m²) Rhizomes & Roots (tubers)	Mean water level (cm)
Phragmites communis										
2 years old	5	2. (50 cm × 25 cm)	Oct. 66	176	180	240	—	1763	1179	+40
Several years old	6	6. (50 cm × 50 cm)	16.8.67	76	295	370	—	1718 1158–2472	—	+50
Various clones	0·5	32. (50 cm × 100 cm)	19.9.67	61 41–87	310	370	4·4	1410 1086–1994	—	+50
Clone A	3	5 × 1 m²	26.7.68	58 42–81	255	340	4·7	1087 605–1975	—	+30
Clone B	3	5 × 1 m²	26.7.68	120 80–137	200	300	8·8	1930 1473–2823	—	+30
Terrestrial, saline	0·5	4. (50 cm × 100 cm)	19.9.67	142	260	—	3·8	1250	—	−15
Typha latifolia										
1 year old	0·1	shoots 4·1 m² underground 4. (50 cm × 50 cm)	30.7.66	—	—	—	—	889	496	+10
2 years old	5	2. (50 cm × 25 cm)	Oct. 66	24	192	220	—	—	904	+40
Established	10	4 × 1 m²	28.9.66	28 21–32	220	280	3·3	1620	—	+60

Table 3.—*continued*

Type of stand	Area of stand (ha)	Area sampled	Date	Shoot no. per 1 m²	Shoot length (cm) mean	Shoot length (cm) max.	Leaf area index	Biomass (g/m²) Shoots	Biomass (g/m²) Rhizomes & roots (tubers)	Mean water level (cm)
Typha angustifolia Established colony	0·02	6 × 1 m² 1 m²	7.9.67	58 53–64	250	300	—	1235 1134–1398	—	+50
Bolboschoenus maritimus ssp. *compactus* Mixed with *Alisma plantago-aquatica*	0·1	shoots 8 . (50 cm × 50 cm) underground 8 . (20 cm × 20 cm)	26.7.66	381	—	—	—	784	759	+15
Pure stand	0·1	shoots 8 . (50 cm × 50 cm) underground 8 . (20 cm × 20 cm)	26.7.66	395	—	—	—	680	1107	+15
Mixed with *Polygonum amphibium*	0·3	3 . (15 cm × 15 cm)	Oct. 66	75	75	75	—	—	2831 (2498 *Bolb.* + 333 *Pol.*)	+10
Bidens tripartitus— Tall stand	0·01	shoots 8 . (50 cm × 50 cm) roots 8 . (20 cm × 20 cm)	19.7.66	220	120	—	—	1188	1221	−20

Low stand	0·01	shoots 8 . (50 cm × 50 cm) roots 8 . (20 cm × 20 cm)	19.7.66	1227	30	—	—	—	380	—	324	−20
Calamagrostis epigeios Pure stand	0·01	shoots 8 . (50 cm × 50 cm) roots 8 . (20 cm × 20 cm)	9.7.66	—	—	—	—	—	759	—	2062	−25
Echinochloa crus-gali Dense stand	0·005	shoots 8 . (50 cm × 50 cm) roots 8 . (20 cm × 20 cm)	28.7.66	—	—	—	—	—	665	—	398	−25
Polygonum aviculare—Plantago major Other species admixed	0·02	shoots 8 . (50 cm × 50 cm) roots 8 . (20 cm × 20 cm)	18.7.66	—	—	—	—	—	482	—	107	−25

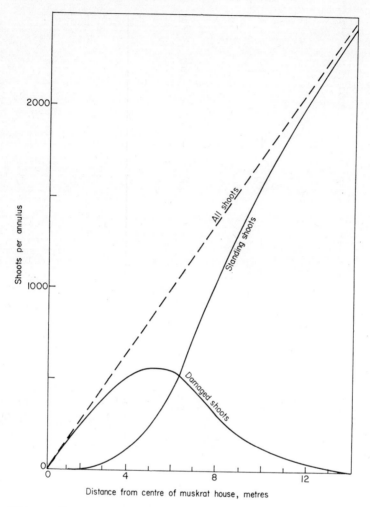

Shoots per annulus

Distance from centre of muskrat house, metres

Figure 5. Damage caused by muskrats to a stand of *Typha latifolia* at the Lake of Kobylí, in dependence on the distance from the centre of a muskrat house (abscissa). Ordinate: numbers of damaged, standing and all shoots in 1 m wide annuli around the muskrat house. (After Pelikán, Svoboda and Kvĕt 1970.)

Established reedswamps

These reedswamps usually develop in relatively sheltered situations with a gently sloping bottom, these conditions favouring the accumulation of gradually decomposing litter; accumulation type of reedswamp community according to Hejný (1970). The sequence of different types of stands is primarily determined by the hydrological conditions. Fig. 6 shows the ideal situation. Nearest to it are the reedswamps along the south-western shore of Nesyt where a smooth transition exists from a saline meadow with admixed dwarf forms of *Phragmites* to terrestrial, limosal and littoral stands, in that order. In the reedswamp, the soil is covered by a thin, 5 to 20 cm, layer of litter and forna mud, the decomposition of which takes some 2 years.

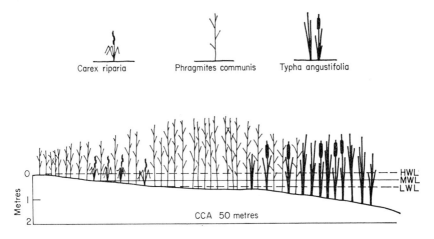

Figure 6. Schematic transect across an established reedswamp at the south-western end of Nesyt. HWL, MWL and LWL—high, mean and low water levels, respectively.

The net primary production of shoots in the *Phragmites*-dominated stands depends largely on the current year's water level. It can be up to 2,000 g/m², when a stand is continuously in the littoral ecophase (Květ, Svoboda and Fiala 1969), but it will fall to about half of this value if the same stand remains in the terrestrial ecophase throughout the growing season (Svoboda and Květ, unpublished). The values of rhizome and root biomass assessed so far in these stands range between 3,500 and 5,500 g/m² (Fiala *et al.* 1968). Limosal to terrestrial *Phragmites*-dominated stands have an undergrowth of other species: *Oenanthe aquatica* (L.) Poir., *Lycopus europaeus* L., *Solanum dulcamara* L., *Polygonum hydropiper* L., *Atriplex hastata* L., *Bidens tripartitus*, *Melilotus dentatus* (W. et K.) Pers., and others, whose biomass may reach as much as 400 g/m² in total. In littoral stands, the admixture of accompanying floating or submerged macrophytes, such as *Lemna* (especially *L. gibba* L.) and *Utricularia vulgaris* L., is very small as long as the canopy is closed and the relative light flux density at water level is 5 per cent or less. The biomass of these species attains appreciable values in the spring and later only in sparse stands or patches of open water. The same holds, *mutatis mutandis*, for the littoral stands with admixed or dominant *Typha angustifolia*. The annual shoot production recorded in a pure stand of *T. angustifolia* at Nesyt amounted to 2592 g/m⁻² while the corresponding rhizome biomass, recorded in the autumn, was 2075 g/m⁻² (Husák 1971).

The established reedswamps represent the main breeding area of waterfowl, because of which the fishponds of Lednice, including Nesyt, were declared a nature reserve in 1953. One of the main conservation measures has been a restriction of reed cutting. Winter cutting is allowed all over the reedswamp area except some 15 ha at the south-western end of Nesyt, where it is done only occasionally and in a haphazard way by the local inhabitants. Summer cutting of the reeds by the fishpond staff is allowed only along the waterward edges of the reedswamps to prevent their advance into the open water. This is done only after the main breeding season of the waterfowl, in late summer or early autumn. The main ecological effect of this summer cutting consists in a nearly complete elimination of the initial stages of reedswamp formation (Hejný 1957, 1960).

The reedswamps along the southern and south-western shores of Nesyt are the breeding area of grey lag geese, *Anser anser* L. These birds act as an important ecological factor in modifying, over relatively large areas, the species composition of the reedswamps. The effects of goose grazing on reedswamp stands have been described by Květ (1970). The geese's order of preference for individual reedswamp species seems to be the following. *Phalaris arundinacea* L., *Glyceria maxima*(Hartm.)Holmbg., *Phragmites communis*, *Bolboschoenus maritimus*, *Schoenoplectus lacustris*, *Typha latifolia* and *Typha angustifolia* on which the geese practically do not graze at all. As *P. communis* and *T. angustifolia* predominate in the Nesyt reedswamps, selective goose grazing has the most marked effects on the balance between these two species. The degree of damage goose grazing causes to *Phragmites* shoots depends on the following factors.

(*a*)   Access to the soft young leaves from open water—at a stand's edge or within a stand of soft emerging shoots—previous year's dead stems represent a highly effective barrier.

(*b*)   Grazing frequency: goose grazing seems to be most intense in the spring and early summer before the goslings can fly and find food elsewhere. At many places, however, grazing of regenerated shoots, after cutting or grazing, persists till autumn.

(*c*)   Depth of the bottom: the damage is usually greater at relatively shallow sites where the geese can clip off whole young shoots or regenerating branches near the bottom.

The grazed *Phragmites* shoots branch, acquire a broom-like appearance after repeated grazing. In this, as well as in other respects, the main direct effect of goose grazing on *Phragmites* resembles that of summer-cutting (Haslam 1970, Husák 1971). Repeated grazing apparently depletes the plants' reserves of assimilated material, destroys their protein-rich young tissues and greatly reduces their leaf area. Grazing maintains the shoots in juvenile state so that aphids—*Hyalopterus arundinis* (F.)—persist on their soft leaves till autumn, long after they have disappeared from normally growing stands. Because of the poorer growth and vegetative reproduction of the grazed *Phragmites*, the dominance of this species over the stand is reduced or lost, and the open niche is filled by other species, usually by *Typha angustifolia*. Where no other tall reedswamp species are available and grazing has taken place over large areas, patches of open water arise, with rich growth of algae, *Lemna*, *Riccia fluitans*, *Hippuris vulgaris* L. and other macrophytes (e.g. *Myriophyllum* spp., *Ceratophyllum demersum* L.). The slightly shaded or unshaded *Typha* shoots grow taller and assimilate more nutrients available for vegetative reproduction. Depending on the degree of damage inflicted by the geese upon *Phragmites*, mixed stands of *Phragmites* and *T. angustifolia* arise in situations where *Phragmites* would normally be the only dominant. The transect, presented in Fig. 7, shows that various types of stands, ranging from pure *Phragmites* to those of pure *Typha*, exist in small patches, probably corresponding to areas of more or less intense goose grazing in the past years.

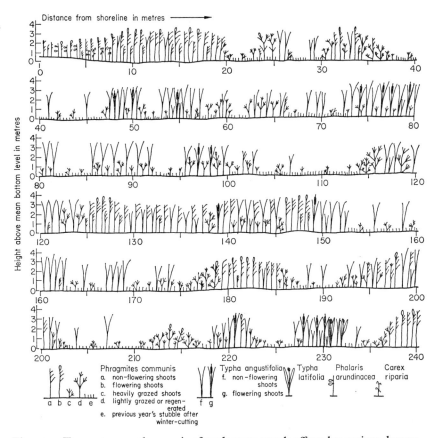

Figure 7. Transect across the mosaic of reedswamp stands affected to various degrees by past goose grazing. Recorded at the south-western end of Nesyt in October 1969.

The hydrological conditions are not without influence either: the pure or nearly pure *T. angustifolia* stands seem to have persisted only at depressions or other permanently wet sites whereas *Phragmites* seems to have regained its dominance more readily in stands growing at shallower sites. In these mixed stands, the ungrazed *Typha* shoots appear to restrict the geese's access to the shoots of *Phragmites*, thus enabling it gradually to restore its dominance.

The whole process of replacement of grazed *Phragmites* by *Typha* and gradual return to the dominance of *Phragmites* has the character of a cyclic succession triggered off by some outer influence. The small scale and irregularity of the pattern of the patches of different stands within the whole reed-swamp (Fig. 7) indicates the same. The most probable reason is the winter cutting of small areas of reed by man, when the water level is low or water is absent, followed by an increase of water level in the spring, by which the barrier effect of the remaining stubble is eliminated, and the geese have free access to the emerging young *Phragmites* shoots. Table 4 shows records of sample plots in different types of stands resulting after goose grazing, as well as in a pure *Phragmites* stand which had not been cut for several years. Such stands tend to degenerate because of the excessive accumulation of litter (Haslam 1970) and increased attack by insect pests, especially by stem borers, such as *Lipara* and *Nonagria*, hibernating in the dead stems. Both the stand density and vigour of individual shoots are affected, and the primary productivity of these stands decreases. In the long-term, the sheltering quality of uncut stands becomes poorer and the accumulated litter and förna mud may raise the bottom level, which increases the probability of occurrence of the limosal to terrestrial ecophases, and of the establishment within the stand of other plant species: e.g. *Carex riparia* Curt., *Solanum dulcamara* L.

Winter cutting thus appears to prevent the progression to further successional stages, and to trigger off goose grazing which combined with hydrological conditions brings about a greater species diversity within the established reedswamps.

Unstabilized reedswamps

These reedswamps are found along the wind- and wave-battered eastern shore of Nesyt. The waves blown over a 3 km distance by the prevailing western winds erode the sandy bottom as well as depositing drifts of both living and dead organic material (filamentous algae and aquatic macrophytes, seeds, pieces of cut reeds and rushes, etc.), covered with a dense mixed stand of *Bolboschoenus maritimus* ssp. *compactus*, *Polygonum lapathifolium* L., *Calystegia sepium* L. (R.Br.), *Oenanthe aquatica*, *Tripleurospermum maritimum* (L.) Koch, *Atriplex hastata*, *Bidens tripartitus*, *Sonchus arvensis* L., *Cirsium arvense* (L.) Scop., *Rorippa amphibia* (L.) Bess., *Lycopus europaeus*, *Epilobium*

Table 4. Numbers, lengths and maximum diameters of shoots (leaf bases in *Typha*) of *Phragmites communis* and *Typha angustifolia*, recorded in specimen sample plots of 20 cm × 200 cm in 8 stands affected to different degrees by goose grazing in the previous years as well as in the current growing season. South-western end of Nesyt, 22 to 23 October, 1966. In *Phragmites*, the damage by geese is classified in increasing amount from none (o) to 4, regenerated undamaged shoots (i.e., branches originating at the stem bases) are presented separately (r.). In *Typha*, undamaged shoots (o) and those affected by insect stem borers (+) are presented separately. The total numbers of shoots and the numbers of flowering ones among them (fl.) as well as the numbers of emerged autumn buds (b) are given for each of the two species. The mean shoot heights (in cm) and maximum diameters (in mm) are given in the form of fragments below the respective number of shoots. Note the relatively greater lengths of *Phragmites* shoots in the *Typha*-dominated stands situated in slight depressions of the bottom.

Type of stand:	*Phragmites communis* Degree of damage by geese to shoots						Total no. of shoots	fl.	b.	*Typha angustifolia*		Total no. of shoots	fl.	b.
	o	1	2	3	4	r.				o	+			
I Pure *Phragmites* Established stand uncut in previous two winters	31	5	0	0	0	0	36	17	52	0	0	0	0	0
	305/7·2	295/7·4	—	—	—	—				—	—	—		—
II Pure *Phragmites* Heavily grazed in the spring	12	2	7	11	19	29	80	3	16	0	0	0	0	0
	180/6·7	189/5·8	150/5·7	90/3·8	51/3·5	116/3·7				—	—	—		—
III Pure *Phragmites* Completely grazed	0	0	0	0	0	0	0	0	10	0	0	0	0	0
	—	—	—	—	—	—				—	—	—		—
IV Dominant *Typha* Early stage	0	0	0	5	4	9	18	0	8	16	0	16	0	21
	—	—	—	167/4·7	123/3·6	170/3·4				241/20	—			—
V Dominant *Typha*, *Phragmites* recovering	4	1	1	1	1	4	12	1	7	9	0	9	0	11
	297/7·4	323/12	238/8·0	230/5·5	115/4·0	158/3·9				319/30	—			—
VI *Phragmites* Regaining dominance over *Typha*	16	3	0	0	1	8	28	9	17	3	0	3	0	5
	252/7·4	201/5·2	—	—	60/5·0	150/3·8				267/24	—			—
VII *Typha* Dominance of *Typha* established	5	0	0	0	1	3	9	2	4	12	6	18	5	22
	329/9·1	—	—	—	30/5·0	221/4·7				329/22·5	140/21			—
VIII Pure *Typha* Stand, established	0	0	0	0	0	0	0	0	0	28*	0	28	2**	17
	—	—	—	—	—	—				288/20	—			—

* Including 2 shoots of *Typha latifolia*   ** Including 1 shoot of *Typha latifolia* *hirsutum* L., *Urtica dioica* L., etc. The environmental conditions in this erosion-accumulation type of community (Hejný 1970) depend on the current year's water level and its fluctuations, and so does the deposition of the drifts.

The zonation of the littoral stands varies from place to place, and schemes of two situations, an exposed and a relatively sheltered one, are presented in Figs. 8 and 9, respectively. *Bolboschoenus maritimus* ssp. *compactus* colonizes

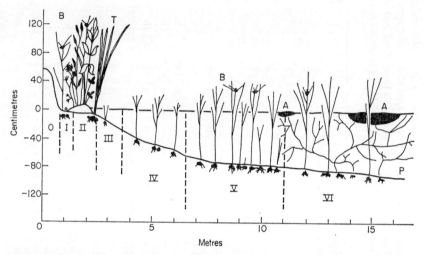

Figure 8. Transect across an unsheltered part of the eastern shore of Nesyt, recorded in June 1970. Abscissa: Distance from shore in metres. Ordinate: distance from water level in centimetres. Zones: O—Steep shore. I—Pool behind the drifts, with prevailing *Bolboschoenus maritimus* ssp. *compactus*, *Oenanthe aquatica* and *Lemna gibba*. II—Drifts of decomposing dead plant parts covered with a dense mixed stand and with a drifted colony of *Typha angustifolia* (T). III—No emergent macrophytes or only a few plants of *Bolboschoenus* (B). IV and V—Sparse and relatively denser (about 10 plants/m²) *Bolboschoenus*, respectively. VI—Sparse *Bolboschoenus* stand with filamentous algae (A) —mainly *Cladophora* and *Enteromorpha intestinalis*, and submerged macrophytes— mainly *Potamogeton pectinatus* L. (P).

most of the exposed shores, but its shoots usually do not emerge in the very narrow zone adjacent to the drift zone, probably because of both wave action and grazing by various water birds, ducks and others, including geese, clipping off parts of the leaves and pulling out the tubers from the bottom. Also the sparse stands in the deeper water are heavily grazed whereas the shoots growing from tubers deposited in the drifts seem to have extremely favourable conditions for their existence. The limosal ecophase and large amounts of nutrients available apparently enhance the formation of the assimilatory system. On the other hand, the plants growing in deep water spend much of their reserves on growth in height till they reach the water level above which

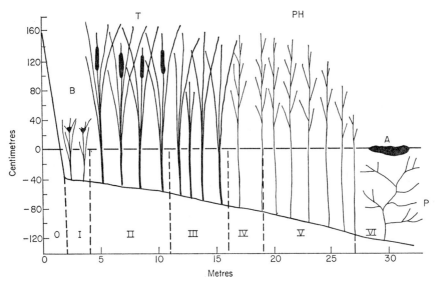

Figure 9. Transect across the unstabilized reedswamp stands at the eastern shore of Nesyt in a relatively sheltered situation, recorded in June 1970. Abscissa and ordinate as in Fig. 8. Zones: O—High shore; I—Sparse stand of *Bolboschoenus* (B.); II—Pure stand of *Typha angustifolia* (T) with flowering shoots; III—Ditto without flowering shoots; IV—Mixed stand of *Typha angustifolia* and *Phragmites communis* (PH); V—Pure stand of *Phragmites communis*, with edge grazed by water birds; VI—Open water with the same submerged vegetation as in VI of Fig. 8. III to V cut in August of the previous year.

they develop their foliage—much of which is soon destroyed by the birds (Fig. 10). These factors seem to limit the presence of *Bolboschoenus* to depths rarely exceeding −90 cm. A shallow littoral to limosal ecophase, occurring over larger areas in dry years, seems to favour the regeneration of these *Bolboschoenus* stands and enable their continuous existence. At high water level, the limosal ecophase is confined only to the narrow drift zone and to the pools behind it. All our observations agree with Hejný's (1960) outline of the ecology of *B. maritimus* in Pannonia. In heavily grazed *Bolboschoenus* stands, *Typha angustifolia* gains the ground and locally eventually suppresses *Bolboschoenus* by a similar mechanism as *Typha latifolia* (see p. 249). This succession takes place only at relatively sheltered places.

Along the east shore of Nesyt, colonies of either *Typha angustifolia* or *Phragmites communis* are distributed only in patches which have developed from vegetative diaspores, originating from other stands, transported and deposited by the waves. The diaspores are portions of the rhizome systems of different size. A small diaspore of *T. angustifolia* is shown in Fig. 11. The position of each colony depends on the height of the water level at the time the diaspore is anchoring its new roots in the bottom. The zonation of the

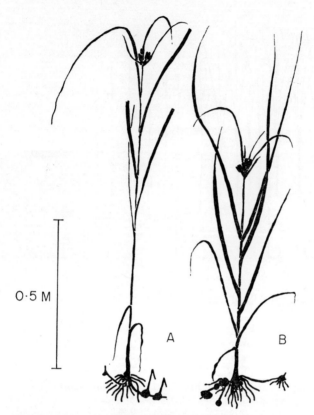

Figure 10. Flowering plants of *Bolboschoenus maritimus* ssp. *compactus* growing along the eastern shore of Nesyt: A, in deep water (about −80 cm); B, in the drifts of decomposing organic material deposited along the shoreline.

established stands (Fig. 6) applies only roughly; purely terrestrial colonies of *T. angustifolia* have been observed which are probably of limited duration. They have apparently started from diaspores deposited during periods of exceptionally high water level. The colonies of both *Typha* and *Phragmites* thrive better nearer the shoreline where they are protected from machine cutting in the summer. Wind damaging the shoots along the edge of the *Typha* colonies restricts their spread. *Phragmites*, being more resistant to wind action and to summer cutting, sometimes shelters the *Typha* colonies and also encircles them on the water-ward side where *Typha* would normally grow better. Such a seemingly reversed zonation of reedswamp stands is shown in Fig. 9.

The vegetative disapores of *Phragmites* and *Typha* which are brought to the eastern shore of Nesyt most probably originate from both human and animal activity. Parts of the rhizome systems are either pulled out from the bottom when the marginal stands are being cut, or they are released by muskrat grazing. This seems to hold particularly for *T. angustifolia,* of which a large colony along the north-western shore of Nesyt is populated by muskrats.

The presence of individual species in the unstabilized reedswamps as well as the balance between them therefore depends on the outcome of the inter-action of physical factors (water level, wind and wave action) with grazing by birds and also by muskrats in stands providing the diaspores, as well as on the management of the fishpond by man.

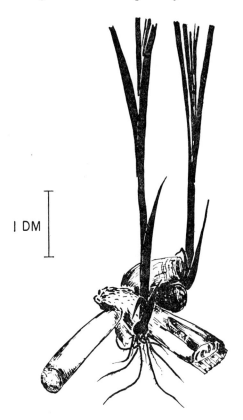

Figure 11. A small vegetative diaspore of *Typha angustifolia* drifted at the eastern shore of Nesyt. June 1970. The two shoots present had 8 leaves each; total length was 825 cm (from 13 to 88 cm per one leaf) and the leaf widths ranged from 3 to 8·5 mm.

Discussion

Our observations on the ecology and growth of individual reedswamp species seem to be in agreement with those of other authors: Smirenskij (1951), Vam-pilov (1951), Pearsall & Gorham (1956), Neuhäusl (1959, 1965), Isambaev (1964*a, b*), Buttery & Lambert (1965), Rudescu (1965), Rudescu *et al.* (1965), Gaevskaya (1966), Dykyjová (1967, 1971), Haslam (1968)—besides the authors quoted before. Much the same principles seem to apply to the South Moravian reedswamps investigated as to others in the stagnant waters of temperate Eurasia. The special conditions of water reservoirs with widely fluctuating water levels, such as those encountered in rice fields (Hejný 1960) or in the south-western Siberian pan-formed lakes (Smirenskij 1951) existed, to a certain extent, at the Lake of Kobylí. Nesyt, on the other hand, with relatively greater differences in water level between years rather than within one year, preserves the character of a fishpond (Hejný 1970), resembling, at the same time, the slightly saline large Pannonian shallow lakes, e.g. Neusiedler See.

Our approach is primarily production ecological, but we have tried to show that production ecological investigations can yield information useful for the interpretation of broader ecological phenomena, such as the assessment of effects of selective animal grazing on the species composition of plant communities, as well as for the choice of the correct management for conservation.

Our observations have proved, once again, the well-known experience that the conservation of any single component of an ecosystem cannot be isolated from that of other, perhaps less precious, components. The Lednice fishponds are a nature reserve primarily because of their ornithological value. Yet, for example, the perpetuation of intense breeding of grey lag geese at Nesyt requires a certain management of the reedswamp plant cover by man rather than leaving the stands to themselves. This apparently does more harm than good, and winter cutting of all stands, maybe in a 2 to 3 year's rotation, would perhaps be the most satisfactory management; it would provide shelter for wild-life in the winter as well as sufficient food for the geese in the growing season. At the same time, the degradation of the reedswamp community to pure and degenerating *Phragmites* stands would be prevented, as well as the formation of a terrestrial habitat, from the accumulated förna mud.

All three types of reedswamps described in our paper require a certain management for their preservation.

The early stages of reedswamp formation are of a short-term nature and are consequently most difficult to preserve. In a cultivated landscape such as South Moravia, temporary flooding of some arable land is perhaps the easiest way of inducing reedswamp formation. As this is hardly feasible, careful observations and records of emergency situations—like that at the Lake of Kobylí—or of newly established water reservoirs are the only substitute.

The other two situations, observed in both the stablilized and unstabilized reedswamps, are longer-lasting and are included in the existing nature reserves. Their management should aim to preserve the existing variety of both plant and animal species as well as the varied plant-animal interactions which contribute substantially to the rapid energy flow and turnover in the reedswamp ecosystems. In addition to the conservation measures discussed before, the management should comprise the induction of certain fluctuations of water level between years, including the creation of a limosal ecophase over larger areas for a whole growing season once in 3 to 5 years. This measure would particularly favour the regeneration of the Scirpion maritimi communities as well as the germination of *Phragmites* and *Typha latifolia* and the consequent establishment of new clones; the variety of genotypes present in the local populations of these species would thus increase. Unfortunately, this requirement contrasts with the present needs of fish-farming, and thus conservation has to rely on the occasional dry seasons with high evaporation and little rainfall. They are, however, not all that uncommon at Nesyt, the English translation of the fishpond's name being 'Never Saturated'.

References

BJÖRK S. (1967) Ecologic investigations of *Phragmites communis*. Studies in theoretic and applied limnology. *Folia limnol. scand.* **14**.

BUTTERY B.R. & LAMBERT J.M. (1965) Competition between *Glyceria maxima* and *Phragmites communis* in the region of Surlingham Broad. I and II *J. Ecol.* **53**, 163–81; 183–95.

DYKYJOVÁ D. (1967) *Primary productivity of littoral stands in the Basin of Třeboň* (*S. Bohemia*). Leaflet guide no. 8 for the BES 1967 Summer Meeting in Czechoslovakia. Mimeographed document, 4 pp.

DYKYJOVÁ D. (1971) Ekomorfózy a ekotypy rákosu obecného *Phragmites communis*. *Preslia* **43**, 120–38.

FIALA K. (1970) Rhizome biomass and its relation to shoot biomass and stand pattern in eight clones of *Phragmites communis* Trin. In: *PT-PP Report*, no. 1. Ed. Dykyjova D., 95–8 Czechoslovak IBP National Committee. Praha.

FIALA K. (in press) Seasonal changes in the growth of clones of *Typha latifolia* in natural conditions. *Folia geobot & phytotax.* **6**.

FIALA K., DYKYJOVÁ D., KVĚT J. & SVOBODA J. (1968) Methods of assessing rhizome and root production in reed-bed stands. In: *Methods of productivity studies in root systems and rhizosphere organisms*, pp. 36–47. Nauka, Leningrad.

GAEVSKAYA N.S. (1966) *Rol vysshikh vodnykh rastenii v pitanii zhivotnykh presnykh vodoemov* (Role of aquatic higher plants in the nutrition of animals inhabiting freshwater reservoirs.) 327 pp. Nauka, Moskva. In Russian.

HASLAM S.M. (1968) The biology of reed (*Phragmites communis*) in relation to its control. *Proc. Brit. Weed Control Conf.* 9th, 392–7.

HASLAM S.M. (1969a) Stem types of *Phragmites communis* Trin. *Ann. Bot. N.S.* **33**, 127–31.

HASLAM S.M. (1969b) The development and emergence of buds in *Phragmites communis* Trin. *Ann. Bot. N.S.* **33**, 289–301.

HASLAM S.M. (1970) Variation of population type in *Phragmites communis* Trin. *Ann. Bot. N.S.* **34**, 147–58.

HEJNÝ S. (1957) Ein Beitrag zur ökologischen Gliederung der Makrophyten in den Niederungsgewässern der Tschechoslowakei. *Preslia* **29**, 349–68.

HEJNÝ S. (1960) *Ökologische Charakteristik der Wasser- und Sumpfpflanzen in den Slowakischen Tiefebenen (Donau- und Theissgebiet)*. 492 pp. Naklad. SAV, Bratislava.

HEJNÝ S. (1970) Plant sociological and synecological characteristics of the reed communities in South Bohemian and South Moravian fishponds. In: *PT-PP Report* no. 1, Ed. Dykyjová D., 65–70. Czechoslovak IBP National Committee, Praha.

HOLUB J., HEJNÝ S., MORAVEC J. & NEUHÄUSL R. (1967) Übersicht der höheren Vegetationseinheiten der Tschechoslowakei. *Rozpr. čsl. Akad. Věd, A,* 77, 1–75.

HUSÁK Š. (1971) *Vliv seče na porosty Phragmites communis Trin. a Typha angustifolia* L. (Effect of cutting on the stands of . . .). Dipl. Thesis. Purkyně University of Brno, Dept. of Botany, Brno. Manuscript. In Czech.

HUSÁK Š. & KVĚT J. (1970) Productive structure of *Phragmites communis* and *Typha angustifolia* stands after cutting at two different levels. In: *PT-PP Report* no. 1, Ed. Dykyjová D., 117–19. Czechoslovak IBP National Committee. Praha.

ISAMBAEV A.I. (1964a) Vlianie khozaistvennogo ispolzovaniya trostnikovykh zarosley na ikh vozobnovlenie i proizvoditelnost. (Effect of economic exploitation of reed stands on their regeneration and productivity). *Trudy Inst. Bot. Alma-Ata.* 19, 231–60.

ISAMBAEV A.I. (1964b) Podzemnye pobyegi trostnika obyknovennogo v razlichnykh ekologicheskikh usloviyakh. (Underground shoots of common reed in different ecological conditions.) *Trudy Inst. Bot. Alma-Ata* 19, 185–202. In Russian.

KLIKA J., NOVÁK V. & GREGOR A. (Ed.) (1954) *Praktikum fytocenologie, ekologie, klimatologie a půdoznalství.* Nakladat. ČSAV. Praha. In Czech.

KROTKEVICH P.G. (1966) Klassifikatsiya biotopov trostnika na ekologicheskoy osnovye. (Classification of reed biotopes on ecological basis). *Sb. Trud. ukr. nauch.-issled. Inst. Tsellyulozno-bumazhnoy Prom. Moskva,* 9, 28–50. In Russian.

KVĚT J. (1970) Destruction of reed stands by grey-lag goose. In: *PT-PP Report* no. 1, Ed. Dykyjová D., 121–3. Czechoslovak IBP National Committee. Praha.

KVĚT J. & HUDEC K. (in press) Effect of grazing by grey-lag geese and reedswamp plant communities.

KVĚT J. & SVOBODA J. (1970) Development of vertical structure and growth analysis in a stand of *Phragmites communis* Trin. In: *PT-PP Report* no. 1, Ed. Dykyjová D., 84–7. Czechoslovak IBP National Committee. Praha.

KVĚT J., SVOBODA J. & FIALA K. (1969) Canopy development in stands of *Typha latifolia* L. and *Phragmites communis* Trin. in South Moravia. *Hidrobiologia* 10, 63–75.

LUTHER H. & RZÓSKA J. ed. (1969) *Project Aqua.* IBP Central Office, London.

LOSOS B. & HETEŠA J. (1967) *Fishponds of Lednice (S.Moravia).* Leaflet guide no. 16 for the BES 1967 Summer Meeting in Czechoslovakia. Mimeographed document, 6 pp.

NEUHÄUSL R. (1959) Die Pflanzengesellschaften des SO-Teiles des Wittingauer Beckens. *Preslia* 31, 115–47.

NEUHÄUSL R. (1965) Vegetation der Röhrichte und der sublitoral-Magnocariceten im Wittingauer Becken. In: Synökologische Studien über Röhrichte, Wiesen und Auenwalder. *Vegetace ČSSR ser. A,* 1, 11–117. Academia, Praha.

PEARSALL W.H. & GORHAM E. (1956) Production ecology I. Standing crops of natural vegetation. *Oikos* 7, 193–201.

PELIKÁN J., SVOBODA J. & KVĚT J. (1970) Destruction of *Typha latifolia* production by muskrats. *Zool. Listy.*

ROTHMALER W. ed. (1962) *Exkursionsflora von Deutschland. Gefässpflanzen.* 3rd ed., 503 pp. Volk und Wissen Volkseigener Verlag, Berlin.

RUDESCU L. (1965) Neue biologische Probleme bei den *Phragmites*-kulturarbeiten im Donaudelta. *Arch. Hydrobiol. Suppl. Donauforschung II.* 30, 80–111.

RUDESCU L., NICHULESCU C. & CHIVU I.P. (1965) *Monografia Stufului din Delta Dunării.* 540 pp. Editura Acad. Rep Soc. Romănia. Bucureşti. In Roumanian.

SMIRENSKIJ A.A. (1951) Struktura vodnykh okhotnichikh ugodii zapadnosibirskoy lesostepi. Soobshchenie I. Obshchaya strukturnaya kharakteristika osnovnykh tipov ozer blyudyets. (Structure of aquatic hunting grounds of the West Siberian steppe woodlands. Communication I. General structural characteristic of the main types of pan-formed lakes). *Trudy vses. nauchno-issled. Inst. okhotnichego Promy.* 9, 122–86. Gosud. Izd. Tekh. i Ekon. Lit., Moskva. In Russian.

VAMPILOV V.N. (1951) Uvelichenie kormovoy proizvoditelnosti i uluchenie gnezdovykh i zashchitnykh uslovii ondatrovykh ugodii delty Selengi (Vostochnoe Pribaykalie). (Increase of food production and improvement of breeding and sheltering conditions in the muskrat hunting grounds in the Selenga river delta—East Baykal region.) *Trudy vses. nauchno.-issled. Inst. okhothichego Prom.* 9, 187–201. Gosud. Izd. Tekh. i Ekon. Lit., Moskva. In Russian.

VICHEREK J (in press) Die Pflanzengesellschaften der Halophyten- und der Subhalophyten-vegetation der Tschechoslowakei. *Vegetace ČSSR, ser. A.*, Academia, Praha.

WESTLAKE D.F. (1965a) Some basic data for investigations of the productivity of aquatic macrophytes. *Memorie Ist. ital. Idrobiol.*, 18, Suppl., 229–48.

WESTLAKE D.F. (1965b) Theoretical aspects of the comparability of productivity data. *Memorie Ist. ital. Idrobiol.*, 18, Suppl., 313–22.

Some effects of organic enrichment on benthic invertebrate communities in stream riffles

H.A.HAWKES and L.J.DAVIES *Department of Biological Sciences, University of Aston in Birmingham*

Introduction

Under natural conditions organic matter, such as leaves, enters the stream ecosystem from the land; such gains of allochthonous material help to make good the continuous loss of materials to the sea. The discharge of organic effluents, such as sewage and those resulting from the processing of food and other biological materials, increases the amount of organic matter naturally present in the stream. The ecological consequences of the resultant increases in organic concentration have been studied since early this century by biologists throughout the world. Their findings have been reviewed (Hynes 1960, Hawkes 1962). Within the stream the introduced organic matter is progressively broken down by biological activity. The increased populations of saprobic micro-organisms and scavengers, responsible for the breakdown, in turn support a larger population of animals feeding on them. The activity of the increased saprobic microbial population, both planktonic and benthic, increases the oxygen demand and this may result in deoxygenation of the water, which affects other organisms according to their degree of tolerance to oxygen depletion. Thus organic enrichment has a differential effect upon members of the stream community, resulting in a succession of communities becoming established at distances below the discharge in relation to the degree of oxidation and mineralization of the organic matter. Typical communities in this ecological succession are represented diagrammatically in Fig. 1. Such a succession is evidence of the homeostatic properties of stream ecosystems which enables them to deal, within limits, with man's organic discharges. The development of benthic saprobic micro-organisms may be in the form of undesirable growths known as sewage fungus. Such growths change the physical nature of the stream bed and thus indirectly affect the macro-invertebrate community. The organic matter or its breakdown

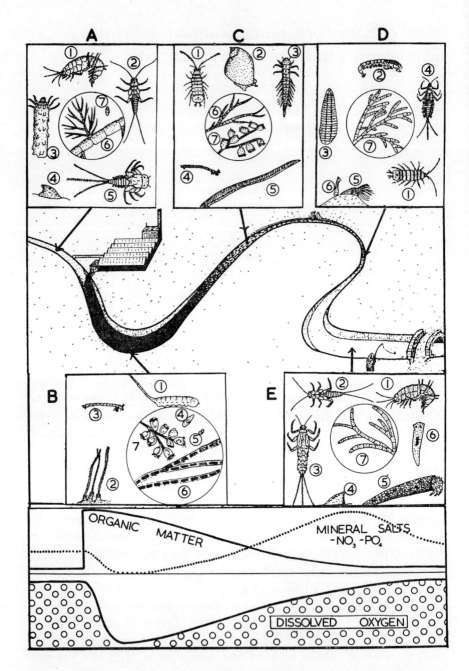

Figure 1. Representative organisms of different benthic communities associated with different degrees of recovery from organic pollution. (Courtesy of *Effluent and Water Treatment Journal*).

Key to organisms in Fig. 1 (micro-organisms shown within circles)

A	B	C	D	E
1. *Gammarus pulex* (Fresh-water shrimp)	1. *Eristalis tenax* (Rag-tailed maggot)	1. *Asellus aquaticus* (Water hog-louse)	1. *Asellus aquaticus* (Water hog-louse)	1. *Gammarus pulex* (Fresh-water shrimp)
2. *Nemoura* (Stone-fly nymph)	2. *Tubifex* (Sludge worm)	2. *Lymnaea pereger* (Wandering snail)	2. *Hydropsyche* (Case-less caddis larva)	2. *Nemoura* (Stone-fly nymph)
3. Limnophilid caddis	3. *Chironomus riparius* (Blood worm)	3. *Sialis lutaria* (Alder-fly larva)	3. *Glossiphonia* (Leech)	3. *Ephemerella* (May-fly nymph)
4. *Ancylus fluviatilis* (Limpet)	4. *Paramecium caudatum*	4. *Chironomus riparius* (Blood worm)	4. *Baetis rhodani* (May-fly nymph)	4. *Ancylus fluviatilis* (Limpet)
5. *Ecdyonurus* May-fly larva	5. *Colpidium*	5. *Erpobdella* (Leech)	5 & 6. *Simulium ornatum* Pupa and larva of black fly	5. *Stenophylax* (Caddis larva)
6. *Draparnaldia* (Green alga)	6. *Sphaerotilus natans* (Sewage fungus)	6. *Stigeoclonium* (Green alga)		6. *Dugesia* (Flat-worm)
7. *Cocconeis* (Diatom)	7. *Carchesium* (Sewage fungus)	7. *Carchesium* (Sewage fungus)	7. *Cladophora* (Blanket weed)	7. *Cladophora* (Blanket weed)

products may be toxic and if particulate solids are present in the discharge these may settle on the stream bed, changing its character. Thus organic pollution cannot be regarded as a single factor affecting the stream ecology, but as a multiplicity of factors.

Earlier workers in Germany (Kolkwitz & Marsson 1908, 1909) classified organisms according to the degree of organic degradation with which they were associated. They introduced the term 'saprobia' to apply to organisms associated with the different stages of oxidation of organic matter in enriched waters and to express their dependence on decomposing organic nutrients. They recognized four saprobes; poly-, alpha meso-, beta meso- and oligo-, on the basis of progressive increasing degree of mineralization. This formed the basis of the 'Saprobiensystem' of assessing the degree of organic pollution by using indicator organisms. Over the years this has been developed by several workers throughout Europe (Fjerdingstad 1964). In other parts of the world similar work has resulted in comparable but less formal systems.

Much effort has gone into classifying organisms according to the degree of organic degradation with which they are associated and into developing indicator systems. As outlined above, however, organic enrichment may affect benthic organisms through several different ecological factors, the relative importance of which differs with respect to different organisms and the nature of the organic matter involved. It is also probable that the relative importance of these different factors changes with natural seasonal changes in environmental conditions. This paper reports investigations comparing the benthic invertebrate populations associated with different degrees of organic enrichment and the effects of seasonal fluctuations in conditions.

Description of streams and methods

Most of the investigations were carried out on the upper stretch of the River Cole, a small stream which arises to the south-west of Birmingham and flows through a rural then residential area before entering a highly industrialized zone of the city. This study was carried out on the upper stretch of the river which received organic enrichment in the form of an effluent from an over-loaded sewage works.

Six sampling stations (I–VI) were selected in riffle zones, one above the effluent from the overloaded sewage works and the other five, approximately equidistant, over the 6 km stretch below, representing different stages of mineralization of the organic matter. The river upstream of the effluent had, unfortunately, received some minor organic enrichment which had mostly been mineralized before the major discharge entered. As a basis for comparison a station was selected in a riffle of Dowles Brook—a good-quality tributary stream of the River Severn which flows through Wyre Forest to enter the River Severn just upstream of Bewdley. The station selected was at Far Forest on the western edge of the forest.

Quantitative samples of the benthic invertebrate populations were taken using a cylindrical sampler which enclosed 1/20th m² of the stream bed. The lower edge was serrated to facilitate it being pushed into the stream bed. Water flowed into the cylinder through a perforated plate facing upstream and passed out through a sampling net of 40 mesh/in (16 mesh/cm) attached to an opening in the downstream portion of the sampler. The area enclosed by the sampler was sampled by disturbing and removing the stones detaching any attached organisms; the flow carried the catch into the net from which they were then transferred to a container and preserved in formalin for subsequent examination in the laboratory. Usually triplicate samples were taken from each station at any one time. At the same time water samples were taken for analysis, the following determinations being carried out—dissolved oxygen, temperature, biochemical oxygen demand, ammonia, oxidized nitrogen, phosphate, hardness, pH and alkalinity. Samples were taken from Dowles Brook and the six stations on the River Cole each month throughout a year.

Results

The results of the intensive study are summarized in Table 1. The populations of different species and groups expressed as the average number per unit area of stream bed, found at the seven different stations studied, are compared. Since the average is influenced by the incidence of the species throughout the year, the highest monthly figure is also given—in brackets. The station on Dowles Brook may be taken as representing a natural stream riffle. Station I in the River Cole although above the major organic discharge represented a recovery stage from an upstream effluent. Stations II–VI represent successive stages of mineralization of the organic effluent discharged between stations I and II. The Turbellaria, because they were not readily recognized in the sample after preservation, were not recorded. *Dendrocoelum lacteum* (Müll), however, was common at station VI, associated with *Asellus*, which forms their food (Reynoldson & Young 1966). The distribution of some of the more commonly occurring taxa along a length of the River Cole is shown in relation to the organic discharge and resultant oxygen sag as histograms in Figs 2 and 3.

The results in the tables and histograms based on yearly average figures confirm and quantify trends, many of which have previously been established. Yearly averages however mask some interesting effects involving the influence of seasonal changes in induced conditions on the seasonal incidence of some species. Fig 4. illustrates the seasonal incidence of the larvae of a chironomid

Table 1. Number of animals per 0·1 m² of stream bed. Yearly average (monthly maximum is shown in brackets).

	DOWLES BROOK	RIVER COLE					
		Above Effluent		Below Effluent			
		1	2	3	4	5	6
OLIGOCHAETA							
Tubificidae	12 (42)	162 (426)	407 (2719)	879 (3374)	1049 (4616)	1159 (3492)	468 (1173)
Enchytraeidae	0·2 (3)	4 (34)	48 (181)	515 (3541)	117 (1065)	17 (46)	4 (22)
Lumbriculidae	47 (136)	73 (414)	12 (82)	10 (50)	41 (139)	9 (34)	9 (37)
HIRUDINEA	2 spp.	5 spp.	3 spp.	3 spp.	4 spp.	4 spp.	5 spp.
Erpobdella octoculata (Linn.)	0·1 (1)	55 (127)	0·1 (1)	0·3 (1)	1 (6)	14 (30)	4 (12)
Erpobdella testacea (Sav.)	0 (0)	0 (0)	0·3 (2)	0·1 (1)	2 (18)	2 (10)	2 (6)
Haemopsis sanguisuga (Linn.)	0 (0)	0 (0)	0 (0)	0 (0)	0 (0)	0 (0)	0·15 (2)
Glossiphonia complanata (Linn.)	0 (0)	3 (10)	0·1 (1)	0 (0)	0·7 (4)	0·6 (4)	0·6 (1)
Helobdella stagnalis (Linn.)	0 (0)	2 (8)	0 (0)	0·1 (1)	0·4 (1)	45 (92)	1·2 (8)
Batracobdella paludosa (Carena)	0 (0)	0·3 (1)	0 (0)	0 (0)	0 (0)	0 (0)	0 (0)
Piscicola geometra (Linn.)	0·1 (1)	0·3 (1)	0 (0)	0 (0)	0 (0)	0 (0)	0 (0)
CRUSTACEA							
Gammarus pulex (Linn.)	55 (153)	71 (266)	0·5 (2)	0·6 (4)	0·6 (4)	0·15 (1)	6 (28)
Asellus aquaticus (Linn.)	0 (0)	8 (30)	0·4 (2)	0·6 (2)	3 (10)	182 (494)	46 (345)
PLECOPTERA	14 spp.	3 spp.	0 spp.	0 spp.	0 spp.	0 spp.	0 spp.
Leuctra moselyi (Morton)	2 (12)	0 (0)	0 (0)	0 (0)	0 (0)	0 (0)	0 (0)
Leuctra inermis (Kempny)	1 (12)	0 (0)	0 (0)	0 (0)	0 (0)	0 (0)	0 (0)
Leuctra hippopus (Kempny)	2·5 (13)	0 (0)	0 (0)	0 (0)	0 (0)	0 (0)	0 (0)
Nemoura cinerea (Retzius)	0·1 (1)	2 (14)	0 (0)	0 (0)	0 (0)	0 (0)	0 (0)
Nemoura erratica (Claassen)	0·1 (1)	0 (0)	0 (0)	0 (0)	0 (0)	0 (0)	0 (0)

	1	2	3	4	5	6	7
Nemoura avicularis (Morton)	0 (0)	0·6 (8)	0 (0)	0 (0)	0 (0)	0 (0)	0 (0)
Capnia bifrons (Newman)	5 (37)	0 (0)	0 (0)	0 (0)	0 (0)	0 (0)	0 (0)
Chloroperla torrentium (Pictet)	0·5 (3)	0 (0)	0 (0)	0 (0)	0 (0)	0 (0)	0 (0)
Chloroperla tripunctata (Scopoli)	0·2 (3)	0 (0)	0 (0)	0 (0)	0 (0)	0 (0)	0 (0)
Protonemura praecox (Morton)	0·3 (2)	0 (0)	0 (0)	0 (0)	0 (0)	0 (0)	0 (0)
Amphinemura sulcicollis (Stephens)	2·5 (33)	0·15 (1)	0 (0)	0 (0)	0 (0)	0 (0)	0 (0)
Brachyptera risi (Morton)	1 (8)	0 (0)	0 (0)	0 (0)	0 (0)	0 (0)	0 (0)
Rhabdiopteryx anglica (Kimmins)	0·1 (1)	0 (0)	0 (0)	0 (0)	0 (0)	0 (0)	0 (0)
Isogenus nubecula (Newman)	0·1 (1)	0 (0)	0 (0)	0 (0)	0 (0)	0 (0)	0 (0)
Isoperla grammatica (Poda)	2 (9)	0 (0)	0 (0)	0 (0)	0 (0)	0 (0)	0 (0)
Small plecoptera	19 (47)	0·6 (3)	0 (0)	0 (0)	0 (0)	0 (0)	0 (0)
EPHEMEROPTERA	5 spp.	1 spp.	1 spp.	1 spp.	1 spp.	1 spp.	1 spp.
Ecdyonurus dispar (Curt.)	17 (95)	0 (0)	0 (0)	0 (0)	0 (0)	0 (0)	0 (0)
Baetis spp.	40 (136)	131 (742)	2 (22)	6 (30)	6 (44)	3 (18)	2·5 (16)
Rhithrogena semicolorata (Curt.)	49 (127)	0 (0)	0 (0)	0 (0)	0 (0)	0 (0)	0 (0)
Ephemerella ignita (Poda)	14 (94)	0 (0)	0 (0)	0 (0)	0 (0)	0 (0)	0 (0)
Ephemera danica (Müll.)	2 (7)	0 (0)	0 (0)	0 (0)	0 (0)	0 (0)	0 (0)
TRICHOPTERA	8 spp.	2 spp.	1 spp.	0 spp.	0 spp.	1 spp.	1 spp.
Hydropsyche fulvipes (Curtis)	19 (69)	0 (0)	0 (0)	0 (0)	0 (0)	0 (0)	0 (0)
Hydropsyche angustipennis (Curtis)	0 (0)	241 (1766)	0·4 (1)	0 (0)	0 (0)	0·1 (1)	0 (0)
Rhyacophila dorsalis (Curtis)	4·0 (14)	0 (0)	0 (0)	0 (0)	0 (0)	0 (0)	0 (0)
Polycentropus flavomaculatus (Pictet)	2·5 (7)	0 (0)	0 (0)	0 (0)	0 (0)	0 (0)	0 (0)
Agapetus spp.	1·7 (26)	3 (18)	0 (0)	0 (0)	0 (0)	0 (0)	0·4
Silo spp.	2·1 (10)	0 (0)	0 (0)	0 (0)	0 (0)	0 (0)	0 (0)
Limnephilidae	1 (4)	0 (0)	0 (0)	0 (0)	0 (0)	0 (0)	0 (0)
Lepidostomatinae	0·1 (1)	0 (0)	0 (0)	0 (0)	0 (0)	0 (0)	0 (0)
Goëra pilosa	0·1 (1)	0 (0)	0 (0)	0 (0)	0 (0)	0 (0)	0 (0)
Pupae	0·9 (4)	0 (0)	0 (0)	0 (0)	0 (0)	0 (0)	0 (0)

Table 1.—*continued*

| | DOWLES BROOK | RIVER COLE | | | | | |
| | | Above Effluent | | Below Effluent | | | |
CHIRONOMIDAE	4 spp.	5 spp.	8 spp.	8 spp.	8 spp.	8 spp.	8 spp.
Chironomus riparius (Meigen)	0 (0)	0 (0)	104 (556)	331 (2282)	187 (1977)	7 (32)	4 (30)
Micropsectra atrofasciatus (Kieffer)	0·5 (3)	5 (19)	2·5 (14)	18 (132)	10 (35)	20 (78)	9 (46)
Prodiamesa olivacea (Meigen)	0·2 (1)	0 (0)	1 (4)	13 (34)	29 (76)	3 (6)	28 (86)
Cricotopus sylvestris (Fab.)	0 (0)	0 (0)	0·3 (4)	0·6 (6)	10 (80)	86 (590)	7 (66)
Cricotopus bicinctus (Meigen)	0 (0)	6 (28)	0·2 (1)	7 (58)	51 (188)	421 (2756)	165 (682)
Trichocladius rufiventris (Meigen)	0 (0)	13 (78)	5 (41)	46 (193)	74 (418)	140 (822)	71 (169)
Brillia longifurca (Kieffer)	0·1 (1)	0·2 (1)	1·5 (7)	35 (128)	47 (219)	59 (259)	29 (156)
Brillia modesta (Meigen)	0·2 (1)	1 (4)	0·9 (9)	5 (26)	7 (18)	2 (6)	2 (8)
Eukiefferiella hospitus (Edwards)	0 (0)	7 (42)	1·5 (9)	12 (73)	24 (83)	39 (104)	16 (58)

—*Eukiefferiella hospitus*—at different stations representing different degrees of organic enrichment. It is most abundant in the lower recovery zone where it achieves three peaks in larval numbers per year at stations IV, V and VI, suggesting three generations. Farther upstream, nearer the effluent, at station III where the oxygen is more severely depleted during the summer months, the summer generation was almost eliminated although the spring and autumn peaks were still present. Aerial dispersal of the adults is probably responsible for the re-establishment of the species after the elimination in the summer. At station II, just downstream of the effluent, the summer peak is

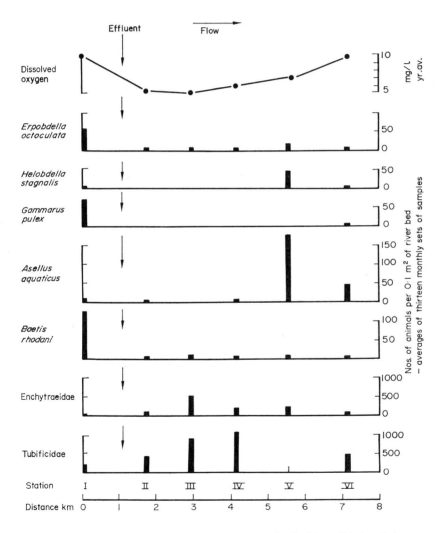

Figure 2. Distribution of some benthic invertebrates in the River Cole in relation to an organic discharge.

eliminated and the spring and autumn peaks markedly suppressed. *Prodiamesa olivacea* reacted in a similar manner. Other chironomid species such as *Brillia longifurca*, which are normally abundant as larvae in the winter-spring period, were less affected (Fig. 5). Other species, such as the nymph of the mayfly *Baetis rhodani*, only made an appearance in the winter months in the organically enriched stations II–V whereas it was abundant in the summer period at station I above the effluent (Fig. 6). *Chironomus riparius* extends its range downstream during the summer and achieves its maximum abundance farther downstream at this time. This is illustrated in Fig. 8 which shows its percentage distribution along the river below the effluent at different seasons.

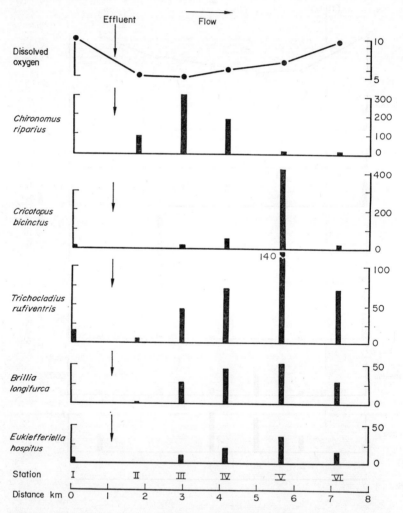

Figure 3. Distribution of some benthic invertebrates in the River Cole in relation to an organic discharge. For explanation of vertical axis values see Fig. 2.

Unlike the insect larvae discussed above, *Gammarus pulex* did not show a winter recovery; this may be due to its lower dispersal powers compared with aerially dispersed insects. Based on results of laboratory work, the absence of *G. pulex* in the winter at the stations below the effluent could not be accounted

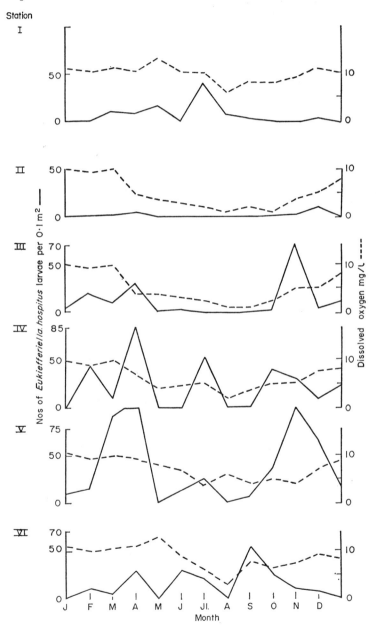

Figure 4. The seasonal incidence of *Eukiefferiella hospitus* larvae in stream riffles subjected to different degrees of organic enrichment. River Cole.

for by the degree of oxygen depletion shown in Fig. 2 and as measured by daytime sampling. At station V, in the recovery zone, the oxygen levels shown should enable *G. pulex* to be present throughout the year. A study of the diel fluctuations in the oxygen concentration (Fig. 7) suggests an explanation. Above the effluent at station I a diel fluctuation occurred due to the effect of light fluctuations on photosynthetic activity of the algae. Below the

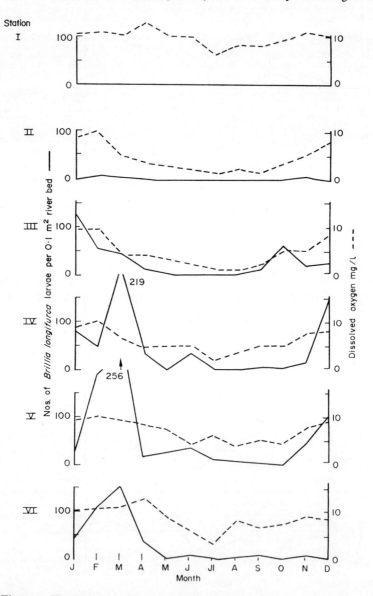

Figure 5. The seasonal incidence of *Brillia longifurca* larvae in stream riffles subjected to different degrees of organic enrichment. River Cole.

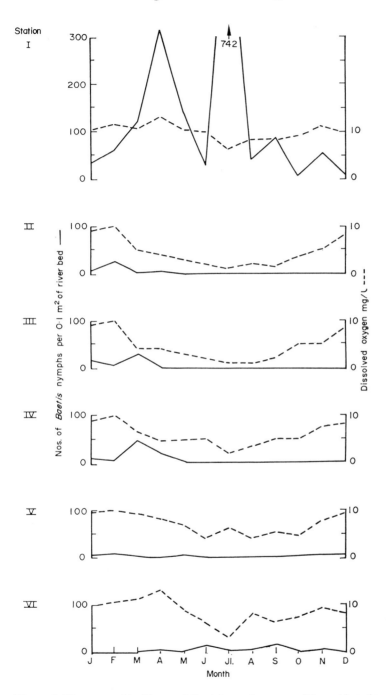

Figure 6. The seasonal incidence of *Baetis* larvae in stream riffles subjected to different degrees of organic enrichment. River Cole.

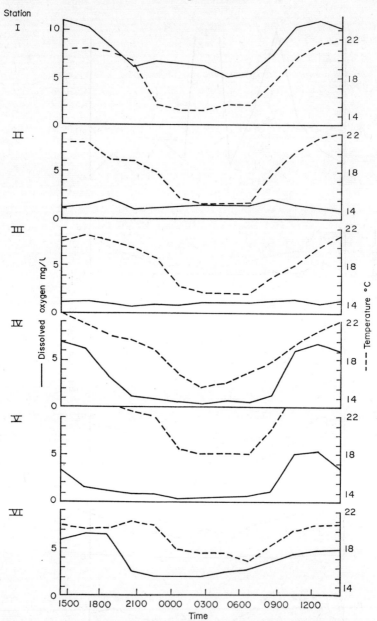

Figure 7. Diel fluctuations in dissolved oxygen and temperature at different stations along the River Cole in relation to an organic discharge.

effluent at stations II and II where the benthic growths were mostly hetero-trophic—sewage fungus, a uniformly low oxygen level existed throughout the 24 hours. At stations IV and V, where the alga *Stigeoclonium* and diatoms had become established a pronounced diel fluctuation occurred with a severe depletion of oxygen throughout the night. In the laboratory investigations it was found that at 20°C and 1 mg/1 o², 50 per cent of the *G. pulex* were killed within a 5-hour period. Thus *G. pulex* would not be expected at stations IV and V during the summer. At station VI although the daytime oxygen concentrations are similar to those at IV and V the night-time depletion is less severe, permitting the presence of a small *G. pulex* population.

Discussion

Organic enrichment may affect benthic organisms by affecting several different autecological factors. Besides the obvious factor of dissolved oxygen, the carbon dioxide concentration, hardness, suspended matter, toxicity of the organic matter and its breakdown products such as ammonia and the effect of temperature and pH on these factors may be important. Of the factors studied in the laboratory, oxygen proved to be the most important one for most organisms tested, although its effect on several organisms was influenced by other factors such as temperature and carbon dioxide concentration. Ammonia toxicity may also have been an important factor, especially with some species. The results of this investigation confirm quantitatively previous findings that some groups such as the Plecoptera and most of the Ephemeroptera and Trichoptera which are common inhabitants of natural stream riffles suppressed or eliminated by organic enrichment of the water. Other groups, however, such as the Enchytraeidae, Tubificidae, Hirudinea and Chironomidae, species of which are either absent or rare in the natural riffle community, become dominant in riffles in organically enriched waters. The distribution of such saprobic species will be determined by the degree to which they are able to withstand low oxygen tensions to enable them to utilize the increased organic food available either directly or indirectly via food chains. Because of differences in the nutritional requirements and tolerance to depleted oxygen tensions and other factors, a succession of dominant species occurred associated with the reduction in organic concentration downstream of the effluent. The reduction in the population of these species downstream, with improved oxygen conditions, is probably due to reduced food content and increased competition. It has, however, been found that larvae of the *Chironomus plumosus* group survive longer at low oxygen levels and are adversely affected by high oxygen levels (Fox & Taylor 1955). It is doubtful, however, whether the oxygen levels in the River Cole were sufficiently high in the recovery zone, at station V for example, to suppress the *C. riparius* population in this way.

Sprague (1963) found that the relative tolerance of four freshwater crustaceans accounted for their distribution in Canadian streams. Other workers have taken as a criterion the effect which decreasing oxygen tension had on the respiratory rate of different species. Mann (1956) found that after acclimating to low oxygen the leech *Erpobdella testacea* showed a reduction in respiratory rate only below about 2 cc/1 o² whereas *E. octoculata* and *Piscicola geometra* showed an effect over a wide range of oxygen tensions. *Glossiphonia complanata* and *Helobdella stagnalis* also showed an effect only below 2 cc/ 1 o² without acclimating. Mann (1961) discusses the adaptive significance of the life history of *E. testacea* in relation to fluctuating seasonal conditions. Edwards and Learner (1960) found that the respiratory rate of *Asellus aquaticus* was relatively independent of oxygen tension between 8·3 and 1·5 mg/1 o², the rate only being reduced by 15–20 per cent over this range.

The distribution of some species is determined more by the availability of their food source; the leech *Helobdella stagnalis* for example follows closely the distribution of its prey organisms (*Asellus aquaticus*) (Fig. 2).

The overall effect of organic enrichment of a stream may be regarded as a synecological one whereby the decomposer component of the stream eco-system is increased in relation to the producer and consumer components. In this process the riffle communities, which in natural streams are mostly inhabited by producers and consumers, are invaded by species of the de-composer community. Organic enrichment thus induces changes both in the proportional species composition and in the structure of benthic com-munities.

Many biological systems of assessing organic pollution make use of the presence or absence of indicator taxa. In many cases, however, the conditions induced by different degrees of organic enrichment are more evident as changes in the relative populations rather than in the appearance or dis-appearance of species. For example, *Gammarus pulex* and *Asellus aquaticus* were recorded from all stations in the River Cole but their relative abundance is closely associated with the degree of organic enrichment. Furthermore the results reported above indicate that seasonal changes need to be taken into account in determining the timing and frequency of sampling.

Most indicator systems are based on the fact that different species and communities are associated with different degrees of degradation of organic matter. This was appropriate to conditions in the past when unoxidized sewage was commonly discharged to rivers and self-purification occurred in the river. However, different ecological conditions are created when complex organic matter is present in very low dilutions as when a small organic effluent discharges to a large river. More relevant to present-day conditions in this country is the situation where large volumes of highly oxidized effluents are discharged to small streams affording little dilution. The eco-logical conditions in such streams—such as the River Ray quoted later—are quite different and may be regarded as eutrophic.

Conservation

In practical terms conservation may be regarded as the maintaining of our natural resources in such a condition as to optimize their use for the community as a whole. The scientific management of our stream benthic communities to this end resolves itself into water management—both quantitatively by flow regulation, and qualitatively by pollution control. Man is exerting increasing demands on the use of rivers for such purposes as water supplies (public and industrial), navigation, fisheries, agricultural irrigation, recreation and for the disposal of our effluents. Management of streams for such diverse but legal purposes, some of which are in themselves conflicting, presents difficulties.

Although organic enrichment may increase the productivity of some waters, the adverse conditions created by excessive discharges of organic matter generally reduce the usefulness of streams for many purposes. In a technologically-based society to deny the use of all the rivers for the carriage of our domestic and industrial used-waters would not only be unrealistic but could seriously limit the availability of water to towns downstream at times of dry weather flow. It is no more possible to conserve all our rivers in their primeval state than it is to conserve the whole country as a nature reserve. Nevertheless it is certainly desirable that some selected rivers and streams should be so preserved and all discharges into them prohibited. Other rivers, however, will need to be used to convey our effluents. Although present levels of waste-water treatment technology make it possible to treat economically such effluents to prevent nuisance in the receiving water, they do cause detectable changes in the benthic communities so that some species are affected. In such rivers it may be that the water quality should be managed so as to conserve those species which it is considered both feasible and desirable to encourage in man's interests. Fortunately most large effluents are not discharged to upland trout streams where the more sensitive species live. It should be possible to treat effluents to such a degree that the receiving river will support coarse fisheries and, although the fauna may be restricted in variety, if the water quality does not adversely affect the fish directly then fish-food organisms are unlikely to be affected and in the nutritionally enriched waters productivity could be increased.

The flow in some rivers is mostly sewage effluent and however purified the effluent, to present-day standards, the fauna is likely to be severely restricted although the species present may develop large populations. The River Ray, a tributary of the Upper Thames, which receives the highly oxidized sewage effluent from Swindon, is such a river. Results of surveys carried out on this river (Silveyra 1969) are shown in Fig. 9. At station I, above the effluents, a fauna dominated by *Gammarus pulex* typical of a small

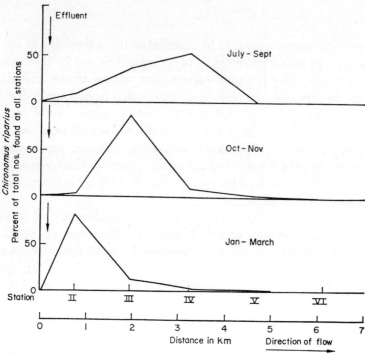

Figure 8. The percentage distribution of *Chironomus riparius* larvae along the River Cole below a sewage effluent at different seasons.

stream was found. After receiving minor discharges the fauna at station II was more restricted but the marked change occurred below the major sewage effluent discharge which is some six times the volume of the stream. Unlike the discharge of the organically rich effluent to the River Cole there was no serious oxygen sag, the most marked effect chemically being the increase in nitrate and phosphate concentrations. The diel fluctuations in oxygen (Fig. 10) were less severe than in the River Cole (Fig. 7) and the night oxygen levels were not so low. Another feature of difference was the stability of the River Ray water in contrast with the chemical changes associated with the self-purification of an organically polluted river. Associated with this chemical stability was the absence of any marked ecological succession along the 6-mile stretch of the River Ray downstream of the effluent to the Thames. Along the whole length below the effluent the only benthic invertebrates occurring in any numbers were tubificid worms, chironomid larvae and *Asellus aquaticus* with a few leeches and the snail *Lymnaea pereger* at some stations. Fig. 9 shows the distribution of *Asellus aquaticus* along the length of the River Ray in contrast with the sharp peak in its distribution in the River Cole (Fig. 2). A striking feature of the river was the high population of *Asellus aquaticus* along the length of the river below the effluent. Another feature was the

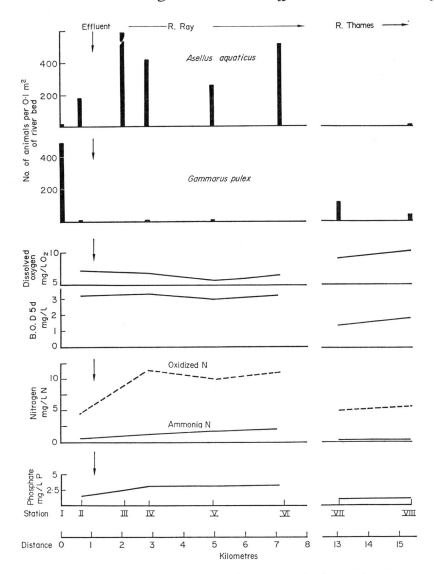

Figure 9. Distribution of *Gammarus pulex* and *Asellus aquaticus* in the River Ray (Wiltshire) in relation to changes in water quality induced by the discharge of a highly oxidised sewage effluent.

dense thick growths of *Cladophora* which covered the river bed, reflecting its high degree of eutrophy. It was only after dilution with a much smaller volume of Thames water that the natural river fauna was re-established at stations in the Thames below the confluence.

The major threat to conservation in rivers receiving such effluents is the sudden breakdown of the treatment processes resulting in untreated or

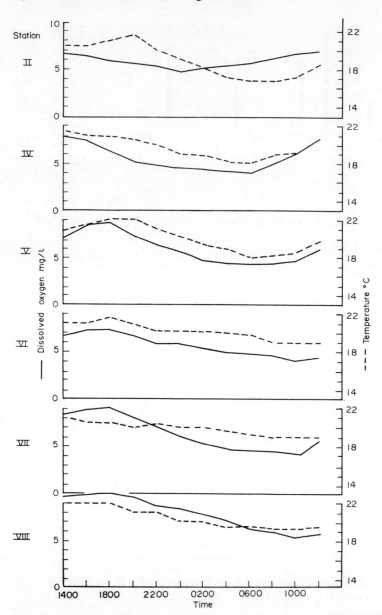

Figure 10. Diel fluctuations in dissolved oxygen and temperature at different stations along the River Ray (Wiltshire) in relation to a discharge of a highly oxidised sewage effluent.

partially treated sewage passing into the river causing high organic and ammonia concentrations and serious deoxygenation, such as occurred during the 1970 strike of sewage works' operators in the U.K. Another less spectacular, though equally serious practice, which suppresses stream communities in stretches of urban rivers receiving no regular discharge of effluent, is that of discharging overflows from sewers at times of high flow. Such discharges although intermittent can have serious effects. A 5-mile stretch of the River Cole running through suburban Birmingham is thus affected. Before 1957 this stretch received a daily overflow of crude sewage at its upper limit which suppressed all macro-invertebrate life throughout the stretch. The construction of a larger trunk sewer relieved the situation and it was hoped that in the absence of regular effluent discharges, the fauna in this stretch would recover. The recovery up to 1960 has been recorded (Hawkes 1963). Chironomid larvae, tubificid worms, and *Lymnaea pereger* (Müll) reappeared along the whole length, the latter being especially abundant in the lower end of the stretch above a major sewage effluent discharge. Apart from these, the leech *Erpobdella*, which reappeared at some stations, and *Chironomus riparius*, which occurred at the lowermost station, no other macro-invertebrates had become established by 1960. During the 10 years since then the fauna has fluctuated somewhat but apart from the appearance in small numbers of *Asellus aquaticus* at the lowermost station, there has been no overall recovery. This is attributed to the storm overflows on the trunk sewer which discharge to the river at several points along this stretch. Industrial toxic effluents as well as untreated sewage are suspected.

It is appreciated that in accepting that some rivers will only support a restricted fauna the resultant simplified ecosystem will be less stable and as a result problems may arise. But just as in agriculture simplified ecosystems are managed to man's advantage it should be possible to manage our rivers in a similar way. Indeed, the management of our non-polluted rivers, such as weed cutting, is essential to maintain amenity value. To enable us to manage our aquatic environment more successfully we need to study the functioning of natural aquatic ecosystems and investigate the effects on them of man's interference.

Summary

1 Benthic riffle communities react sharply to organic enrichment of the water.
2 Some taxa such as the Plecoptera—with the exception of *Nemoura cinerea*, the Ephemeroptera—with the exception of *Baetis rhodani* and to a less degree the Trichoptera—with the exception of *Hydropsyche angustipennis*, were adversely affected by slight organic enrichment.
3 Other taxa such as the Oligochaeta, Hirudinea and Chironomidae increased both in variety and in numbers in different degrees of organic enrichment and degradation, associated with the stages of self-purification of an excessively enriched stream.

4 The saprobic benthic communities associated with different levels of organic enrichment were distinguished more by differences in the percentage species composition rather than their species lists.

5 The seasonal incidence of some species at a given station was affected by the degree of organic enrichment. The summer incidence of some species such as *Baetis rhodani* and *Eukiefferiella hospitus* being progressively suppressed the higher the degree of organic concentration. More tolerant species such as *Chironomus riparius* extended its range and achieved its maximum abundance farther downstream during the summer.

6 Low night-time dissolved oxygen levels accounted for the absence of some species, such as *Gammarus pulex*, in some organically enriched waters, where day-time oxygen conditions were satisfactory.

7 Although some rivers should be preserved in their natural state and all unnatural discharges to them prohibited, many rivers will need to be used for conveying our effluents. Such a practice will inevitably affect the benthic communities and simplify the stream ecosystem especially where the flow of natural diluting water is low. It should, however, be possible to manage such rivers by flow regulation and pollution control to enable them to support a benthic community beneficial to man.

8 Attention is drawn to the dangers of the breakdown of otherwise efficient treatment plants discharging to such rivers and to the adverse effects on benthic communities of permitting the intermittent discharge of sewer overflows into urban streams.

Acknowledgements

The authors wish to acknowledge the financial support received from N.E.R.C. in the form of a Research Studentship (L.J.D.) and of a Research Grant (H.A.H.), the work reported in this paper forming part of the N.E.R.C. supported research programme—investigating the environmental factors responsible for changes in stream bed biocoenoses induced by polluting discharges.

Assistance with the identification of the chironomid larvae was received from P. Bright (Bristol), M.A.Learner (U.W.I.S.T.) and B.Styczynski (Warsaw), whose help is gratefully acknowledged.

References

EDWARDS R.W. & LEARNER M.A. (1960) Some factors affecting the oxygen consumption of *Asellus. J. exp. Biol.* 37, 706–18.

FJERDINGSTAD E. (1964) Pollution of streams estimated by benthal phytomicroorganisms. 1. A saprobic system based on communities of organisms and ecological factors. *Int. Revue ges. Hydrobiol.* 49, 1, 63–131.

Fox H.M. & Taylor A.E.R. (1955) The tolerance of oxygen by aquatic invertebrates. *Proc. roy. Soc. B.* **143**, 214.

Hawkes H.A. (1962) in Klein, L. *River Pollution.* 2 Biological Aspects of River Pollution. 329–432. Butterworths, London.

Hawkes H.A. (1963) Effects of domestic and industrial discharges on the ecology of riffles in Midland streams. *Int. J. Air. Wat. Poll.* **7**, 565–83.

Hynes H.B.N. (1960) *The Biology of Polluted Waters.* Liverpool Un. Press. 70–85.

Kolkwitz R. & Marsson M. (1908) Oekologie der Pflanzlichen Saprobien. *Ber dtsch. bot. Ges.* **26A**, 505–19.

Kolkwitz R. & Marsson M. (1909) Oekologie der tierschen Saprobien. *Int. Rev. Hydrobiol.* **11**, 126–52.

Mann K.H. (1956) A study of the oxygen consumption of five species of leech. *J. exp. Biol.* **33**, 615–26.

Mann K.H. (1961) The life history of the leech *Erpobdella testacea* Sav. and its adaptive significance. *Oikos.* **12**, 164–69.

Reynoldson T.B. & Young J.O. (1966) The relationship between the distribution of *Dendrocoelum lacteum* (Müll) and *Asellus* in Britain and Fennoscandia. *Verh. int. Limnol.* **16**, 3, 1633–9.

Silveyra J. (1969) *Some effects of Swindon sewage effluent on the River Ray and Upper Thames.* M.Sc. Course Project Thesis, Univ. of Aston in Birmingham.

Sprague J.B. (1963) Resistance of four freshwater crustacea to lethal high temperatures and low oxygens. *J. Fish. Res. Can Bd.* **20**, 338.

The role of introduced fish in fish production in Ceylon's freshwaters

C.H.FERNANDO *Department of Biology, University of Waterloo, Waterloo, Ontario, Canada*

Introduction

In an FAO publication (Anon 1968) the annual freshwater fishery resources were estimated at a high of 134,000 and a low of 44,000 metric tons. Incidentally the high value is more than the total fish production for Ceylon now from marine, brackish and freshwaters. It represents a *per capita* catch of 10 kg for the 11·5 million inhabitants of the country.

The freshwater fish production in Ceylon up to 1956 was estimated at a mere 400 metric tons annually. In 1958 this figure had doubled and in 1965 the figure was 7,000 metric tons. The catch for 1968 was 8,000 metric tons. The basis for the optimism reflected in the FAO estimates for future fish production from freshwaters is the phenomenal increase in the fish catches from 'natural' waters in the last ten years. The reason for this increase was the introduction in 1951 of *Tilapia mossambica*. Besides constituting 50–90 per cent of the fish catch by weight in the numerous man-made lakes, the abundance of this species has enabled some of the economically important local species to be exploited commercially (Fernando 1965).

Questions, however, have been raised from time to time regarding the wisdom of having introduced foreign species and especially *T. mossambica*. Claims have been made that *T. mossambica* was displacing indigenous species (the names of indigenous fish follow Munro 1955) by predation or competition. Also to some nationalistically-minded people importing foreign species amounted to admitting some deficiency which should not exist in a natural fauna.

In the present paper I shall attempt to analyse the reasons for the success of *T. mossambica* in Ceylon.

The freshwater fish production of Ceylon comes almost entirely from man-made habitats. Considerable expansion and diversification of this resource is occurring now and will continue at least till the end of this century. The optimum development of the fisheries by management must take into consideration fish production goals and conservation of the indigenous fauna.

Pre *T. mossambica* period

Views generally held by fishery scientists in Ceylon to account for the low freshwater fish production were: 1, that there are no indigenous species feed-

Table 1. Indigenous freshwater fish fauna: Families, mean sizes and feeding habits. (H—Herbivorous, O—Omnivorous, and C—carnivorous).

	No. (Species)	Mean size* (cm)	H	O	C	Remarks
Cyprinidae:						
Carplets	19	7	16	3	—	8 endemic species
Large (sport)	1	75	—	1	—	
Large (rare)	1	37	—	1	—	
†Large	4	32	3	1	—	
Cobitidae:	3	5	—	3	—	
Mastacembelidae:	2	44	—	2	—	
Siluroidea:						
Small	2	11	—	2	—	One feeds on molluscs
†Large	4	30	—	3	1	One feeds on molluscs
†Very large	1	150	—	—	1	Important predator
Anguillidae:	2	80	—	2	—	
Cyprinodontidae:	3	5	—	3	—	
Ophiocephalidae:						
Small	3	15	—	—	3	
†Large	2	75	—	—	2	Important predators
Cichlidae:						
Small	1	7	—	1	—	
†Large	1	30	—	1	—	Feeds on molluscs
Anabantidae:						
Small	3	5	—	3	—	1 endemic species
Large	1	15	—	1	—	
Gobiidae:	1	36	—	—	1	Important predator
Totals	54		19	27	8	

* Sizes taken from Munro (1955). Probably refer to large specimens. Averages for more than 1 species.
† Includes one or more economically important species.

ing on coarse vegetable matter (Amirthalingam 1949, Schuster 1957); and 2, that all the valuable food fishes are predatory (Willey 1910). Fernando (1956a) discussed these views and showed that coarse vegetable feeders did occur among the indigenous fish fauna. It is also known that some of the economically important species like the carp *Labeo dussumieri* are herbivorous.

A significant fact, however, is that there are relatively few large species among the indigenous fauna (Table 1). There is also a very poor fauna and no economically important species in numbers in the hill country.

The phenomenal increase of fish production from freshwaters due to the introduction of *T. mossambica* made me restudy the problem of natural deficiencies in the fish fauna. Fernando (1965) stated that since all lakes in Ceylon are man-made there has been no evolution of typical lake species and that the fauna of lakes were recruited from rivers and marshes.

Indigenous fish fauna

Ceylon has an area of 65,863 km². It was separated from the Indian sub-continent in the Miocene. The mountain-stream fish fauna which invaded India during the Pliocene did not therefore reach Ceylon (Darlington 1957). During the Pleistocene marked pluvial and interpluvial periods occurred with conditions much wetter and much drier than at present (Abeywickrema 1956).

The main freshwater habitats consist of 103 rivers flowing more or less radially. The larger perennial rivers arise in the central highlands. Lake-like marshes (Sinhalese-Villu) are present in the lower reaches of a few of the rivers (Fig. 1). The south-western portion of the island receives two monsoons and an average rainfall of over 75 in annually, and is referred to as the wet zone. Parts of the other zone, the dry zone, may receive as little as 25 in annually, mainly during one monsoon.

The fish fauna consists of fifty-four true freshwater species (Table 2). This is certainly a low figure for a tropical island so close to the continental mass. In comparison Singapore, an island 100 times smaller, has seventy recorded species (Alfred 1961). The fish fauna consists of river- and marsh-dwelling species. The nine endemic species, eight of them carplets, are restricted to perennial streams in the wet zone. Eleven species have accessory respiratory organs and a number of others can withstand periods of drought in deoxygenated waters, e.g. *Macrones* spp., *Wallago attu* and *Ompok bimaculatus*. Some can survive in liquid mud, e.g. *Puntius vittatus* (Deraniyagala 1930), or can live buried in caked mud, e.g. *Mastacembelus armatus* and *Macrognathus aculeatus*. The fish fauna was probably impoverished during interpluvial periods. Speciation seems to have occurred only in the small perennial streams. However, ten subspecies can be distinguished from Indian

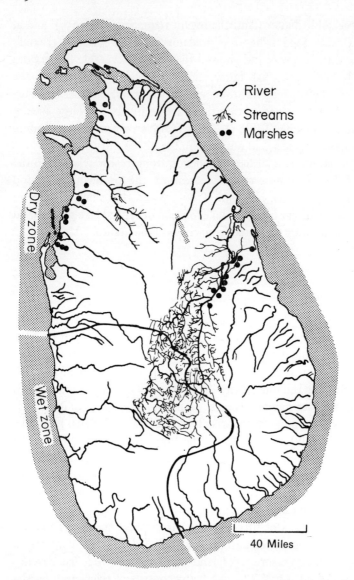

Figure 1. Natural freshwater habitats. Streams are shown for only two rivers. They are more numerous for rivers in or draining the wet zone.

forms according to Deraniyagala (1959), this includes species living in rivers and marshes. It is likely that the freshwater fauna has lost some large species found in the Indian mainland which has a freshwater fauna of about 400 species (Day 1889). It has gained by speciation no large species. But if it is any consolation, all the endemics are valuable aquarium fishes. The loss of species found on the Indian sub-continent, if such loss has occurred, could

Table 2. Distribution of indigenous freshwater fishes in the major types of habitats in Ceylon.

Species	Rice fields	Ponds	Reservoirs		Rivers and streams
			0–300 m above sea level	over 300 m above sea level	
Total number	36	38	36	15	54
Economically important	6	10	10	1	10
Endemic genera	1	—	—	—	2
Endemic species	1	—	—	—	9

Economically Important Species: (contribute 5% or more of the total catch of indigenous species).	*Puntius dorsalis, P. sarana, Labeo dussumieri, L. porcellus, Wallago attu, Ompok bimaculatus, Ophiocephalus striatus, O. marulius, Etroplus suratensis, Heteropneustes fossilis.*
Endemic species:	*Puntius titteya, P. melanampyx, P. cumingi, P. nigrofasciatus, P. pleurotaenia, Garra ceylonensis, Rasbora vaterifloris.*
Endemic genera:	*Horadandiya atukorali, Malpulutta kretseri.*

well prove a blessing, since we have the opportunity of introducing species capable of giving higher yields. The conservation of the nine endemic species is desirable for aesthetic reasons and they could become very valuable commercially.

Estuarine species play little part in colonizing freshwaters though Munro (1955) lists thirty species as entering freshwater. Candidates for invasion of freshwaters are, however, present in estuaries, e.g. *Lates calcifer*. One of them, *Etroplus suratensis*, has been successfully introduced into lakes where it has become economically important. The negligible role of estuarine species is probably due to a number of factors. There is hardly any tidal influence around Ceylon and no natural lakes exist.

Freshwater habitats

Natural freshwater habitats consist of: a, rivers and streams, the latter very numerous in the wet zone; b, marshes which are either connected to rivers or represent seasonally contracted flood plains isolated from rivers (Fig. 1); and c, ponds which vary from ephemeral to permanent.

Man-made habitats dominate the standing waters. They consist of: (i) lakes (English—tanks; Sinhalese—wewa; Tamil—kulam) (these vary in size from a few hectares to 65 km² at full supply level (F.S.L.); tank construction in Ceylon dates back about 1,500 years and consisted of an intricate water supply system for rice cultivation; over 10,000 such tanks were built (Fig. 2); (ii) irrigation channels, and (iii) rice fields. In recent years development of river valleys on a multipurpose basis has been undertaken and hydro-

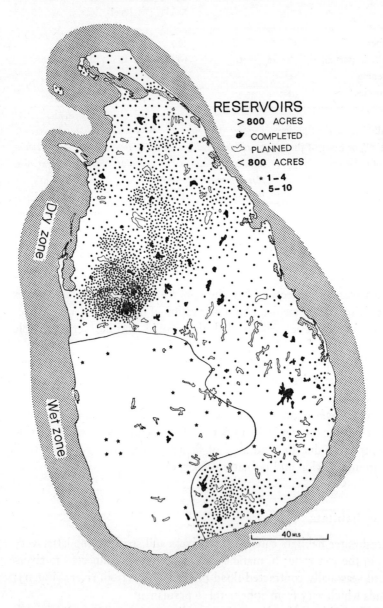

Figure 2. Man-made freshwater habitats. Distribution of small lakes adapted from Abeywickerema (1955).

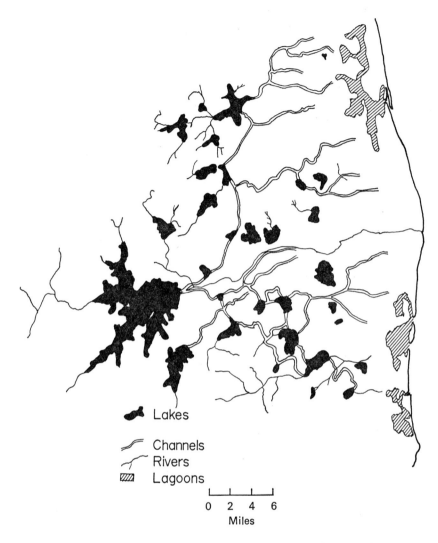

Figure 3. Lakes, channels and rivers in Gal Oya Valley, a multipurpose river valley development scheme. Total area 1,800 km². Note extensive irrigation channels.

electric power, irrigation and flood control schemes have been integrated. Tanks with accompanying irrigation channels will encompass the whole country. Man-made habitats are shown in Figs. 2 and 3 and their extent, together with that of natural habitats, is given in Table 3. In addition about 8,000 km² of rice fields carry water for periods varying from a few weeks to four months. These serve as nurseries for many species of fishes (Fernando 1956*b*) and are rich in food for fish (Weerekoon & Samarasinghe 1958).

Table 3. Freshwater resources of Ceylon.

	Present		Projected	
	No.	Area (000 ha)	No.	Area (000 ha)
1. NATURAL HABITATS				
(a) Rivers				
† Large	9	*	—	—
Small	94	*	—	—
Total length	—	(4,563 km)	—	—
Total runoff (34,088 × 10⁶ cu. m.)	—	—	—	—
% precipitation as runoff (27·2)	—	—	—	—
(b) Villus (marshes)	*	12·5	—	—
(c) Small ponds	*	*	—	—
(d) Streams	*	*	—	—
2. MAN-MADE HABITATS				
(a) Lakes (> 333 ha)	52	59·1	84	104·2
(b) Lakes (< 333 ha)	9000	41·6	1200	12·5
(c) Rice fields	—	833·3	—	208·0
(d) Irrigation channels				
Total length	—	(2,400 km)	—	(4,800 km)

† Runoff over 600 × 10⁶ cu. m. annually.
* Indeterminate because of variability of areas or numbers.

Notes: Exact areas for 'lakes' unobtainable. Figures refer to approximations at full supply levels. River lengths refer to main river only.

Introduction of foreign species

The earliest introductions were sport fishes, which included trout and carp, into lakes and streams in the hill country. *Osphronemus goramy* was accidentally introduced in 1927, and is of some importance as a food fish. The introduction of food fishes commenced in 1948 and was halted temporarily in 1952. On the basis of recommendations (Fernando 1965) three additional species were introduced in 1969 (Table 4). Altogether fifteen species have been introduced.

Of the introduced species *T. mossambica* has made by far the greatest impact on the fish catch. We have data of species composition and total fish catch from one lake, Parakrama Samudra (2,264 ha) from 1949 to 1966 (Fig. 4B) and also for three other lakes for shorter periods (Table 5). The total freshwater fish catch for Ceylon is given in Fig. 4A. In general it can be said that *T. mossambica* accounts for about 90 per cent of the fish catch by weight in the larger shallow lakes of the low country. These lakes account for at least 75 per cent of the total fish catch from freshwaters. In a deep lake, Senanayake Samudra, the percentage of *T. mossambica* was about 40 per cent and in a

Table 4. Fish introductions into Ceylon's freshwaters.

Species	Origin	Date	Breeding	Remarks
Salmo trutta	Europe	1882–1893	+	stocks supplemented from hatchery annually
Salmo gairdneri	N. America	1899–1902	+	
Cyprinus carpio	Europe	1915 (cold water)	+	
	Singapore	1948 (warm water)	+	Breeding 1966
Carassius carassius	Europe	1915	+	
Osphronemus goramy	Indonesia	1927	+	Accidental introduction. Important food fish
Ctenopharyngoden idellus	China	1948		
Hypopthalamichthys molitrix	China	1948		
Catla catla	India	1942		
Trichogaster pectoralis	Malaysia	1951	+	
Tilapia mossambica	E. Africa	1951	+	Very important
Helostoma temmencki	Thailand	1951		
Etroplus suratensis	Coastal lagoons and estuaries of Ceylon	1950	+	Important food fish
Tilapia hornorum	E. Africa	1969		
Tilapia melanopleura	E. Africa	1969		
Tilapia zilli	E. Africa	1969		

Table 5. Fish catches from four 'lakes' in Ceylon showing the percentage of *Tilapia mossambica*

Habitat	Period	Total catch (Kg)	Catch Kg/ha annum	% *T. mossambica* by weight
Parakrama Samudra (2,264 ha)	1961–1964	1,546,692	224	84·5
Minneriya tank (2,552 ha)	Oct. 1965–Sept. 1967	564,454	73	91·2
Karapala villu (Marsh about 810 ha)	Oct. 1965–Sept. 1967	84,390	34	65·1
Senanayake Samudra (7,939 ha)	1961–1964	497,510	22·4	38·8

marsh 65 per cent (Table 5). Hardly any fish are caught in the deep, mid and hill country reservoirs, where *T. mossambica* cannot survive because of lower temperatures and lack of suitable breeding sites on the steep margins of these lakes. The indigenous fauna of these reservoirs is poor (Table 2).

The outcome of *Tilapia mossambica* introductions has been varied. They have sometimes been eliminated by competition or predator pressure from open waters and stunting has occurred both in pond culture and in open waters. Johnson and Soong (1963) found that in Singapore *T. mossambica* colonized only waters not usable by local species (e.g. polluted). Lowe-McConnell (1969) reports the failure to establish *T. mossambica* in flooded

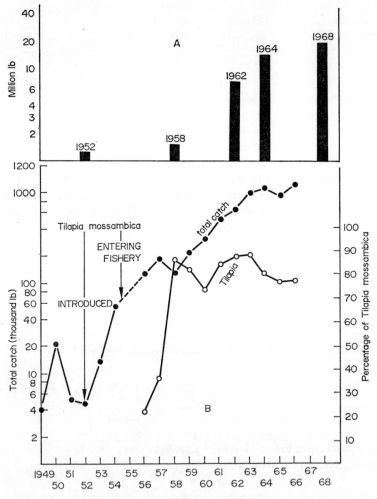

Figure 4. A. Fish production from Ceylon's freshwaters.
B. Fish catches (o) and percentage of *Tilapia mossambica* (●) from Parakrama Samudra, a lake of 2264 ha.

sugar-cane fields in Guyana due to predator pressure. Ling (1953) states that this species was eliminated from open waters in Thailand by predator pressure. At a recent symposium (Anon 1969) held in Calcutta on fisheries of reservoirs *T. mossambica* is mentioned in only two of fifty-one papers on Indian reservoir fisheries and in one of these the catch of *T. mossambica* had diminished from 5 per cent. *T. mossambica* is however cultured widely in ponds in South East Asia though not in Ceylon. Lin (1953) reports that in Haiti *T. mossambica* constitutes 90 per cent of the catch in open waters.

The success of *T. mossambica* in open waters of Ceylon is twofold. It is responsible for a great increase in the fish catches and the size attained by the fish is relatively high. The abundance of *T. mossambica* is perhaps due to the poor indigenous fauna and the availability of suitable habitats (shallow lakes). The large size attained is certainly influenced by levels of predation and by restriction of breeding sites. There is some direct evidence that the large carnivorous fishes have increased in numbers since the introduction of *T. mossambica*. The size of *T. mossambica* varies greatly in different open-water habitats in Ceylon (Table 6). The smallest mean sizes of fish caught in gill nets of mesh size 3–5 in. (8–13 cm) are those from shallow lagoons and lakes without a marked fluctuation in water levels. Some difference is also found between shallow and deep lakes. The breeding areas were mapped for three lakes having fish of varying mean sizes (Fig. 5). There appears to be an

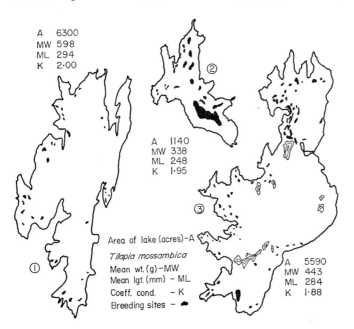

Figure 5. The 'status' of *Tilapia mossambica* in three lakes showing the influence of the extent of breeding areas on size. (Adapted from Fernando & Indrasena 1969.)

Table 6. The status of *Tilapia mossambica* in some habitats in Ceylon (adapted from Fernando and Indrasena 1969).

| Name of Habitat | Habitat | | | Fish | | | Fish catch (kg/ha/annum) |
	max. depth (m)	area (ha) F.S.L.	Description	Mean length (cm)	Mean weight (gm)	Coefficient of condition (K*)	
Beira lake	6·1	60·75	Brackish highly fertilized	15·9	93	2·25	2244
Batticoloa lagoon	18·3	11,950	Brackish	20·4	144	1·70	(28–56)
Fish ponds	1·22	0·101	Freshwater	17·6	90	1·79	1795
Karapola villu	9·15	810	Freshwater marsh, connected to river	26·8	443	2·10	84
Tabbowa tank	9·15	461·7	Freshwater lake (shallow)	24·8	338	1·95	(56–84)
Parakrama Samudra	12·2	2,264	Freshwater lake	28·4 (34·2 in 1957)	443	1·88	180
Minnerya tank	18·3	2,552	Freshwater lake (deep)	29·4	598	2·00	118
Kandalama tank	21·35	984·2	Freshwater lake (deep)	31·4	651	2·02	(56–84)
Senanayake Samudra	45·75	7,939	Freshwater lake (very deep)	—	400	—	9

$$*K = \frac{W \times 10f}{Lf}$$

W = wt. in gm.
L = length in mm.

All samples taken in 1964-65.
Fish production values for 1963.
Figures within brackets are rough estimates.

inverse relation between the extent of breeding sites and mean size. Beauchamp (1958), Lowe-McConnell (1959) and Welcomme (1966) have commented on the importance of nursery areas in influencing the numbers of *T. mossambica* in African lakes. In Ceylon predator pressure and restriction of breeding sites combine to give population levels under which stunting is not severe.

The overall effect of fish introductions has been beneficial to the commercial fisheries. However, some questions must be raised: 1, what are the effects on the indigenous fish fauna; 2, what adverse effects have so far been in evidence; 3, are future introductions likely to be beneficial and if so what species should be introduced?

The indigenous fish fauna has not been adversely affected so far. All the indigenous species are found in rivers and streams and this habitat has not been invaded to any extent by introduced species. Under drought conditions the indigenous species which are better adapted are more likely to be at an advantage than introduced species. In lakes the abundance of indigenous species has not been affected by the presence of *Tilapia mossambica*.

The nine endemic species are all rare and are the most likely to be eliminated by unfavourable conditions. If this happens it is more likely to come about by destruction or alteration of their habitat than by introduced species.

Some adverse effects have occurred. A cestode *Bothriocephablus gowkonensis* was introduced with chinese carp and occurs in an indigenous species (Fernando & Furtado 1963). This parasite is destructive to pond fish and has spread into eastern Europe and South East Asia (Fernando & Indrasena 1969). Its effects on wild fish have not been studied. The common carp was introduced into the low country reservoirs from 1958 to 1966. Recently it was found breeding in some of the lakes (Fernando & Indrasena 1969). This species might adversely affect the breeding of *T. mossambica* and other species of *Tilapia*.

Future introductions

As regards future introductions the different types of habitats should be considered separately (Table 7). For the large low country lakes no further introductions are necessary for the present. The deeper lakes in the mid and hill country with their poor fish fauna (Table 2) and negligible fish production can certainly benefit from introduction of both herbivorous and carnivorous species. The river fauna could perhaps be strengthened by the addition of herbivores. The small lakes in the low country should be considered on the same lines as fish-ponds and fast-growing species introduced after the monsoons. There is an abundance of species, both freshwater and estuarine,

Table 7. Introduction of economically important species.

	Present	Proposed
Rice fields	*Trichogaster pectoralis*	
Small ponds	*Trichogaster pectoralis*	
Villus (marshes)	*Tilapia mossambica* *Osphronemus goramy*	Will be colonized via rivers
Rivers and streams	*Osphronemus goramy*	*Labeo* spp.; Other large herbivorous fishes
Irrigation channels	*Trichogaster pectoralis* *Osphronemus goramy*	Same as for rivers
Large lakes (> 333 ha)		
(*a*) Low country	*Tilapia mossambica* *Osphronemus goramy* *Cyrinus carpio* *Tilapia zilli* *T. melanopleura* *T. hornorum*	No additional introductions
(*b*) Mid and up country	*Cyprinus carpio*	*Tilapia zilli* Gervais *T. melanopleura* Dum., *T. hornorum* Trewawas. *T. sparmanni* (Castelnau), *T. galilaea* (Ardeti) *Notopterus chitala* (Ham.) *Mugil cephalus* L. and *Chanos chanos* (Forskal).
Small lakes (< 333 ha)		
(*a*) Permanent	*Tilapia mossambica* *Osphronemus goramy* *Cyprinus carpio*	As for low country lakes over 333 ha
(*b*) Temporary	none	Annual post-monsoon stocking of fingerlings of fast growing local and introduced species. Also estuarine species, e.g. *Mugil cephalas*, *Chanos chanos* and the prawn *Macrobrachium*

including crustaceans (Ling 1962), to choose from. Some technical problems of breeding and transport need to be solved. Also, some investment of funds so sadly lacking at present should be injected into the scheme on a long-term basis.

Summary

Ceylon has an indigenous fish fauna poor in species, lacking especially typical lake species to use efficiently the numerous man–made lakes. *Tilapia mossambica* has successfully occupied the lake habitat and increased fish production immensely. At the same time it has not shown marked stunting.

The success of *T. mossambica* is due to the fortuitous combination of suitable predator pressure and some restriction of breeding sites. It has not, as far as is known, adversely affected the indigenous fish fauna.

The future management of the abundant freshwater resources of Ceylon for fish production should include introduction of suitable species into the rivers and deeper lakes in the mid and up-country and the use of small lakes as fish-ponds.

The nine endemic species which are valuable aquarium fishes should be conserved.

References

ANON. (1968) *Fisheries in Asia and their development prospects.* F.A.O. Publ. 79507 E/E, 25 pp.

ANON. (1969) *Ecology and fisheries of freshwater reservoirs.* Seminar Central Inland Fisheries Res. Inst. Barrackpore, India No. 2, November 1969, 34 pp.

ABEYWICKEREMA B.A. (1956) The origin and affinities of the flora of Ceylon. *Proc. Ceylon Ass. Advmt Sci.* (1955) Pt. 2, 99–121.

ALFRED E.R. (1961) Singapore freshwater fishes. *Malay. Nat. J.* **15**, 1–19.

AMIRTHALINGAM C (1949) The wealth of Ceylon waters. *Proc. Ceylon Ass. Advmt Sci.* (1948) Pt 2, 77–86.

BEAUCHAMP R.S.A. (1958) Utilizing the natural resources of L. Victoria for the benefit of fisheries and agriculture. *Nature, Lond.* **181**, 1634–6.

DARLINGTON P.J. (1957) *The geographical distribution of animals.* John Wiley, New York, 675 pp.

DAY F. (1889) *The fauna of British India, including Ceylon and Burma.* 2 vols.

DERANIYAGALA P.E.P. (1930) The Eventognathi of Ceylon. *Spolia zeylan.* **16**, 1–41.

DERANIYAGALA P.E.P. (1959) The evolution of sub-species in Ceylon. *Proc. Ceylon Ass. Advmt Sci.* (1958) Pt. 1, 220–4.

FERNANDO C.H. (1956*a*) The food of four common freshwater fishes of Ceylon. *Ceylon J. Sci. Ser. C* **7**, 201–17.

FERNANDO C.H. (1956*b*) The fish fauna of paddy fields and small irrigation ditches in the Western lowlands of Ceylon; and a bibliography of references to fish in paddy fields. *Ceylon J. Sci. Ser. C* **7**, 223–7.

FERNANDO C.H. (1965) The development of Ceylon's fisheries. XI. The role of inland waters in relation to the development of Ceylon's fisheries; and a note on the pearl oyster fishery. *Bull. Fish. Res. Stn Ceylon* **17**, 291–7.

FERNANDO C.H. & FURTADO J.I. (1963) A study of some helminth parasites of freshwater fishes in Ceylon. *Z. Parasitkde.* **23**, 141–63.

FERNANDO C.H. & INDRASENA H.H.A. (1969) The freshwater fisheries of Ceylon. *Bull. Fish. Res. Stn Ceylon* **20**, 101–34.

JOHNSON D.S. & SOONG M.H.H. (1963) The fate of introduced fish in Malaya. *Proc. 16th Int. Congr. Zool.*, p. 246.

LIN S.Y. (1953) Fish culture projects in Haiti and the Dominican Republic. *Fish. Bull. F.A.O.* 6, 230–4.

LING S.W. (1953) Inland fishery project in Thailand. *Fish. Bull. F.A.O.* 6, 223–30.

LING S.W. (1962) Studies on the rearing of larvae and juveniles and culturing of adults of *Macrobrachium rosenbergi* (De Man). *Indo-Pacif. Fish. Counc. Curr. Afr. Bull.* No. 35, 1–11.

LOWE-MCCONNELL R.H. (1959) Breeding behaviour patterns and ecological differences between *Tilapia* species and their significance for evolution within the genus *Tilapia* (Pisces: Cichlidae). *Proc. Zool. Soc. Lond.* 132, 1–30.

LOWE-MCCONNELL R.H. (1969) Speciation in tropical freshwater fishes. *Biol. J. Linnean Soc. Lond.* 1, 51–75.

MUNRO I.S.R. (1955) *The marine and freshwater fishes of Ceylon*. Canberra, 351 pp.

SCHUSTER W.H. (1957) *Report on a survey of the inland fisheries of Ceylon*. Ceylon Govt. Session Paper No. 24, 15 pp.

WEEREKOON A.C.J. & SAMARASINGHE E.L. (1958) Mesofauna of the soil of a paddy field in Ceylon. Preliminary report. *Ceylon J. Sci. bio. Sci.* 1, 155–70.

WELCOMME R.L. (1966) Recent charges in the stocks of *Tilapia* in Lake Victoria. *Nature, Lond.* 212, 52–4.

WILLEY A. (1910) Note on the freshwater fisheries of Ceylon. *Spolia zeylan.* 7, 88–106.

Water management in nature reserves

L.W.G. HIGLER *Research Institute for Nature Management, Netherlands,** *Leersum*

Introduction

The department of Hydrobiology of the Research Institute for Nature Management is dealing with the following types of investigation.

1 Making an inventory of all types of water in the Netherlands in, as well as outside, Reserves. This basic research is necessary, as little was known about the hydrobiology of Dutch waters except for some oligotrophic 'vens' and for brackish waters (Redeke 1922, 1933).

2 Characterization and classification of these waters with the help of chemico-physical analysis, geomorphological observations and in particular the study of biocommunities of micro- and macro-organisms.

3 Geographical and ecological research on rare or threatened species, which includes experiments in the laboratory and for larger animals work in the field (Higler 1967).

4 Basic research on problems such as eutrophication, pollution, etc.

The information gathered in this way is used for giving directions for the purchase and management of nature reserves or newly created landscapes like 'polders', sand diggings, recreation parks and so on. The management *sensu stricto* is performed by the owners or managers of reserves or by governmental authorities. One of our tasks is to investigate the effects of the advisory measures after they have been executed. On the basis of geomorphological and historical data a classification of Dutch waters has been made, but from a hydrobiological point of view this is not satisfactory. Our goal is the characterization and classification on the basis of biological criteria, but for the time being we are using the old system. The main stagnant waters in the Netherlands, for example, can be divided into dune lakes, broads, 'vens', old dyke breaks and old river branches. A number of representative examples of each category has been purchased as nature reserves.

* R.I.N. Communication nr. 18.

Marshes with open water

They form a fascinating variety of land, water and all the transitional stages in between with a rich abundance of flora and fauna. The broads were created from peat pits by the action of wind and water. They are shallow and contain fresh water rich in nutrients. One of the most interesting characteristics of these areas is the autochtonic swamp succession.

The transition between open water and floating vegetation, consisting of *Stratiotes aloïdes* L., turned out to be especially rich in aquatic organisms. For evaluation of these broads we need a good insight into the structure of the ecosystem. Studies on the presence and distribution of macro-organisms adhering to *Stratiotes* plants showed a specific distribution pattern for a number of insect larvae (Fig. 1). We constructed a scheme of potential

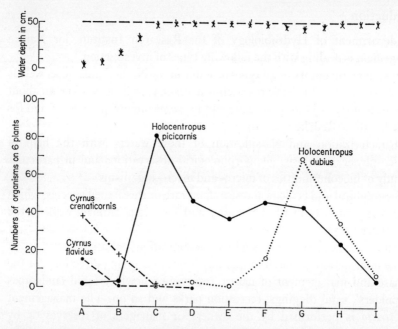

Figure 1. Distribution of *Polycentropodidae* larvae in an autochtonic swamp succession with *Stratiotes aloïdes* (Venematen, July 1967).

occupation of *Stratiotes* plants by larvae of Trichoptera and Ephemeroptera in a well-developed autochtonic swamp succession during the summer (Fig. 2). We found that the numerical differences between samples (consisting of six plants each), in the series from open water to shore, were significant for all the animals considered. Using simple methods for numerical analysis we found that corresponding stages in the swamp succession in different broads were characterized by the presence or absence of a few specific animals

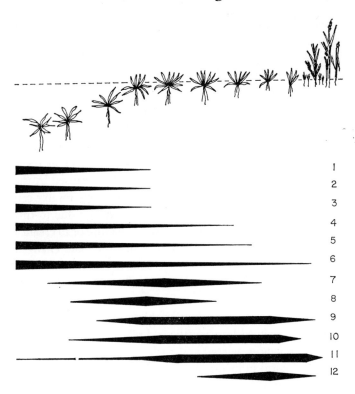

Figure 2. Distribution of larvae of Trichoptera and Ephemeroptera in an autochtonic swamp succession with *Stratiotes aloïdes* (end of June/end of July).

1. *Cyrnus crenaticornis*
2. *Cyrnus flavidus*
3. *Caenis horaria*
4. *Caenis robusta*
5. *Agraylea multipunctata*
6. *Oxyethira costalis*
7. *Agraylea pallidula*
8. *Cyrnus insolutus*
9. *Oecetis furva*
10. *Holocentropus picicornis*
11. *Oxyethira fagesii*
12. *Holocentropus dubius*

according to the scheme in Fig. 2 (Brantjes & Higler 1970). We are able to use this scheme as a measure in comparable situations. A better knowledge of the autecology of the animals considered makes the scheme directly applicable for the interpretation of established dissimilarities. The scheme represents the situation in an undisturbed and unpolluted broad.

The threats to these reserves are severe; they make the management very difficult. Leentvaar (1964) establishes that in the Netherlands nearly all waters form part of a system of canals in which the water is kept by dykes, pumps and sluices and that the need for regulation of the amount of water influences, at the same time, its quality. That is why these marshes are threatened more and more by pollution. The polluting effect is in many cases enlarged by a decrease of seepage water in those reserves where seepage plays an important role in the water management. Solutions to this problem are difficult to find. In a number of cases it is possible to replace the inflowing water by clean water from other places, or to purify the incoming water by using a few peat pits as natural purification plants.

As a matter of course these areas are extraordinarily attractive for recreation. This often causes an inadmissible disturbance of the very sensitive vegetation, if not direct pollution (e.g. spilled oil from motor boats, etc.). An adequate enlightenment and careful supervision can be effective in these cases. Another big problem in managing this type of reserve is caused by the autochtonic swamp succession itself. In about 30 to 40 years open water can be changed into land. The richness and value of the broads is due to this process. However, it is not easy to freeze this dynamic structure or to create a brand-new starting-point for the same situation under the now changed circumstances. In nature reserves experiments are done to test the possibilities of 'freezing' (by thinning out the *Stratiotes* plants) and recycling the swamp succession (by digging out peat pits as far as the mineral bottom). It is absolutely necessary to find solutions to these problems, for the significance of these reserves is not only defined by scientific and recreational importance but also by such economic factors as reed and rush culture, fisheries and in particular by their hydrological influence on the surrounding meadows and haylands (Schroevers & Segal, 1964).

Running waters

So far we have not mentioned running waters, although there are hundreds of streams in the Netherlands. They form a distinct category of 'lowland-rivulets' (Redeke 1948). These streams are dependent on rainfall, so they have a very variable water drainage. The speed of the current varies from 0 to about 100 cm/sec and the bottom correspondingly consists of silt, sand, pebbles or small boulders. The fauna is partially that of fast-running water, partially that of stagnant water and partially a type typical for this special kind of stream.

Many of the rivulets have been canalized and most of them are polluted by waste water or agricultural drainage. The undisturbed ones are few in number and they are threatened by the same risks. Management is difficult, in particular if there is no supervision on the upper course. Reserves ought to be formed in such a way that the total basin is under control. In practice one has to look for the best management for sections of a water course within a reserve. The necessity of canalization of a section under management can sometimes be removed by short-circuiting the stream, but a much better solution appears to be the partial covering of a cross-section with boulders without cementing them. In some cases this can be practised without much digging or disturbance of the natural course of the rivulet. A number of stream-sections in reserves are involved in such experiments.

The pollution of running waters as well as remedies for this evil are too well known to discuss here. An exception must be made for a special kind of pollution we meet in some areas of the Netherlands where there are concentrations of fattening farms for calves and pigs. The pollution caused by the liquid manure of these animals is characterized by a high ammonia content. One of the most important 'lowland rivulets', the 'Hierdense beek', is situated in a region where about 36,000 calves are raised. Though periodical chemical samples were taken by governmental authorities no trace of this kind of pollution was observed for some years. A biological evaluation showed a community typical of slightly polluted water in a number of sections and from this it was possible to determine the sources of pollution. We used an adaptation of the known saprobe-systems in order to estimate the degree of pollution. This method has functioned better in this case than the traditional methods of chemical sampling. The illegal drainage of the liquid manure at irregular times makes management extraordinarily difficult. We have proposed the pumping of all liquid manure by a pipe-line to a nearby purification plant which raises the costs per calf by about 6 guilders (about 70p).

New developments in the fight against sewage-water drainage include the possibility of treatment of this water in the surrounding woods. In the Hierdense beek area, experiments will be done in which the liquid manure is pretreated in simple biological plants. Further purification entails the horizontal passage of the prepared liquid manure through the sandy soil. If these experiments succeed, we are nearer to the solution of many sewage-water problems.

References

BRANTJES N.B.M. & HIGLER L.W.G. (in press). Een numerieke vergelijking van macrofauna in Stratiotesverlandingen. *Med. Hydrobiol.* 4, (2).

HIGLER L.W.G. (1967) Some notes on the distribution of the waterbug, *Gerris najas* (Degeer, 1773), in the Netherlands (Hemiptera-Heteroptera). *Beaufortia*, 14, 87–92.

LEENTVAAR P. (1964) Management and changing of water quality in the Netherlands. *Proc. MAR Conf. Int. Un. Conserv. Nat. nat. Resour.*, New Series no. 3, 267–70.

REDEKE H.C. (1922) Zur Biologie der niederländischen Brackwassertypen. *Bijdr. Dierk.*, 22, 329–35.

REDEKE H.C. (1933) Über den jetzigen Stand unserer Kenntnisse der Flora und Fauna des Brackwassers. *Proc. Congr. int. Limnol.*, 6th, 46–61.

REDEKE H.C. (1948) *Hydrobiologie van Nederland. De zoete wateren.* Amsterdam, 580 pp.

SCHROEVERS P.J. & SEGAL S. (1964) The economic significance of the phytocenological research in the marsh-regions of the Netherlands. *Proc. MAR Conf. Int. Un. Nat. Conserv. nat. Resour.*, New Series no. 3, 260–6.

Part 4
Habitat Management for
Wildlife in Africa

African grassland management—burning and grazing in Murchison Falls National Park, Uganda

D.H.N.SPENCE and A.ANGUS *Department of Botany, The University, St Andrews, Fife*

Introduction

In 1961, Buechner and Dawkins described how, as a result of the increase in human population and subsistence agriculture round the boundaries of Murchison Falls National Park, elephant and fires within the Park were causing the rapid replacement of woodland and the few fragments of high forest by uniform grassland. Since then the destruction of woodland and deterioration of grassland has continued (Plate 1). Laws (1970) has related these changes to the general alteration of habitat brought about by elephant in East Africa.

Steps have recently been taken by the Parks' authorities to manage this situation and, if possible, to restore a diverse habitat. Ultimately this diversity will only be maintained by a system of management involving regulation of numbers, and movement, of large mammals and the control of fire. One of Buechner and Dawkins's pleas was for an immediate reduction in numbers of elephant and hippopotamus. Between 1965 and 1967 cropping was carried out on both banks of the River Nile (Laws and Parker 1968, Laws *et al.* 1970); and a controlled burning programme has been initiated (Report, Acting Director, Uganda National Parks dated 31/3/67; unpublished). The next need is to assess the relative importance of fire and grazing in certain vegetation types. A start was made at Joliya in 1965 by excluding large mammals, with a ditch, from a plot in the widespread *Hypparrhenia* grassland (Fig. 1, *J*). At Chobe, representing an area in which cropping had recently taken place, plots were set out during 1967 in *Sporobolus-Setaria* grassland (Fig. 1, *G*) (which may be a facies of *Hypparrhenia* grassland) and in *Combretum-Terminalia* woodland (Fig. 1, *W*). These Chobe plots were to be subjected over a number of years to controlled burning, or total protection, in the presence or absence of large grazing mammals.

The long-standing practice of deliberate burning of vegetation in tropical

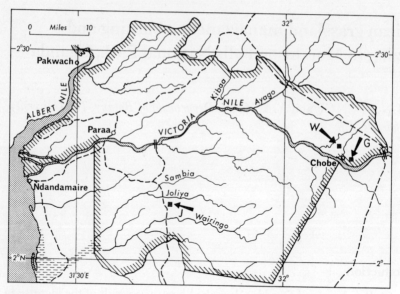

Figure 1. Location of research areas in Murchison Falls National Park. At Chobe, W = woodland plots (VII to XII) and G = grassland plots (I to VI). Map references respectively 403250, 405248 in series Y503, Sheet Na –36–6, Ed. 2–USD. J = Joliya plot which is not discussed in the present account.

and sub-tropical Africa is carefully reviewed by West (1965), who also outlines many of the burning experiments which have been carried out on that continent. Much of this work has been initiated and studied from the point of view of the use and abuse of fire in the management of pasture for cattle; how, for example, to control the spread of bush at the expense of pasture grasses. Comparatively little has been done to assess precisely, by the use of enclosures, the effects of fire and grazing on vegetation in the more complex environment of National Parks. Recent work by Lock (1966) on grasslands in part of Queen Elizabeth National Park, Uganda, indicates how informative such studies can be. Results from enclosures supported the idea of a gradient of decreasing grazing intensity with distance from water. Grassland 3 miles from water appeared to be a fire climax; nearer water, grazing replaced and excluded fires.

The present authors agreed with the Director of Uganda National Parks, the late Mr Francis Katete, to sample the vegetation of the Chobe plots in Murchison (Fig. 1) for several years and to record the changes, whilst the Parks' staff maintained the plots and firebreaks and carried out the controlled burning. This paper assesses, in management terms, some of the data collected so far, bearing in mind that a first aim of Park management should be the re-creation of a diverse habitat.

In this preliminary account change under controlled conditions is repor-

Plate 1. Derived *Sporobolus* grassland (cf. Plate 6). Moribund *Terminalia* woodland with elephants in the middle distance.

Plate 2. Woodland plots in September 1967. Ditch for ungrazed plots and firebreaks between ditched plots are nearing completion. Treatments of 1 acre, ditched, plots from left to right have since been late burn, early burn and no burn. The unditched plots are in the foreground lying parallel to the ditched plots; firebreaks have still to be made round them.

Plate 3. Woodland plot no. 7 (at right of Plate 2) in August 1969 showing, compared with Plate 7, the effect of complete protection for 2 years from burning and from grazing by large mammals.

Plate 4. Woodland plot no 10 (right foreground of Plate 2) in August 1969 protected for two years from fire only. Data in paper show substantial increase in shrub growth compared with burnt and grazed woodland plots.

Plate 3

Plate 4

Plate 5

Plate 6

ted only in terms of variation in representation and height of named species. Accepting these criteria of diversity, is it possible to say after 2 years' experiments if *Sporobolus-Setaria* grassland or *Combretum-Terminalia* woodland can be improved by controlled burning, or must the access of large mammals, a much less feasible operation, also be controlled?

The vegetation

The vegetation of the Chobe area is mapped by Langdale-Brown *et al.* (1964) as a catena with *Terminalia* woodland on higher parts and derived *Vitex-Phyllanthus-Sapium* woodland in the valleys. In fact, the grassland plots in this lower ground now support a grass savannah with scattered *Acacia sieberiana* trees, while the woodland plots are dominated by *Combretum* spp. (*binderianum* and *gueinzii*) and *Terminalia glaucescens*. Soils are red-brown loams, with brown surface layers.

Relics of many of the woody species comprising *Combretum-Terminalia* woodland persist in the grassland as short coppice shoots which sprout during the growing season from underground stocks, but fail to develop further because of annual fires and/or grazing by large mammals. Much of this grassland appears, from the presence in it of the remains of dead trees, to be derived fairly recently from woodland as Buechner and Dawkins (1961) reported for similar areas 9 years ago. Grassland is probably more heavily grazed than woodland; the greater quantity of *Sporobolus pyramidalis sensu lato* also suggests this (Chippindall 1955, Rattray 1954), while both Lock (1966) and Field (1968) consider the *Sporobolus* grasslands in the vicinity of the Mweya peninsula in Queen Elizabeth Park, Uganda, to be the result of hippopotamus grazing.

Grassland and woodland areas share the same dominant grasses and most other species. Grassland has more *Acacia sieberiana*, all less than 2 ft (61 cm) tall apart from a few trees, while the woodland has scattered trees of *Terminalia glaucescens* and *Combretum molle* (Plate 2) and abundant bushes more than 2 ft (61 cm) tall, mainly of *Combretum*. Species of *Desmodium*, *Indigofera*, *Acalypha* and *Ampelocissus* occur more abundantly in woodland. Buried pottery and a large pit were exposed during the digging of the ditch (see below) for the grassland plot. It is of interest therefore that *Imperata cylindrica*, a species held by Langdale-Brown *et al.* (1964) to indicate former cultivation, is locally abundant in grassland and almost absent from the woodland.

Plate 5. Grassland plot no. 3 ungrazed and unburnt since May 1967, photographed in August 1969 protection. Recovery of tree species, mainly *Acacia sieberiana*, compared with 'control' conditions illustrated in Plate 6.

Plate 6. Grassland plot no. 4 August 1969 unditched, and therefore grazed and subjected to two late burns, since the adjoining ditched plots (e.g. no. 3 in Plate 5) were set up in May 1967.

Large mammals

The principal large mammals present in the area in which the plots are situated are elephant *Loxodonta africana*, hippopotamus *Hippopotamus amphibius* and buffalo *Syncerus caffer*. In the riverine zone of Murchison, south of the Nile, their estimated standing crop biomass in 1969 (based on aerial counts) was 269·7 kg/ha of which hippopotamus contributed 190 kg/ha, elephant 34 kg/ha and buffalo 30 kg/ha; the north bank of Murchison, including the Chobe region, was probably similar with respect to hippopotamus and buffalo but lower in terms of elephant (Laws, *in litt.*). There are no up-to-date estimates of densities of elephant and other species on the north bank. Laws's estimate of elephant densities on the riverine strip of the south bank are 1·0–2·0 per km² while his north bank data of 1964 and 1967 for hippopotamus, based on aerial counts in a 2–mile riverine zone of grazing, give densities in block 2, including grassland plots (*G*), of 19·3 and 12·2 per km² in 1964, and 1967 respectively. The corresponding figures for block 3, which include woodland plots (*W*) are 23·5 and 22·2 per km². Their grazing density is assumed to be the same, overall, in both blocks (Laws *in litt.*), but should be lower in the woodland which lies further from the Nile than the grassland since hippopotamus are restricted to grazings adjacent to permanent water, and are at least in part the cause of the gradient in grazing intensity in similar terrain in parts of Queen Elizabeth Park (p. 320).

Methods

There is one set of plots in grassland (I to VI) and one set in woodland (VII to XII). Each set comprises six contiguous plots, each 70 yds (64 m) square, separated from each other by maintained firebreaks (Fig. 2). Three contiguous plots at each site are also surrounded by a ditch which, following Lock (1966) who used similar plots in Queen Elizabeth Park, are 10 ft wide with 6 ft high, vertical sides. Three treatments are being applied to the ditched and unditched areas, with one plot per treatment: no burn, 'early burn' after onset of the dry season (18 December 1967, 3 January 1969, January 1970) and 'late burn' towards the end of the dry season (28 February 1968, 11 March 1969, March 1970). The ditched grassland plots (I to III) were completed by April 1967 and first sampled in September 1967. The ditched woodland plots (VII to IX) were first sampled in September 1967, and completed by October 1967 (Plate 2).

Three sets of data are being gathered in each of the twelve plots. 1) Presence of all species of flowering plants in thirty-six permanent quadrats 1 yd² (0·84 m²) in extent laid out in a co-ordinate grid (Fig. 2) with concrete, numbered posts for corners, ordinates and abscissae. Lines may be run out

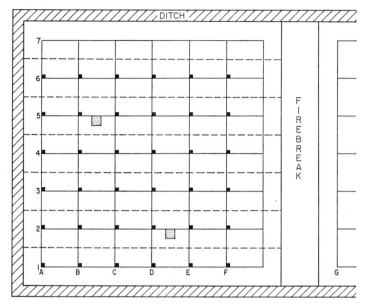

Figure 2. Plot I, showing ditch, firebreak and method of identifying ordinates and abscissae so that each permanent quadrat (dark square) has its own grid reference. Corners and intermediate points are marked on the ground by concrete posts, to which lines are attached for re-surveying. The small, shaded squares mark the position of randomly selected production quadrats. The grid method was applied to all 12 plots, 6 in grassland (Plots I to VI) and 6 in woodland (Plots VII to XII). The grid in each plot measured 60 yds by 60 yds (55 by 55 m), and each permanent quadrat 1 yd² (0·84 m²).

for re-location. 2) Standing crop of all above-ground parts and of litter determined in randomly selected areas of 50 ft² (4·65 m²). 3) Number and height of individuals of all woody species within three, alternate, longitudinal strips of the grid system; each strip being 10 yds (9·14 m) wide and 60 yds (54·84 m) long (area 0·013 ha). Only some quadrat and tree height data are dealt with in the present account.

Results

It has already been noted that, even prior to enclosure, *Sporobolus pyramidalis* was less abundant in woodland (Fig. 3) and this was attributed to lighter grazing there compared with grassland. After enclosure, *Sporobolus pyramidalis*, *Hypparhenia filipendula* and *H. rufa* among the dominant grasses are reduced primarily by lack of grazing, but the reduction is enhanced by lack of burning also (dotted line in Fig. 3). Of the herbs, *Glycine javanica* (Leguminosae) seems to be particularly susceptible to grazing. It is, consistently, twice as frequent in woodland as in grassland, again confirming a gradient in grazing intensity (Fig. 3). The high level attained in ditched grassland in 1967

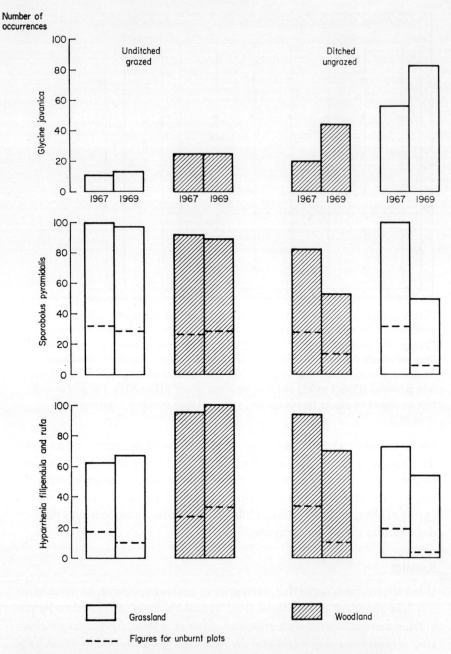

Figure 3. Comparison of the effects of grazing or its absence, with and without burning, in grassland plots which have been ditched to exclude large mammals since May 1967, or left accessible: and woodland plots which have been ditched since October 1967 or left accessible to large mammals. Plots have been subsequently unburnt or subjected to burning early (December 1967, 1968) or late (March 1968, 1969) in the dry season. Sampling dates: September 1967 and August 1969. Total possible occurrences per column is 108.

probably arises from the fact that while ditching was completed by April 1967, the recording of vegetation was not carried out until September 1967, after 5 months' growing season. *Sporobolus* by contrast obviously responded more slowly to enclosure and the absence of grazing. Assuming the 1967 and 1969 levels for *Glycine* in grazed grassland approximate the levels in the ditched plot at the time large mammals were excluded, there has by 1969 been an eightfold increase in *Glycine* in the absence of grazing for three growing seasons. When ungrazed in this habitat, which may be presumed to be less shaded than woodland, *Glycine* smothers tracts of vegetation, and regenerating shrubs such as *Acacia sieberiana* (Plate 4). Many less abundant but perhaps nutritionally important, herbs are also commoner in woodland and also increase in all plots in the absence of grazing (Fig. 4).

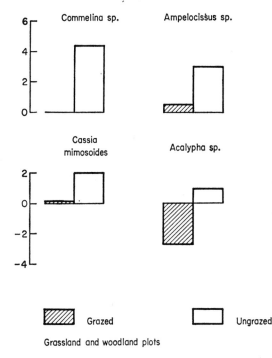

Figure 4. Number of occurrences of named species in August 1969, as relative increase from number in September 1967, in grassland and woodland plots which in the intervening years have been grazed, or ditched and ungrazed, by large mammals.

Of woody species, *Lonchocarpus laxiflorus* decreases with cessation of grazing, as Buechner and Dawkins (1961) would predict for this species. Other woody species increase rapidly. *Acacia sieberiana* is the potential dominant, of which both the number of plants and their stature are greatly increased if grazing is stopped (Fig. 5). Plates 3 and 4 provide visual evidence of change in grassland which has been ungrazed for three growing seasons.

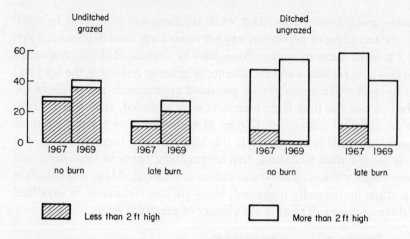

Figure 5. Number of *Acacia sieberiana* plants per 0·3 acre (0·013 ha) in grassland plots which have been ditched, or left accessible to large mammals. Plots were unburnt or subjected to late burns in March 1968 and March 1969.

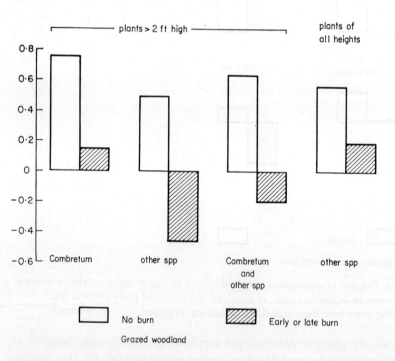

Figure 6. Number of woody plants per 0·3 acre (0·013 ha) in August 1969, as relative increase or decrease from number in September 1967, in *grazed* woodland plots (X to XII). The plots have been unburnt for at least two years, or subjected to two, annual early (December) or late (March) burns. Data from early and late burns are combined here.

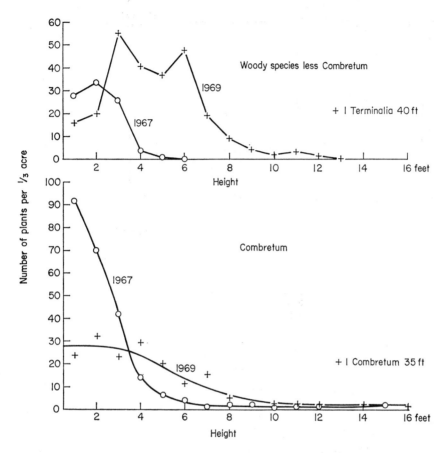

Figure 7. Height distribution of plants of *Combretum* species and other woody species, in September 1967 and August 1969, in woodland plot VII, unburnt and ungrazed by large mammals since ditching was completed at the initial sampling period.

In woodland which is grazed for two years, absence of burning increases the amount of *Combretum* and other woody species (Figs. 6, 7). Without grazing, woody species increase even in the presence of burning, but most markedly in its absence (Fig. 8 and Plates 5, 6). Comparison of grazing and its absence in unburnt woodland plots (Fig. 9) shows that *Combretum* is more susceptible to burning than to the existing levels of grazing. Other woody species, however, respond to the absence of grazing also. Thus, by excluding grazing from unburnt woodland for two years, other woody species have increased by almost twice if all height classes are considered, by fivefold if only those over 2 ft high are counted. We have included shrubby *Desmodium* and *Indigofera* species in the category of woody species other than *Combretum*, and these two groups of species account for much of the increase. As with

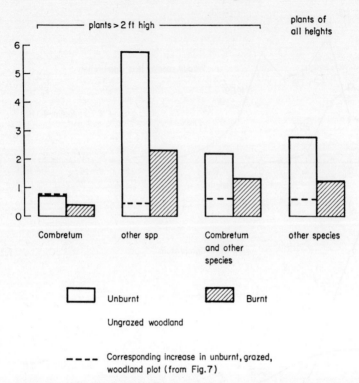

Figure 8. Number of woody plants per 0·3 acre (0·013 ha) in August 1969, as relative increase from number in September 1967, in *ungrazed* woodland plots (VII to IX). Since initial sampling in 1967, these have been inaccessible to large mammals and treated with early, late or no burning, as Plots X to XII (Fig. 7). The corresponding increase in unburnt, grazed, woodland plot X (from Fig. 6) is indicated by a dotted line.

Glycine, these members of the Leguminosae appear to be particularly susceptible to grazing; *Piliostigma* (Caesalpinoidae) does not.

Conclusions

From present evidence, shrub regeneration and herb improvement in *Sporobolus-Setaria* grassland will only follow reduction of grazing. Another season may show if the marginal improvement in shrubs, with grazing and a late burn, is real. Fire protection in these grasslands without respite from grazing is probably of little value. Lock (*pers. comm.*) reaches a similar conclusion for the grazing enclosures in *Hyparrhenia* savannah at Joliya.

In *Combretum-Terminalia* woodland, absence of both grazing and burning produces the most spectacular changes, but even the cessation of burning alone for as little as two years has brought about an increase in shrub cover and diversity. Plants of *Combretum* and other woody species more than 2 ft

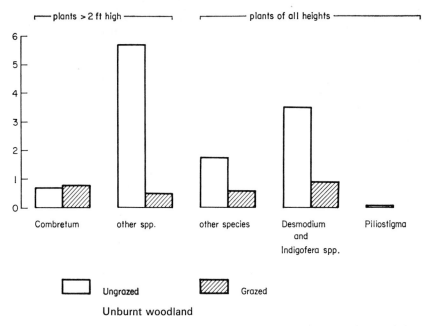

Figure 9. Number of woody plants per 0·3 acre (0·013 ha) in August 1969, as relative increase from number in September 1967, in woodland plots (VII, X) which have been *unburnt* since 1967 and either ungrazed or grazed by large mammals.

(61 cm) tall have increased by 50 per cent. These findings confirm quantitatively Buechner and Dawkins's (1961) recommendation that the important *Terminalia glaucescens* woodland, of which the present plots are part, should be conserved by fire protection. Even greater improvement would rapidly follow exclusion of grazing.

These plots were originally sited in areas which had been subjected to heavy browsing and grazing, and from which large numbers of hippopotamus and elephant had just been removed by culling. From the evidence provided by grazed, control plots over two growing seasons, culling does not appear to have caused any immediately obvious change in composition of the vegetation, particularly in contrast to the marked and often rapid changes in the plots from which grazing has been excluded. A principal omission from the present data is a current estimate of densities of large mammals in the areas round these plots. A problem is their diet. Field (1968) provides information on grass species eaten by hippopotamus and buffalo in certain parts of Queen Elizabeth Park, Uganda, while Laws and Parker (1968) give, for stomachs of elephants, proportions of 'browse', bark and grass taken on the north and south bank of the Nile in a number of localities in Murchison. There is little information on buffalo, in particular and, for all three species, on quantity and types of herbs eaten. What, for example, takes *Glycine* and the 'woody' Leguminosae?

Meanwhile, a detailed study of two vegetation types in controlled conditions has already distinguished precisely between the effects of fire and of grazing by large mammals, and indicates that fire control is unlikely to improve *Sporobolus-Setaria* grassland; large mammals there must be excluded or greatly reduced in number. Control of movement of, and access by, large mammals may be desirable but there are obvious practical difficulties. It is more immediately feasible to eliminate fire by creating firebreaks, especially to reduce the danger of widespread casual burning of the type prevalent in early 1967, where 'almost the whole Park was burned over by poachers' during the remaining dry season in spite of efforts by the Parks staff over many days to put out the fires (Rep. Acting Director, N.P./1/89 dated 31/3/67).

In his article in this volume, Gimingham outlines Picozzi's findings that grouse populations are largest on heather moors in eastern Scotland when a mosaic of small areas of diverse age is maintained by burning. The aim in Murchison should be the re-creation of a similar, suitably scaled, diversity. Provided fire exclusion is made part of a general burning plan so that over-grazing of localized areas is avoided, our results indicate that *Combretum-Terminalia* woodland on the North Bank of Murchison Falls can be conserved immediately by the strict exclusion of burning.

Acknowledgements

Mr Roger Wheater, Deputy Director of the Uganda National Parks, initiated these experiments. Much of the recording has been undertaken by Mr Gelasio Busigye, Assistant Warden, and in 1967 by Mr Sam Mukuru and Mr David Okioga of Makerere, Miss Marion Moffat and Miss Sarah Lowe of St Andrews. Dr J.M.Lock helped with recording and with identification of species. Mr Anthony Ziegler, lately Warden, Chobe Sector, carried out the burnings and helped in numerous ways on our visits to the Park. To all these individuals, and many junior Parks staff, our thanks. Mr Francis Katete, Director of the National Parks until his tragic death in a car accident in June 1970, gave every encouragement and support. First, the Carnegie Trust for the Scottish Universities and then the Royal Society—IBP (CT) Committee financed us, the latter as part of the U.K. contribution to IBP. Finally, we should like to thank Dr R.M.Laws for permitting us to quote some of his un-published data on densities and biomass of large mammals in Murchison.

References

BUECHNER H.K. & DAWKINS H.C. (1961) Vegetation changes induced by elephants and fire in Murchison Falls National Park, Uganda. *Ecology*, 42, 752–66.

CHIPPINDALL L. (1955) A guide to the identification of grasses in South Africa. In: *The grasses and pastures of South Africa*. Central News Agency, Johannesburg.

FIELD C.R. (1968) A comparative study of the food habits of some wild ungulates in Queen Elizabeth National Park, Uganda: preliminary report. *Symp. zool. Soc. Lond.*, 21, 135–51.

LANGDALE-BROWN I., OSMASTON H.A. & WILSON J.G. (1964) *The Vegetation of Uganda and its bearing on land-use*. Govt. Printer, Entebbe, Uganda.

LAWS R.M. (1970) Elephants as agents of habitat and landscape change in East Africa. *Oikos*, 21, 1–15.

LAWS R.M. & PARKER I.S.C. (1968) Recent studies on elephant populations in East Africa. *Symp. zool. Soc. Lond.*, 21, 319–59.

LAWS R.M., PARKER I.S.C. & JOHNSTONE R.C.B. (1970) Elephants and their habitats in North Bunyoro, Uganda. *E. Afr. Wildl. J.*, 8, 163–80.

LOCK J.M. (1966) *Vegetation in relation to grazing and soils in Queen Elizabeth National Park, Uganda*. Unpublished Ph.D. thesis, University of Cambridge.

RATTRAY J.M. (1954) Some plant indicators in Southern Rhodesia. *Rhodesia agric. J.*, 51, 176–86.

WEST O. (1965) *Fire in vegetation and its use in pasture management with special reference to tropical and subtropical Africa*. Commonwealth Agricultural Bureaux mimeographed publn. no. 1/1965. Commonwealth bureau of Pastures and Field Crops, Hurley, Berkshire.

Destruction or utilization of a wildlife habitat?

R.M.LAWTON *Land Resources Division, Directorate of Overseas Surveys, Tolworth, Surrey*

Introduction

The middle reaches of the Luangwa Valley, north-eastern Zambia, form one of the finest surviving wildlife areas in Central Africa. The habitats owe their survival to a number of factors, the main one probably being the difficulty of access. The area is bounded to the west by a steep escarpment over 300 m high; to the east the black alluvial soils near the Luangwa are impassable during the rains, that is from November to April. Furthermore, the soils over part of the valley are covered with a mantle of large rounded pebbles that make them unsuitable for cultivation. Finally, the valley is very hot, it supports a large tsetse-fly population and is therefore not an ideal human habitat.

There are two large game reserves covering a total area of 14,000 km² (5,000 miles²), separated by a corridor of approximately 2,900 km² (1,100 miles²). Most of the observations have been made within this corridor, which supports a rich and varied wildlife population and a small human population of about 7,000 people concentrated in a few large villages.

In 1965 the Game Department decided that the habitat was being destroyed by overgrazing and overbrowsing and that it was necessary to crop elephant (*Loxodonta africana*), buffalo (*Syncerus caffer*) and hippopotamus (*Hippopotamus amphibius*). The decision was based on a few aerial reconnaissances and counts and on 'a rapid assessment of the severe modification of vegetation caused by the activities of the larger game animals' (Game and Fisheries, Zambia 1966). The term 'severe modification' implies a change in the appearance and perhaps composition of the vegetation brought about by grazing and browsing. As far as appearance is concerned, there is certainly a difference between a grazed and browsed stand of vegetation and untouched vegetation, but the point at issue is whether this is destruction or intensive utilization of the vegetation. The Game Department considering it to be destruction, have built a permanent abattoir in the Southern Game Reserve, and in 1966 cropped 200 elephant, 200 hippopotamus and 100 buffalo.

At this stage it must be emphasized that where wildlife populations are confined (e.g. where their migratory routes are closed by areas of cultivation), it may be necessary to control them, perhaps by cropping; but in the Luangwa Valley the elephants are free to roam over the uninhabited escarpment and on to the edge of the plateau, where the human population is low. If they cross into cultivated land east of the Luangwa River they may be shot by the elephant control service which accounts for 300–500 animals each year. Hunting and poaching are human activities that can be controlled, but not eliminated, in an area as large as the Luangwa Valley. Therefore an allowance must be made for the numbers taken annually by poachers, before a cropping scheme can be considered.

Grazing

All my observations have been made at the end of the dry season, from September to November, that is at a time when the utilization of the habitat is most intensive. Near the banks of the Luangwa, patches of perennial grasses are grazed to ground level, but they are still alive and will flush after the first storm. Good stands of *Echinochloa stagnina*, *E. pyramidalis* and *Setaria* sp. were observed in November at the end of the dry season; where they have not been burnt these grasses are grazed throughout the dry season by elephant, buffalo and hippopotamus. An elephant was observed grazing a stand of *Hyparrhenia* grass in the riverine zone in November. Trampled grass near the river provides a good cover for the soil surface. To the west away from the river the corridor is dominated by a vast undulating grassy plain, the Chifungwe plain; one of the dominant grasses there, *Setaria eylesii*, remains palatable throughout the dry season. This is a most important grazing area, but in most years it is swept by fire and destroyed. There are coppice shoots of trees and shrubs in the grassland but they are burnt back by the frequent fires. Further west, at the foot of the escarpment, tall *Hyparrhenia* spp. grasses are trampled and grazed; a fire at this stage creeps along the ground and is less destructive than a fire in a stand of 2 m high, untrampled grass. Grass on the alluvial flats, bordering a tributary of the Luangwa River near the base of the escarpment, is grazed continuously by puku (*Kobus vardoni*), a small antelope, and remains green throughout the year. All these examples are of perennial grasses. If the habitat had been overgrazed there would have been large areas without any grass cover, but this is not so. There is also a good reserve of grazing left at the end of the dry season, provided it has not been burnt.

Browsing

During the dry season, browse is an important source of food. In September *Combretum ghazalense* flushes, by late October it had been heavily browsed by elephant, but the trees had not been noticeably damaged. The shallow, surface rooted, *Colophospermum mopane* is probably the most important source of browse; it flushes soon after the first storm in October–November. In a wild-life habitat a stand of mopane is mainly of value to large herbivores as a reserve of browse. Elephant cause pollard growth of mopane by pushing down trees that are usually fire-damaged at the base, and so bring the canopy down to browse level for themselves and for rhinoceros (*Diceros bicornis*), eland (*Taurotragus oryx*) and other browsers. In this way patches of mopane are reduced to coppice but the trees are not killed. They will then grow to 2 m high pollarded stems. The difference between a mopane woodland canopy and a pollard canopy is illustrated by an enumeration; in the woodland sample six trees were recorded, compared with fifty-two pollards and three trees in a pollarded stand of the same area. Many trees are so heavily browsed that their shape is determined by browsing. For example, the crowns of *Piliostigma thonningii* and other species are flat, but the trees have not been killed. This is considered to be utilization not destruction. An understanding of the relationship between *Colophospermum mopane* and elephant is the key to the ecology of the Luangwa Valley. Examination of aerial photographs shows that there is a good reserve of accessible mopane woodland and pollarded stands in the valley.

Discussion

What are the forces of destruction in the habitat? The principal one is fire, usually man-made, although rare natural fires caused by lightning may occur at the beginning of the rains. The fires sweep through the woodland, destroying dry season grazing and browse. In most years the Chifungwe plain is burnt, cracks form at the soil surface, and the first storm may open these up into erosion gullies. In one instance where an elephant path had stopped a fire near the edge of the plain, no surface cracks could be found under the grass-covered area. These paths are clearly visible on the aerial photographs, but do not appear to be related to erosion gullies. If the populations of large herbivores are reduced there will be more unused, untrampled vegetation and therefore more combustible material in the area.

The Luangwa River frequently changes its course and erodes its banks, but this is natural erosion and is not caused by the activities of the wildlife population. Although often overlooked, another natural force of destruction is flooding. If the rainfall in the head waters and on the plateau is high, the rivers and oxbows in the valley may be in spate for a few months, and some trees may be drowned, perhaps accounting for the dead trees often found around the edges of oxbows.

Elephants do strip the bark off trees, sometimes ring-barking them and killing the stems, but most of the trees coppice from the roots. The baobab, *Adansonia digitata*, does not survive this treatment.

The Luangwa valley is of value as an almost natural ecosystem. Its value for tourism, recreation and scientific purposes should take priority over its potential as a source of protein. Wildlife should certainly be used as a source of food, as it always has been. The Luangwa valley is a traditional hunting area, on a tribal boundary, an area of no-man's-land, mainly used for hunting expeditions by neighbouring tribes. In pre-colonial times the human population was much lower than it is now, and the large present day urban population of the Copperbelt could destroy the protein resources of the Luangwa within a few years. It is therefore recommended that the present game reserves should be maintained as sanctuaries, and wildlife should be ranched or raised in semi-domesticated herds around the periphery for exploitation. Wildlife is resilient, and may recover from the present exploitation. In the early 1930s the hippopotamus population was very low, but now schools of 200–300 may be seen; few calves are seen in these large schools, and the Luangwa is probably stocked to capacity with hippo. This species could be cropped, but management is not necessary on grounds of habitat destruction. The disturbance caused through cropping hippo at night may cause the population to disperse to areas where it is no longer protected.

Summary

In the Luangwa valley cropping of elephant, hippopotamus and buffalo began in 1966 in order to prevent habitat deterioration. The observations presented in this paper suggest that the habitat is not being destroyed by overgrazing or overbrowsing, but that fire is the main cause of destruction.

Reference

GAME & FISHERIES, ZAMBIA (1966) *Annual report for the year 1965*. Govt. Printer, Lusaka.

The seed biology of *Themeda triandra* Forsk. in relation to fire

J.M.LOCK *Nuffield Unit of Tropical Animal Ecology, P.O. Queen Elizabeth Park, Lake Katwe, Uganda. Now at Department of Botany, University of Ghana, P.O. Box 55, Legon, Ghana*
T.R.MILBURN *Department of Botany, Makerere University, P.O. Box 7062, Kampala, Uganda*

Introduction

Themeda triandra is a perennial savannah grass widespread in tropical and sub-tropical Africa, extending eastwards to Arabia and India. A closely related species, *Themeda australis* R.Br., occurs in Australia, and is often considered to be conspecific with *Themeda triandra* (Ewart 1930, Maire 1952). In Africa, *Themeda triandra* is commonest at medium altitudes, in areas where there are regular dry seasons. It is scarce in West Africa (Prain 1934), and rare in North Africa (Maire 1952, Quezel & Santa 1962), where scattered populations may be relics from moister periods when grasslands extended northwards across the present Sahara Desert. It has attracted much attention as a grazing grass, particularly in South Africa, but recent work in Uganda (Marshall & Bredon 1967) showed that it was both unpalatable and of low nutritive value. Many workers (e.g. Bews 1913, Edwards 1935) have noticed its inability to withstand heavy grazing. Throughout the range of *Themeda triandra* it has been noticed that regular burning in the dormant season appears to be essential to the persistence of *Themeda* grassland (reviewed by West 1965). *Themeda australis* appears to be very similar in its ecology (Tothill 1969).

Themeda triandra has no means of extensive vegetative spread, although individuals may split following the death of the centre. Although it is a perennial, field observations on marked plots suggest that individual plants do not live very long. Seed germination and seedling establishment must therefore be important in the maintenance and persistence of *Themeda*-dominated grasslands. In the Queen Elizabeth National Park, Western Uganda, seedlings of *Themeda triandra* appear after burning of the grassland, and have not been seen at any other time under natural conditions. Water, of course, is also needed, and germination thus follows burning when sufficient rain has fallen. On one occasion, some *Themeda* grassland burned on 12 March; heavy rain fell the same evening; on 17 March seedlings of *Themeda* were common in the burnt area, but completely absent outside it. It is clear from these observations that the seeds are not destroyed by fire, and that burning somehow stimulates germination.

Edwards (1942) showed that the dispersal unit of *Themeda triandra* could bury itself in the ground by hygroscopic movements of the awn. He suggested that the buried seed would be protected from fires. The present paper confirms and amplifies Edwards's results, and attempts an analysis of the factors causing germination of *Themeda* seeds.

Fire evasion

The structure of the dispersal unit

The dispersal unit of *Themeda triandra* (Fig. 1) consists of the caryopsis, enclosed by the lower glume and the lemma. These are dark brown, hard, and shiny, and tightly appressed to the caryopsis. They are also heavily silicified.

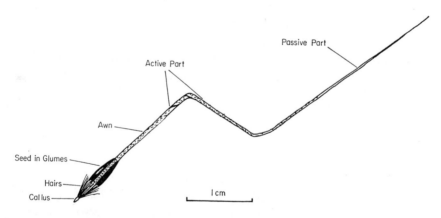

Figure 1. Dispersal unit of *Themeda triandra*.

The stalk of the dispersal unit abscisses obliquely to leave a sharp-pointed callus (Tothill 1969). This bears stiff brown hairs directed away from the point. The lemma bears a geniculate awn about 70 mm long. There are two bends in the column of the awn in its dry state, but one of these disappears when it is wetted. The proximal and median parts of the awn are grooved, twisted, and hygroscopic. The distal section is terete and inactive, and tapers to a fine point.

The hygroscopic behaviour of the awn

Darwin (1876) observed the hygroscopic behaviour of the *Themeda* awn (as *Anthesteria ciliata*) and showed that it twists and untwists in response to changes in humidity. He discussed the mechanism of torsion and traced it to the individual cells. The mechanism of torsion in *Stipa* was further discussed and explained by Murbach (1900). Our observations confirm that awn movement takes place in response to humidity changes, and not only in the presence of liquid water. Awns placed in atmospheres of known humidity showed that most of the movement takes place between 100 per cent and 50 per cent R.H. Records from a hygrograph showed that fluctuations over this range occurred on most days in *Themeda* grassland.

When the dispersal unit falls from the parent plant the awn is almost straight, as it is when wet. The awn thus acts as a flight, tending to make the seed fall point foremost, easily able to lodge in a crack in the soil, or in a plant base. Edwards (1942) showed that seeds placed on a cracked soil surface entered the cracks as a result of the awn movements. He also suggested that seeds might be better able to bury themselves near the parent plant, where the awn would be most likely to meet obstructions. We have observed that some seeds excavated in the field have the callus hairs spirally twisted round the seed, suggesting that the seed had been actively screwed into the soil. If the inert distal part of the awn is prevented from rotating, the twisting of the proximal part will instead be transmitted to the seed, screwing it into the ground.

To test the suggestion that seed burial is most likely to take place near the parent plant, the positions of seedlings and plant bases were plotted in five 0·5 m squares in recently burnt *Themeda* grassland. The results (Table 1),

Table 1. Distribution of Themeda seedlings in grassland.

	Plant bases	Bare ground
Ground cover (%)	24	76
Seedling distribution (%)	57	43
(107 seedlings plotted)		

show that more seedlings occur within established plants than in the spaces between them. In addition, 500 cm² of grass clump, and 1500 cm² of bare ground were dug over and searched for *Themeda* seeds. The smaller area of grass clump yielded sixteen seeds against the four found under bare ground, excluding the possibility of differential germination of seeds buried in plant bases.

The mean depth of burial of 100 seeds dug up from an area burned in June 1966 was 11 mm. Many workers have measured soil temperatures during grass fires, and there is general agreement that at depths of around 1 cm little rise in soil temperature occurs as a result of the passage of a normal grass fire (Masson 1948; Norton & McGarity 1965; Tothill & Shaw 1968). A few measurements made in Queen Elizabeth Park support these conclusions. It seems clear that the burial of the seed by the movements of the awn will protect the seed from fire damage.

Stimulation of germination

Field Experiments

When a grassland is burnt, various changes potentially capable of stimulating germination take place. These can be summarized as follows:

1   the heat of the fire;
2   ash from the fire;
3   the removal of the plant cover.
   This leads to:

(*a*)   more light reaching the soil surface;
(*b*)   changes in the spectral composition of the light reaching the soil surface;
(*c*)   higher soil temperatures, and greater temperature fluctuations;
(*d*)   removal of a potential source of inhibitors.

   Field experiments were carried out in the grasslands of the northern part of the Queen Elizabeth National Park. *Themeda triandra* is abundant in the drier parts of the park on black or dark brown loams derived from Pleistocene volcanic ashes. Some 700–800 mm of rain fall each year in two rather irregular wet seasons, March–May and October–December. Much of the grassland in the park is burnt at least once every two years during the dry season. *Themeda triandra* is usually co-dominant with *Hyparrhenia filipendula* (Hochst.) Stapf, with *Bothriochloa insculpta* (A.Rich.) A.Camus, *Chloris gayana* Kunth, *Heteropogon contortus* (L.) Roem. & Schult. present in smaller amounts, and with the dwarf tussock-forming grasses *Sporobolus stapfianus* Gand. and *Microchloa kunthii* Desv. forming a lower layer and flowering only after burning.

Experiment 1

This was designed to compare the effects of clipping and burning of *Themeda* grassland on the germination of *Themeda* seeds. Four plots for each of four treatments were laid out in a randomized block design. The treatments were control, burn, clip and leave, and clipping followed by sweeping off of all cut grass and litter. Each plot was 20 ft (6·2 m) square. The whole area was surrounded by a firebreak 10 ft (3·1 m) wide, and plots were separated from each other by paths 5 ft (1·5 m) wide. The controls and the clip and leave treatments were all destroyed by a violent fire which crossed the firebreak during 5 very dry weeks which followed the setting-up of the experiment. After a further 2 weeks, during which 60 mm of rain fell, seedlings were counted in ten 5 dm² quadrats placed randomly within each plot in the surviving treatments. Grassland near the plot which had escaped the fire was used as the control. One hundred seedlings were dug up in each treatment and the depth of burial of the seeds measured.

Results are shown in Table 2. It is clear that burning is not necessary for

Table 2. Germination of *Themeda* seeds, and depth of burial of germinating seeds, in clipped and burnt grassland.

Treatment	Replicate	Seedlings/m²	Depth of burial (mm)
Burnt			12·5
	1	16·0	
	2	7·6	
	3	11·6	
	4	17·2	
Clipped			12·3
	1	14·0	
	2	15·2	
	3	32·4	
	4	14·0	

stimulation of germination of buried seeds of *Themeda triandra*. Removal of the plant cover alone is sufficient. It is also clear that few seeds are destroyed by the fire, even those which are shallowly buried. If many shallowly buried seeds had been destroyed, the mean depth of burial of germinated seeds would have been greater in the burnt area.

Experiment 2

The second experiment attempted to compare the effectiveness of light and heat in promoting germination after cutting and burning. In a preliminary small-scale experiment, 1 m² blocks were burnt and cut, and others were similarly treated and immediately covered with black polythene. In a later experiment, larger areas, 3 × 1 m, were clipped, and two were immediately covered with black polythene. Clipping and covering were done in the late evening so that the covered areas received very little light before being covered. Insufficient rain fell after this experiment to give full germination. Results are shown in Table 3. These suggest that light may be important in stimulating germination, although the shading by the black polythene may also have lowered temperatures beneath it.

Table 3. Light and germination of *Themeda triandra* in the field.

Treatment	Area	Germination under black polythene	Germination on open ground
Burn	2 × 1 m²	7	37
Clip	2 × 1 m²	o	8
Clip	2 × 3 m²	o	5

Temperature changes after cover removal

Very large changes occur in the soil temperature regime after removal of the cover by clipping or burning. Temperatures after burning tend to be slightly higher because of the black ash left by the fire. Measurements of soil and air temperatures were made in burnt and unburnt *Themeda* grassland at Katojo, Western Uganda, five miles south of the Equator, in June 1966. Soil temperatures were measured with mercury-in-glass thermometers. The surface temperature was taken with the bulb of the thermometer covered with the thinnest possible layer of dust. Wet-bulb and dry-bulb readings were taken with a whirling hygrometer, 4 ft (1·3 m) above ground level. The results are shown in Fig. 2 and summarized in Table 4. Similar results, but from

Table 4. Soil temperatures (°C) in *Themeda* grassland, and the effect of removal of the plant cover.

Treatment	Depth	28 June 1966		
		Maximum	Minimum	Range
Burnt	Surface	59·0	16·0	43·0
Unburnt	Surface	37·5	17·8	19·7
Burnt	1 cm	37·7	20·1	17·6
Unburnt	1 cm	28·8	19·1	9·7
Burnt	5 cm	32·4	21·7	10·7
Unburnt	5 cm	25·9	20·7	5·2
		10–28 May 1969		
		Mean Maximum	Mean Minimum	Range
Cut	1 cm	40·7	18·3	22·4
Uncut	1 cm	28·3	19·2	9·1
		5–11 May 1970		
Cut	1 cm	45·9	18·6	27·3
Uncut	1 cm	28·9	18·3	10·6

clipped areas, and at one depth only, are also included in the table. They were obtained from a Grant Miniature Temperature Recorder, using thermistor probes. The figures given in the table are the means from three thermistor probes placed at the same depth and in the same conditions.

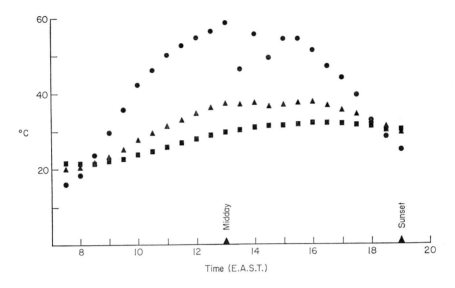

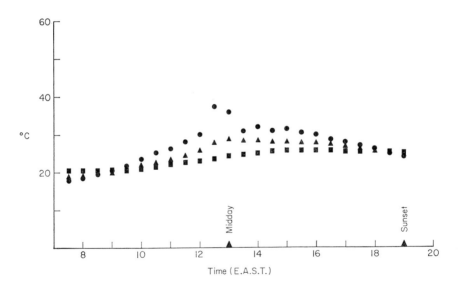

Figure 2. Soil temperatures in burnt (*a*) and unburnt (*b*) *Themeda* grassland on 28 June 1966. ●—surface (see text); ▲—1 cm; ■—5 cm.

Laboratory tests on germination of Themeda triandra

Seed of *Themeda triandra* is difficult to collect in quantity, and viability of seeds is often low due to infestation by insects and fungi. The tightly appressed glumes also make it impossible to see if the dispersal unit contains a viable seed. Laboratory tests were thus often made on small samples, but replication was usually good, and only tests which were repeated at least once are reported here. Seeds were collected either by hand picking, or by driving a Land Rover through a mature stand of *Themeda* and collecting the seeds in a trough fitted between the front bumper and the radiator. The seeds were dried in the shade for a few days before being stored in airtight tins. Germination trials were carried out in plastic petri dishes, on two layers of Whatman No.1 Filter paper, moistened with 4 ml of distilled water. Petri dishes were placed in polythene bags to reduce water loss, but were opened daily to check germination. Dark treatments were given in black polythene bags. In controlled-temperature experiments, the dishes were placed on a large copper plate resting on a water bath. Temperatures in the dishes were checked with thermistor probes. Temperatures were maintained to within $\pm 1°C$. Seeds being treated at temperatures above ambeint were given additional light for 12 hours each day from six fluorescent tubes (three Warm White, three Tropical Daylight), in addition to diffuse daylight.

The results of germination trials on seed of different ages are shown in Fig.3. They suggest strongly that there is an after-ripening period, which

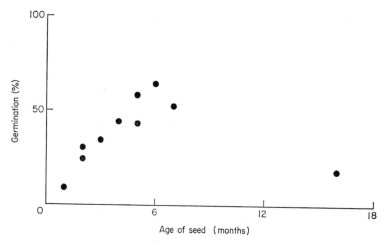

Figure 3. Germination of dispersal units of *Themeda triandra* at different ages.

lasts about six months, during which the seed gradually becomes germinable. Further trials, to test various effects of light, temperature and other treatments, are summarized in Table 5.

The contrast between the germination behaviour of *Themeda* seeds in the field and in the laboratory suggested that the seeds might undergo changes as a result of burial in the soil. In a preliminary trial, 88 seeds were dug up from *Themeda* grassland, removed from the glumes, and 44 were set to germinate in total darkness, and 44 in 12 hr light/dark cycles, at laboratory temperatures

Table 5. Laboratory trials on germination of *Themeda triandra* seeds.

Age of seed (months)	+ or − glumes	Pretreatment	Treatment during germination		% Germination
1	+	None	L/D	20–25°	10
1	−	None	L/D	20–25°	39
1	−	None	L/D	35°	48
1	−	None	L/D	21–35°	56
1	−	48 hrs at 55°	L/D	20–25°	47
1	−	12 hrs dark hydration, then 10 hrs R	Dark	20–25°	56
1	−	ditto but 10 hrs FR	Dark	20–25°	59
1	−	Hydration in dark	Dark	20–25°	57
6	−	None	L/D	20–25° Distilled Water	90
6	−	None	L/D	20–25° *Themeda* leaf washings*	78
4	+	None	L/D	20–25°	63
4	+	None	Dark	20–25°	59

L/D—12 hrs light followed by 12 hrs dark.
R—red light.   FR—far-red light.
* Derived from chopped leaves soaked in a minimal volume of distilled water for 2 hrs.

(20–25°C); 37 germinated in total darkness, and 41 in the light/dark treatment. Germination of these seeds was rapid, being complete in 3 days, as against 1 week for fresh seed.

In a further experiment, freshly collected seeds were sealed into small, thin, perforated polythene bags, and buried 1 cm deep in *Themeda* grassland. After 5–6 weeks they were dug up at night, and immediately placed in two black polythene bags. They were carried back to the laboratory and transferred to petri dishes in a darkroom. The treatments and results are shown in Table 6. The results from these experiments suggest that burial in soil may induce a light requirement in the seeds.

Table 6. Germination of *Themeda* seeds after burial in soil.

Burial time (weeks)	Germination temperature (C)	Light		Dark	
		Number of seeds	% Germination	Number of seeds	% Germination
5	20–25	65	6	9 36	3 8
6	30	177	42	24 57	1 2
6	30	41	10	25 78	8 10

Discussion

Seed burial

The burial of *Themeda* seeds by the hygroscopic movements of the awn places them in a generally more equable environment than the soil surface provides. The insulating properties of the soil not only protect the seed from fire, but also from the high surface temperatures which follow the removal of plant cover. The early root system of the seedling is also well placed in the moister, cooler layers of the soil. Although the burial mechanism provides protection from extremes, and improves the chances of seedling establishment on bare soil, it is also likely (Table 1) to place the seed in the base of another plant, where competition for water and light will be maximal.

Stimulation of germination

Seeds of *Themeda triandra* appear to differ greatly in their germination requirements according to storage conditions. Seeds stored in the laboratory appear to germinate in a wide range of conditions, as opposed to the special conditions under which germination occurs in the field. It seems unlikely that results from laboratory-stored seed bear much relation to field behaviour. Laboratory-stored seeds appeared to be aphotoblastic and insensitive to high temperatures.

Laboratory tests show no inhibition by washings from *Themeda* leaves and stems. Although auto-inhibition has been postulated widely as a germination control mechanism, it has rarely been demonstrated satisfactorily. For example, Muller, Hanawalt & McPherson (1968) have claimed that herb growth in the chaparral vegetation of California is regulated by inhibitors produced by the dominant shrubs. Herbs are abundant only for a few years after fires, which are believed to destroy accumulated inhibitors and allow germination of herb seeds. In spite of the doubt attached to laboratory tests on *Themeda* seeds, it seems unlikely that auto-inhibition is involved here.

It is clear from Experiment 1 that the role of fire in promoting germination of *Themeda* is an incidental one. It appears to act only by removing the cover. Tothill (1969) found that *Heteropogon contortus* behaved similarly in Queensland. This species also has awned dispersal units which bury the seed. He attributed germination to the higher temperatures which, in his area, allowed germination in cleared or burnt areas when temperatures were too low to permit it below a grass cover.

In *Themeda* grassland, large changes in the temperature regime of the seeds occur when the cover is removed. These could easily stimulate germination. Removal of the cover, followed by covering with black polythene, was an attempt to separate the effects of light and heat. Black polythene also caused some lowering of temperature beneath it as well as excluding light, and the experiments were otherwise somewhat unsatisfactory. However, the results do suggest that light could be stimulating germination.

Removal of the cover alters both the quantity and quality of the light reaching the seeds. Mature *Themeda* grassland reflects or absorbs up to 95 per cent of the incident radiation, in Western Uganda. Cumming (1963), and Taylorson & Borthwick (1968) have demonstrated that the light beneath a plant canopy is enriched in the inhibitory far-red wavelengths, and that light of similar composition could inhibit germination of some photoblastic seeds. Laboratory-stored seeds of *Themeda* showed no response to red and far-red light, but the photoblastic response shown by seeds after burial for 6 weeks might be mediated by the phytochrome system.

There remains the question of whether sufficient light penetrates to the buried seed to activate a photochemical reaction. The soil under most *Themeda* grasslands cracks deeply during the dry season, and these cracks appear before the soil is completely dry. In a laboratory trial, light was easily detectable through a 3 mm layer of soil allowed to dry in a petri dish. Light penetration increased as the soil dried. Furthermore, in a heavy storm, the saturation of the upper layers of the soil would provide ideal conditions for light penetration by total internal reflection. Light could certainly reach some of the more shallowly buried seeds, but seeds have been found germinating from 25 mm and it is hard to believe that any light can reach this depth.

Since stored seeds differ so markedly from buried ones in their germination behaviour, it seems likely that burial of the seeds induces extra germination requirements. Seeds which were buried and dug up were stimulated to germinate by a combination of light and high temperature. These seeds were buried for only 6 weeks; in nature a seed would be unlikely to remain buried for less than 12 weeks. The seeds dug up from under *Themeda* grassland (Table 6) germinated well in both darkness and light at room temperature. The soil was not completely dry when these seeds were dug out. They were put into white trays in the sun, which, if they were partially hydrated, could have fulfilled their light requirement. They also doubtless became hot. Both these unintentional pre-treatments could have stimulated germination later.

Conclusions

On the basis of these experiments a life history of a *Themeda* seed can be constructed. In western Uganda there are two wet and two dry seasons each year. *Themeda* flowers in the wet season and the dispersal units are shed towards the end of it. They fall to the ground and bury themselves by hygroscopic awn movements. The after-ripening period prevents germination before the onset of the dry season. During the dry season the seed after-ripens, but also develops new germination requirements. Lack of water also prevents germination. In the next wet season light and temperature conditions are unfavourable for germination. During the second dry season (in this case) the grassland burns. At the beginning of the rains the seed hydrates, light and temperature requirements are fulfilled, and germination takes place.

Grasses with awned dispersal units appear to be important constituents of regularly burnt grasslands in many parts of the world. It is possible that fire-related germination mechanisms like that of *Themeda triandra* are widespread. These rather specialized germination requirements may partially explain the disappearance of *Themeda* when burning is discontinued. The possibility of their wider occurrence should be borne in mind when preparing management programmes for regularly burnt grasslands.

Summary

Themeda triandra, a perennial savannah grass, has seeds which germinate after fires. The seed is buried by hygroscopic movements of the awn to a mean depth of 1 cm, where it is protected from the heat of fires. Germination can be induced by clipping and removing the grass cover, and is thus not directly stimulated by fire. Field and laboratory experiments suggest that germination is induced by a combination of light and high temperatures, which is produced by cover removal. Awned grasses are widespread in regularly burnt grasslands, and seed burial and post-fire germination, if found to be widespread, could be important in grassland management.

References

BEWS J.W. (1913) An ecological survey of the Midlands of Natal, with special reference to the Pietermaritzburg District. *Ann. Natal Mus.* 2, 485–545.

CUMMING B.G. (1963) The dependence of germination on photoperiod, light quality, and temperature in *Chenopodium* spp. *Can. J. Bot.* 41, 1211–33.

DARWIN F. (1876) On the hygroscopic mechanism by which certain seeds are enabled to bury themselves in the ground. *Trans. Linn. Soc. Lond. 2nd Series, Bot.* 1, 149–67.

EDWARDS D.C. (1935) The grasslands of Kenya. 1. Areas of high moisture and low temperature. *Emp. J. exp. Agric.* 3, 153–9.

EDWARDS D.C. (1942) Grass-burning. *Emp. J. exp. Agric.* 10, 219–31.

EWART A.J. (1930) *Flora of Victoria.* Melbourne.

MAIRE R. (1952) *Flore de l'Afrique du Nord.* Vol. 1. Paris.

MARSHALL B. & BREDON R.M. (1967) The nutritive value of *Themeda triandra*. *E. Afr. agric. for. J.* 32, 375–9.

MASSON H. (1948) La temperature du sol au cours d'un feu de brousse au Senegal. *Bull. agric. Congo belge* 40, 1933–44.

MULLER C.H., HANAWALT R.B. & McPHERSON J.K. (1968) Allelopathic control of herb growth in the fire cycle of California chaparral. *Bull. Torrey bot. Club* **95**, 225–31.

MURBACH L. (1900) Notes on the mechanism of the seed-burying awns of *Stipa avenacea*. *Bot. Gaz.* **30**, 113–17.

NORTON B.E. & McGARITY J.W. (1965) The effect of burning of native pastures on soil temperatures in northern New South Wales. *J. Br. Grassld Soc.* **20**, 101–5.

PRAIN D. (1934) *Flora of Tropical Africa*. Volume IX. London.

QUEZEL P. & SANTA S. (1962) *Nouvelle flore de l'Algerie et des regions desertiques meridionales*. Tome I. Paris.

TAYLORSON R.B. & BORTHWICK H.A. (1968) Light filtration by foliar canopies: significance for light-controlled weed seed germination. *Weed Sci.* **17**, 48–51.

TOTHILL J.C. (1969) Soil temperatures and seed burial in relation to the performance of *Heteropogon contortus* and *Themeda australis* in burnt native woodland pastures in Eastern Queensland. *Aust. J. Bot.* **17**, 269–75.

TOTHILL J.C. & SHAW N.H. (1968) Temperatures under fires in bunch spear grass pastures of south-east Queensland. *J. Aust. Inst. agric. Sci.* **34**, 94–8.

WEST O. (1951) Vegetation of Weenan County, Natal. *Mem. bot. Surv. S. Afr.* **23**.

WEST O. (1965) Fire in vegetation and its use in pasture management with special reference to Tropical Africa. *Mimeogrd Publ. No.* 1/1965 *Commonw. Bur. Past. Fld Crops*.

Comparative food preferences of five East African ungulates at different seasons

D.R.M. and J.STEWART *Research Division, Kenya Game Department, P.O. Box 241, Nairobi. Now at 2 Kyrchil Lane, Colehill, Wimborne, Dorset, England*

Introduction

There has been a considerable increase recently in both the amount and scope of research into herbivore food habits in Africa. The earlier, largely qualitative, studies were summarized by Stewart and Stewart (1970); they mostly consisted of lists of plants eaten by various animals, or were studies of individual species' feeding behaviour or of preferences shown by various species for vegetation types. Talbot (1962) and Lamprey (1963) were among the first to publish quantitative data on the selection of different plant species and to compare the preferences of different animal species feeding together.

Recent work has concentrated upon the quantitative assessment of food preferences in relation to the relative availability of food plants and to seasonal changes in plant growth, chemical content and 'palatability'. This work includes studies of individual species (e.g. Field 1969; Goddard, 1968, 1970; and of groups of species (e.g. Bell 1969; Casebeer and Koss 1970; Gwynne and Bell 1968; Stewart and Stewart 1970).

The present study investigated the preferences of five species, feeding together in an area of *c.* 300 ha, at three stages of plant growth: (i) just after the beginning of a wet season in April 1967 when there was a flush of new growth and when much of the pasture had previously been heavily grazed or burnt; (ii) in June 1967 at the end of the wet season when the grasses were mature but still green; (iii) in August 1969 at the end of a prolonged dry season when the remaining foliage was brown and dry. (Unusually wet climatic conditions caused the delay in carrying out iii.) The five species were Coke's hartebeest, *Alcelaphus buselaphus cokii* Günther, Grant's and Thomson's gazelle, *Gazella granti* Brooke and *G. thomsonii* Günther, wildebeest, *Connochaetes taurinus* (Burchell), and zebra, *Equus burchelli* (Gray). The study area, at *c.* 1760 m a.s.l. in Nairobi National Park, Kenya, is mostly flat or

351

gently sloping but is intersected by valleys containing permanent water. The vegetation consists of scattered tree/grassland on reddish-brown clay, with some patches of *Acacia drepanolobium* Sjostedt on grey-black clay ('black-cotton' soil).

The area was chosen because it attracts a variety of species throughout the year and because the accessibility of permanent water means that the animals use a conveniently small range.

Methods

Food preferences were investigated by the identification of plant epidermis in faeces. At each stage of the study the area was first visited for five consecutive days, at a different time each day, and the position of the animals was mapped. A sample of faeces from each of ten fresh piles of droppings from every species was collected on the sixth day, by which time the faeces contained only plant material from the range covered during that period (Stewart 1967).

The different grassland associations occurring throughout this range were then mapped. At stages i and ii of the study the percentage composition (by bulk of foliage) of the grass component of the pasture was assessed with a 1 m-square quadrat, divided into four, placed at 10 m intervals along 100 m transects in each association. Transect means were adjusted according to the relative area occupied by each association, and hence an overall mean figure for each available grass was obtained. Foliage of non-flowering grasses was either identified in the field by gross vegetative characteristics, using a reference collection, or in the laboratory by microscopic epidermal characters (Stewart 1965); to facilitate this, and to ensure that every species present was recorded, all grasses flowering near the transects were also listed. At stage iii the condition of the pasture made it possible to record only the approximate abundance, on a subjective scale, of each grass every 10 m along similar transects; hence the approximate abundance throughout the range was assessed. At each stage the dicotyledons and other monocotyledons occurring near the transects were listed.

Faecal samples were treated and slides prepared according to Stewart and Stewart (1970): 100 fragments of grass epidermis were recorded from each sample (except where noted below) using reference slides and a key. Small fragments bearing insufficient characters to allow identification were ignored; larger unidentifiable fragments were recorded as 'unidentified' and included in the 100 records. Some fragments from certain genera (e.g. *Eragrostis*, *Sporobolus*) could not be identified to the species, so that all records for such a genus were lumped.

The relative abundance of material from dicotyledons in each sample was simply recorded on a subjective scale.

Results

Stage i (April 1967)

During the five days preceding faecal collection the animals ranged over an area of *c.* 220 ha. About 50 per cent of this area consisted of dense dry grass, mostly in tussocks, 30–45 cm high excluding inflorescences; some new growth was present. Two-thirds of this section were located on sloping valley sides and were dominated by *Cymbopogon pospischilii*. Other common grasses included *Bothriochloa insculpta*, *Digitaria macroblephara*, *Hyparrhenia lintonii*, *Pennisetum mezianum* and *Themeda triandra*. The remaining third, on flat black-cotton soil, was dominated by *P. mezianum*; *D. macroblephara*, *T. triandra*, *Ischaemum afrum* and *Lintonia nutans* were common. (Authorities for names of grasses are given in Tables 1–3.)

A further 25 per cent of the area, on flat higher ground, had previously been burnt and bore a flush of new growth to 5–10 cm. This section was also dominated by *P. mezianum*; *Cynodon dactylon*, *Digitaria scalarum*, *D. macroblephara*, *Eustachys paspaloides* and *T. triandra* were common.

The remaining 25 per cent had been heavily grazed during the preceding dry season; half this section was on the flat higher ground and was dominated by *D. macroblephara*, *D. scalarum* and *Harpachne schimperi*. *Microchloa kunthii* was also very common. The other half lay on valley sides where the co-dominants were *C. pospischilii*, *D. macroblephara* and *T. triandra* and other common species were *C. dactylon*, *Eragrostis braunii* and *E. tenuifolia*.

Twenty-four dicotyledons were recorded along the transects, the commonest being *Aspilia mossambicensis* (Oliv.) Wild (often noted as having been eaten), *Dyschoriste radicans* Nees, *Indigofera volkensii* Taub; *Orthosiphon parvifolius* Vatke and *Sida ovata* Forsk. Ten other monocotyledons were recorded, the commonest being *Aneilema hockii* De Wild., *Commelina* spp. and the sedge *Mariscus macropus* (Boeck.) C.B.Cl.

Table 1 compares the overall percentage composition of the grass component of the pasture with the results of the faecal analyses. The latter are expressed firstly as frequency, or presence/absence, data; i.e. the number of faecal samples (P) from each animal species which contained a particular grass, for comparison with the number (n) examined. (Only nine samples could be obtained for Thomson's gazelle.) Secondly the mean percentage ($\bar{x}$) of each grass (by numbers of fragments) in the samples is shown; 100 grass fragments were recorded per sample except for five Grant's gazelle samples and one from Thomson's gazelle, where the scarcity of grasses meant that lesser totals, which were converted to percentages, had to suffice. Finally, dicotyledons in the faeces are expressed as the number of samples in which they were abundant, frequent or occasional/nil.

Table 1. Food preferences of five ungulates, assessed by analysis of the faeces and compared with pasture composition, following the start of a rainy season

Ephemeral/ perennial	Grazing value[1]	Composition of pasture — Grasses	% foliage	All species n=49	H n=10			GG n=10			TG n=9			W n=10			Z n=10		
				P	P	$\bar{x}$	s	P	$\bar{x}$	s	P	$\bar{x}$	s	P	$\bar{x}$	s	P	$\bar{x}$	s
p	high	Digitaria macroblephara (Hack.) Stapf	20	6	1	0·2		2	1·0			—		3	0·4		—		
p	low[3]	Pennisetum mezianum Leeke	18	24	4	0·6		6	5·5	7·4	8	2·0		4	1·4		2	0·2	
p	low[3]	Cymbopogon pospischilii (K. Schum.) C.E. Hubbard			1	0·1		1	0·1		—			—			—		
p	high	Themeda triandra Forsk.	13	49	10	74·6	8·3	10	42·5	23·0	9	62·8	13·4	10	81·3	6·9	10	56·8	13·4
p	high	Digitaria scalarum (Schweinf.) Chiov.	10	5	1	0·1		2	0·8		1	0·1		1	0·1				
p	high	Cynodon dactylon (L.) Pers.	7	42	8	1·4		8	29·6	23·3	9	7·8	15·5	9	2·1		8	3·0	
p	high	Eustachys paspaloides (Vahl) Lanza & Mattei	5	21	4	0·5		3	0·9		4	1·1		5	0·7		5	0·8	
p	high[4]	Hyparrhenia lintonii Stapf	4	22	9	4·7		5	1·4		3	0·8		2	0·3		3	2·0	
p	low	Harpachne schimperi A. Rich.	4	3				—											
p	medium	Bothriochloa insculpta (A. Rich.) A. Camus	3	22	6	2·0		5	1·8		6	1·9		4	0·5		1	0·1	
p,e		Eragrostis spp.[2]	2	8	—			3	2·0		2	0·2		2	0·3		1	0·1	
p,e		Aristida spp.[2]	2	26	7	3·8		3	0·8		7	1·9		4	1·0		5	0·8	
p	high	Cenchrus ciliaris L.	<2	3	—			1	0·4		1	0·1		—			1	0·1	
p	low	Enneapogon elegans (Nees) Stapf	<2																
p	high[4]	Heteropogon contortus (L.) R. & Sch.	<2	12	8	3·1		7	0·5		2	1·5		10	7·3	5·9	1	0·1	
p	low	Ischaemum afrum (J. F. Gmel.) Dandy	<2	45	9	6·8	5·5	7	8·6	8·4	8	16·7	13·4				10	28·8	12·2
p	low	Lintonia nutans Stapf	<2	1	1	0·1								1	0·1				
p	low	Microchloa kunthii Desv.	<2	3	—			1	0·1		1	0·1		2	0·2				
p	high	Panicum coloratum L.	<2	11	1	0·2		4	1·1		1	0·2					3	0·6	
p	low[3]	Pennisetum stramineum Peter	<2	1	—			1	0·1										
p	medium	Rhynchelytrum repens (Willd.) C. E. Hubbard	<2																
p	low	Setaria phleoides Stapf	<2	8	1	0·1		2	0·5								4	1·2	
p,e		Sporobolus spp.[2]	<2	28	2	0·2		6	1·6		6	1·1		9	3·8		2	5·0	14·3
		Unidentified grasses in faeces		25	7	0·8		5	0·7		5	0·9		5	0·5		3	0·4	
		Dicotyledons	a		3			6			5			6			3		
			f		7			4			4			4			7		
			o																

H hartebeest, GG Grant's gazelle, TG Thomson's gazelle, W wildebeest, Z zebra, n = no. of samples examined. P = no. of samples in which the grass concerned was identified; $\bar{x}$ = mean % of fragments recorded; s = standard deviation (for grasses scoring ⩾ 5%), a abundant. f frequent. o occasional/nil.

[1] As assessed by cattle usage (Bogdan 1958).
[2] Including Aristida adoensis Hochst., A. keniensis Henrard; Eragrostis braunii Schweinf., E. ?lehmanniana Nees, E. superba Peyr., E. tenuifolia A. Rich.; Sporobolus discosporus Nees, S. pellucidus Hochst., S. phyllotrichus Hochst., S. pyramidalis Beauv., S. stapfianus Gaud.
[3] Prior to flowering.   [4] Except when young.

Stage ii (June 1967)

During the relevant five days at the end of the wet season movements of the animals were largely restricted to a smaller area of *c.* 100 ha within the April range. About 25 per cent of the area lay on valley slopes dominated by *Cymbopogon pospischilii* and *Bothriochloa insculpta*; *Cenchrus ciliaris*, *Digitaria macroblephara*, *Hyparrhenia lintonii*, *Pennisetum mezianum* and *Themeda triandra* were also common. Most grasses were flowering, with foliage often 90–120 cm high. The remaining 75 per cent lay on flat black-cotton soil, much of it dominated by *P. mezianum*, accompanied by abundant *D. macroblephara* and *Ischaemum afrum*. Many of the grasses (including these three species) had been grazed; their foliage was only 15–30 cm high, or less, with comparatively few flowering stems remaining. The 26 dicotyledons recorded (including *Aspilia*), on the other hand, showed few signs of use with the exception of *Commelina* spp. Three other monocotyledons were recorded, two (the sedges *Cyperus kilimandscharicus* Kukenth. and *Mariscus assimilis* (Steud.) Podlich) being common.

Table 2 compares the pasture composition with the faecal analyses. Only seven Thomson's gazelle and nine wildebeest samples were obtained, and <100 fragments were recorded for all Grant's samples.

Stage iii (August 1969)

The range used in August 1969, at the end of a long dry season, occupied *c.* 160 ha; only half of this overlapped parts of the earlier ranges. About 50 per cent of the area had been heavily grazed; three-quarters of this section lay on valley slopes where *Themeda triandra* was probably the most abundant species and *Cymbopogon pospischilii*, *Cynodon dactylon*, *Digitaria macroblephara*, *Eragrostis braunii*, *E. superba*, *E. tenuifolia*, *Harpachne schimperi*, *Panicum ? massaiense* and *P. poaeoides* were all common; however, the state of the pasture made a precise determination of relative abundance impossible. The remaining quarter lay on flat higher ground dominated by *T. triandra* and *Pennisetum mezianum* on brown and black soil respectively. *T. triandra* was also common on the latter, and *D. macroblephara* on the brown soil.

The remaining 50 per cent of the area had been fairly heavily, but more patchily, grazed; three-quarters of this lay on valley slopes dominated by *C. pospischilii*; *Aristida adoensis*, *D. macroblephara*, *Hyparrhenia lintonii* and *T. triandra* were locally common. A quarter, which had been less well grazed, lay on higher ground dominated by *E. tenuifolia*, *P. mezianum* and *T. triandra*; *D. macroblephara*, *P. ? massaiense* and *P. poaeoides* were also common.

Absence of flowering material prevented the identification of all the dicotyledons present; however these included many of the species recorded during stages i and ii.

Table 2. Food preferences of the five ungulates at the end of the rainy season

Ephemeral/ perennial	Grazing value[1]	Composition of pasture: Grasses	% foliage	All species n=46	Analysis of faeces														
					H n=10			GG n=10			TG n=7			W n=9			Z n=10		
				P	P	x̄	s	P	x̄	s	P	x̄	s	P	x̄	s	P	x̄	s
p	low[3]	Pennisetum mezianum	25	21	5	0·8		6	7·7	9·2	5	1·0		4	0·7		1	0·2	
p	low	Ischaemum afrum	18	44	10	31·0	16·4	8	9·8	9·7	7	23·0	10·1	9	25·4	11·7	10	65·9	13·5
p	high	Digitaria macroblephara	17	43	10	3·7		9	11·8	7·3	7	14·4	6·8	9	7·4	2·9	8	1·5	
p	low	Cymbopogon pospischilii	7	—															
p	medium	Bothriochloa insculpta	6	26	5	0·8		1	0·8		5	2·3		9	3·4		6	1·0	
p	high	Themeda triandra	6	46	10	57·0	14·4	10	22·3	13·8	7	47·8	6·1	9	48·1	11·8	10	14·4	4·5
p	low	Lintonia nutans	4	27	6	1·3		4	2·0		5	2·0		6	1·0		6	0·7	
p	high	Eustachys paspaloides	2	31	4	0·6		6	4·3		6	1·9		8	2·7		7	1·7	
p	medium	Andropogon schinzii Hack.	2	—															
p	low	Aristida adoensis	<2	4	2	0·2		1	0·4		1	0·1					1	0·1	
e	medium	Brachiaria cruciformis (Sw.) Gris.	<2																
p	high	Cenchrus ciliaris	<2	1															
p	high	Cynodon dactylon	<2	41	6	2·6		9	19·4	13·2	7	4·1		9	6·7	4·4	10	8·2	6·2
p	high	Digitaria scalarum	<2	1							1	0·3							
e	low	Dinebra retroflexa (Vahl) Panzer	<2	19	2	0·2		8	17·9	17·5	3	1·4		4	0·5		2	0·2	
e	low	Enneapogon elegans	<2	—															
p,e	—	Eragrostis spp.[2]	<2	1	1	0·1													
e	high	Eriochloa nubica (Steud.) Thell.	<2	—															
p	low	Harpachne schimperi	<2	—													1	0·1	
p	high[4]	Heteropogon contortus	<2	—										1	0·1		1	0·1	
p	high[4]	Hyparrhenia lintonii	<2	—													1	0·1	
p	low	Microchloa kunthii	<2	—															
e	medium	Panicum atrosanguineum A. Rich.	<2	10				2	0·8		3	0·6		4	0·8				
p	high	P. coloratum	<2	2	1	0·1		1	0·4					1	0·1				
p	high	P. ? massaiense Mez	<2	—															
p	medium	Rhynchelytrum repens	<2	—															
e	low	Setaria pallide-fusca (Schumach.) Stapf & C. E. Hubbard	<2	—															
p	low	S. phleoides	<2	16	3	0·4		1	0·4		3	0·4		2	0·2		7	1·0	
p,e	—	Sporobolus spp.[2]	<2	24	4	0·7		2	1·6		1	0·1		8	2·0		9	3·8	
		Unidentified grasses in faeces		18	4	0·5		1	0·4		2	0·4		6	0·7		5	1·0	
		Dicotyledons a			—			10			1			—			1		
		f			2			—			5			2			1		
		o			8			—			1			7			9		

[2] Including Eragrostis braunii, E. cilianensis (All.) Lutati, E. superba, E. tenuifolia ; Sporobolus discosporus, S. pellucidus, S. phyllotrichus, S. stapfianus. For abbreviations and remaining footnotes see Table I.

Table 3 lists the grasses in four groups: (*a*) the species (*Themeda triandra*) which was, overall, the most abundant in the range used; (*b*) species which, overall, were ranked 'occasional' but which were locally frequent or abundant; (*c*) rarer species which were sometimes locally common, and (*d*) the remaining species recorded. During the faecal analyses <100 grass fragments were recorded for two Thomson's gazelle and all ten Grant's gazelle samples.

Discussion

The technique

This study attempted to compare the food preferences of a selection of animal species with the composition of the pasture they were using. The quantitative assessment of food-plant availability is not entirely straightforward, since 'availability' is not simply a question of the proportions of different plants present; it is also affected by their age and growth form (which may vary widely), their position in relation to other plants, and by factors such as the proximity of water or predator-cover and the way in which soil conditions influence animal movement. No quantitative allowance could easily be made for such factors. Nevertheless, an attempt must be made in food-habits studies to assess availability in quantitative terms if the maximum value is to be obtained from the results and if they are to be at all comparable.

Faecal analysis was used because it permits the sampling of large numbers of individuals, with minimum disturbance, under entirely natural conditions; it is also practicable when direct observation is impossible because of pasture conditions. However, several limitations of the technique as applied in this study must be mentioned. Firstly, information was only obtained about leaf-blades in the diet, since sheath epidermis is often much less differentiated and thus difficult to identify. Secondly, Stewart (1967) showed that epidermis of different grasses may be digested to different extents, and that it may break up in the digestive tract into fragments varying significantly in mean size between grasses. Thus the proportions of epidermis in the faeces, even if measured by surface area rather than by numbers of fragments, do not accurately represent the proportions ingested. However, the experiments suggested that large differences in proportions by numbers are meaningful, especially if (as in this study) very small fragments are ignored; this avoids bias in favour of certain species which are more easily identifiable from small fragments than others.

There remains the possibility that some plants might be completely digested, which would invalidate even qualitative data. However, the same series of experiments indicated that any perennial grasses eaten (with the possible exception of those eaten spasmodically or in very small quantities)

Table 3. Food preferences of the five ungulates at the end of a long dry season

| | | Composition of pasture | | All species | Analysis of faeces | | | | | | | | | | | | | | |
| | | | | | H | | | GG | | | TG | | | W | | | Z | | |
Ephemeral/perennial	Grazing value[1]	Grasses	Abundance[5]	n=50 P	n=10 P	$\bar{x}$	s	n=10 P	$\bar{x}$	s	n=10 P	$\bar{x}$	s	n=10 P	$\bar{x}$	s	n=10 P	$\bar{x}$	s
p	high	*Themeda triandra*	f–la	50	10	64·2	14·4	10	32·9	17·8	10	48·4	26·9	10	35·2	12·1	10	44·3	21·4
p,e	—	*Aristida* spp.[2]	o–lf	40	9	3·8		8	4·7		7	1·3		9	3·9		6	1·0	
p,e	high	*Digitaria macroblephara*	o–lf	36	8	2·3		7	5·0	5·0	3	0·5		9	6·8	3·8	9	4·3	
p	—	*Eragrostis* spp.[2]	o–lf	25	8	1·1		3	1·6		1	0·1		7	1·5		6	1·9	
p	low	*Harpachne schimperi*	o–lf	23	7	2·0		1	0·5		3	1·0		7	1·4		5	1·5	
p	low[3]	*Pennisetum mezianum*	o–la	6	—			3	0·8					1	0·1		2	0·2	
p	medium	*Botriochloa insculpta*	r	41	7	1·3		9	7·1	5·4	8	4·3		10	5·3	3·5	7	3·1	
p	low	*Cymbopogon pospischilii*	r–la	26	3	0·5		5	2·8		6	3·9		4	0·7		8	2·0	
p	high	*Cynodon dactylon*	r–lf	48	10	9·9	4·9	8	11·8	11·0	10	16·9	10·0	10	29·2	13·6	10	13·0	13·2
p	low	*Enneapogon elegans*	r	2	1	0·1											1	0·2	
p	high[4]	*Hyparrhenia lintonii*	r–lf	11	1	0·1		1	0·5		5	2·0		1	0·1		4	1·6	
p	low	*Microchloa kunthii*	r–lf	12	1	0·1								3	0·3		7	3·7	
p	high	*Panicum ?massaiense*	r–lf	—															
p	high	*P. poaeoides* Stapf	r–lf	3	2	0·2								1	0·1				
p	high	*Cenchrus ciliaris*	trace	3	—									1	0·2		2	0·4	
p	high	*Chloris gayana* Kunth	trace	3	—									1	0·1		1	0·1	
e	low	*C. pycnothrix* Trin.	trace	8	3	0·3					1	0·4					4	0·6	
p	high[4]	*Heteropogon contortus*	trace	34	8	6·7	6·1	3	2·0		1	0·1		9	2·9		6	3·1	
p	low	*Ischaemum afrum*	trace	31	9	6·1	7·0	7	11·1	11·8	8	2·5		5	4·4		9	13·9	12·8
p	high	*Lintonia nutans*	trace	6	1	0·1		1	0·3		1	0·1		1	0·1		1	0·1	
p	low[3]	*Panicum coloratum*	trace	21	3	0·3		3	12·9	22·7	2	0·3		6	3·0		1	0·1	
p		*Pennisetum stramineum*	trace	1	—						8	8·1	11·7				1	0·1	
p	medium	*Rhynchelytrum repens*	trace	4	—			2	0·5		1	0·1					1	0·1	
p	low	*Setaria phleoides*	trace	7				2	1·0		1	0·1		1	0·1		3	0·4	
p,e	—	*Sporobolus* spp.[2]	trace	29	5	0·7		4	1·2		3	0·4		8	2·8		9	2·8	
		Unidentified grasses in faeces		24	2	0·2		4	2·1		7	9·3	12·4	6	1·9		5	0·8	
		Dicotyledons a			—			10			10			—			—		
		f			—			—			—			2			—		
		o			10			—			—			8			10		

[2] Including *Aristida adoensis, A. keniensis*; *Eragrostis braunii, E. cilianensis, E. exasperata* Peter, *E. hispida* K. Schum., *E. superba, E. tenuifolia*; *Sporobolus discosporus, S. festivus* Hochst., *S. phyllotrichus*.

[5] f frequent, o occasional, r rare (= overall assessment in area); la locally abundant, etc.

For abbreviations and remaining footnotes see Table 1.

can be identified in the faeces; information was not obtained on ephemerals (which are unimportant constituents of East African grasslands—e.g. see Tables 1–3—although they are very important in grass-steppe areas) or on dicotyledons. There is also circumstantial evidence against the possibility that some grasses might be completely digested. First, it is often the case that a common grass which is absent from most faecal samples on a particular occasion nevertheless occurs abundantly in a few samples from both the same and different animal species. It is unlikely that there could be such a widely-differing degree of digestion, especially between individuals of the same species, and much more likely that this reflects a true difference in intake. Secondly, the great majority of grasses, except for very small or obviously unpalatable species, do occur from time to time in considerable quantity in faecal samples. Thirdly, epidermal fragments in faeces from zebra, a non-ruminant, are larger and less well digested than those in ruminant faeces; nevertheless zebra faeces do not tend to contain greater numbers of grass species.

In this context the danger of drawing conclusions from plants noted to have been eaten must be mentioned. During stage ii of this study *Pennisetum mezianum* was recorded as being well eaten, but the faecal analyses tended to contradict this. Conversely, at the same time dicotyledons were recorded as being much less well used than at stage i, but the analyses did not support this. The presence of herbivores other than those being studied (such as warthog, *Phacochoerus aethiopicus* (Pallas), ostrich, *Struthio camelus* Linnaeus and hare, *Lepus* sp. in the present case), and the effects of the times of through-put and elimination of material from the digestive tract (Stewart 1967), mean that the absence of faecal material from plants which have apparently been utilized does not necessarily imply that they have been completely digested.

The standard deviation (s) of means $\geqslant 5$ per cent is shown in Tables 1–3 to indicate the degree of variation between individual samples, but further statistical analysis of these data is deliberately omitted to avoid overstating their value; they must be used with caution and only large differences should be regarded as meaningful. The latter, however, taken in conjunction with the frequency data (P), provide an indication of the relative importance of different grasses as food plants, and of differences in the diets of the animals concerned. Dicotyledonous material in the faeces was recorded simply on a relative abundance scale because of the lack of experimental evidence about digestibility, and because much of this material consisted of hairs which are difficult to record quantitatively.

It must be stressed that the choice of food plants by herbivores in any particular situation will depend, amongst other factors, on the choice of plant species available. Thus dogmatic conclusions about preferences cannot be reached, and considerable variation in the use made of a particular species may be expected at different times and places. Nevertheless, it is worth comparing the results of different studies and as the number of the latter increase certain trends are likely to emerge.

Utilization of grasses

The only grass occurring in every faecal sample at all stages of this study was *Themeda triandra*. At stage i it provided only 10 per cent of the available grass foliage, but in all samples it formed a high proportion of the epidermal fragments (Table 1) and was undoubtedly selected. At stage ii it provided 6 per cent of the foliage and was still being strongly selected, although in all species it formed a lower proportion of the fragments (Table 2), with a particularly marked drop in Grant's gazelle and zebra. At stage iii, after a two-year gap and at the end of a long dry season, it was the most abundant grass available. Considering its much greater availability than at stages i and ii, however, relatively much less use was being made of it at stage iii (Table 3). *T. triandra* is usually regarded as one of the most important food plants of African wildlife (Bayer 1955) and stock (Edwards and Bogdan 1951), and is recorded by Stewart and Stewart (1970) and Talbot and Talbot (1963) as being strongly selected by various wild species, although Lamprey (1963) found that in the Tarangire Game Reserve, Tanzania, its proportion in the diet of wildebeest and zebra simply reflected the proportion in the pasture. Grzimek and Grzimek (1960) recorded that examination of the pasture at various times and places in the Serengeti, Tanzania, did not suggest that *T. triandra* was much used; it seems possible, however, that this conclusion underlines the difficulties stressed by Heady (1964) and already mentioned in this paper of assessing forage utilization in this way.

Cynodon dactylon was never abundant in the pasture, but occurred in a high proportion of faecal samples. Whereas it was strongly selected by Grant's gazelle at stages i and ii, the data suggest that it was of most importance to other species when the pasture dried out (Table 3). This species is another of the most valuable African grasses (Edwards and Bogdan 1951; Scott 1955). Bredon and Horrell (1961) record that cattle also tend to graze it mainly in the dry season; Lamprey (1963), Grzimek and Grzimek (1960), Stewart and Stewart (1970) and Talbot (1962) all found that it was selected by various wild herbivores.

Ischaemum afrum, regarded by Edwards and Bogdan (1951) as 'unpalatable (except possibly when quite young) and useless in pastures', figured prominently in the faeces throughout, although its availability was high only during stage ii. It was clearly selected by zebra at all stages, and also by Thomson's gazelle at stage i and Grant's gazelle at stage iii. In an earlier study involving the same animal species at a season corresponding to stage iii, Stewart and Stewart (1970) again found that *I. afrum* figured rather more prominently in the diet of zebra than of other species, and at another site at the same time, when zebra were absent, it was favoured particularly by hartebeest and to some extent by Grant's gazelle and wildebeest, but was hardly touched by Thomson's gazelle (cf. Table 3).

Other grasses which show evidence of having been selected by certain animals at certain seasons include *Bothriochloa insculpta* (by several species at stage iii), *Heteropogon contortus* (at stage iii, especially by hartebeest), *Panicum coloratum* (at stage iii, especially by the two gazelles) and *Sporobolus* spp.—mainly *S. phyllotrichus* (by wildebeest and zebra at all stages). All are regarded by Bogdan (1958) as useful food plants, although *H. contortus* becomes less palatable to cattle when flowering because of its awns. The present study bears this out, as it was almost unused at stage ii; by stage iii few inflorescences remained.

In contrast to those which were clearly selected, several grasses figured prominently in the pasture but not in the faeces. *Pennisetum mezianum*, mostly in a very stemmy, tussocky growth-form, was abundant at stages i and ii; it was present in about half the faecal samples at these times, but only in Grant's gazelle, in which it was consistently most abundant at all three stages, did it form an appreciable proportion of the epidermal fragments. Bogdan (1958) records this grass as being little used by stock except possibly when young. Its usage by wild animals probably varies considerably with growth-form. Talbot (1962) found that it ranked second in importance in the diet of Thomson's gazelle and wildebeest in western Masailand, over periods of 10 and 15 months respectively. However, Lamprey (pers. comm., 1970) considered that it was largely ignored in the Tarangire Game Reserve. He states that in the Serengeti National Park new growth of *P. mezianum* is grazed to some extent, but that nevertheless the new growth of other species is preferred; mature stands remain ungrazed even though other grasses in the same area are being heavily grazed. Casebeer and Koss (1970) likewise found that the proportion of *P. mezianum* in the diet of four herbivores in south-eastern Masailand was much lower than its proportion in the available pasture. Stewart and Stewart (1970) found that at three sites in Masailand where *P. mezianum* was common it was largely ignored, but at a fourth site it ranked second in the diet of six species.

Digitaria macroblephara was also a common constituent of the pasture; nevertheless, although it appeared in a high proportion of faecal samples at stages ii and iii its availability appears to have exceeded its usage, a result also recorded by Casebeer and Koss (1970). Elsewhere, however, this species has been reported to be very palatable to stock (Bogdan 1958). *Cymbopogon pospischilii* was again fairly common, but its scent and taste tend to make it unpalatable (Eggeling 1947). It was probably used to a small extent by several species at stage iii simply because of the scarcity of other food.

Most of the remaining grasses present were eaten on occasion, but show no striking difference between availability and utilization.

The preceding paragraphs consider the results primarily from the point of view of the overall importance of different grasses as food plants. Certain apparent differences between animals with respect to their utilization of these grasses have also been indicated, but these are much less clear-cut and often could not be proven even if it were legitimate to test their significance. These differences tended to be greatest at stages i and ii, and least at the end of the dry season when what grass foliage remained was dry and brown. (Turner and Watson 1965 record a similar increase in the overlap of herbivore diets as the dry season advances in the Serengeti.)

At stage i, although *Themeda triandra* was heavily selected by all species, Grant's gazelle probably made rather less use of it, and considerably more of *Cynodon dactylon* and *Pennisetum mezianum*, than did other animals. At this stage hartebeest probably made more use of the clumped species on the un-burnt valley slopes, such as *Heteropogon contortus* and *Hyparrhenia lintonii*, than other animals and zebra made noticeably more use of *Ischaemum afrum*.

At stage ii Grant's gazelle and zebra showed the same tendencies as at stage i, and both species show a particularly marked decrease in their use of *T. triandra*. The two gazelles apparently made rather more use of *Digitaria macroblephara* than other animals. No marked differences are apparent at stage iii.

The differentiation of diet on the basis of the grass species used was thus not very great, but it must be borne in mind that these results only concern the relative proportions of leaf from different grasses in the diet. Had a study been made of the relative proportions of leaf, sheath and stem much greater differentiation would probably have been indicated; it was clear during the analyses of samples at stage iii, for instance, that wildebeest had consumed a much lower proportion of leaf than other species. Gwynne and Bell (1968) found marked differences in the selection of plant parts when analysing stomach contents from four species in the Serengeti.

Utilization of dicotyledons

Despite the simple, subjective method of assessment a clear pattern emerges of the use made of dicotyledons (Table 4). They were never important to hartebeest, wildebeest or zebra, although most use was made of them in the early wet season when there was a flush of new growth, after which the use progressively decreased. The converse is true for the two gazelles. Dicotyledons were already abundant in over half the Grant's gazelle samples at stage i, and were abundant in all samples at stages ii and iii. Thomson's gazelle

Table 4. Relative abundance of dicotyledons in the faecal samples at the three stages of plant growth

Stage: Season:		i early wet	ii late wet % of faecal samples	iii late dry
Hartebeest	a	—	—	—
	f	30	20	—
	o	70	80	100
Grant's gazelle	a	60	100	100
	f	40	—	—
	o	—	—	—
Thomson's gazelle	a	—	14	100
	f	55	71	—
	o	45	14	—
Wildebeest	a	—	—	—
	f	60	25	20
	o	40	75	80
Zebra	a	—	—	—
	f	30	10	—
	o	70	90	100

a abundant, f frequent, o occasional/nil.

made only moderate use of dicotyledons at stages i and ii, but heavy use of them at stage iii.

The relative proportion of dicotyledons to grasses, however, was always much higher in Grant's samples. At stage i grasses were already sparse in half the Grant's samples, and were uncommon in all samples at stages ii and iii. In Thomson's gazelle, despite the increasing use of dicotyledons, grasses remained common until stage iii, when there were noticeably few in 30 per cent of the samples.

Gwynne and Bell (1968) obtained similar results in the Serengeti regarding the relative utilization of grasses and dicotyledons by Thomson's gazelle, wildebeest and zebra, as did Talbot (1962) for wildebeest and the two gazelles, and Stewart and Stewart (1970) for all five species considered in the present study. Lamprey (1963), however, found that Grant's gazelle in Tarangire ate 90 per cent grass, although he notes that other food plants may have been underestimated.

Utilization of sedges

Sedges formed an insignificant proportion of the available foliage at stage i, and by stage iii they had dried out and almost disappeared. At stage ii, however, two species (see 'Results') formed *c.* 5 per cent of the total monocotyledon foliage, and a record was made during the faecal analyses of the number of sedge fragments encountered per 100 grass fragments. The mean number for Grant's gazelle was 123·2, and for Thomson's gazelle 15·5. For the remaining animals it was <5·5.

Acknowledgements

We are grateful to the Director, Kenya National Parks, for permission to carry out this study in Nairobi National Park and to the Wardens of the Park for their support. We are also grateful to the staff of the East African Herbarium for assistance in identifying plants, and to the staff of Dr J.M.King for assistance in collecting faecal samples.

Summary

The food habits of five ungulates feeding together on a limited area of East African scattered tree/grassland were investigated at three stages of plant growth: (i) early in the rains, (ii) at the end of the rains, and (iii) at the end of a long dry season. The composition of the diet was investigated by the identification of plant epidermis in faeces, and was related to the relative abundance of different plants in the pasture. A detailed assessment was made of the importance of different grasses in the diet, whilst the use made of dicotyledons was recorded without any attempt to identify the species concerned.

Differences between animals in the extent to which different grasses were utilized were not very clear-cut and there was considerable overlap in diets, especially towards the end of the dry season. Comparison of the relative availability of different grasses with the extent to which they were utilized indicated that certain species were clearly selected; i.e. they formed a much higher proportion of the diet than of the available foliage. Conversely, several abundant species clearly tended to be ignored. Some seasonal changes in these respects were apparent.

Distinct differences were apparent in the extent to which dicotyledons were eaten; these formed a large part of the diet of Grant's gazelle at stage i, and were the major source of food at stages ii and iii. In Thomson's gazelle dicotyledons also formed a significant part of the diet, increasing in importance as the pasture matured and dried out, but grasses remained important at all stages. Dicotyledons were unimportant to hartebeest, wildebeest and zebra, although all three species made rather more use of them following the beginning of the rains than at other times.

Sedges were used in preference to grasses by Grant's gazelle at stage ii, but formed an insignificant part of the diet of other species.

References

BAYER A.W. (1955) The ecology of grasslands. In *The grasses and pastures of South Africa* (Ed. by D.Meredith), pp. 539–50. Capetown.

BELL R.H.V. (1969) *The use of the herb layer by grazing ungulates in the Serengeti National Park, Tanzania.* Ph.D. thesis, Manchester University.

BOGDAN A.V. (1958) *A revised list of Kenya grasses.* Nairobi.

BREDON R.M. & HORRELL C.R. (1961). The chemical composition and nutritive value of some common grasses in Uganda–1. *Trop. Agric. Trin.* 38, 297–304.

CASEBEER R.L. & KOSS G. (1970) Food habits of wildebeest, zebra, hartebeest and cattle in Kenya Masailand. *E. Afr. Wildl. J.* 8, 25–36.

EDWARDS D.C. & BOGDAN A.V. (1951) *Important grassland plants of Kenya.* London.

EGGELING W.J. (1947) *An annotated list of the grasses of the Uganda Protectorate.* 2nd ed. Entebbe.

FIELD C.R. (1969) A study of the feeding habits of the hippopotamus (*Hippopotamus amphibius* Linn.) in the Queen Elizabeth National Park, Uganda, with some management implications. *Zoologica Africana* 5 (1), 71–86.

GODDARD J. (1968) Food preferences of two black rhinoceros populations. *E. Afr. Wildl. J.* 6, 1–18.

GODDARD J. (1970) Food preferences of black rhinoceros in the Tsavo National Park. *E. Afr.. Wildl. J.* 8, 145–61.

GRZIMEK M. & GRZIMEK B. (1960) A study of the game of the Serengeti plains. *Z. Säugetierk.* 25, 1–61.

GWYNNE M.D. & BELL R.H.V. (1968) Selection of vegetation components by grazing ungulates in the Serengeti National Park. *Nature, Lond.* 220 (5165), 390–3.

HEADY H.F. (1964) Palatability of herbage and animal preference. *J. Range Mgmt* 17(2), 76–82.

LAMPREY H.F. (1963) Ecological separation of the large mammal species in the Tarangire Game Reserve, Tanganyika. *E. Afr. Wildl. J.* 1, 63–92.

SCOTT J.D. (1955) Pasture plants for special purposes. In *The grasses and pastures of South Africa* (Ed. by D.Meredith), 653–66. Capetown.

STEWART D.R.M. (1965) The epidermal characters of grasses, with special reference to East African plains species. *Bot. Jb.* 84(1), 63–116, and (2), 117–74.

STEWART D.R.M. (1967) Analysis of plant epidermis in faeces: a technique for studying the food preferences of grazing herbivores. *J. appl. Ecol.* 4, 83–111.

STEWART D.R.M. & STEWART J. (1970) Food preference data by faecal analysis for African plains ungulates. *Zoologica Africana* 5(1), 115–29.

TALBOT L.M. (1962) Food preferences of some East African wild ungulates. *E. Afr. agric. for. J.* 27(3), 131–8.

Talbot L.M. & Talbot M.H. (1963) The wildebeest in Western Masailand, East Africa. *Wildl. Monogr.* no. 12, 1–88.

Turner M.I.M. & Watson R.M. (1965) An introductory study on the ecology of hyrax (*Dendrohyrax brucei* and *Procavia johnstoni*) in the Serengeti National Park. *E. Afr. Wildl. J.* 3, 49–60.

The effect of creating additional water supplies in a Central African National Park

J.S.WEIR *Department of Zoology, University of Leicester, England*
(*formerly University College, Rhodesia*)

Introduction

With an area of approximately 1·25 million ha (*c.* 5,000 sq. miles) Wankie National Park, Rhodesia, is one of the largest parks in Southern Africa. Much of this area is covered with deep deposits of aeolian Kalahari sand. The area covered by the flat Kalahari sand deposits is also separated climatically from the hotter and wetter northern region of the Park (Fig. 1). These sands are outstandingly deficient in minerals and organic matter, even in comparison with other African soils (Saunder 1964), and have been assessed as unsuitable for agricultural purposes other than forestry (Vincent and Thomas 1961).

The Park evolved originally by the accretion of various areas of land until it became a Game Reserve, and subsequently achieved National Park status. Mammals of several species are supposed to have migrated northwards from the area of Botswana to drink at permanent pools in the Gwaai and other rivers to the north during the dry season (May to November). With the onset of the wet season these animals would disperse over the Kalahari sands, drinking from temporary waterholes formed in clay pans filled with rainwater. The development of farms on the Permian and Triassic sedimentary rocks and basalts along the Gwaai River and to the north of the Gwaai River led to fencing and the utilization of restricted dry-season water supplies for cattle.

Consequently, in an effort to preserve the natural fauna, to prevent interference with farming, and to utilize the tourist potential of the National Park, additional water supplies have been created within the Park boundary to sustain migratory herds throughout the relatively long dry season.

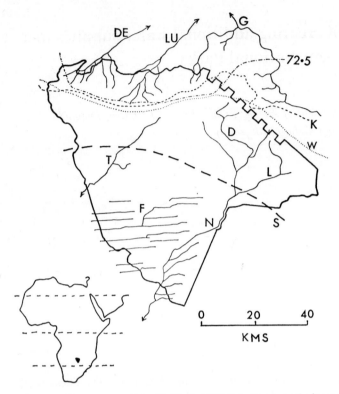

Figure 1. The position of Wankie National Park is shown on the inset map of Africa. The detailed map shows the division of the Park into regions. The 72·5°F isotherm is marked and runs close to the northern boundary of the Kalahari Sand deposits (K) and the effective watershed (W). To the north the rivers Deka (DE), Lukosi (LU) and Gwaai (G) are marked while the 'fossil watercourses' of the Dopi (D), Linkwasha (L) and other non-flowing rivers (T, F, N) mark shallow valleys with occasional pans. The possible extent of a vegetation change (S) is marked, though this is ill defined and of doubtful significance.

Creation of additional water supplies

There are few permanent natural waterholes in the Kalahari sand region, and no rivers or streams under present climatic conditions. In the northern and western parts of the Park there are some rivers which hold water throughout the year (e.g. the Deka) but many streams which dry up. The deep fine and medium sands reduce surface run-off to a minimum (<1 per cent), and only on grassland within 3 or 4 km of pans does the clay content of the top soil rise to more than 3 per cent or 4 per cent and increase the water retention of the soil.

Additional water supplies have been created since 1935 in a variety of ways. In the north-western section of the Park, boreholes with pumps (either wind driven or diesel powered), supply water to pools in river beds or to small man-made dams on watercourses. In the Kalahari sand areas, certain natural clay pans have been deepened by scraping mud from them during the dry season. Their water-holding capacity is increased and in normal years such pans hold rainwater throughout the year. Other pans have been supplied with water pumped continuously from boreholes either directly into the pan or via a concrete reservoir.

Animal populations at man-made waterholes

This policy has been successful, and large populations of herbivores congregate at these man-made waterholes throughout the dry season. They form an obvious tourist attraction and the road system has been planned to enable tourists to view populations gathered at selected pans where viewing platforms have been constructed. Although herds penetrate to farms on the northern side of the Park boundary and control measures are necessary, one has to assume that in the absence of artificial waterholes all animals requiring water would have had to reach the Gwaai and rigorous control would have eliminated many of them.

The present paper is not directly concerned with economic or political aspects of National Park policy, but deals with the effects on the animals and on their environment of the new situation which has been created by man. Observations and measurements described here were made during the period 1961–6, and refer to conditions in the Park at that time.

Animal populations in relation to waterholes

Spatial and temporal segregation of animal populations

Records of the number of animals drinking at a pan during a period of 24 hours were made at selected pans by members of staff of the Department of National Parks and others, during the peak of the dry season. These were taken over a period of 6 years (1957–63). Data from these censuses were used by Weir and Davison (1966) in an examination of the temporal separation of animal species at waterholes. Some species were shown to drink during the day (warthog *Phacochoerus aethiopicus*, sable *Hippotragus niger*, roan *H. equinus*), while others showed a pronounced peak in the evening, but also drank in the afternoon and during the night (elephant *Loxodonta africana*, giraffe *Giraffa camelopardalis* and buffalo *Syncerus caffer*). While some species seldom encountered each other at waterholes (e.g. warthog and buffalo), others were frequently seen together (elephant, buffalo, giraffe). To some extent therefore the species present showed temporal separation in the use of the waterholes.

Censuses are used here to assess the relative numbers of each species drinking at particular pans. There were clear differences in the composition of the faunas at different pans (F test p <0·01 per cent). Table 1 shows the percentage composition of ten common species at seven pans all supplied with water from boreholes. This can be compared with Table 2, which measures the general structural types of vegetation found within 10 km of the seven selected pans, as assessed from aerial photographs. Obviously some animals were distributed

Table 1. Percentage composition of Fauna at seven selected pans

	Shapi	Dom	Guvalalla	Nyamandhlovu	Kennedy I	Ngwashla	Makwa
Buffalo (*Syncerus caffer* Sparrmann)	5·71	16·33	6·07	33·89	17·89	45·44	59·73
Eland (*Taurotragus oryx* Pallas)	0·24	2·04	0·58	1·29	22·48	1·01	4·53
Elephant (*Loxodonta africana* Blumenbach)	44·05	28·34	85·84	42·91	16·51	31·98	15·99
Giraffe (*Giraffa camelopardalis* Linn.)	1·67	7·48	0·58	6·45	4·36	0·72	5·33
Kudu (*Tragelaphus strepsiceros* Pallas)	1·67	3·85	3·76	2·58	3·44	1·45	0·53
Roan (*Hippotragus equinus* Desmarest)	3·10	2·04	0·58	0·18	0·69	2·17	0·0
Sable (*Hippotragus niger* Harris)	6·19	6·58	1·45	0·55	2·98	9·70	3·73
Warthog (*Phacochoerus aethiopicus* Pallas)	0·71	5·67	0·0	2·03	3·67	4·05	1·60
Wildebeeste (*Connochaetes taurinus* Burchell)	1·19	7·26	0·0	4·60	25·23	1·74	5·60
Zebra (*Equus burchelli* Gray)	35·48	22·45	1·16	5·34	2·98	2·03	2·93

Table 2. Percentage composition of vegetation within 10 km

	Grassland	Scrub	Woodland
Shapi	59	31	10
Dom	21	40	40
Guvalalla	10	72	19
Nyamandhlovu	14	59	26
Kennedy I	9	60	31
Ngwashla	7	65	27
Makwa	5	45	50

in relation to certain structural types of vegetation—zebra *Equus burchelli* for instance were associated with the large amounts of grassland at Shapi and Dom (Table 3).

Table 3. Percentage contribution of zebra, elephant and buffalo to the fauna

	Zebra	Elephant	Buffalo	All species average number per census
Shapi	36	44	6	420
Dom	23	28	16	441
Guvalalla	1	86	6	346
Nyamandhlovu	5	43	34	543
Kennedy I	3	17	18	436
Ngwashla	2	32	45	691
Makwa	3	16	60	375

The distribution of certain other species did not correspond to the vegetation types. Elephant and buffalo showed a clear variation in numbers which did not correspond to any vegetation trend, either in structural composition or plant species distribution. Elephant numbers did not form a constant proportion of the total animals recorded (Table 3). Detailed investigations of the factors affecting elephant distribution at these pans suggested that the sodium content of the borehole water was important, as was the availability of soil sodium within 2 to 3 km of the pan. Localized soil sodium deposits occurred near pans, and had been exposed by elephant at pans where the sodium content of the water was moderate or low (Fig. 2). Elephant ingested this soil and may have derived quantities of water-soluble mineral salts such as calcium, magnesium and sodium bicarbonate from it (Weir 1969a). Some pans supplied with water from boreholes were avoided by elephant. These had a low sodium content and no soil sodium was available locally. Thus it appears that elephant distribution was determined by a behavioural preference for sodium. This seems likely to be a physiological requirement imposed by a ruminant-like digestion (Blair-West *et al.* 1963).

In deciding where to instal new boreholes there is a clear opportunity to regulate to some extent the species of animals one wishes to encourage at waterholes, both by careful assessment of the vegetation of the surrounding region and by geochemical and hydrological assessment of water quality and soil chemistry. Water quality as far as elephant are concerned depends on the sodium content, though this could affect other species adversely. It should now be possible for accurate predictions to be made on the direct effect on animal populations of creating new waterholes.

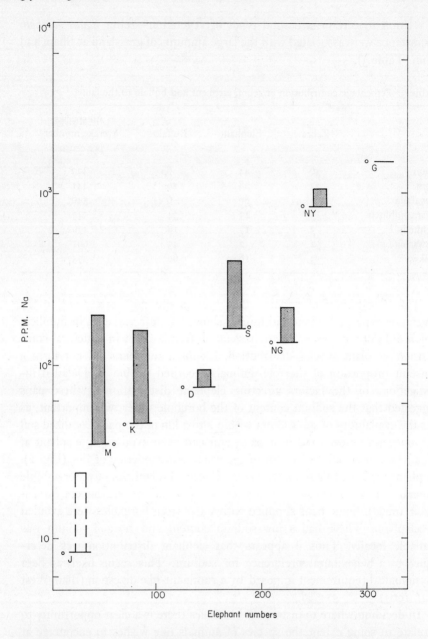

Figure 2. Mean numbers of elephant censused per pan per night are shown in relation to the mean sodium content of the water in the pan. An estimated relative value for the numbers of salt licks developed near each pan is inserted as a histogram beside the relevant pan. Dotted histogram shows relative numbers of scrapes not salt licks.
G = Guvalalla, NY = Nyamandhlovu, NG = Ngwashla, S = Shapi, D = Dom, K = Kennedy I, M = Makwa, J = Jambile.
Dom is close to Nyamandhlovu, so animals may move freely between these two pans.

Effect of animal populations on vegetation near pans

At a 'high-sodium' pumped pan Boughey (1963) showed by investigations during 1960 and 1961 that animals, elephant in particular, were altering the vegetation. This pan (Guvalalla) had been first supplied with borehole water in 1957, so the effects measured by Boughey were those of the initial build-up of a large population averaging 300 elephant drinking per day. Nyamandhlovu Pan, however, was first supplied with borehole water in 1936 (Weir 1968) and so any extensive destruction of vegetation at this pan (also with a high-sodium input and an average of 230 elephant and over 200 other animals per night) would have been expected to be evident by 1966. In fact large trees occurred within a few hundred metres of the pan and woodland was abundant within a few kilometres (Table 2, 26 per cent of total area within 10 km is forest). In some areas near this pan there had been extensive destruction of trees of certain species.

Some tree destruction occurred also at pans with moderate sodium content and moderate elephant numbers. As many of these pans had been maintained for ten years or more the general nature of any elephant damage should have been apparent. There was, however, no evidence, in 1966, of elephant damage comparable in scale or extent to that seen in Tsavo National Park, Kenya, during 1969. Yet this vegetation had never been subjected to intensive dry season utilization by animals prior to maintenance of water supplies in pans.

At natural seasonal pans, perennial grasses dominated the grassland up to the pan edge. At most maintained pans, the grassland within a few hundred metres of the pan edge was composed of annuals. The area affected was large at a pan such as Nyamandhlovu, but proportionally smaller at pans with smaller animal numbers. Evidence from soil analyses suggested that grasslands extending for several kilometres round pans are edaphic and represent former deflation basins subsequently filled with fine sand and clay by sheet wash (Weir 1969*a*). The woodland fringe adjoining these grasslands frequently showed signs of damage by elephant, with occasional trees destroyed and branches broken off.

Effect of animal populations on pans

The clay pans into which water was pumped probably increased in size following prolonged usage for many years by large herds. Observations by local residents suggested that Nyamandhlovu Pan had increased considerably in size since water was first supplied to it. The means of increase must be either by the removal of mud in suspension in the water consumed by herds, or by the removal of mud on the body when animals wallow or splash in the pans. The amount of material in suspension in the water was very high during the dry season when animals were drinking in large numbers and continually stirring up mud with their hooves. Weir (1968) reported 8·00 gm and 3·00 gm dry wt. per litre from two such pans.

Many natural pans will ultimately be filled in by soil erosion following the development of superficial salt licks, usually slightly above natural or maintained pans. Material from such excavated licks is readily washed by sheet erosion into the adjacent pan and blown by high winds into it (Weir 1969a).

Effect of populations of large animals on the fauna of pans

The natural pan fauna is adapted (Weir 1960, 1968, 1969b) to overcome an obligatory hot dry season lasting a few weeks or a few months. The very characteristic crustaceans, Conchostraca, and Anostraca, were abundant both in species and numbers. Permanent water in a pan eliminated these almost completely, but provided refugia for forms such as Notonectidae and Hydrophilidae which do not have a desiccation-resistant stage in the life history. Many Odonata survived as adults during the dry season but others flew in with the onset of the rains. A few such permanent pans could act as effective refugia increasing freshwater arthropod species diversity and numbers, but the addition of the omnivorous fish *Clarias mossambicus* to most of these permanent pans for use as food by park rangers, reduced their potential as refugia.

The increased numbers of animals at maintained water supplies resulted in increased deposition of dung near such water throughout the wet season. This dung had the effect of increasing the phosphorus, nitrogen and organic content of pools of all sizes. There was effectively an increase in fertility and productivity in pools of all sizes. Numbers of amphibian tadpoles were high in such pools and were associated with air-breathing Anisops and syrphid larvae. Deoxygenation occurred readily and pools showed various stages of eutrophication. Natural pools with clear, acid water and emergent vegetation with a large diverse insect population, were not commonly found near sodium-rich pans where dung deposition by elephant was greatest.

Studies related to dung deposition

Dung deposition near pans

Herds gathered at pans deposited quantities of dung throughout the surrounding region (Fig. 3). The deposition and fate of dung was assessed by means of experimental plots and by marked areas from which dung was

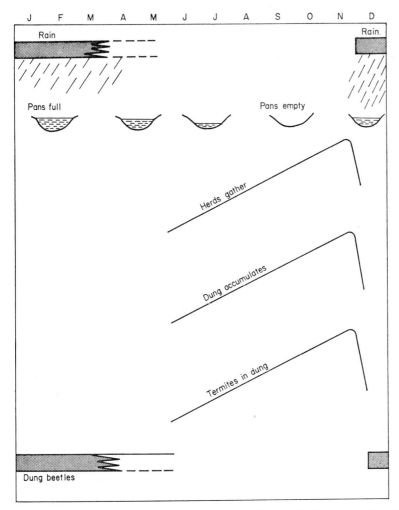

Figure 3. Diagram showing seasonal changes in rainfall, correlated successively with natural pans filling with rainwater, mammals gathering at maintained waterholes in the dry season, surface dung accumulation in the dry season, termite activity in surface dung, and the occurrence of dung beetles during the wet season.

removed periodically and weighed. Dung of certain species could not be readily differentiated, so pellet groups were assessed on an arbitrary basis.

(1) *Small pellets*

Kudu (*Tragelaphus strepsiceros* Pallas)
Wildebeeste (*Connochaetes taurinus* Burchell)
Roan (*Hippotragus equinus* Desmarest)
Sable (*Hippotragus niger* Harris)
Immature giraffe (*Giraffa camelopardalis* Linn.)
Immature eland (*Taurotragus oryx* Pallas)

(2) *Large pellets*
   Mature eland (*Taurotragus oryx* Pallas)
   Mature giraffe (*Giraffa camelopardalis* Linn.)
(3) Zebra (*Equus burchelli* Gray)
(4) Buffalo (*Syncerus caffer* Sparrman)
(5) Elephant (*Loxodonta africana* Blumenbach)

The distribution and dry weight of dung in these five categories in early November is shown in Figs. 4 and 5. Measurements showed that surface dung

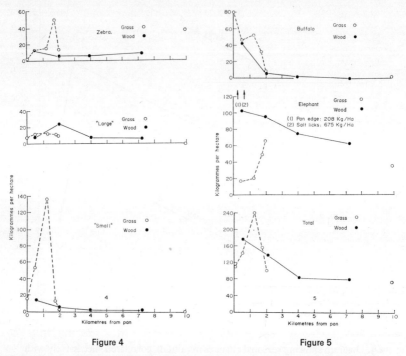

Figure 4   Figure 5

Figures 4 and 5. Surface accumulation of dung of various kinds at the end of the dry season, as measured from 99 quadrats each of 232 m², at various distances from a pan (Makwa) with a moderate elephant population. Two general habitats are differentiated—woodland and grassland. Values in kgm/hectare dry weight. Zebra, buffalo and elephant dung could be readily differentiated, but not dung of certain other herbivores, here differentiated on the basis of pellet size into 'large' and 'small'.

in all areas increased from May until the start of the wet season in November, when there were considerable surface accumulations. These were largely broken down and dispersed by rain and possibly soil arthropods in December until within a week there was little 'old' dung remaining on the surface. Some old pellet groups deposited during the dry season lasted for two complete seasons, but were not readily recognized as pellet groups except when marked on experimental plots. Experiments were carried out to determine the amount of dung removed and the agents of removal during the dry season.

Dung removal

The three main removal agents were: (1) Fire, which in October or November removed all dung on the soil surface in woodland but usually left unaffected any on grassland near pans. (2) Termites which were very active in the period August to November in dung (Fig. 3). (3) Trampling and hoof action by herds which tended to break up and destroy dung on the surface by incorporating it into the surface layers of the soil. Hoof action was intense in some areas near pans and prevented the completion of growth experiments or removal experiments using dung.

The effect of termites, hoof action and fire obviously varied with the distance from the pan. Termite activity reached a maximum in the woodland—scrub fringe (Table 4), where dung deposition was high and damage to vegeta-

Table 4. Termite removal rates in per cent per month (from all experiments)

| | Woodland | | Scrub woodland 'islands' | Grass near pan |
Distant	Average	Fringe		
3	6	14	26	20

tion was most obvious. Termite activity in dung varied seasonally, and during the wet season dung beetles were responsible for the removal and burial of almost all dung (Fig. 3).

Fire in October (a 'late' burn) resulted in almost complete removal of dung (by ashing) from soil surface in woodland, but left unaffected dung on grassland. The scattered litter and dung on grassland was unable to maintain a fire (Table 5). Hoof action was maximal nearest pans, but difficult to assess experimentally, separately from termite activity.

Table 5. Rates of removal of dung—percentage per month. (Experiment II)

		(September–November) Woodland	Scrub	Grassland
Not burned	Hoof scatter	0·2	0·8	? > 0·9 Max. 5·0
	Termites	10	18	18
	Residue (November)	58	10	8
Burned in October	Percentage lost in October burn			
	Loss by burning	55	6	0
	Residue (November)	2	8	8

Spatial transport of dung

All grass throughout the region in both woodland and grassland was dead and consisted of dry straw stubble by October. As there was little, if any, of this material left upright on the grassland by November, it seemed unlikely that dung deposited on such grasslands was derived from plant material living on the grassland. Dung accumulating in grassland was examined, and in the case of elephant clearly included much fibrous and woody material. Spatial transport of nutrients from woodlands to grasslands was occurring at this time. The exact measurement of the amount and origin of the transported material presented some difficulty.

Dung was deposited in a centripetal pattern and in consequence estimates could be made of the total dung in the region round a maintained waterhole (e.g. within 15 km) by conversions of the measurements of dung per hectare to the amount of dung in successive circular zones (annuli) at known distances from the waterhole, allowing for differences in types of vegetation in successive annuli (Fig. 6). Calculating the total weight of dung estimated to have been deposited within this area and relating this to the total area, if animals were depositing dung randomly throughout the region, the percentage of

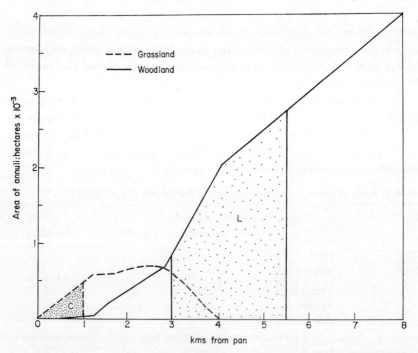

Figure 6. Shows the total area of grassland and woodland within 18 km of Makwa pan. Area marked C is the area of grassland in which nutrients are concentrated and area L is area of woodland from which nutrients are lost.

dung falling on any one annulus would be related to the area of that annulus. In fact the ratio of the percentage dung to the percentage area shows that proportionally more dung is recorded on the surface of annuli nearer the pan. However, these values do not include dung removed from the soil surface by fire, termites or hoof action. Fire is an intermittent agent, and hoof action is important only near pans. The action of termites was measured experimentally (above) and has been shown to be the major factor involved.

Conversion of recorded amounts of dung on the soil surface in November to that which would have been recorded on the soil surface in November in the absence of termite action, shows a marked increase in dung deposited near the waterhole (Fig. 7). This large effective spatial transport of dung is

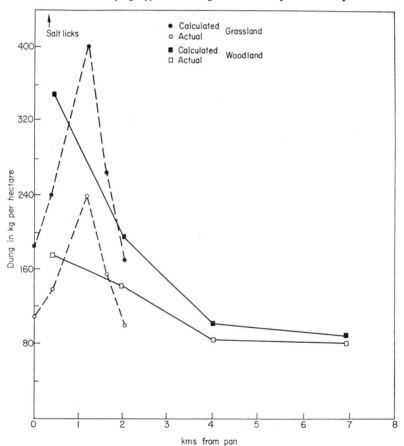

Figure 7. The total weight of dung actually measured on the soil surface in woodland as kgm/hectare dry weight at various distances from Makwa pan in grassland and in woodland is here compared with a series of calculated equivalent values based on experimental measurements of the rate of removal of dung by termites. The calculated value shown is the weight of dung which would have accumulated on the soil surface in November in the absence of termites, and the difference is the weight of dung calculated to have been removed by the termites.

masked by the localized activity of termites near waterholes, in removing the dung.

Mineral nutrient availability and the spatial transport of dung

Dung contains significant quantities of plant nutrients, such as nitrogen and phosphorus, and the weights of dung deposited per hectare can be reinterpreted as weights of nutrients. Mean values of phosphorus content (as percentage P_2O_5) were measured in dung as follows: elephant 0·67 per cent, buffalo 0·96 per cent; large pellets 0·77 per cent, and zebra 0·43 per cent. Dung therefore represents a valuable source of minerals in this particularly deficient environment. Soil phosphorus was measured during the dry season along a transect near a pan, and up to 10 km from it. These values (from anion exchange measurement) can be compared with values of the phosphorus content of grass (measured in January during the wet season) along the same transect line (Fig. 8).

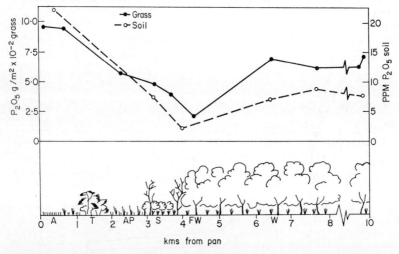

Figure 8. Phosphorus (as gm $P_2O_5 \times 10^{-2}$) in grass per sq. metre cropped during January (wet season) and phosphorus (as p.p.m., P_2O_5) in soil during October along a transect from Makwa pan. Corresponding vegetation types are shown diagramatically. A = annual grassland; T = thicket; AP = annual and perennial grasses; S = scrub with dense perennial grasses; FW = fringe woodland with tree destruction by elephant; W = woodland with scattered clumps of perennial grasses.

The woodland in general appears to have consistent values of soil and grass phosphorus except in the fringe bordering the pan, where very low values were found both at the damaged woodland edge and in the border of scrub and low bush. The typical grassland values were similar to those for woodland, but rose to a high level in both soil and grass near the waterhole.

The most obvious explanation for this series of values is that it may represent the result of the spatial transport of dung by animals feeding in the woodland fringe close to the pan and defaecating frequently on their way to or from the pan. This process repeated by scores of animals of varied species each year over a long period of time will eventually result in a complete change in the mineral status of these regions. It is probable that the fringe of annual grasses round the pan are enabled to compete with perennials by the relatively high phosphorus level of the environment. Equally, it seems likely that species changes in grasses, already occurring in the scrub and fringe area will result in grasses of increasingly low phosphorus content becoming dominant. The relative palatability of grass species to the herbivores has not been investigated here. A gradual soil impoverishment and subsequent species change in grass in the woodland fringe may affect the herbivores responsible for the initiation of this process.

There is evidence from dung accumulation and termite activity, that the degree to which this spatial transport of nutrients occurs varies with the numbers of animals congregated near the pans. At pans with few animals (e.g. Jambile, Livingi) there was relatively little dung transport from woodland and few annual grasses at the pan edge. At pans with large animal populations the amounts of dung recorded were correspondingly large and the fringe of annual grassland became a broad belt. The amounts quoted here refer to a pan (Makwa) with a moderate to low elephant population (60) recorded during the dry season.

Grass growth in response to dung

Experiments which will not be described in detail here, showed that grass does in fact respond to applications of buffalo dung and elephant dung, the response being proportional to the amount applied within wide limits. The response was measured in dry weight of grass of different species produced and in number and height of flowering shoots. These experiments were carried out in woodland, and the effect of fire in burning over the applied dung on some plots at the end of the dry season enabled comparisons to be made of the effect of fire on grass growth in such an experiment. There was no detectable difference in the response of the grass as measured up to 12 weeks later. From this it appears that the major contribution to grass growth may come from mineral components (P, K, Mg, etc.) rather than from organic matter and nitrogen which was lost on combustion.

Utilization of phosphorus by vegetation and termites

Radioactive P_{32} was used to determine the fate of phosphorus in dung when subjected experimentally to various treatments. Known amounts of P_{32} were mixed into fresh buffalo dung which was then 'cast' from plastic containers to the approximate shape and size of an average lump of buffalo dung. These were placed in various situations throughout the environment and the environment examined regularly to determine what was happening to the phosphorus. This was carried out at a number of pans so that effects could be compared under a variety of conditions.

Phosphorus in dung 'set' near a maintained pan appeared rapidly in the soil litter at the pan edge following destruction of the synthetic buffalo dung heap by hoof action. Following the first thunderstorms annuals in the soil germinated and these grasses showed varied degrees of activity. Dung had been scattered for distances of 30 m. Green algae from the surface muds at the edge of the water were also radioactive and showed that some of the surface dung near the pan was reaching the pan in surface flow after thunderstorms. This dung formed the basis for the freshwater life in the pans (Weir 1969b).

During the dry season dung containing radiophosphorus remained generally 'static' when placed in woodland until taken by termites, destroyed by fire, or moved by hoof action. Minute quantities of fluid from freshly deposited dung were detected on the twigs and branches of adjacent trees and bushes, to which they were transferred by occasional flies or other insects, which moved from the fresh dung to the plants. Once the dung had dried out on the surface, the only movement of radioactive material was that by termites (which seldom removed all the available dung). While termites in the area showed levels of radioactivity for some weeks following ingestion of labelled dung, no radioactivity was detected in adjacent vegetation during the dry season. Thus, removal of nutrients by termites to mounds or colonies did not result in this material becoming accessible to plants during the dry season. The effect of fire in ashing dung was to cause some scattering of minerals in the soil within 6–10 cm. from the former dung heap. Such phosphorus was not removed by termites.

At the start of the wet season, radioactive phosphorus appeared rapidly in vegetation near the points at which labelled dung had been deposited. At points where the remains of the original synthetic dung heap had been removed by me following termite removal of some of the dung, some slight activity was detected in vegetation during the wet season. It appears possible that some of the mineral content of dung removed by termites may eventually become available to plants when the wet season starts. This low activity could have come from small fragments of the original dung which had been overlooked by the termites and also missed when the remains of the dung were removed. There was no evidence that a significant quantity of the phosphorus in the dung actually removed by termites reached vegetation within five months, nor was it possible to trace the actual fate of the phosphorus in dung removed by termites. At sites where dung had been ashed by fires, plants in the area showed a high level of activity at the start of the wet season, suggesting that minerals from ashed material were readily available to the plants. There was some dispersal of phosphorus-laden ash by wind over the soil surface.

Discussion and conclusions

The effects of creation of additional water supplies in this region are diverse, affecting soil vegetation and invertebrates and including the initiation of processes the final results of which cannot as yet be measured. Direct effects on animal populations, following the preference of certain species for particular combinations of vegetation or for water qualities, lend themselves to manipulation by man in park management. They offer means to regulate the distribution and numbers of certain mammal species and also to regulate the use and status of vegetation in particular areas. At the time this work was carried out (prior to 1966) the criteria for the use of particular pans as maintained waterholes lay primarily in the political and social requirements of keeping animals within the park and in the economic value of animal populations as tourist attractions. Thus the ecological importance of such man-made waterholes has perhaps not been fully explored. Certain aspects remain to be investigated, such as the role of small artificial reservoirs of different shapes and perimeters as a means of causing or preventing population interaction while drinking.

The potential of man-made waterholes as refugia in which certain types of invertebrates could be maintained throughout the dry season has not so far been utilized. The supply of permanent water to such dung-laden waterholes alters their invertebrate fauna. This effect has to be coupled with that of elephant which, near certain maintained pans, are eliminating many natural pans of certain physical kinds (pans with acid, clear water, Weir 1968) by the creation of numerous shallow, erosion-prone salt licks which readily cause gully formation and surface run-off of sand into adjacent natural pans. Thus the entire freshwater habitat is exposed to environmental pressures which could alter its general nature.

The interaction of wildlife, fire and vegetation has long fascinated African ecologists. Vegetation is being affected in some areas by elephant in this Park (Boughey 1963), but little attention has been paid to equivalent changes in the soil fauna. Here it can be shown that termites and fire are in 'competition' for dung in woodland, but not in grassland where fire is generally unable to penetrate. This is coupled with the transport of nutrients in dung from woodland, centripetally towards the pan. The result of these effects is that a large percentage of the mineral nutrients moved from woodland towards the pan tend to be removed by termites from grassland areas near the pan. These are lost from short-term circulation and use by vegetation. Minerals in dung burned in woodland remain available to vegetation but not to termites, and appear rapidly in grass and bushes at the start of the wet season. These effects vary with the numbers of animals involved. Termite activity was very marked at pans with large elephant populations. Thus experiments on the effect of nutrients on grass growth were more successful in some areas than others, following the nutrient enrichment of the annual grassland near the pan compared with the perennial grasses further from the pan. Experiments on controlled burning, excluding animals, would be expected to produce equally varied results, depending on the induced nutrient status of the area in question. It would be difficult to interpret the results of such experiments without a knowledge of the processes (e.g. nutrient shifts) which have previously occurred, to which vegetation may not have adjusted, or on which vegetation may be dependent, and which may be affected by soil invertebrates.

The management policy in this area should still rest on the judgement of those in charge, as the present work shows only some of the long-term processes of biogenic environmental differentiation, which have been induced by the growth and development of a large animal population in a uniform habitat not previously accessible to them. There are now numerous descriptions of the status of animal and plant communities in National Parks and elsewhere in Africa, and of changes in the status of these communities. Experimental analyses or other evidence on the nature of the environmental processes which have led to the production of these communities and to changes in them is notably lacking. The assumption that such processes are similar to those which have been shown to operate in North America or Europe is almost certainly unfounded, and management policies based on such assumptions are unlikely to be successful. It would be necessary to measure and to predict the outcome of these long-term processes and interactions in order to formulate a meaningful long-term ecological policy which could then be integrated with the economic and political parameters involved to produce a realistic management policy.

Summary

Ungulate herds in Wankie National Park, Rhodesia, gather at artificially maintained water supplies during the dry season. Differences in species distribution can be related to vegetation differences (e.g. zebra) or to water quality (e.g. elephant). Herbivore dung accumulated on the ground during the dry season, but was removed continuously by termite activity and by hoof action. Dung accumulation was greatest near pans, as was termite activity, hoof action, and tree destruction. Maintenance of water in pans throughout the year affected the species composition of the freshwater fauna, while dung washed into such pans increased their productivity. These effects are discussed in relation to the spatial movement of nutrients by herbivores and it is concluded that the creation of such artificial waterholes initiates processes which will eventually alter the environment, and necessitate continuous revision of management policies. The creation of artificial water supplies has proved to be a useful approach to the problems of this Park, and the results achieved should facilitate the further manipulation of such populations and environments to meet ecological, social, and political requirements.

Acknowledgements

I am indebted to the Director and members of staff of the Department of National Parks and Wildlife Management of Rhodesia, for their willing co-operation and help. In particular, I am indebted to E.C.Davison, B.Austen and H.Cantle. The assistance of G.Nyamakunda and P.Nhariwa is gratefully acknowledged, and I am indebted to Mr R.J.Fenner and others in the Government Soil Laboratory, Salisbury, for certain analyses.

References

BLAIR-WEST J.R., BOTT E., COGHLAN J.P., DENTON D.A., GODING J.R., WINTOUR M. & WRIGHT R.D. (1963) The regulation of electrolyte metabolism of ruminant animals in arid zones. In: *Environmental Physiology and Psychology in arid conditions.* Unesco Paris 1963, 289 pp.

BOUGHEY A.S. (1963) Interaction between animals vegetation and fire in Southern Rhodesia. *Ohio J. Sci.* 63, 193–209.

SAUNDER D.H. (1964) Exploring the potential of Rhodesian Soils. *Proc. Trans. Rhod. Sci. Ass.* 50 16–28.

VINCENT V. & THOMAS R.G. (1961) *An agricultural survey of Southern Rhodesia. Part I: Agro-Ecological Survey.* 124 pp. Govt. printer, Salisbury, Rhodesia.

WEIR J.S. (1960) A possible course of evolution of animal drinking holes (pans) and reflected changes in their biology.—*Proc. 1st Fed. Sci. Cong., Salisbury, Rhodesia.* 5 pp. Mardon and Co.

WEIR J.S. (1968) Seasonal variation in alkalinity in pans in Central Africa. *Hydrobiologia* 32, 69–80.

WEIR J.S. (1969a) Chemical properties and occurrence on Kalahari sand of salt licks created by elephant. *J. Zool.* 158, 293–310.

WEIR J.S. (1969b) Studies on central African Pans: III. Fauna and Physico-chemical Environment of some ephemeral pools. *Hydrobiologia* 33, 93–116.

WEIR J.S. & DAVISON E.C. (1966) Daily occurrence of African game animals at water holes in dry weather. *Zool. Afr.* 1, 353–68.

Influence of indigenous animals on the dynamics of vegetation in conservation areas

R.KNAPP *Institute of Botany, University of Giessen, Germany*

Introduction

Until recent years the influence of indigenous animals has been largely neglected in vegetation studies in central Europe. This is due partly to a reduction of their numbers in many areas or to their effect being obscured by a number of activities connected with agriculture and forestry. In recent years a research programme has begun dealing with these influences and concentrating on conservation areas (Knapp 1967*a*, *b*; 1969; 1970*b*).

This work was stimulated by studies and observations in other continents, such as Africa, North America, and southern Asia. In these continents the outstanding influence of populations of large indigenous herbivorous mammals has been documented in several areas with predominantly natural vegetation (Knapp 1965*a*, *b*; 1966; 1967*a*; 1970*a*, *b*).

Large indigenous wild animals can also influence the vegetation structure in central Europe and some of our results are summarized here under three headings.

Influence of animal food preferences on vegetation succession

Vegetation types on different sites and of varied successional stages are influenced by these animals in various ways. There is a tendency for animals to concentrate for feeding and resting on certain plant communities (Talbot & Talbot 1962; Knapp & Knapp 1953 Klötzli 1965; Gwynne & Bell 1968), and in case of seral stages, vegetational succession in these communities will be interrupted or deflected by their influence. Therefore, certain communities dominated by grasses, herbs and shrubs can remain rather stable under a regime of recurrent grazing and browsing by wild ungulates, even in some potential forest climax areas. Regressive successions can also occur in such places. For example, in extreme cases forest can be gradually replaced by bush vegetation or grassland under the influence of high densities of large herbivorous animals. But, where it is composed of plant species not preferred by such animals, forest vegetation may be locally less affected or not degraded. In this way, a park-like vegetation can develop and be maintained by the influence of wild mammals. Such areas may be covered by vegetation complexes consisting of a mosaic of forest, thicket and patches of open grassland.

The most striking effects of this kind observed in central Europe were due to the influence of red deer (*Cervus elaphus*), wild hog (*Sus scrofa scrofa*) and chamois (*Rupicapra rupicapra*, in certain areas of the Alps). In Africa, elephant (*Loxodonta africana*), cape buffalo (*Syncerus caffer*), hippopotamus (*Hippopotamus amphibius*) and eland (*Taurotragus oryx*) are among the species with most influence on vegetation, but a number of other African ungulate species also have major effects.

Promotion of nitrophilous vegetation

Nitrophilous vegetation, very different from the surrounding plant cover, can develop on the resting places of large wild mammals, and also in association with bird colonies. These nitrophilous types include plant communities regarded hitherto mainly as due to the influence of agriculture, husbandry and permanent human settlement. Stands of such plant communities, owing their origin to the influence of indigenous animals, have obviously been centres for the expansion of ruderal and other nitrophilous vegetation after the introduction of agriculture and stock breeding.

Influence of burrowing animals

Bare areas fit for development of initial successional stages of vegetation can be created by burrowing animals. In this way early seral stages can be maintained in areas devoid of steep slopes, torrents and other agents that induce bare sites for initial colonization. This influence of burrowing animals is apparently very important for the continued survival of a number of plant communities in certain plains areas, for example, open vegetation with affinities to the continental south-east European steppe (rich in 'Pannonian' and 'Pontic' flora elements). Locally, such xerothermic plant communities, associated with dry microclimates, can belong to the final stages of successional series on steep southern slopes and the slope edges above them in the hill country of some parts of central Europe (mainly areas with mean annual rainfall of 450–600 mm, 18–24 in) (Knapp, 1970*b*). But such sites do not usually exist in plains areas. Species like *Jurinea cyanoides*, *Kochia arenaria*, *Corispermum marschallii*, *Koeleria glauca* and *Alyssum montanum* ssp. *gmelinii* were found concentrated on heaps of calcareous sands, resulting from burrowing activity of wild animals, in some parts of the northern region of the Upper Rhine Plains (Knapp 1970*b*). The occurrence of such plants was virtually limited to places opened by burrowing animals in the natural landscape. Today, the species mentioned can also be found on sandy sites opened by vehicles, sand pits for construction work, and other human activities (Ackermann 1952).

Discussion

In the floras of many central European plains areas only a small proportion of the total number of species occurs in vegetation regarded by several authors hitherto as the potential natural vegetation. Many other species live in plant communities regarded under present conditions mainly as anthropogenic. These plant communities are dependent on man and his activities, such as agriculture, pasture management, and industry. But our results suggest that a high percentage of the species in these plant communities could also persist in areas modified by the activities of indigenous mammals. Such species could, therefore, be members of natural ecosystems.

In the scientific management of conservation areas it seems to be quite feasible to preserve a variety of plant communities in combination with the protection of certain indigenous mammals. Under certain conditions these mammals can partly replace the pressure of grazing by domestic stock, of occasional selective cutting, of prescribed burning, and of other means often suggested now for preserving some vegetational types of seral character. The difficulty is that the precise influence (in quantitative terms) of indigenous free-living animals on a limited area is not predictable. The size of a conservation area for simultaneous protection of indigenous mammals and rare or desirable plant communities must, therefore, be rather large. But the conservation areas in central Europe are usually small, and protected plant species survive only in small numbers of individuals and over very restricted areas. The influence of indigenous mammals is very variable and on occasion can even be deleterious in such small protection areas. There are cases of serious harm by burrowing or grazing wild mammals on small, scarce stands of rare plants. In any case the influence of these mammals must be extensively studied and if necessary controlled.

Summary

Vegetation complexes of forests, thickets and grassland can be promoted and preserved by the action of certain large indigenous herbivorous mammals. Indigenous nitrophilous plant communities can live on the resting places of wild mammals and in bird colonies. A number of plant communities can survive as a result of the effect of burrowing animals on the habitat in certain areas. Thus indigenous herbivorous mammals can contribute to the preservation of desirable plant communities in large conservation areas, but this favourable influence is less reliable in small protection areas. These conclusions result from studies on the interrelations between vegetation and wild mammals and birds in central Europe and other continents.

References

ACKERMANN H. (1952) Die Vegetationsverhältnisse im Flugsandgebiet der nördlichen Bergstrasse. *Schr.-Reihe d. Naturschutzstelle Darmstadt* **2**, 1–134.

GWYNNE M.D. & BELL R.H.V. (1968) Selection of vegetation components by grazing ungulates in the Serengeti National Park. *Nature Lond.* **220**, 390–3.

KLÖTZLI F. (1965) Qualität und Quantität der Rehäsung in Wald und Grünland-Gesellschaften des nördlichen Schweizer Mittellandes. *Veröff. geobot. Inst., Zürich* **38**, 1–186.

KNAPP G. & KNAPP R. (1953) Über Pflanzengesellschaften und Almwirtschaft im Ober-Allgäu und angrenzendem Vorarlberg. *Landwirtschaft. Jahrb. f. Bayern* **30**, 548–88.

KNAPP R. (1965a) *Die Vegetation von Nord- und Mittelamerika und der Hawaii-Inseln.* 40 + 373 pp. G. Fischer, Stuttgart.

KNAPP R. (1965b) Pflanzengesellschaften und höhere Vegetationseinheiten von Ceylon und Teilen von Ost- und Central-Afrika. *Geobotan. Mitteilungen* **33**, 1–31.

KNAPP R. (1966) Höhere Vegetationseinheiten von West-Afrika unter besonderer Berücksichtigung von Nigeria und Kamerun. *Geobotan. Mitteilungen* **34**, 1–16.

KNAPP R. (1967a) Wild und Vegetation in den Tropen, Subtropen und anderen Gebieten. *Ber. Oberhess. Ges. Naturwiss. Abt. N.F.* **35**, 157–75.

KNAPP R. (1967b) *Experimentelle Soziologie und gegenseitige Beeinflussung der Pflanzen.* 2. Aufl. 266 pp. Ulmer, Stuttgart.

KNAPP R. (1969) Induktive und experimentelle Untersuchungen über Probleme der Syndynamik von Pflanzengesellschaften. *Vegetatio* **18**, 82–90.

KNAPP R. (1970a) Wald und offene Flächen in der Naturlandschaft. *Ber. Oberhess. Ges. Naturwiss. Abt. N.F.* **37**, 87–118.

KNAPP R. (1970b) *Einführung in die Pflanzensoziologie.* 3. Aufl. 384 pp. Ulmer, Stuttgart.

TALBOT L.M. & TALBOT M.H. (1962) Food preferences of some East African wild ungulates. *East Afr. agric. for. J.* **27**, 131–8.

Part 5
Ecological Studies on the Conservation and Control of Large Mammals

The ecological and economic basis for game ranching in Africa

I.S.C.PARKER & A.D.GRAHAM *Wildlife Services Ltd,*
P.O. Box 30678, Nairobi, Kenya

Introduction

Game ranching is here taken to mean the 'husbandry of presently wild animals for the same ends as conventional ranching: that is the production of food and utilities and as a means of occupancy of land by man'.

The literature on this subject is extensive (Talbot *et al.* 1965 list over 450 sources). However, it is a notable feature of game ranching that it remains more talked of than done. There are instances of success (Dasmann & Mossman 1961; Riney 1963; Parker 1964; Roth 1966 and Bindernagel 1968 among others), but for the most part the concept has won only limited acceptance.

This paper examines some of the human ecological limitations that govern man's relations with other animals. The observed motives for game ranching, which are not always rational, are discussed and speculations are made on their relevance to modern man. It has seemed to us necessary to do this before the essential nature of the ecology and economics of game ranching can be discerned. It is hoped that we can help to resolve some of the apparent contradictions that surround modern man's relation with wild and domestic animals in Africa today, and indicate ways in which game ranching can be realistically attempted.

Game Ranching

The first use of wild animals by man on the African continent was made by primitive hunters and gatherers such as are represented today by the Hadza of Central Tanzania and the Bushmen of the Kalahari regions. These people make no planned attempts to influence primary or secondary productivity, but live as simple tertiary converters, existing in a state of equilibrium with their resources. Free from other human interference they could undoubtedly continue to do so. Contrary to popular belief these hunters and gatherers often live a life of considerable nutritional affluence. Woodburn (1968) found that the Hadza diet was nutritionally adequate and that they spent less time obtaining their subsistence than do neighbouring agricultural tribes. Lee (1968) observed that in the 'Kung bushmen average daily food collection exceeds minimum energy requirements by 165 calories and 33 grams of protein. In addition he noted that to obtain this only 2–3 days' work per week are required in what is considered very inhospitable terrain by other men. Although most of their food is vegetable, about 20 per cent is animal and in view of the success of this basic form of game use, it is surprising that it has not persisted and been incorporated into the modern systems of human land use that are displacing it.

Other African peoples have practised communal hunting that constitutes a more organized form of game use. For example, the Acholi of Uganda enforced 'close-seasons' and other measures that were in effect management practices. However, these traditional methods of exploiting wildlife have tended to atrophy under western influences, and the reduction of animal populations that has accompanied human expansion.

Attempts at organized game ranching have been made over the past 15 years in a number of African countries. Descriptions of some of these endeavours in the Republics of South Africa, Rhodesia, Zambia, Tanzania, Kenya and Uganda are given by Riney (1963), Parker (1964), Roth (1966), Savory (1967), Steel (1968), Bindernagel (1968) and Parker & Archer (1970) among others. They can be classified politically into three categories:
(i)   private landowners using their own wild animals on their own land,
(ii) private landowners having to obtain state permission to use animals on their own land, and
(iii) Government or quasi-Government authorities, or contractors to them, using wildlife on state land.

Much of the game ranching carried out in the Republic of South Africa comes under category (i). In many instances, the animals are initially acquired from the state and placed on farmland from which genuinely wild animals have long been absent. In this sense the reintroduced 'wild' animals are more truly domesticants. As far back as 1959 there were between 2,000 and 3,000 farms carrying such animals in the Transvaal alone. Much of the game ranching in Rhodesia falls under the second category, ranchers being allocated quotas which they may take on their own land. The animals here are genuinely wild. In Zambia and the East African states such attempts as have been made have mostly been on state land by government authorities, with indigenous wild animals.

The profitability of many of these attempts has tended to support the belief that wild animals are better converters than domestic stock, at least on so-called 'marginal' lands (Riney & Smithers 1960, Harthoorn 1961, Mossman & Dasmann 1962, among others). However, it should be understood that with the more outstanding successes (i.e. those dependent on such produce as zebra, elephant and hippo hides) this has not been due to anything other than 'salesmanship'. Fashion-dependent luxuries are entirely different commodities to essential utilities and foods. Thus zebra, elephant and hippo are not competing in the markets with domestic stock; their use by man is additional to his other animal interests.

Comparison between the returns from game and beef on Rhodesian ranches (Dasmann & Mossman 1961) are limited in value when there are separate standards for preparing the product. Present hygiene requirements for game meat production are much lower than those for beef in modern abattoirs. While there may be reason for pursuing such a course in the short term, it is difficult to see how deviation from the hygiene optima can be tolerated in the long run. Further, some of the comparisons between game and cattle in Rhodesia (where most experimental game ranching has been done) have been made where poor management of the latter has been apparent (Savory 1967).

Part of the argument favouring game maintains that wild animals do not cause extensive erosion in fragile habitats whereas this is common with domesticants. However, there are well-documented cases in which game have 'abused' habitats and caused erosion as extensive as any caused by cattle (Petrides & Swank 1958; Laws 1968). It has never been demonstrated that wildlife productivity at the lower end of the rainfall regime is any higher than it is possible to achieve with domestic animals. Some wild species can be independent of water for long periods, an advantage in the use of arid zones (Taylor 1969). However, the value of this tends to be nullified by the difficulty man himself has in occupying waterless land. Once the provision of water permits man to live in such areas, it is only a short step to watering other animals. It is worth noting here that the highest wild animal biomasses encountered in East Africa are in fact at the upper end of the rainfall scale (Field & Laws 1970), as is the case with cattle (Watson 1970a, b).

Talbot *et al.* (1965) state that one of the advantages wild ungulates offer is that they have 'differential, non-duplicating preferred diets'. However, the more detailed work of Bell (1969) and Field (1970) indicates that this is not wholly true in that the food preferences of all ungulates, including cattle, are probably mainly expressed in differing plant growth forms. In fact Bell (1969) showed that the numerous grazing species of the 'marginal' Serengeti area, far from being independent, were interdependent with a range of competitive and facilitative relationships.

As the case that game is 'better' than domestic stock in some areas is not proven, there are grounds for suspecting that it does not rest on rational land use planning alone. Anyone interested in the 'cause of preservation' cannot but be aware of the strong human emotions that centre on it. Often these seem illogical and conflicting. It is therefore important to examine man's relationship with other animal life in order that the principles underlying the various approaches may be clearly understood.

Man and Animals

Man classifies animals into three broad categories: pets, domesticants and wild. These can be described as follows.

1   Pets are kept in order to satisfy personal relationship needs in their keepers. These may have several psychological origins, are essentially affairs of the individual, and form part of an anthropocentric world.

2   Domesticants are kept mainly to provide food, and also services such as ploughing, transport, guarding, etc. Animals kept for food are invariably gregarious, as are the majority of all domestic species. The relationship between man and domestic beast is commensal, whereas this is not necessarily so with pets.

3   Wild animals are those that live independently of man and characteristically resist his interference with avoidance or aggression. 'Wildness' in itself, of course, exists only in the mind of the beholder; it is not a property of nature.

Pets

Some observations on the phenomenon of pets are appropriate here. The case of a childless woman keeping small dogs or cats seems to be a relatively simple case of substitution. The same applies to the elderly or those lacking close relationships with other people. However, it is not generally appreciated that the widespread desire to preserve wildlife, exemplified by the creation of National Parks, is often an extension of the compulsion to keep pets. We also suggest that the killing of animals for pleasure ('sport hunting') is closely allied to it. The well-known change from a bloodthirsty hunter to a passionate preservationist, the adage of the poacher making the best park warden, far from being a swing from one end of the spectrum to the other, is more probably a case of inversion, the one being the antithesis of the other, with identical neurotic origin. The former desire to slay, inverted into the desire to preserve, seems the consequence of repressed aggression towards humans (which aggression probably has nothing to do with true hunting), the animals here representing people.

Lack of space prevents further examination of man's compulsion to keep pets. It has been a human trait over a great span of time, for which psychological explanations are to be found. In modern times the instinct has reached unprecedented proportions and assumed the character of a chronic neurosis as evidenced by the abandonment of reason in its pursuit. On a grand scale this is probably best exhibited by the amount of money spent on keeping pets in Britain, Europe and North America (which annually must exceed £100,000,000), while at the same time people in these societies experience malnutrition, not to mention psychic distress.

The pet-syndrome (a term specifically relating here to neurotic aspects and not the overall phenomenon of pets) seems allied to three main factors: high human density, minimal contact with competitive animal life, and affluence. The salient point is that, in the context of land use, this sort of indulgence is not a basic requisite of life and is quite distinct from man's biological relationship with other forms of life. Failure to appreciate this has led to considerable misunderstanding in our attitudes to ecological research, not least among the confused being some scientists.

Domestication

The advantages of domesticating animals to ensure continuity of food supplies (mainly protein) are obvious, but one is astonished at how few animals man has domesticated in the past. He has invaded and occupied most of the world's surface and exploited it mainly through only five mammalian groups; cattle (*Bos* spp.), sheep (*Ovis aries* L.), goats (*Capra* spp.), pigs (*Sus scrofa* L.), horses (*Equus caballus* L.) and donkeys (*E. asinus* L.), and a few birds, (Phasianidae, Numididae, Anatidae, Columbidae, etc.) In the process he has displaced many indigenous herbivores that flourished in these environments prior to his arrival, e.g. the American bison (*Bison bison* (L.)). That this does not imply some intrinsic limit on the range of domesticable species is shown by his use, in climatic extremes where the conventional six mammals were unsuitable, of such animals as yaks (*Bos grunniens* L.), water buffalo (*Bubalus bubalis* (L.)), camels (*Camelus bactrianus* L. and *C. dromedarius* L.), and llamas (*Lama* spp.). Nevertheless, the absence of a wider range of domesticants does suggest the existence of a major barrier of some sort. We must consider what this might be if game ranching is to become practicable in the long term.

Man and wild animals

Nowhere is the lack of a wider range of domesticants more puzzling than in Africa. Here, as far as is known, man has existed longer than on any other continent. At the same time he has coexisted with a wider range of herbivores than elsewhere. Apparent incentives seem obvious; tsetse fly (*Glossina* spp.) barred much of the land to the conventional six mammalian domesticants, and protein deficiency among many agricultural Africans appears to have been chronic for a long time. That at least some species of wild animals are susceptible to domestication in the classic sense is demonstrated by the use of eland (*Taurotragus oryx* Pall.) in the Ukraine over the past 75 years (Treus and Kravchenko 1968), and in Rhodesia (Posselt 1963). African elephant (*Loxodonta africana* Blumenbach) were successfully domesticated in the former Belgian Congo (Philippson 1934), ostrich (*Struthio camelus* L.) are farmed in South Africa and the tractability of many other species in zoos around the world suggests that most of them are available for domestication. So long as one regards the origin of domestication as rational planning on the part of intelligent man, its absence remains an enigma. However, there is evidence that it may have come about unintentionally, in which case the facts surrounding it become more understandable. In this we support the view of Zeuner (1963) that domestication was essentially fortuitous, rather than intended.

The essence of domestication is the disappearance of the prey reaction to a predator (man) on the part of the domesticant. In the absence of pain or other alarming stimuli emanating from man, animals soon relax their avoidance of him or aggression towards him—they become tame. This is readily observed in a number of national parks in many parts of the world. The Murchison Falls and Queen Elizabeth National Parks in Uganda are examples. Because they are comparatively small with high tourist traffic, animals have become relatively tame through frequent non-alarming contact. This sustained association outweighed the traumas of cropping, and the animals have remained tame despite the shooting of 2,000 elephant and approximately 10,000 hippopotamus (*Hippopotamus amphibius* L.)

We believe that we have observed incipient domestication similar to the original process actually occurring at the Wankwar ranger post in the Murchison Falls Park. This post is situated in an area of *Hypharrenia* grasses, that for most of the year are coarse and unpalatable (Field 1968). In the vicinity of the post this is kept mowed short and not permitted to mature. It thus offers an oasis of palatable grazing in a generally unfavourable area, and has attracted a number of old male buffaloes (*Syncerus caffer* Sparrman). The staff do not disturb them and though old males are widely considered to be the most aggressive individuals of this species, they have become so tame that they now permit considerable abuse without displaying aggressive or avoiding reactions. The rangers' children ride them and they are frequently struck with broom handles and the like when found blocking doorways. They are essentially domesticated, except that man has not yet exploited them. They belie Zeuner's (1963) contention that man had to learn the art of domestication by first using docile species.

Once an animal is tame, and providing its contacts with man continue to be beneficial or non-traumatic on balance, it will stay tame. It is then domesti-cated. Subsequent breeding for submissiveness, and other qualities, will enhance the initial condition. Thus cattle endure branding with hot irons, castration, etc, without becoming wild for more than a fleeting period. This whole process is greatly facilitated by using gregarious animals in which the individual's response can be damped by communal non-reaction. The essen-tial requirement is a period in which contact with man is without trauma for sufficient time to extinguish the prey response entirely. The original critical human factor was probably indifference to the animal, rather than any posi-tive reaction or intention.

We have noted earlier that man, when a hunter and gatherer, in Africa is nutritionally affluent. His success depends on the vigour of his opportunism, not only nutritionally but in many other ways. The principle of opportunism (i.e. exploit *all* opportunities) produced in effect an ecological prohibition against a relaxation of the predator-prey relationship. In addition, these hunters were nomadic and unlikely to have resided long enough in a given spot for the completion of relationships that require time to mature; nor did they modify vegetation, thus negating the possibilities for attracting herbi-vores to them.

There is evidence that the African agriculturalist without domestic stock has been protein deficient for a long time. History records frequent famines. In such circumstances they were necessarily also opportunists, particularly towards meat. It would be difficult for anyone in a chronic state of protein hunger to forgo eating an animal one day in the hope that it might later reproduce or grow bigger. Man in this state could not afford the period of taming essential to domestication. Animals that came near enough to tame were simply eaten.

We thus offer an hypothesis to account for the lack of domestication—the hunter gatherer had no need to, the agriculturalist could not afford to. It was man's own ecological prerequisites that kept him from domesticating wild African animals. With today's affluence and technology, these blocks to domestication have disappeared. (Pet keeping existed in primitive African societies, but we have pointed out earlier that this is a very different phenome-non to the use of animals for basic utilities, and was in itself a barrier to such use.) We can now consider the idea of ranching game in the light of future necessities.

Man's Requirements

Although protein deficiencies are widespread in Africa (Manson-Bahr 1960), this, paradoxically, does not mean that traditional food sources are inadequate. The vast inland lakes and oceans of the continent are far from fully exploited.

Other countries produce protein surpluses that could be marketed in Africa. It is obvious, then, that conventional sources are still abundant. If they are not being fully exploited it is because of some intrinsic factor in the human condition, as recognized by Talbot *et al.* (1965), and not because of a protein famine. There is therefore no reason to use wild animals *per se* as a new meat source.

As was pointed out earlier, it is fallacious to assume that game cannot cause land degradation. Man's mismanagement of both wild and domestic animals has the same result. What then has created interest in ranching game in recent years? Undoubtedly it has arisen in the main from a preoccupation of certain people with wildlife as a phenomenon in itself. In this instance the maximization of productivity, or any exploitation at all, is far removed from the real psychological objectives. Undoubtedly much of the work carried out so far to investigate the possibilities for game ranching has arisen out of this strong desire to preserve wild animals, and consequently there is motivation to arrive at predetermined conclusions irrespective of the facts. As a result there is no well-documented exposition of game ranching as a competitive form of land use.

In terms of land use the diversity of African herbivores might be more productive of man's requirements than the exclusive use of his present range of domestic beasts. This concept does not exclude mixed use of existing domesticants and what are today wild animals. In introducing such an approach, and as man is central to the ideas, we need to consider some of the ecological limitations and requirements of man before seeing how animals may fit into these.

Man as an animal has ecological optima and his manipulations of environment will inevitably tend toward these. It has long been accepted that man evolved as an open country species and one of his most prominent activities is the creation of open habitat. Only very specialized people live in forest (traditionally a fearsome place associated with demons and the like) and even here they tend to make clearings. With the need for openness goes his endeavour to gain control over plant life. It follows that the fewer the plants, the easier control becomes; therefore in the interests of economy in a broad sense he will try to limit rather than increase diversity of plant life (and thus its dependent animals). The history of his exploitation of plant and animal communities bears this out. Therefore it does not necessarily follow that the wide range of adaptations in wild animals in fact are to man's ecological advantage. (There is evidence that the observed success of wildlife in much of East Africa's savanna, commented on by Grzimek & Grzimek (1960) and others, has only been made possible through man's own opening and exploitation of these areas.) In what might be called his 'climax rural situation', vegetation is modified to consist largely of grassland, with woody types occurring only in cultivated forests and hedgerows. The phenomenon of burning bush and grassland whenever possible that occurs everywhere, but is so characteristic of Africa today, becomes understandable as part of the deep-seated need to gain control over vegetation and maintain open environments. The rationalization that it is to ensure good grazing we consider to be secondary and it follows the domestication of ungulates.

It follows that if man's ecological needs tend toward open country, animals suited to such situations will be attractive to him. Thus species most likely to conform to his requirements are grassland types, particularly gregarious species which, because of their behaviour, are more susceptible to control. A herd of 500 cattle is easily directed by five men in open country. This is more difficult in thick bush and virtually impossible in forest with the same manpower. The factors of open country, gregariousness and controllability are correlated.

Increases in human populations inevitably lead to competition for basic resources. This gives rise to the phenomenon of ownership, the basic purpose of which is to ensure the security of essential food supplies. The intensity of the need to exert ownership rises with population density. Consequent upon this the maintenance of status demands that the individual strive throughout life to extend his power of 'ownership'. In modern communities its measure is money, and even land is so valued. In less-developed communities land is the measure for agriculturalists, and livestock for pastoralists. It is expressed ownership in one form or another, individual or communal, that is the means whereby man attains his ambitions (Gulliver 1955; Dyson-Hudson 1966). Herein lies the probable reason for the abandonment of the original hunters' and gatherers' affluent way of life—a rise in density brought about the ecological necessity for ownership, which took many cultural forms. Wild animals cannot be demonstrably owned and therefore a resource on which man had long relied was abandoned. Ownership forms a major obstacle to the long-term use of wild animals in an undomesticated state by man in high density situations. While land lies vacant, communal ownership of an animal resource on it is possible in a crude sense, but when it becomes occupied (and continuously rising populations imply that all land will become occupied) and owned by the individual, he must be able to exercise his ownership totally. The animals on it must be domesticated. It is of particular interest that the practice of game ranching in Africa is most widespread and successful in South Africa where it is practised under full ownership. It is least developed and meets the greatest opposition where ownership of wild animals is denied the individual, even on his own land. To suggest to a pastoralist that he abandon his only possessions, i.e. his livestock, in favour of un-ownable wild things, is akin to suggesting to Aristotle Onassis that he give up money and revert to cowrie shells (*Monetaria moneta* L.)

A further ecological characteristic of man is his well-known resistance to change. For game ranching to become a readily acceptable form of land use in the absence of a real need for it, some device is required to overcome the inevitable psychological conservatism that will be encountered. The only such device that appears to be available to anyone (except the rational scientist) is the astonishingly powerful force of neurotic sentimentalism. As a tool, however, it bears consideration.

Conclusions

Although a number of attempts to ranch African game have been made these have achieved only limited success. As yet the ecology and economics of this form of land use remain largely conjectural. In a continent with abundant wild animals the absence of game ranching needs explaining. We have attempted to do this in terms of human ecological limitations, particularly those dictating man's choice of habitat and social requirements.

In view of the present lack of any need to augment protein production we have questioned some of the previous arguments put forward for game ranching. This has led us to consider man's various activities with animals and to recognize that two of the most basic of these, pet-keeping and domestication, are very different in origin and purpose. The anthropomorphism inherent in the former prohibits the use of pets for food and utilities; the purpose of the latter is the provision of these basic necessities. The concept of game ranching has received greatest support from people preoccupied with wildlife *per se*, as a rationalization for its preservation. We suggest that, paradoxically, resistance to game ranching from the same sources stems from a failure to recognize this. It has therefore been necessary to re-examine the concept.

The puzzling lack of indigenous African domesticants might suggest that the continent's wild animals are unsuitable for intensive use by man. However, we suggest that the block existed within man, not with the animals, and that in the modern situation some of its causes have been removed. But new obstacles have arisen as a result of increased human density, manifest in the phenomena of occupancy and ownership. These prohibit the long-term use of animals in a wild state. In the future, as human populations increase, they can be expected ultimately to invade and occupy all available land. While doing so there will be a tendency toward the creation of more open habitats which will discriminate against wild animals dependent on thicket and forest. Rising human density will gradually displace all wild animals and only domesticants will survive in the long run. This process will affect the most productive areas first in that they are the ones most desired by man.

The ecology of game ranching must focus on a better knowledge of the process of domestication and take into account more of man's own ecology.

The most suitable species for domestication would appear to be gregarious types adapted to grassland. It may be that within the great diversity of African wildlife lies a potential for increasing productivity. In terms of today's needs there is no case for game-ranching; its possible value to man lies in the future. The true economics of this form of land use will only become apparent when the actual contributions of game ranching to man's situation are realized.

Meanwhile, wildlife can be put to a variety of uses on thinly populated or vacant land. Certain species in their wild state might be used as meat sources. However, unless techniques that ensure minimal disturbance are used, particularly with gregarious animals, extensive and continuous hunting will lead to population declines as described by Geist (this volume).

Acknowledgements

We wish to acknowledge the many useful and stimulating discussions with Drs R.M.Watson and R.M.Laws on this and many related subjects. We thank R.Denney and A.D.Forbes-Watson for their comments on the manuscript, and Mrs A.C.Parker for its preparation.

References

BELL R.V. (1969) *The use of the herb layer by grazing ungulates in the Serengeti national park*. Ph.D. Thesis, Manchester University.

BINDERNAGEL J.A. (1968) Game cropping in Uganda. *Uganda Game Dept. Mimeographed Report.*

DASMANN R.F. & MOSSMAN A.S. (1961) Commercial utilization of game mammals on a Rhodesian ranch. *The Wildlife Society, California section. Mimeographed report*, 8 pp.

DYSON-HUDSON N. (1966) *Karamojong politics*. Oxford University Press.

FIELD C.R. (1968) The food habits of some wild ungulates in relation to land use and management. *E. Afr. agric. for. J.* 33.

FIELD C.R. (1970) Feeding habits of hippopotamus. *Zool. Afr.*, 5.

FIELD C. & LAWS R.M. (1970) The distribution of the larger herbivores in the Queen Elizabeth National Park, Uganda. *J. appl. Ecol.* 7, 273–94.

GRZIMEK B. & GRZIMEK M. (1960) *Serengeti shall not die*. Hamish Hamilton Ltd, London.

GULLIVER P.H. (1955) *The family herds*. Routledge & Kegan Paul Ltd, London.

HARTHOORN A.M. (1961) Some aspects of game cropping. In *Conf. on Land Management Problems, Lake Manyara, Tanganyika*. 14 pp., mimeographed.

LAWS R.M. (1968) Interactions between elephant and hippopotamus populations and their environments. *E. Afr. agric. for. J.* 33, 140–7.

LEE R.B. (1968) What hunters do for a living, or, how to make out on scarce resources. In *Man the hunter*. (Ed. Lee R.B. & Devore I.) Aldine Publishing Co., Chicago.

MANSON-BAHR P. (1960) *Manson's Tropical Diseases*. 15th Edition. Cassel & Co., London.

MOSSMAN A.S. & DASMANN R.F. (1962) Game ranching handbook for Southern Rhodesia. *Mimeographed report*, 15 pp.

PARKER I.S.C. (1964) The Galana game management scheme. *Bull. epizoot. Dis. Afr.* **12**, 21–31.

PARKER I.S.C. & ARCHER A.L. (1970). The status of elephant, other wildlife and cattle in Mkomazi game reserve with management recommendations. *Wildlife Services Ltd. report to Tanzania Government*, 61 pp.

PETRIDES G.A. & SWANK W.G. (1958) Management of the big game resource in Uganda, East Africa. *Trans. N. Am. Wildl. Conf.* **23**. 461–77.

PHILIPPSON P. (1934) Domesticating the African elephant: experiments in the Belgian Congo. *Field* 163.

POSSELT J. (1963) The domestication of the eland. *Rhod. agric. Res.* **1**: 81–7.

RINEY T. (1963) Utilisation of wildlife in the Transvaal. *I.U.C.N. pub. no. 1 (new series)* 303–5.

RINEY T. & SMITHERS R. (1960) Wildlife and human values in Southern Rhodesia. *Proc. 1st Fed. sci. congr. Salisbury S. Rhod.*, 307–17.

ROTH H.H. (1966) Game utilisation in Rhodesia. *Mammalia* **30** (3).

SAVORY C.A.R. (1967) The utilization of wildlife on Rhodesian marginal lands and its relationship to humans, domestic stock and land deterioration (drought). *1st Rhod. sci. congr. Bulawayo.*, 118–28.

STEEL W.S. (1968) The technology of wildlife management game cropping in the Luangwa Valley Zambia. *E. Afr. agric. for. J.* **33**.

TALBOT L.M., PAYNE W.J.A., LEDGER H.P., VERDCOURT L.D. & TALBOT M.H. (1965) The meat production potential of wild animals in Africa. *Commonwealth Agric. Bureau Tech. Commun.* **16**.

TAYLOR C.R. (1969) The eland and the oryx. *Scient. Am.* **220** (1).

TREUS V. & KRAVCHENKO D. (1968) Methods of rearing and economic utilization of eland in the Askaniya-Nova zoological park. *Symp. zool. Soc. Lond. No. 21*, 395–411.

WATSON R.M. (1970a) Aerial livestock surveys of Kaputie division Samburu district and North Eastern Province. *Reports to Kenya Government Ministry of Economic Planning and Development. Unpublished MS.*

WATSON R.M. (1970b) Aerial livestock surveys of Kajiado Narok and Kitui Districts. *Reports to Kenya Government Ministry of Economic Planning and Development. Unpublished MS.*

ZEUNER F.E. (1963) The history of the domestication of cattle. *R. anthrop. inst. Occasional paper 18. Man and Cattle*, 9–15.

Field trials of the line transect method of sampling populations of large herbivores

PATRICK HEMINGWAY *College of African Wildlife Management,
Tanzania*

Introduction

Field trials were undertaken by students of the College of African Wildlife Management to test the utility of systematic strip sampling of extensive areas of rangeland as habitat for large herbivorous mammals.

The number of animals of a given species in an area under study is often called the population of that species. I have intended that meaning in the title, but strictly speaking it is the area of rangeland that we consider which is the population in the statistical sense, the animals being characteristics or items of this community which we wish to estimate by sampling. The recording unit we employ is a 50 m square (0·25 ha). We sample a total of 40,000 such units in a day's work, typically arranged in a matrix of 200 rows and the same number of columns. For convenience the area is divided into ten equal and parallel strips each 10 km × 1 km. In each strip a separate team walks a centrally aligned transect as long as the strip and the number of units inspected by all the teams as they walk their transects makes up the sample.

Because the sampling design is systematic, we must assume a model for the population in order to estimate parameters. The one tested (Gates, Marshall & Olson 1968; Gates 1969) is that of the population in 'random' order (Cochran 1963). This is the simplest of all statistical models and, if pertinent, enables parameters to be estimated as in simple random sampling.

A further complication in the method is introduced by the necessity to measure units in the sample by horizontal, line-of-sight scanning. If there exist potential obstructions to vision in the horizontal plane, there is always a chance of non-response, that the eye will fail to measure some of the units.

We have interpreted that portion of the model that predicts the pattern of non-response as meaning that the human eye sees all potential target animals of a particular species out to a characteristic distance which we call its reach for that kind of target animal. Beyond its reach, the eye can still see animals, but we can no longer be certain that it will see all the animals that are there to be seen. If there exist in addition to the target animals potential obstructions to vision in the horizontal plane, there is a chance that the eye will fail to see animals that are within its reach. This chance of non-response caused by obstruction to vision is predicted in the model by an exponential probability density function. With no obstruction to vision in the horizontal plane; the eye scans a strip equal to twice its reach in width. With potential obstructions to vision in the horizontal plane, the model predicts that the scanned strip will be equivalent to twice the reciprocal of the exponential parameter in width, although units will be drawn from the area all the way out to the eye's reach. It is also assumed that the exponential parameter will be large enough so that the chance of seeing animals at the eye's reach is negligibly small.

Since we know the size of the sample area from the sample strip width and the length of the transects, the estimate of the total numbers of an animal species is the product of our estimate of the number of occupied units in the population and the mean number of animals in an occupied unit. In rangeland containing potential obstructions to vision in the horizontal plane, we are no longer certain of the sample area, as the exponential parameter is not known but estimated from the trial. This additional source of variance and how to deal with it is the problem that is solved here for the first time in the model proposed by Gates.

Methods

One disadvantage of the human eye is that it is not very good at judging distance or bearing of a line from itself to an observed object. Although bearing can be measured well enough with a prismatic compass, there is no such simple device that will measure distance of a tie line to an unoccupied station. In the data presented here, the tie line distances are all ocular estimates. Teams measure their elapsed track along their compass course by pacing, a method sufficiently accurate considering the other components of the system.

A day's work is planned the evening before, making use of the excellent 1 : 50,000 topographic maps available for the whole of the three East African countries in which we work. Transect courses are plotted on the map with an air navigation type protractor and scale.

Transect teams are transported to the starting-points of their assigned morning walks immediately after breakfast and are picked up just before lunch at the end points. Walking along their transect course by the aid of a prismatic compass, they scan with their unaided eyes as far as they can see ahead and to both right and left of their line of travel. When they see an animal or group of animals, they halt and record on a *pro-forma* sheet their elapsed track distance and the bearing and distance of the tie line from their position to the position of the animal or animal group in an occupied unit. Using binoculars, they also note details of age, sex and behaviour of the animals in the occupied unit. Afternoons are free to work up data or to do some other project.

We are pleased to report that despite the bad reputation of some of the dangerous species of African big game, no team member has ever been injured by an animal in five years of transect work. For that matter, neither have any animals been hurt, for the crews are unarmed. Crews have retreated gracefully from snarling lionesses protecting their cubs, climbed trees to avoid ill-tempered rhinos and fled before the rage of demonstrating elephants without sustaining more than a few scratches and skinned knees.

Results

Figure 1 is the plot of a day's work devoted to measuring the position and

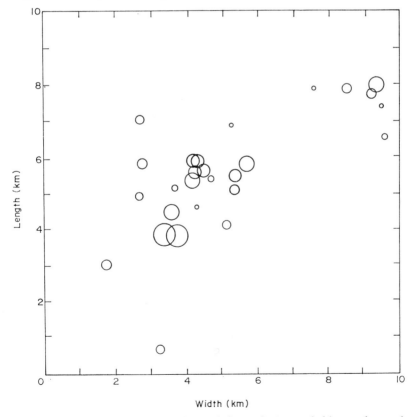

Figure 1. Distribution of Thomson's gazelle in 100 km², sampled in one day on the Simanjuru Plains, Northern Tanzania (see text).

numbers of Thomson's gazelle (*Gazella thomsoni*) on the Simanjiru Plains in Northern Tanzania. The area of each circle is proportional to the number of individual animals within the occupied unit at its centre. In this pure grass-land habitat there were no potential obstructions to vision in the horizontal plane and the sampling fraction was 0·6, with the eye's reach taken as 300 m. Looking at this plot it is evident that the spatial distribution of the occupied units that were observed does not appear to be 'random'. There is a marked tendency for the occupied units to occur in clusters, also the number of animals in an occupied unit is not 'randomly' ordered, and there is a very great variation in the number of animals in occupied units. It is likely that the model will give both biased and imprecise results under such conditions. There is no way of determining the amount of bias, but the estimate of total numbers, under the assumptions of the model, is rather imprecise for such a high sampling fraction, with a coefficient of variation of about 8 per cent of the estimated 241 gazelle.

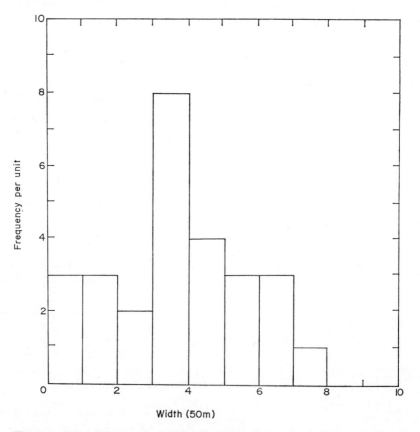

Figure 2. Histogram showing, for the area in Fig. 1, number of observations in equal strips of unit width at increasing distances from the track.

One must expect such unfavourable spatial distributions for any sort of sampling in plains-dwelling antelope and gazelle for the behavioural reasons explained by Walther (1966). We have found that the spatial distribution among those species that prefer rangeland containing a woody element in the vegetation is much more likely to be approximated by the 'random' order model. There is less variation in the size of the groups, the number of animals in an occupied unit and the occupied units themselves are more evenly scattered over the population.

Figure 2 is a histogram for the same day's work showing the number of observations in equal strips of unit width as these strips lie at increasing parallel distances from the track. The relatively high output from the fourth strip is most conspicuous. We think this is not a real output but indicates some sort of bias, for the high output at the centre is balanced by a lower than expected output in all of the other strips except one. Further evidence for some sort of bias not yet understood by us is provided by the data summarized in Fig. 3. This is a histogram of the relative sightings of animals per unit

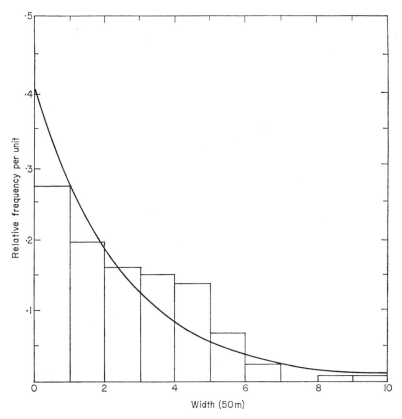

Figure 3. Relative frequency of sightings of impala per unit strip width on a trial in the Selous Game Reserve.

strip width made from the results of a trial in wooded and bushed grassland at the Miombo Research Centre, Selous Game Reserve, South-eastern Tanzania. The species involved was impala (*Aepyceros melampus*). In this vegetation type there is, of course, potential horizontal obstruction to vision. Gates's model underestimates scanner output as shown by the theoretical curve's fit to the histogram. Although a half-normal model would better predict the pattern of non-response there still remains a slightly higher than expected output in the middle strips. Gates's model estimates the sampling fraction as 0·25 while the half-normal gives 0·387 as an estimate for the same parameter.

Cost

In an extensive survey, the area of the population would be many thousands of square kilometres. The size of the *Julbernadia-Brachystegia* woodland in the wildlife estate in Tanzania alone has been estimated as over 150,000 km². In such a vast area it would be necessary to estimate the total numbers of many different species for a great number of different purposes. Many of the species are likely to differ in density, variability of numbers in occupied units, and preferences for habitats with varying degrees of visibility. For many practical reasons, not the least of which is the need for careful planning and supervision of transect teams by qualified personnel, some sort of cluster sampling would be necessary.

Such an extensive survey as that required to assess the Miombo woodland portion of the wildlife estate in Tanzania would have to be completed in a single dry season after the annual burning of the grass, a period of four months. If ten crews under the supervision of one qualified person comprised the survey team they could handle seventeen shifts of base camp in one season if they remained in a camp for four days and took on the average three days to shift camp. The 150, 000 km² would be divided up into 166 blocks of 900 km² each. From these 166 blocks, eighteen would be selected randomly and a base camp would be set up in the centre of each chosen block. Within each block, three secondary blocks of 100 km² each would be randomly chosen for sampling by the line transect method. This would take three days to do and leave one day of rest between shifts of base camp. With this size survey team a rough estimate of the total field cost would be E.A. Shs. 10,000/-.

In the 100 km² block selected for the day's transect work, it would be necessary always to stratify the area so that each stratum would have as uniform visibility conditions as possible. Otherwise there would be a bias introduced by more than one value for the exponential parameter in a given set of transects and consequently a different sampling fraction in each visibility type. Such stratification could be easily and quickly done from aerial photographs which were taken in order to make the topographical maps.

The relation between components of total field cost and the standard errors for the different animal species could be used to answer various questions about the overall cost of a given standard of precision. Knowledge of the precision attainable at a fixed cost with different animal species and various combinations of primary and secondary sampling units is needed. Methods of establishing these points are covered in detail, with many practical examples, by Loetsch & Haller (1964) for a situation very similar to ours. They describe a tropical forest inventory in Northern Thailand, where they used cluster sampling.

Acknowledgement

I am indebted to Mr Leslie Robinette who introduced me to the line transect method and who brought Gates's model to my attention.

Summary

Field trials of the line transect method of sampling populations of large herbivores by students of the College of African Wildlife Management are described.

Results of the field trials are analysed with the aid of a theoretical model for the line transect method. The model is least successful in dealing with plains-dwelling animals under conditions of unrestricted visibility, but gives satisfactory results for those species that prefer rangeland containing a woody element which restricts visibility.

The cost of an extensive wildlife survey using the line transect method in cluster sampling is discussed.

References

COCHRAN W.G. (1963) *Sampling techniques*. John Wiley & Sons, New York.
GATES C.E., MARSHALL W.H. & OLSON D.P. (1968) Line transect method of estimating grouse population densities. *Biometrics* **24**, 135–45.
GATES C.E. (1969) Simulation study of estimators for the line transect sampling method. *Biometrics* **25**, 317–28.
LOETSCH F. & HALLER K.E. (1964) *Forest inventory*. BLV Verlagsgesellschaft, Munich.
WALTHER F. (1966) *Mit Horn und Huf*. Verlag Paul Parey, Berlin.

A behavioural approach to the management of wild ungulates

V.GEIST
Environmental Sciences Centre, The University of Calgary,
Calgary 44, Alberta, Canada

Introduction

In the wisdom of hindsight, the content of this paper is based on elementary animal behaviour. However, nothing in my earlier training in animal behaviour quite prepared me for what I was to find in the field, and ethologists visiting my study area appeared just as surprised as laymen. Evidently, some very important aspects of animal behaviour have not yet fully penetrated circles of professional behaviourists, let alone those of wildlife managers. Today there is interest in game ranching, not only in Africa but also in New Zealand and even North America (Fuller 1962; Scotter 1969; Klein 1970). Our national parks are strained by visitor use, Alaska and Canada's arctic areas are subjected to ever-increasing oil and mining developments, while managers of public lands in North America are faced with ever greater demands by conflicting interests, one of which is the conservation of the native fauna. All this touches on the lives of our native large mammals. Although the contents of this paper should become common knowledge in the management of wild ungulates, they are likely to strike many biologists as rather odd. Of the three major points a behaviourist could raise, two will be dealt with here.

First, we can take advantage of the learning ability of ungulates for the sake of conservation, management, and research. We are educating wild ungulates with every contact we make, and, whether we like it or not, or acknowledge this fact, the lessons are usually neither to their benefit nor to ours. By perpetuating ungulates in a 'wild' state we are likely to endanger even more species. We can be constructive, however, as pointed out later.

Second, human disturbances can cause severe alterations to the behaviour of a species with repercussions on the physiology, population dynamics,

413

and ecology of the animals. On this subject we must become much better informed so as to protect faunas from apparently innocent human actions.

Third, a knowledge of the relation of social and ecological adaptations can be used in management to achieve desired objectives. This will be treated in detail in another paper, using the mountain sheep *Ovis c. canadensis* as an example. Leuthold (1969) dealt with ethology in relation to game management in a paper given to the Ninth International Congress of Game Biologists in Moscow, while several papers imply or discuss some management implications of behavioural research in ungulates (Nievergelt 1967; Geist 1967b, 1968; Walther 1969).

Learning, habituation, and taming

There is a widespread notion that most large mammals will not coexist with humans. This idea is coupled with a deep pessimism about the future of 'shy, wilderness species', since with human encroachment they obviously cannot survive. I consider it to be largely a myth, and a dangerous one, for conservation, since it prevents the initiation of actions that would safeguard the existence of these species. If a species gets along with animals other than man, it can also get along with man, and get along splendidly. However, it is up to us to act in such a manner that we become acceptable, and remain a harmless part of that species' environment.

That this can be done has been demonstrated conclusively by a number of investigators who habituated 'wild' species to their presence. Schaller (1963) accomplished it with gorillas (*Gorilla gorilla*), Goodall (1968) with chimpanzees (*Pan troglodytes*), Holroyd (1967) with mountain goats (*Oreamnos*), Welles and Welles (1961) with desert bighorns (*Ovis canadensis nelsoni*). Some investigators took advantage of animals habituated to human presence, or entirely tame, in national parks, for example, Schaller (1969) with lions (*Panthera leo*), Schenkel (1966) with lions and rhinos (*Diceros bicornis*), Kühme (1965) with hunting dogs (*Lycaon pictus*), Walther (1964) with Thomson's gazelles (*Gazella thomsoni*), Estes (1969) with gnu (*Connochaetes taurinus*) and gazelles (1967), and Geist with mule deer (*Odocoileus hemionus hemionus*) (1966) and mountain sheep (*O. c. canadensis*) (1967a).

In addition, in many national parks mammals have taken humans for granted as part of their environment, and even benefit from visitors, towns and various other alterations to the landscapes. Bighorn sheep in Banff, Waterton, and Kootenay national parks in Canada have taken advantage of seeded and fertilized road banks, and well-tended lawns around hotels, mixing quite freely with visitors along roads, at viewpoints and car parks, and approaching them occasionally for food.

Bighorn sheep inhabiting Mount Norquay in Banff National Park are thriving despite the Trans-Canada Highway and a paved road up the mountain; despite a chair-lift, a hotel, a ski lodge, a coffee-shop, and the heavy recreational use of the mountain environs. These sheep graze the extensive cuttings and embankments left by highway construction, the large areas cleared of timber for ski runs, and are commonly fed by delighted tourists (Plate 1). Some of them are killed annually by traffic on the Trans-Canada Highway and others are removed by trapping to serve as stock for reintroduction elsewhere. These sheep are large individuals, characterized by high reproduction and rapid growth of juveniles; and this despite severe landscape alterations and human use of the area.

In Waterton Lakes National Park a home-range group of mule deer have settled in the small town. They and the human residents have grown accustomed to, and ignore, each other, and the same is true for some bighorns that occasionally visit the town. The deer feed and rest on the lawns, horn carefully-planted trees and shrubs, and use the houses as shelters from the gales that sweep the town so very often (Plates 2 and 3). In autumn it is not uncommon to see school-children and rutting bucks walking along the road, with neither paying attention to the other; but woe to the dog or cat the deer catch on the streets. These deer are large-bodied, carry large antlers, and have a high reproductive rate.

The bighorns from Norquay and mule deer from Waterton are a living lesson that, given protection from hunting and poaching, large mammals will learn to accept humans, take advantage of them, and live in prosperous populations. However, one can go further and systematically profit from the learning abilities of ungulates, an insight I owe to the late E. J. Stenton, a warden of Banff National Park. He tagged adult bighorns and caught lambs without traps, drugs, ropes, without wrestling panic-stricken animals to the ground; in fact without upsetting the animals greatly. First he taught adult bighorns to lick salt from his hand (Plate 4), then he taught them to accept his hand on their face and side of head, then he clipped a tag into their ear (Plate 5). He caught lambs by hunching down and extending his hand past the front legs of the mother which licked salt. The lambs invariably came close to investigate, and Stenton closed his fingers around one leg and lifted the lamb up for inspection and tagging. It was that simple. When I came to Banff National Park in 1963 to study bighorn behaviour, Stenton had been tagging sheep in the manner described for fourteen years.

Unfortunately, Stenton did not realize the importance of his approach, and did not take full advantage of it. Although he read the tags occasionally, and looked forward to the return appearance of several well-known individuals each year, he was only interested in knowing if any of his sheep had been shot outside the park (a few were). Since the animals were quite tame, it was possible to approach and, with some practice, read their tags, wherever these sheep were found. It was possible (*a*) to check if chronological age coincided with the number of horn segments, to determine (*b*) the loss of individuals from Stenton's home-range group of sheep to other home-range groups, (*c*) the extent of wandering by rams and their home-range fidelity, and (*d*) the age of the oldest individuals. It also became possible to (*e*) tame other sheep, previously unaccustomed to man, with the aid of the tame ones, and (*f*) for me to lead groups of these animals to areas they had previously not visited and to which they were unaccustomed. I purposely did not reinforce these movements. I have reported on this research and the insights gained from working with tame sheep, in several publications (Geist 1967*a*, 1967*b*, and in press).

From these experiences, from working with free-living mule deer that were habituated to man, or tame; from taming in the wilds a fox, a weasel, several squirrels, and Canada jays; from having followed various habituated moose, elk, and bears in national parks; from the published reports of other workers; and from the principles of learning as long-established by animal psychologists, the following can be concluded: The behaviour of 'wild' ungulates toward human beings is largely a consequence of our behaviour towards them; they are as 'wild' as we teach them to be. They are not 'inherently wild' any more than their counterparts under human care are 'inherently domesticated', or humans are 'inherently cultured'. Free-living ungulates can be expected to treat humans at first as any strange object, and thereafter adjust their response on the basis of the following behaviour of humans. If hunted, stalked, and repeatedly frightened they will flee. This response is likely to continue for a long time even if all hunting stops (confirmed for red deer, Batcheler 1968). The young are conditioned to flee at the sight of humans, and these in turn are likely to stalk close to the animals, thus unwittingly reinforcing the flight response upon being discovered. If ignored, ungulates will ultimately ignore humans. If rewarded by the appearance of humans they will search out their presence and willingly work for a reward. This means that wild, but unhunted populations of ungulates can be habituated to humans; tamed in their native habitats; marked; weighed; measured and inspected without restraining methods; led to localities previously unutilized by them or taught not to visit others; and can be cropped without hunting. We can take advantage of their behaviour to control them without the aid of fences or expensive labour, and make use of their adaptations to their native ecosystem. This can be done without domesticating the animals. They will be free to roam and continue their normal life, but will live with man as a constant part of their environment and come to us when and where we want them to. The method of achieving this is likely to vary somewhat with each species. Mammals appear to be 'learning machines' and

Plate 1. Bighorn sheep grazing and resting below a hotel in the town of Banff (Banff National Park, Alberta, Canada).

Plate 2. A mule deer buck in the town of Waterton, resting below a porch in the centre of the town (Waterton National Park, Alberta, Canada).

Plate 3. Yearling mule deer bucks, sparring in the camp ground within Waterton town limits.

Plate 4. A bighorn ram tamed in the wilds, licking salt from investigator's hand.

Plate 5. One of the bighorn rams tagged without restraining the animal. Note tag in left ear.

the increase in relative size of their brains from the early to the late Tertiary (Jerison 1961) should give anybody pause.

Disturbances

The effect of disturbance on the biology of wild ungulates has received little study to date. However, those investigations conducted by agriculturists and experimental psychologists as well as the practical experience gained in reindeer husbandry and ungulate control in New Zealand (Batcheler 1968) give little cause for complacency. It appears that there is sufficient evidence to suggest that we should be much better informed on the direct and indirect effects of hunting, tourism, mineral exploration, construction, and harassment by light aircraft.

A conceptual model of the ruminants 'Umwelt' may help us to visualize when and how disturbance acts. In general, the animal strives to live, and best functions physiologically in a thoroughly familiar (predictable) physical and social environment. It is born with a variety of means to achieve this, including a number of learning mechanisms, and curiosity, but also with alarm responses and means to adjust itself or the environment until it is predictable and not dangerous. It appears to be typical of mammals that there is a programming period early in life during which the individual stores information; discards all actions leading to unpleasantness; habituates to common but neutral stimuli; conditions certain responses by imitating larger companions; learns its home ranges by anticipating the physical features of the localities it moves to; and associates localities with appetites and a variety of stimuli with flight. We call much of this programming 'play'. In addition the animal is able to generalize from one stimulus to classes of similar stimuli —that is, it is able to generalize stimuli, localities, and experiences. For every stimulus the animal appears to attain an appropriate response, which reduces 'indecision'. If something unfamiliar appears, the animal experiences an alarm reaction, and prepares itself physiologically for flight. If severe disturbance follows, it forms an extremely strong aversion towards this object or situation. It (1) becomes excited if the unpleasant object or any evidence associated with it is sensed, and remains excited even after the object disappears; (2) avoids the locality where the disturbance was experienced; and (3) generalizes to all similar objects and localities and avoids them or becomes disturbed upon sensing them. Hence, there are repercussions. If the disturbance is common and localized in time and space, the animal soon learns to avoid it. The disturbance is likely to be most detrimental if it is frequent and unpredictable, so that the animal cannot escape it. In experimental animals this unpredictability causes neurosis, loss of weight, loss of appetite, malfunctioning of horn growth, susceptibility to predation, reduced reproduction, or death (Barnett 1967, Liddell 1954, 1958, 1961, Calhoun 1963). We need to know (1) which factors cause disturbance, and the extent of physiological upset caused by each factor; (2) the physiological effects of prolonged excitement on development, growth, mortality and reproductive performance of individuals (with particular emphasis on the developing embryo); (3) the increase in accidents and deaths caused by confused running and exertion during flight; and (4) the extent of voluntary withdrawal from available habitat, the consequent alteration of the species' ecology, and its effects on reproductive performance and individual growth.

What is known of the effects of disturbance is disquieting. Excitation is costly because it elevates metabolism (Graham, in Blaxter 1962), and raises the energy cost of living, thus competing directly with energy otherwise available for reproduction and growth. Psychic stress induced in gestating domestic ewes by leading them into unfamiliar environments greatly raised adrenocorticoid levels in the blood, and could precipitate pregnancy toxemia (Reid & Miles 1962). In the volume on reindeer husbandry edited by Zigunov (1961) there is constant emphasis on reducing all possible forms of disturbance and unnecessary exercise to ensure calm grazing (pp. 90, 95, 96, 100, 101, 103, 108, 110). Disturbances cause loss in body weight (pp. 101, 311); weaken the animals and increase susceptibility to diseases (pp. 99, 101, 247); and may cause emphysema if reindeer are forced to exert themselves in very cold weather (p. 277). Disturbance may also cause absorption of embryos if maternal body weight loss exceeds 17 per cent (p. 111), or precipitate abortions if pregnant does are exerted (p. 33) or chased through crusted snow where the abdomen hits against the hard surface or a covered obstacle (p. 65). They may cause desertion (p. 115) or trampling of new-born fawns, or displacement of foetus at calving time, and hence difficult deliveries or dystocia (p. 98). At certain critical times of their annual cycle reindeer are particularly susceptible to damage by disturbance, such as during late pregnancy and calving; during the fly season; and during severely cold weather in winter. That exertion is damaging, and must be compensated for by increasing the consumption of high-quality food and by rest, is revealed by the fact that working stags are susceptible to emphysema (p. 277) and necrobacillosis despite supplementary feeding (p. 211), while gestating reindeer does used as working animals become barren unless fed concentrates (p. 33). Moreover, working reindeer need extensive periods of rest (p. 214).

The most damaging effect of frequent disturbance could be decrease in the birth weight of the reindeer calves and hence their viability, leading to lowered reproductive performance of the population. We do not know the average minimum weight required to assure the calves' survival during a calving period with average or normal weather. However, there will be such a weight below which the calf is too weak and ill-developed to survive. In a normal population at carrying capacity the average birth weight of a calf is likely to be *below* that required to survive the neonatal period, so that only the heavier calves, about 25 per cent on the average, or less in caribou, survive their first week of life. We can conceive of the female's goal in winter as producing a calf of a survivable size, a goal she is hard pressed nutritionally to attain and usually misses. Any drain on her resources reduces even further her chances of raising an offspring. A significant drop in the average birth weight would hence result in lower reproduction. In addition, excitement of pregnant females could affect their young behaviourally, as is indicated by Thompson's (1957) work on rats. I have discussed this for mountain sheep, and shown how female sheep are adapted to reduce unnecessary energy expenditures (Geist, in press). This thinking is based largely on the work on neonatal mortality in domestic lambs (Alexander *et al.* 1959; Alexander 1961; Watson & Elder 1961).

For other species there is less information on the possible effects of harassment, but Bannikov *et al.* (1961) report that saiga antelope, chased by hunting parties in cars, died of pulmonary oedema. Nishikawa & Hafez (1968) mention that mares exerted during late pregnancy are likely to abort. Liddell (1954, 1958, 1961) showed that experimentally-induced stress caused weight loss in domestic goats, severely impaired horn growth, increased neonatal mortality, and caused death in lambs if they were deprived of the presence of their mothers. It led to neurosis in domestic sheep, and made them susceptible to predation by stray dogs. Disturbance is likely to be least detrimental to vigorous, healthy individuals living in large populations.

Another serious consequence of persistent disturbance is voluntary withdrawal from available habitat and the confinement of the population to a smaller and maybe less favourable area. This is a conclusion Batcheler (1968) came to when he reported on the effects of control measures on one chamois (*Rupicapra rupicapra*) and two red deer (*Cervus elaphus*) populations in New Zealand. Persistent hunting appeared to cause the animals to shift from favoured habitat into escape cover and assume secretive, nocturnal habits. Batcheler (1968) suggested that this resulted in worsened living conditions for the animals, as evidenced by decreased reproductive rate, and significantly lower fat deposition. In one population, barren hinds became evident, while after several years the hinds apparently became smaller. It can be predicted that in addition to this the average age at sexual maturation has increased, the antler growth of the males is retarded, the average birth weight of fawns has declined, and the mothering behaviour of hinds has probably degenerated somewhat.

In this instance a reduction in the controlled populations was desired, although usually in conservation one is interested in the opposite effect. Habitat left unused is wasted. Moreover, once suitable habitat has been lost by the animals' withdrawal, it may be quite difficult for certain species to return, i.e. bighorn sheep (Geist 1967b, 1968, in press), elk (*C. e. nannodes*) (McCullough 1969), or pronghorn antelope (*Antilocapra*) (Einarsen 1948).

From purely theoretical considerations it is evident that loss of favourable habitat to the species due to disturbance will vary with the species. It is likely to be insignificant in forms characterized by high reproductive rates, 'broadcast' dispersal of juveniles, short life expectancy of juveniles, and the ability to adopt nocturnal habits. For nomadic social species living in open terrain, such as caribou, saiga or pronghorn antelope, the loss may be only temporary, since wandering groups re-enter the area and utilize it as long as they are left undisturbed or until they leave on their own. For social species in which individuals have high life expectancies, low reproductive rates, a retention rather than dispersal of juveniles, and which inhabit widely dispersed patches of stable habitat, the alienation from available habitat is likely to be most severe, as are probably other effects of disturbance. This has been discussed with reference to mountain sheep (Geist, in press). It is such species which have suffered most in the last half-century, as exemplified by bighorn sheep in the United States (Buechner 1960) and in northern Eurasia by the wild sheep (*Ovis ammon*, *O. nivicola*), the ibex (*Capra ibex*, *C. caucasica*), the wild goat (*C. aegagrus*), the markhor (*C. falconeri*), the goral (*Nemorhaedus*), the chamois (*Rupicapra*), the yak (*Poephagus*), and earlier on the wisent (*Bison bonasus*) and aurochs (*Bos primigenius*), the reindeer (*Rangifer*), the wild camel (*Camelus ferus*), the wild horses (*Equus przewalskii*), and the onager (*Equus hemionus*) (Heptner *et al.* 1961). Almost all the genera mentioned have domesticated forms, and all their wild forms are potential candidates for domestication. This is likely to be true for all social ungulates, and where domestication has been attempted it has largely succeeded, as exemplified by African antelope (Robins 1963), musk oxen (Teal 1970), Siberian wapiti and sika deer (Heptner *et al.* 1961).

Discussion

In the North American conception of wildlife management, the amount of wildlife is primarily related to both the amount of available habitat and the quality of that habitat (Allen 1962; Dasmann 1964). It follows that, to maintain or increase wildlife populations, it is necessary to conserve habitat, or create more and improve the existing one. That this is the essential *first* and *major* step in the management of all ungulates, is a conclusion with which it is impossible to quarrel. That it is the *only* step necessary to assure success is a contention to which one can take exception, for reasons already indicated. In retrospect, however, it is not difficult to see why the above concept has been embraced with so much enthusiasm, since it has been applied with unquestionable success to the management of America's most important game species such as rabbits, squirrels, quail, pheasants, grouse, white-tailed deer, black-tailed deer, mule deer, and moose. In short, it works well with species that reproduce heavily and broadcast their young over the countryside; by itself it cannot work well with probably most gregarious ungulates. If we are to conserve and manage all ungulate species in the wild state, knowledge of the total biology of each species is essential, including its diverse behavioural adaptations—not only its habitat requirements. Nothing will hasten this more than the development of commercial game ranching. Here, several species would use the land simultaneously and every square foot of terrain must be utilized. Forage must be converted to animal matter at the greatest efficiency, and harvesting must be done with a minimum of labour and without upset to the animals.

For management of ungulates in national parks and ecological reserves, a thorough knowledge of animal behaviour will become an important tool of park managers. Although the populations must be left largely undisturbed, it is important to know how well they are performing, in order to detect subtle artificial influences or the approaching extinction of the populations, and to take remedial action. Since specimens cannot be collected without markedly altering the populations, one must depend on other information such as the actions and appearance of the living animals, and the interpretation of their signs and remains. Earlier work on mountain sheep (Geist, in press) and work presently in progress, indicate that behavioural parameters are as much affected by the ecology of the animals as are morphological ones. Klein (1964) has shown the latter for deer from Alaska (*Odocoileus hemionus*). In the future we are likely to have behavioural performance criteria which can be sampled at any desired specific population size, since they do not require killing of animals.

In national parks it is vital to know how landscape alterations will affect the ecology and hence growth form and behaviour of the various ungulates. Wild ungulate populations are of greatest cultural value in national parks if they reflect the variables operating under pristine conditions, and not the effects of land cleared for recreational purposes, fertilized road banks, garbage dumps, visitor disturbances, management manipulations (such as population reductions), or the effects of disrupted migrations because snow ploughed off the roads in winter creates impassable barriers. It is also vital to know how visitors behave, and to teach them to behave so as not to alienate mammals or endanger themselves. Where visitors are common, steps may have to be taken to educate both the visitors and the animals. It will not be possible otherwise to maintain natural populations of large mammals.

We must also have studies on the effect of hunting on the biology of ungulates in its fullest ramifications. Only then can we set the rules of hunting in a rational fashion, and ensure maximum production of the resource, be it on public lands or on game ranches. On an *a priori* basis it can be predicted that prolonged and extensive hunting will alter the biology of the species affected. Hunting will select for paedomorphism, early maturation, high reproduction, secretive habits, nervousness, inefficient conversion of ingested food, and increased efficiency in exploitation of escape terrain or cover. This will result ultimately in small, relatively short-lived forms of the species, with small horns or antlers. In addition, where several ungulate species coexist, it is likely that significant changes in habitat preference by one species may lead to the loss of other species in the manner expounded by Krantz (1970).

References

ALEXANDER G. (1961) Energy expenditure and mortality in new-born lambs. *Proc. 4th Int. Congr. Anim. Reprod.* 3, 630–7.

ALEXANDER G., PETERSON J.E. & WATSON R.H. (1959) Neonatal mortality in lambs. *Aust. vet. J.* 35, 433–41.

ALLEN D.L. (1962) *Our wildlife legacy*, revised edition 422 pp. New York, Funk & Wagnalls.

BANNIKOV A.G., ZHIRNOV L.V., LEBEDEVA L.S. & FANDEEV A.A. (1961) *Biology of the saiga.* (English translation.) Springfield: U.S. Department of Commerce.

BARNETT S.A. (1967) *Instinct and intelligence.* London: Macgibbon & Kee.

BATCHELER C.L. (1968) Compensatory responses of artificially controlled mammal populations. *Proc. N.Z. ecol. Soc.* 15, 25–30.

BUECHNER H.K. (1960) The bighorn sheep in the United States, its past, present and future. *Wildl. Monogr. No. 4. Chestertown.*

CALHOUN J.B. (1963) *The ecology and sociology of the Norway rat.* U.S. Dept of Health, Education & Welfare Publication No. 1008. Bethesda, Maryland.

DASMANN R.F. (1964) *Wildlife Biology.* 23 pp. New York: John Wiley & Sons Inc.

EINARSEN A.S. (1948) *The pronghorn antelope and its management.* 238 pp. Washington, D.C.: The Wildlife Management Instit.

ESTES R.D. (1967) The comparative behavior of Grant's and Thomson's gazelles. *J. Mammal.* 48, 189–209.

ESTES R.D. (1969) Territorial behavior of the wildebeest (*Connochaetes taurinus* Burchell 1823). *Z. Tierpsychol.* 23, 284–370.

FULLER W.A. (1962) *The biology and management of the bison of Wood Buffalo National Park.* Canadian Wildlife Service, Wildl. Mgmt. Bull. Ottawa Series *1*, No. 16.

GEIST V. (1966) Ethological observations on some North American cervids. *Zool. Beitr.* (*N.F.*) 12, 219–50.

GEIST V. (1967a) Working with tame mountain sheep. *Animals* 10(3), 119–23.

GEIST V. (1967b) A consequence of togetherness. *Nat. Hist.*, N.Y. 76(8), 24–30.

GEIST V. (1968) Welchen Wert hat die Verhaltensforschung in Wildnisgebieten für eine moderne Wildverwaltung? Tagungsberichte No. 104. *Beiträge zur Jagd und Wildforschung.* Berlin: Deutsche Akademie für Landwirtschaftswissenschaften.

GEIST V. (In press) *Mountain sheep: A study in behaviour and evolution.* Chicago: University of Chicago Press.

GOODALL J.VAN LAWICK. (1968) The behaviour of free-living chimpanzees in the Gombe Stream Reserve. *Anim. Behav. Monogr.* 1(3), 161–311.

GRAHAM N.McC., cited in K.L. BLAXTER. (1962) The fasting metabolism of adult wether sheep. *Br. J. Nutr.* 16, 615–26.

HEPTNER V.G., NASIMOVIC A.A. & BANNIKOV A.G. (1961) *Mammals of the Soviet Union.* (German translation.) Jena: V.E.B. Gustav Fischer Verlag.

HOLROYD J.C. (1967) Observations of Rocky Mountain goats on Mount Wardle, Kootenay National Park, B. C. *Can. Fld Nat.* 81, 1–22.

JERISON H.J. (1961) Quantitative analysis of evolution of the brain in mammals. *Science* 133(3457), 1012–14.

KLEIN D.R. (1964) Range-related differences in growth of deer reflected in skeletal ratios. *J. Mammal.* 45, 226–35.

KLEIN D.R. (1970) Tundra ranges north of the boreal forest. *J. Range Mgmt*, 23, 8–14.

KRANTZ G.S. (1970) Human activities and megafaunal extinctions. *Am. Scient.* 58, 164–70.

KÜHME W. (1965) Freilandstudien zur Soziologie des Hyänenhundes (*Lycaon pictus lupinus* Thomas 1902). *Z. Tierpsychol.* 22, 495–451.

LEUTHOLD W. (1969) *Ethology and game management.* Paper read at Ninth International Congress of Game Biologists, Moscow, U.S.S.R. 15–19 Sept. 1969.

LIDDELL H.S. (1954) Sheep and goats: The psychological effects of laboratory experiences of deprivation and stress upon certain experimental animals. In *Beyond the Germ Theory*, J. Galdston (Ed.), 106–19. New York: Health Education Council.

LIDDELL H.S. (1958) A biological basis for psychopathology. In *Problems of Addiction and Habituation*, P. H. Hoch & J. Zubin (Eds.), 120–33. New York: Grune & Stratton Inc.

LIDDELL H.S. (1961) Contributions of conditioning in the sheep and goat to an understanding of stress, anxiety and illness. In *Lectures on Experimental Psychiatry.* University of Pittsburgh Press.

McCULLOUGH D. (1969) The tule elk. *Univ. Calif. Publs zool.* 88, 194 pp.

NISHIKAWA Y. & HAFEZ E.S.E. (1968) Reproduction of horses. In *Reproduction in Farm Animals*, E.S.E.Hafez (Ed.), 289–300. Philadelphia: Lea & Febiger.

NIEVERGELT B. (1967) Die Zusammensetzung der Gruppe beim Alpensteinbock. *Z. Säugetierkunde* 32, 129–44.

REID R.L. & MILES S.C. (1962) Studies on the carbohydrate metabolism of sheep. The adrenal response to psychological stress. *Aust. J. agric. Res.* 13, 282–95.

ROBINS E. (1963) *Africa's wildlife. Survival or extinction?* 224 pp. London: Odhams Press Ltd.

SCHALLER G.B. (1963) *The mountain gorilla.* Chicago: University of Chicago Press.

SCHALLER G.B. (1969) Life with the king of beasts. *Natn. geogr. Mag.* 135(4), 494–519.

SCHENKEL R. (1966) Zum Problem der Territorialität und des Markierens bei Säugern— am Beispiel des schwarzen Nashorns und des Löwens. *Z. Tierpsychol.* 23, 593–626.

SCOTTER G.W. (1969) *Reindeer husbandry as a land use in northern Canada.* Paper read at Conference on Productivity and Conservation in Northern Circumpolar Lands, Edmonton.

TEAL J.J. Jr. (1970) Domesticating the wild and woolly muskox. *Natn. geogr. Mag.* 137(6), 863–79.

THOMPSON W.R. (1957) Influence of prenatal maternal anxiety on emotionality in young rats. *Science* 125, 698–9.

WALTHER F. (1964) Einige Verhaltensbeobachtungen an Thomsongazellen (*Gazella thomsoni* Guenther, 1884) in Ngorongoro-Krater. *Z. Tierpsychol.* 21, 871–90.

WALTHER F. (1969) Flight behaviour and avoidance of predators in Thomson gazelle (*Gazella thomsoni* Guenther 1884). *Behaviour* 34, 184–221.

WATSON R.H. & ELDER E.N. (1961) Neonatal mortality in lambs. *Aust. vet. J.* 37, 283–90.

WELLES R.E. & WELLES F.B. (1961) *The bighorn of Death Valley.* Fauna Series No. 6. Washington D.C.: U.S. Fauna National Parks.

ZIGUNOV P.S. (Ed.). (1961) *Reindeer husbandry.* (English translation from Russian.) Springfield: U.S.A. Department of Commerce.

Controlled fire in the management of
North American deer

RICHARD D.TABER *College of Forest Resources, University of
Washington, Seattle*
JAMES L.MURPHY *Pacific Northwest Forest and Range Experiment
Station, U.S. Forest Service; and College of Forest Resources, University of
Washington, Seattle*

Introduction

There are two species of *Odocoileus* deer in North America—*O. virginianus*,
the white-tailed deer, and *O. hemionus*, the mule deer. Low trees and shrubs,
with or without a tall tree overstory, are important as both food and cover in
deer habitat. Factors which set back forest communities to a shrub stage
generally favour deer. Fire is one such factor.

Controlled fire is used in the management of North American forest lands
for several purposes. These are: to reduce wildfire hazard by reducing fuel;
to expose mineral soil as a seedbed; to control undesirable plant species; to
improve quality of desirable forage plant species; to control disease in timber
trees; and to improve water yield through plant control.

In contrast to the widespread study and use of fire in livestock and timber
management, there has been relatively little research or operational study on
the use of controlled fire in wildlife management (Komarek 1966). However,
the importance of fire in improving or maintaining deer habitat is widely
recognized (Storer 1932; Stoddard 1936; Leopold 1950; Wing 1952 and
Davis 1959, among others). The prime management function of fire in deer
habitat is to stimulate the production of more abundant, available, and
nutritious forage (Leopold, Sowls, & Spencer 1947; Lutz 1956; Harlow &
Bielling 1961; Silker 1961; and Miller 1963). This is achieved through release
of nutrients to the soil, stimulation of seed germination and root-crown
sprouting, reduction in plant height (deer can browse only to about 4ft,
1·2 m), and increased light through canopy removal.

Effects of fire in major forest regions

Before and during the settlement of North America by European man, fire
occurred throughout most of North America. Recently, control of wildfire

425

has resulted in deterioration of deer habitat. Controlled fire can, however, be used for improving deer habitat without loss of other values. Its consideration in detail is best discussed by major forest regions.

Temperate rainforests of the Pacific Northwest

The climax forest in much of this humid coastal belt is dominated by western hemlock (*Tsuga heterophylla*), western red cedar (*Thuja plicata*) and the true firs (*Abies* spp.). Historically, however, wildfires have been so widespread that the subclimax Douglas fir (*Pseudotsuga menzeisii*), a valuable timber species, is the most abundant tree. The forest-managers have developed silvicultural methods favouring Douglas fir. Timber is harvested in clear-cut units of 30–150 acres (12–60 ha), and these are burned to reduce fire hazard and prepare a seedbed for Douglas fir. This treatment also favours shrub growth, and therefore black-tailed deer (*O. h. columbianus*), especially where tree regeneration is delayed (Longhurst, Leopold, & Dasmann 1952; Brown 1961). Resultant heavy populations of deer often damage young Douglas fir by browsing (Hines 1963). This conflict is not yet resolved.

Western semi-arid regions

The typical forest tree of the semi-arid parts of the North American west, where precipitation is under 25 in (675 mm) is the ponderosa pine (*Pinus ponderosa*), either as a climax or a fire-subclimax species (Davis 1959; Daubenmire 1969).

Before the coming of Europeans, stands were typically open and parklike, with mostly grass as subordinate vegetation. Pine regeneration was often dense where fire burned more intensively; subsequent fires thinned these thickets. Foresters in some areas have simulated the natural process by periodic light surface burning, to expose mineral soil and to thin dense sapling and pole stands (Davis 1959; Weaver 1964).

Clear-cut harvest areas are usually burned to reduce fire hazard and expose mineral soil for regeneration (Cooper 1966).

There can be conflicts between big game management and silvicultural objectives in this type of habitat (Davis 1959). Clear-cutting at least temporarily eliminates needed cover for deer (Society of American Foresters 1961). Selective cuts are seldom heavy enough, 35 per cent or less, to release important browse species (Society of American Foresters 1961). Controlled burning significantly reduces or eliminates important browse species such as bitterbrush (*Purshia tridentata*) (Weaver 1964). If deer are abundant, they can significantly affect the success of natural pine regeneration and coniferous plantations as found in central Oregon (Driscoll 1963).

In high fire hazard areas of continuous timber and brush stands, fuel break networks are now being constructed as conflagration barriers and to provide access for fire crews. Timber and brush stands along major ridges are thinned so that fire cannot cross the ridges through the crowns. This fire control measure improves deer habitat by increasing shrub accessibility and increasing shrub sprouting (Murphy 1963).

The Great Basin area, east of the Sierra Nevadas and southern Cascade Ranges, was once a climax bunch grass association and at higher elevations a mixed shrub association (Longhurst, Leopold, & Dasmann 1952). Heavy use of the range by livestock is thought to have been instrumental in creating the present dominant ground cover of annual cheat grass (*Bromus tectorum*) which is of little benefit to deer. Cheat grass, when cured, is highly flammable, and frequent range fires maintain it at the expense of the shrubs and bunch grass associations.

In contrast, logging and fire on higher altitude summer deer ranges have opened the stands of coniferous timber to the benefit of deer. At the other elevational extreme, the potential deer winter ranges along the lower edge of the ponderosa pine belt may be improved or degraded as deer habitat by fire, depending on season, frequency, and intensity (Longhurst, Leopold & Dasmann 1952).

Inter-mountain and northern Rocky Mountain forests

The forests of western Colorado, Utah, Idaho, and western Montana are seasonally dry and subject to lightning fires; 'fire type' plant associations are common. Trees favoured by fire include western white pine (*Pinus monticola*), lodge pole pine (*P. contorta*), Douglas fir, ponderosa pine, and aspen (*Populus tremuloides*).

Historically, hot, repeated wildfires in these forests produced extensive brushfields in which willows (*Salix sp.*) and redstem ceanothus (*Ceanothus sanguineous*), choice forage for deer and wapiti, were abundant. Big game was abundant. More recently, control of wildfires has permitted plant succession to proceed beyond the optimal habitat type for these animals.

Fire used silviculturally to consume slash or prepare coniferous seedbeds improves deer habitat. Fire also improves aspen stands by stimulating rootsprouting.

Chaparral of California and Arizona

The chaparral is a community of mainly evergreen shrubs found in regions with hot, dry summers and is adapted to repeated burning. It is used by man mainly as watershed cover, for recreational hunting, and to a lesser extent for grazing by sheep. In southern California controlled fire is seldom used in chaparral management, but in central and northern California, and in Arizona, deer management through the use of fire has been intensively studied.

Chaparral is ecologically peculiar in two ways.

(*a*) Growth-form: there are rarely trees in the chaparral, and herbaceous plants are a relatively minor part of the flora. The dominant vegetation consists of closely-growing shrubs (of which *Adenostema* (chamise) and *Quercus* (live and scrub oak) are the dominant genera in northern California) with very little understory. Summer fires burn accidentally or are set purposely to encourage the sprouts which emerge from the root-crown following burning and are a favourite forage of deer.

(*b*) Succession: chaparral plants, if there is no management, perpetuate themselves, since the climatic climax, an evergreen broad-leaved forest, is deflected by wildfire.

Uncontrolled fire in the chaparral can result in accelerated erosion, loss of fences and houses, and other damage. Because of this, a programme employing controlled fire was developed.

Briefly, the objectives of the programme are to reduce shrub density (to reduce shading and competition for moisture) and stature (to make their foliage available to deer), and to increase grass and forb abundance (for watershed cover and winter deer forage). Controlled burning, followed by seeding with the desired grasses and forbs is carried out to achieve these objectives. The warmer slopes are treated in this way and the cooler ones protected as cover.

The region so managed is called shrubland because of its interspersion of woody and herbaceous vegetation. A study by Taber (1956) compared shrubland to the unmanaged chaparral with respect to their deer populations (Table I).

Table 1. Comparison of black-tailed deer on unmanaged chaparral and shrubland habitat

	Annual available forage (dry wt kg/ha)	
	Chaparral	Shrubland
Herbaceous	5·2	92·6
Woody	197·2	552
Average crude protein level in diet (per cent)	9	14
Ovulation rate (per adult ♀)	0·77	1·65
December population per sq. km	64·7	155·4

As Table I indicates the system of chaparral management through burning and seeding to produce shrubland improves deer habitat by increasing forage availability and quality. The increase in quality is not due mainly to fertilization by ash; this is short-lived. Rather, the increase in quality is due to the increase in shrub sprouts, and the increase in herbaceous forage.

Any biotic community is dynamic, and a continuing system of management is necessary to maintain shrubland over chapparal.

Since the shrubs in the forage areas will be kept in their most productive growth-form (fully available) by moderate deer browsing, and yet may be killed out by excessive browsing, the tools of management include the capability of controlling deer density. If deer density is too light for control of shrubs, a second application of fire kills shrub seedlings and some mature shrubs. A series of burns in rapid succession, however, will eliminate so many of the shrubs important as deer forage that the carrying capacity of the area for deer will be reduced. On occasion, of course, this reduction of deer capacity may actually be a managerial goal. Use of controlled fire to increase or lower deer carrying capacity appears to be applicable to most shrub-dominated plant associations, where the crowns tend to grow above the reach of deer.

Mixed hardwood—conifer forests of the central and north-eastern United States

This general forest type is characteristic of the northern forested states, from Minnesota in the west to New Jersey in the east. The forest is made up of a wide variety of deciduous and evergreen trees, with different responses to local site conditions and different values both commercially and with regard to deer ecology. Typically, these forests are managed for pulpwood or timber, with deer production also a stated objective.

As has been noted, deer can browse heavily on, and deform or destroy, a regenerating commercial forest. The intensity of damage tends to rise with deer population density; Table 2, synthesized from several sources, shows

Table 2. Relation of white-tailed deer density to damage in some North American conifer hardwood forests

Estimated deer density (no./sq km)	Damage to timber seedlings	Reference
323·7	Total	Grange 1949
284·9	Total	Bartlett 1958
90·6–116·5	Heavy	Stoeckler, Strothman, and Krefting 1957
64·7–129·5	Heavy	Graham 1954
51·8+	Moderate	Bennett 1962
51·8	Light	Bartlett 1958
20·7–31·0	Light	Graham 1954
20·7–23·3	Light	Bennett 1962

the general relationship between deer population density and damage to conifer reproduction. It is obvious that it is easy to build deer numbers, in this region, beyond the level compatible with conifer reproduction.

Since the main deer management problem in this region is not deer production, but rather keeping deer herds within the limits of the food supply, there are few examples of the deliberate use of fire to increase deer numbers. Fire can, however, be used to increase food. Aspen and jack pine (*P. banksiana*) are important browse species which are successionally replaced by hardwood trees. Fire induces regeneration of both aspen and jackpine, increasing deer forage (Vogle 1967).

South-eastern pine forests

The south-eastern region of the U.S. has a mixed conifer-hardwood vegetation, similar to that of the Lake States, but this region differs in being largely snow-free so that natural fires are a more important ecological factor. As in the chaparral, where natural fires are frequent, a system of using fire as a managerial tool for both silviculture and wildlife has been developed. The work of Stoddard (1936) is well known with respect to the management of the bobwhite quail, particularly, but also the wild turkey, the white-tailed deer and other wildlife species. All of these frequent the subclimax pine forests of this region and all, but especially the deer, are influenced by the amount of hardwood in the biotic community.

In this region there is a tremendous variety of potential forage plants—78 species of woody plants and 150 herbaceous ones. Timber species (pines) are not highly preferred by deer (Goodrum & Reid 1958). Burning benefits deer by increasing available browse quantity and quality, of which the latter seems more important (Lay 1956 and 1957). Leguminous herbs are also preferred forage and are encouraged by fire (Goodrum & Reid 1958).

With these various examples of the relation of deer, fire, and habitat in mind, we can now consider the basic ecology of fire-vegetation relationships. Fire can improve quantity and quality of food and cover in North American deer ranges, and controlled fire is used in some regions for these purposes. But foresters and wildlife managers ask the question—What is the total effect of fire on the ecosystem?

Summary of reported effects of controlled fire on the ecosystem

The effects of fire on soil moisture vary, but most studies conclude that moisture in the soil is reduced significantly after fire (Eden 1924; Haines 1926; Auten 1934; Isaac & Hopkins 1937; Sampson 1944; Austin & Baisinger 1955; Lutz 1956; Ahlgren 1963).

Because of increased light absorption by the blackened surface, and reduction of insulation, soil temperatures have been found to increase on burned
areas (Isaac 1930; Shirley 1932; Wahlenberg 1935; Tryon 1948; Lutz 1956;
Ahlgren & Ahlgren 1960; Ahlgren 1963). Several investigators reported soil
temperatures high enough to kill seedlings or reduce growth (Isaac 1929;
1930; Tryon 1948). Others suggested that fire is needed to raise temperatures
in order to stimulate growth of shrubs and trees (Went, Juhren, & Juhren
1952).

Most investigators found soil acidity to be decreased by ash left from fire,
since it is highly alkaline (Haines 1926; Isaac & Hopkins 1937; Gibson 1938;
Garren 1943; Tryon 1948; Ferrell & Olson 1952; Austin & Baisinger 1955;
Lutz 1956; Ahlgren & Ahlgren 1960; Biswell 1963). However, studies in
Californian ponderosa pine type (Vlamis, Biswell, & Schultz 1955) and
Australian *Eucalyptus* plantations (Beadle 1940) showed no significant change
in pH after burning. Increases in soil magnesium, calcium, potassium, phos-
phorus, and nitrogen by leaching from ash have been shown by many workers
in many regions (Sampson 1944; Tryon 1948; Ferrell & Olson 1952; Austin
& Baisinger 1955; Lutz 1956; Ahlgren & Ahlgren 1960; Ahlgren 1963; Lotti,
Klawitter, & LeGrande 1960). However, a study in western Washington
(D. Cole & C. Grier, pers. comm.) shows that changes found in the nutrient
levels of soil do not necessarily reflect changes in nutrient levels in the ecosystem. They say most past studies have been orientated toward the *results*
of burning rather than the mechanisms by which results are achieved. They
claim that the potential for ion loss from the system is increased by burning,
through mass transport, volatilization, immobilization, and leaching.

Soil erosion is increased significantly by controlled burning on steep
slopes in California and the Idaho ponderosa pine type (Lowdermilk 1930;
Kolak 1931; Connaughton 1935). However, Silker (1961) in Texas, states
that 'if burns are planned and conducted only when the duff is moist to damp,
soil erosion on steep slopes will be limited'.

Rodent populations may be reduced because of a hot, controlled burn,
but quickly rise, often above pre-burn levels, due to immigration. Various
reasons have been suggested for this, principally animal curiosity and increased availability of seeds and insects (Horn 1938; Bole 1939; Moore 1940;
Garman & Orr-Ewing 1949; Hoover 1953; Tevis 1956; Ahlgren 1963;
Hatchell 1964). A possible additional, or alternative, factor is the breakdown
in social controls due to massive environmental change.

Since fire produces smoke and ash, and since these may significantly
affect air quality, attention has recently been focused on controlled fire as a
potential source of air pollution. Studies thus far have been mostly exploratory. Preliminary indications are that particulate matter in smoke may be
more important than gaseous components. Sophisticated forest burning

techniques and weather management will be necessary to minimize air pollution (Murphy, Fritschen & Cramer 1970).

Prescribed burning in management of North American deer

Because of the threat of ecosystem impairment by loosely planned and 'unscientific' burning, prescribed burning is replacing controlled burning in management of Northern American forest lands. The techniques involved in the use of prescribed fire for deer habitat improvement include a clear statement of the objectives to be attained. Objectives will include avoidance of undesired side-effects such as fire escape and production of offensive smoke levels. They will also include the desired effects of the fire upon the plant community—whether large hardwood trees must be killed by a hot fire, for example, or whether root-sprouting must be stimulated by a lighter ground fire. Fire characteristics, and the effect of fire upon the various components of the vegetation, can then be planned for by taking into account fuel size, distribution, and moisture, air temperature and movement, soil moisture, time of day, and season. If there is a large amount of fine dry fuel, for example, a summer burn would be very difficult to control, but one in autumn, winter, or spring might not. But autumn burning may be undesirable because of the greater air stability, and therefore higher smoke pollution potential. If hardwoods are to be controlled, a late spring fire is more effective than one in winter. Such considerations affect the choice of season, and even the choice of day and hour.

Since there is no practical field method for measuring fuel moisture by size class of fuel, fuel moisture sticks and scales have long been used as fuel analogues. Fuel moisture analogue measures have been successfully correlated with burning results, so that burning results can be accurately predicted (Dixon 1965; Beaufait 1966).

Direct measurements can be made of air temperature, wind speed, and humidity.

Further control of fire effects can be attained through size of burned area, fuel modification, careful planning of type, speed and pattern of ignition, direction of burn, presence of fire breaks. Plans must include systematic but flexible provisions for fire control, mop-up and patrol. A post-burn appraisal will help to improve prescriptions for future burns.

Even so a shortage of precise knowledge about the ecological effects of fire, and a fear of fire escape, tend to limit the use of fire for ecological manipulation.

If fire is to continue to be a tool in management of land, and to become a widely accepted tool in management of deer in North America, carefully planned, scientifically based prescribed burns will be mandatory; a requirement for 'scientific management of animal and plant communities for conservation'.

References

AHLGREN C.E. (1963) Some basic ecological factors in prescribed burning in northeastern Minnesota. *Proc. Annual Tall Timbers Fire Ecology Conference.* Tallahassee, Fla. 2, 143–9.

AHLGREN, I.F. & AHLGREN C.E. (1960) Ecological effects of forest fires. *Bot. Rev.* 26, 483–553.

AUSTIN R.C. & BAISINGER D.H. (1955). Some effects of burning on forest soils of western Oregon and Washington. *J. Forestry* 53, 275–80.

AUTEN J.T. (1934) The effect of forest burning and pasturing in the Ozarks on the water absorption of forest soils. *U.S. Dept. Agric., Forest Service Central States Forest Exp. Sta. Note* 16, 5 pp.

BARTLETT C.O. (1958) *A study of some deer and forest relationships in Rondeau Provincial Park.* Ontario Dept Lands & Forests, Biol. Ser. 66, 137 pp.

BEADLE N.C.W. (1940) Soil temperature during forest fires and its effect on the survival of vegetation. *J. Ecol.* 28, 180–92.

BEAUFAIT W.R. (1966) Prescribed fire planning in the intermountain west. *USDA, Forest Service, Res. Paper Int.* 26 Intermountain Forest and Range Expt. Sta. 24 pp.

BENNETT A.L. (1962) Industrial forestry and wildlife—the northeast. *J. For.* 60, 118–20.

BISWELL H.H. (1963) Research in wildland fire ecology in California. *Pro. Annual Tall Timbers Fire Ecology Conference.* Tallahassee, Fla. 2, 63–97.

BOLE B.P. (1939) The quadrant method of studying small mammal populations. *Sci. Publ. Cleveland Mus. Nat. Hist.* 5, 15–77.

BROWN E.R. (1961) The black-tailed deer of western Washington. *Washington State Game Dept. Biol. Bull.* No 13, 124 pp.

CONNAUGHTON C.A. (1935) Forest fires and accelerated erosion. *J. Forestry* 33, 751–2.

COOPER R.W. (1966) The prescribed fire problem. *Proceedings, National Prescribed Fire seminars Macon, Georgia, USDA Forest Service,* 1–3.

DAUBENMIRE R. (1969) Structure and ecology of coniferous forests of the northern Rocky Mountains. *Coniferous Forests of the Northern Rocky Mountains* (ed. by R. D. Taber) 25–42. University of Montana, Missoula.

DAVIS K.P. (1959) *Forest fire: control and use.* McGraw-Hill.

DIXON M.J. (1965) *A guide to fire by prescription.* USDA Forest Service, Southern Region. Atlanta, Georgia. 32 pp.

DRISCOLL R.S. (1963) Repellents reduce deer browsing on ponderosa pine seedlings. *USDA Forest Service, Pac. NW. For. and Range Expt. Sta. Portland, Research Note PNW* 51, *July* 1963, 8 pp.

EDEN T. (1924) Edaphic factors accompanying the succession after burning on Harpenden Common. *J. Ecol.* 12, 267–86.

FERRELL W.K. & OLSON D.S. (1952). Preliminary studies on the effects of fire on forest soils in the western white pine region of Idaho. *Idaho Univ. Forest, Range and Wildlife Exp. Sta. Res. Notes* 4, 1–5.

GARMAN E.H. & ORR-EWING A.L. (1949) Direct-seeding experiments in the southern coastal region of British Columbia 1923–49. *Brit. Col. Forest Serv., Tech. Publ. T.* 31, 23 pp.

GARREN K.H. (1943) Effects of fire on vegetation of the southeastern United States. *Bot. Rev.* 9, 617–54.

GIBSON J.M. (1938) Comments. *J. Forestry* 36, 1049–51.

GOODRUM P.D. & REID V.H. (1958) Deer browsing in the longleaf pine belt. *Proc. Meet. Soc. Am. Foresters* 1958, 139–43.

GRAHAM S.A. (1954) Changes in northern Michigan deer forest from browsing by deer. *Trans. N. Am. Wildl. Conf.* 19, 526–33.

GRANGE WALLACE (1949) *The way to game abundance: with an explanation of game cycles.* Scribner, 365 pp.

HAINES F.M. (1926) Effect of fire on soil. *J. Ecol.* 14, 33–71.

HARLOW R.F. & BIELLING P. (1961) Controlled burning studies in longleaf pine-turkey oak association on the Ocala National Forest. Reprinted from *Proc. of the 15th Annual Conf. Southeastern Assoc. of Game and Fish Commissioners.* Atlanta, Ga. 16 pp.

HATCHELL G.E. (1964) *Small-mammal species and populations in the loblolly shortleaf pine forest type of Louisiana.* Southern Forestry Exp. Sta., New Orleans, La. 12 pp.

HINES W.W. (1963) Relations of black-tailed deer density to conifer survival. *Proc. Ann. West. Assoc. State Game and Fish Comm.* 43, 188–92.

HOOVER E.F. (1953) Some experiments in baiting forest lands or the control of small seed eating mammals. *Ore. State Bd. of For., Res. Bull.* No. 8, 4 pp.

HORN E.E. (1938) Some wildlife forest relationships. *Trans. N. Am. Wildl. Conf.* 3, 376–80.

ISAAC L.A. (1929) Seedling survival on burned and unburned surfaces. *Pacific Northwest Forest Exp. Sta. For. Res.* Note 3. 17 pp.

ISAAC L.A. (1930) Seedling survival on burned and unburned surfaces. *J. Forestry* 28, 569–71.

ISAAC L.A. & HOPKINS H.G. (1937) The forest soil of the Douglas fir region and the changes wrought upon it by logging and slash burning. *Ecology* 18, 264–59.

KOLAK E.E. (1931) Erosion: a problem in forestry. *J. Forestry* 29, 193–8.

KOMAREK R. (1966) A discussion of wildlife management, fire and the wildlife landscape. *Proc. Annual Tall Timbers Fire Ecology Conference.* Tallahassee, Fla. 5, 177–94.

LAY D.W. (1956) Effects of prescribed burning on forage and mast production in southern pine forests. *J. Forestry* 54, 582–4.

LAY D.W. (1957) Browse quality and the effects of prescribed burning in southern pine forests. *J. Forestry* 55, 342–7.

LEOPOLD A.S. (1950) Deer in relation to plant succession. *Trans. N. Am. Wildl. Conf.* 15, 571–80.

LEOPOLD A.S., SOWLS L.K. & SPENCER D.L. (1947) A survey of overpopulated deer ranges in the United States. *J. Wildl. Mgmt.* 11, 162–77.

LONGHURST W., LEOPOLD A.S. & DASMANN R. (1952) A survey of California deer herds, deer ranges and management problems. *State of California Dept. of Fish and Game, Bureau Game Cons. Bull.* 6, 36 pp.

LOTTI T., KLAWITTER R.A. & LEGRANDE W.P. (1960) Prescribed burning for under-story control in loblolly pine stands of the coastal plain. *Southeastern Forest Exp. Sta. Paper* No. 116, 19 pp.

LOWDERMILK W.C. (1930) Influences of forest litter, run-off, percolation, and erosion. *J. Forestry* 28, 474–91.

LUTZ H.J. (1956) Ecological effects of forest fires in the interior of Alaska. *U.S. Dept. Agr., Tech. Bull.* 1133, 121 pp.

MILLER H.A. (1963) Use of fire in wildlife management. *Proc. Annual Tall Timbers Fire Ecology Conference.* Tallahassee, Fla. 2, 19–30.

MOORE A.W. (1940) Wild animal damage to seed and seedlings on cut-over Douglas fir lands of Oregon and Washington. *USDA, Tech. Bull.* No. 706.

MURPHY J.L. (1963) *Conflagration barriers—a new concept.* Forest Fire conditions of western North America. *Portland, Oregon Western Forestry and Conservation Assoc.* 1963, 68–74.

MURPHY J.L., FRITSCHEN L.J. & CRAMER O.P. (1970) Research looks at air quality and forest burning. *J. Forestry* 68, 530–5.

SAMPSON A.W. (1944) Effect of chaparral burning on soil erosion and on soil moisture relations. *Ecology* 25, 171–91.

SHIRLEY H.L. (1932) Does light burning stimulate aspen suckers? *J. Forestry* 29, 524–5; 30, 419–20.

SILKER T.H. (1961) *Prescribed burning to control undesirable hardwoods in southern pine stands.* Texas For. Serv. Bull. No. 51, 44 pp.

SOCIETY OF AMERICAN FORESTERS (1961) *Forestry handbook.* Ronald Press Co., New York 9, 32.

STODDARD H.L. (1936) Relation of burning to timber and wildlife. *N. Am. Wildl. Conf. Proc.* 1, 399–403.

STORER T.I. (1932) Factors influencing wildlife in California, past and present. *Ecology* 13, 315–34.

TABER R.D. (1956) Deer nutrition and population dynamics in the North Coast Range of California. *Trans. N. Am. Wildl. Conf.* 41, 159–72.

TEVIS L. Jr. (1956) Effect of a slash burn on forest mice. *J. Wildl. Mgmt.*, 20: 405–9.

TRYON E.H. (1948) Effect of charcoal on certain physical, chemical, and biological properties of forest soils. *Ecol. Monogr.* 18, 81–115.

VLAMIS J., BISWELL H.H. & SCHULTZ A.M. (1955) Effects of prescribed burning on soil fertility in second growth ponderosa pine. *J. Forestry* 53, 905–9.

VOGLE, R.J. (1967) Controlled burning for wildlife in Wisconsin. *Proc. Sixth Annual Tall Timbers Fire Ecology Conference.* Tallahassee, Fla. 6, 47–96.

WAHLENBERG W.G. (1935) Effects of fire and grazing on soil properties. *J. Forestry* 33, 331–8.

WEAVER H. (1964) Fire and management problem in ponderosa pine. *Proc. Annual Tall Timbers Fire Ecology Conference.* Tallahassee, Fla. 3, 117–124.

WENT F.W., JUHREN G. & JUHREN M.C. (1952) Fire and biotic factors affecting germination. *Ecology* 33, 351–64.

WING L.W. (1952) *Practice of Wildlife Conservation.* John Wiley and Sons, New York. 408 pp.

Some effects of a change in estate management on a deer population

V.P.W.LOWE *The Nature Conservancy, Merlewood Research Station, Grange-over-Sands, Lancashire*

Introduction

Almost invariably, when major changes in land use are made, the repercussions on the communities of plants and animals involved are complex; and generally, a considerable period of time is required before a new regime can become established. Seldom have such changes been monitored throughout, and in the case of moor burning, perhaps the most widespread management practice in upland country, none of the effects on any of the grazing species has yet been evaluated critically. Similarly, most attempts to manage or control animal populations have proceeded by empirical methods and the results have rarely been fully documented.

Ideally, in order to manage any species and its habitat. 'The first stage in attempted control of the situation should always be the collection of adequate information about the whole ecology of the animals studied. . . . The second stage is to invent practical methods of control' (Elton 1957, p. 85). This advice was particularly relevant to the postwar (1939–45) problem of Red deer (*Cervus elaphus* L.) management in Scotland, for there was almost no information supported by factual evidence on any aspect of their ecology. Furthermore, only on Rhum were there herds available in a suitable location for such a study. These deer, however, had to be controlled in accordance with defined objects of reserve management, after the Nature Conservancy acquired the island in 1957 (Eggeling 1964), and there was, therefore, no opportunity to evaluate the previous system of management. The principal objective, rehabilitation of the vegetation, involved the cessation of commercial sheep farming and the associated management practice of moor burning. Such a grazing regime was unique within the range of the species in Scotland, and the information required as a basis for management, as well as the methods of deer control, had to be collected and developed during the course of the

437

study. It is therefore possible to evaluate only some of the effects due to these changes in management. Furthermore, although red deer were never true forest dwellers, but evolved as inhabitants of the transition zone between forest and steppe (Dzieciolowski 1969a), the results from Rhum cannot be related to red deer in their natural habitat because Rhum is a virtually tree-less island.

Only two other studies of the effects following similar changes in habitat management on deer populations have been sufficiently documented to make some comparison possible. The first was Evans's work on the red deer on Jura between 1878 and 1890 (Evans 1890), which was later summarized by Cameron (1923), and the second was the history of the Kaibab north deer herd (*Odocoileus hemionus* (Rafinesque)) first described by Rasmussen (1941) and more recently by Russo (1964). These are discussed later. The main purpose of this paper is to describe the more important effects on the quality and numbers of red deer on Rhum, with particular reference to body size, antlers, fecundity and dispersal, after monitoring as wide a range of physical and dynamic properties of the deer as possible during the first nine years of the new regime.

Habitat

The island of Rhum lies some 24 km off the west coast of Scotland, in the Inner Hebrides. It is approximately 10,684 ha in extent, consisting mainly of *Molinia*-dominated grasslands with smaller areas of *Calluna* and *Agrostis-Festuca* on the better-drained soils below 300 m (Plate I). Most of the higher ground is rocky and sparsely covered with vegetation, and affords little grazing except during the summer months.

The hills, which are composed largely of igneous rocks, were formed during the Tertiary period by intrusion through the Torridonian sandstone. Except for the basalts in the north-west of the island, the soils, derived from the ultrabasic rocks, felsites and granophyres, generally support only poor-quality grazings. However, where these soils are flushed by mineral-enriched spring waters after rain, small areas of better-quality pasture have developed, and these are the grazings most favoured by the deer.

Since the island is almost treeless, the only shelter from the sun in early summer, from rain (annual average 236 cm), and from frequent high winds and gales, is that provided by topographic features.

Management before 1957

Rhum was last inhabited, by people wholly dependent for their livelihood on the resources of the island and its surrounding coastal waters, in 1826. In 1827–8, the proprietor assisted the entire population (*c.* 400) to emigrate,

Plate 1. View looking eastwards from the centre of the island showing the *Molinia*-dominated grasslands with *Calluna* on the better-drained soils on the low ground and the sparse vegetation on the hills.

mainly to Nova Scotia, and the island was, thereafter, managed almost entirely in the interests of sheep farming. Initially it was stocked with 8,000 sheep, and there were probably never less than 3,000 until 1926, when they were all removed (Eggeling 1964). In 1939, the north and west parts of the island, the sheep ground (see Lowe 1969), were restocked with about 5,000 sheep. After the war (1945) this population was reduced to between 3,700 and 1,700 until 1957, when all the sheep were again removed.

The present stock of red deer dates from 1845, when the stony and more mountainous ground in the eastern and southern parts of the island was set aside as a deer forest. The deer were not, however, restricted to this area but allowed free access to all parts of the island. During thirteen years, 1926–39, the whole island was effectively deer forest, and the only competitors for the grazings were small numbers of goats (*c*. 100) and ponies (*c*. 30). The maximum number of deer on the island during this period is not known because no systematic counting of the deer was undertaken. In April 1957 (first census), 1,584 deer were counted, and it was thought there had been little change in numbers since the war.

Management since 1957

The Conservancy's primary object was to restore the island to the highest level of biological production, commensurate with its environmental resources. The management practice of moor-burning was, therefore, discontinued after the sheep were removed in September 1957, and trials with tree species were started in small fenced plots on a variety of sites as a preliminary to re-establishing woodland cover. Afforestation on a large scale was limited to one enclosure only, in the north-east of the island. Apart from these areas and certain strips of vegetation adjacent to them, which have been burnt periodically since 1963 as firebreaks, there was no positive management of the habitat. Dead grass, mainly *Molinia*, was allowed to accumulate and drains were allowed to become choked, so that only natural factors would influence the future development of the habitat.

Excluding the small herd of ponies (*c*. 20), feral goats (*c*. 120) and very large numbers of *Lepidoptera* (mainly lasiocampids and *Saturnia pavonia* L.), red deer were the only important grazing animals. The number of red deer, however, had to be stabilized to maintain a constant reduction in the former grazing pressure. An increased annual cull was therefore instituted, which, after 1961, remained at one-sixth of the spring-counted adults. This culling of the deer was the only direct interference in an otherwise uncontrolled ecosystem.

Methods and Materials

A team, usually consisting of three or four men, counted the deer every year in late winter or early spring while the majority of the herds were still on their low ground winter grazings and the classes could be most easily distinguished. Deer were classified as stags, hinds, yearling stags and calves of the previous year. The last two classes were still distinguishable at this time of year because, on Rhum, the male calves never developed antler pedicles before June, when they were 12 months of age, unlike those on the continent of Europe, which begin to develop pedicles in February, at the age of 8 months (Dzieciolowski 1969b; Raesfeld 1964).

The whole island was completely searched for dead carcasses at various times each year, but, since most natural deaths occurred during March and the first half of April, searching was intensified during this period so that deer which died before the annual census could be separated from those dying afterwards.

Every year, deer calves were caught, usually within a day or two of birth, and marked with ear tags to provide known-aged individuals in the population for studies of development, behaviour and dispersal. By use of mandibles from such marked individuals of known age, which had subsequently died or been shot, various methods of ageing deer were investigated. The most reliable method was found to be one based on tooth replacement, eruption and wear (Lowe 1967), and all mandibles from deer found dead or shot were aged by this method.

Stags were culled during the period August–October and the hind cull followed during the period October–January. Both sexes were culled in proportion to the numbers present at the time of the spring census in the different areas. The stags, were, to some extent, selectively culled, those bearing antlers with poorly-developed tines, showing distorted antler growth or in in poor condition physically, being shot first each year. Only stags with many or long tines on well-shaped heads (antlers of symmetrical shape and with a width between them at their widest equal to their length) were completely protected, unless in poor condition.

The hind cull followed the normal practice on Scottish deer forests, and consisted mainly of yeld hinds (mature hinds, 12 or more months after failing to breed during the breeding season following parturition). A varying number of immature hinds had also to be shot because there were rarely sufficient yeld hinds to meet the demands of the cull (Table 1). Milk hinds with calves at foot were seldom shot unless both were in very poor condition. This practice conserves the most productive elements of the population and exploits the meat potential of the least fertile whilst they are in their best condition and are readily marketable.

Both sexes were shot with rifles and their carcasses (minus alimentary tracts and blood) were brought off the hill on the backs of specially trained ponies. Whole body-weights were recorded where practicable; at other times only carcass weights, before and after being dressed in the larder, were recorded.

Table 1. *Total numbers of hinds (adjusted to 1 June) and their breeding performance, based on populations reconstructed from material collected up to 1 June 1968*

Year	No. of hinds (all year classes)	Minimum % of hinds known to have calved	No. of sexually mature hinds	Maximum % of sexually mature hinds failing to calve (yeld)
1957	778	40·1	441	29·3
1958	837	42·5	474	25·1
1959	862	41·2	489	27·4
1960	866	37·6	491	33·6

Mandibles for ageing the deer, stags' antlers and ovaries were the only materials collected as a routine every year.

Results

Antlers

Data from all the culls (1957–65) enable us to construct a curve illustrating the acquisition and loss of antler tines in relation to age (Fig. 1). It appeared

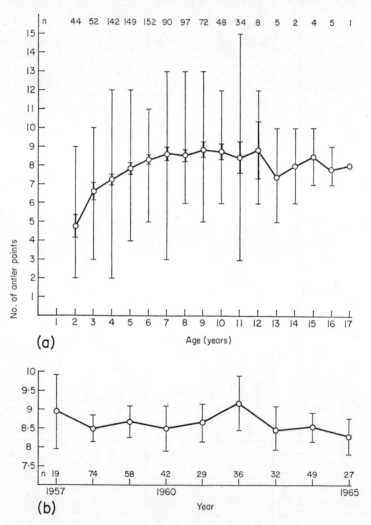

Figure 1. (*a*) Mean number of antler points in relation to age of the stags culled on Rhum, 1957–66, together with 2 × s.e. (vertical thick lines) and the total range for each year class (vertical thin lines).

(*b*) Mean number of antler points on mature stags (7–17 years) in each year's cull.

that an asymptote was not reached until the age of 7 years, one year later than the same part of the curve relating to body weight (Fig. 2). Since the data were mainly from stags, culled because their antlers were considered inferior (see p. 440), the curve probably falls below the true means for the different year classes, particularly after maturity, but its general form is not thought to depart from the real growth curve in any other respect.

When the data for each year from the asymptotic classes were pooled to increase the sample size and the averages were compared, the numbers of

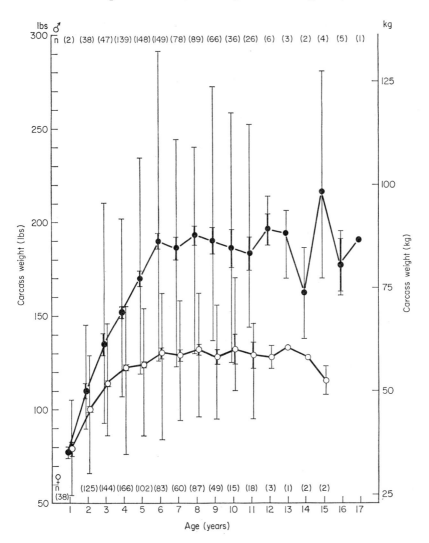

Figure 2. Mean age-specific body weights (less alimentary tracts) of stags ● and hinds ○, culled on Rhum 1957–65, together with 95 per cent confidence limits and the total range.

antler tines, excepting 1962, appeared if anything, to have declined over the period; they certainly did not show the increase expected as a consequence of the culling policy (Fig. 1).

Body weight

Data from all the annual culls were used to construct the growth curves shown in Fig. 2. For comparisons between years, the sample size for each year was increased by pooling all the weights of individuals within the plateau portion of each of the growth curves, i.e. the physically mature age classes. In the stags, for instance, the weights of the 6–9-year-olds were pooled because they alone were similar, all except one exceeding 85 kg (13 st 7 lb).

The weights of the hinds also reached a plateau at 6 years, but weights did not begin to decline before the age of 11 years; again with one exception, the average weights of these year classes all exceed 58·5 kg (9 st 3 lb).

The weights of younger and older stags and hinds could not be similarly compared between years because the size of the samples varied too widely, and further pooling of data was not possible because, as in other red deer populations (Dzieciolowski 1969a; Raesfeld 1964), the average weights of individual year classes were too widely separated on both the steeply ascending and descending parts of the growth curve.

When the significance of the linear regressions between the weights of the mature deer and the years in which they were shot, was tested, the results showed that the average weights of mature animals of both sexes had declined significantly (stags, $t = 3·61$, 380 d.f., $p < 0·001$; hinds, $t = 5·72$, 348 d.f., $p < 0·001$) during the period. The weight of the stags ($Y = 21·453 - 0·129 X$) had declined by a calculated 6·5 kg or 7·3 per cent and the weight of the hinds ($Y = 15·808 - 0·106 X$) showed a decline of a calculated 5·4 kg or 8·7 per cent during the nine years. But, whereas stags living largely on grazings on the low ground (Lowe 1966) began to lose weight immediately after the change in management, the hinds, living mainly on pastures higher up the hills, remained unaffected for the first four years (Fig. 3a).

Fecundity

After pooling the data from all the annual culls of young and yeld hinds, two age-specific fecundity curves were constructed (Fig. 3b). The one, linking together all the open circles, represents hinds which had had access to areas of heath or grassland, burnt within two years of their being shot; the other represents the performance of hinds which had been grazing only unburnt pastures or moorland for at least two years before their deaths.

The cessation of moor-burning was followed by a highly significant (x^2

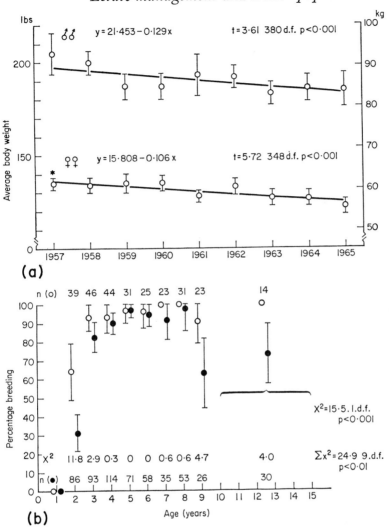

Figure 3. Time trends in (*a*) size, and (*b*) breeding performance of deer on Rhum.
(*a*) Mean body weights (less alimentary tracts) of mature stags (6–9 years of age) and mature hinds (6–11 years of age) for the period 1957–65. 95 per cent confidence limits are indicated.
(*b*) Breeding performance of young and yeld hinds, (○) having had, (●) not having had, access to burnt areas within two years of being culled.
* All age classes pooled for 1957 following the removal of the labels from the mandibles by Hooded crows (*Corvus cornix*).

= 15·47, 1d.f., p <0.001) decline in the breeding performance of all age classes of hinds. The age classes which were most affected were the two-year-olds and hinds, nine years of age or older. Only 31·4 ± 10·0 per cent of the two-year-olds attained puberty in their third year after the discontinuation of moor burning in contrast with the 64·1 ± 15·4 per cent which had done so previously. Fecundity of the nine-year-olds and older declined by about 25 per cent.

This decline in fecundity was shown to be easily reversed; the fecundity of two-year-olds, having access to areas burnt as fire breaks after 1962, recovered significantly to around its former level (70 per cent: p = 0·044) in contrast to the 30·5 per cent of the others (Lowe 1969).

Changes in population

Population size and structure

The only way by which it was found possible to test the validity of the annual census, was by checking the counted totals against the numbers calculated to have been present after reconstructing the original populations by ageing all the deer subsequently recovered dead. By 1966 it was calculated that more than 80 per cent of each of the first four years' counted populations (1957–60) had died, and the totals estimated for these (i.e. dead and probable survivors) differed from those counted by only 2·1 ± 1·6 per cent (Lowe 1969). However, errors in classification were greater; 11·3 ± 2·6 per cent of the stags were found to have been classified as hinds during the counts and the hinds appeared to have been overestimated by 17·3 ± 8·6 per cent. A rather variable number of calves had also tended to be classified as hinds (13·0 ± 19·0 per cent).

By 1968 it was calculated that more than 80 per cent of each of the first five years' populations (1957–61) had been recovered dead, and it was therefore possible to re-estimate the differences between the counts and reconstructions over a longer period. Overall, the estimate of the error in counting had increased slightly to 3·0 ± 1·3 per cent (Table 2). Errors in classification also showed slight differences; this time stags appeared to have been underestimated by 10·0 per cent and hinds overestimated by 19·2 per cent.

Effects of culling

Figure 4 depicts the changes in numbers of stags and hinds counted during the ten annual censuses, the observed class values having been corrected for misclassification (Lowe 1969). It will be seen that the numbers of each sex increased to begin with, following the removal of the sheep and a traditional low cull in the first year (1957). But, whereas the stags continued to increase in numbers up to 1964, when their numbers fell sharply, the hinds increased in numbers only during the first two years; after 1959 they gradually decreased in numbers and, except for 1964 and 1965, they continued this decline for the following seven years.

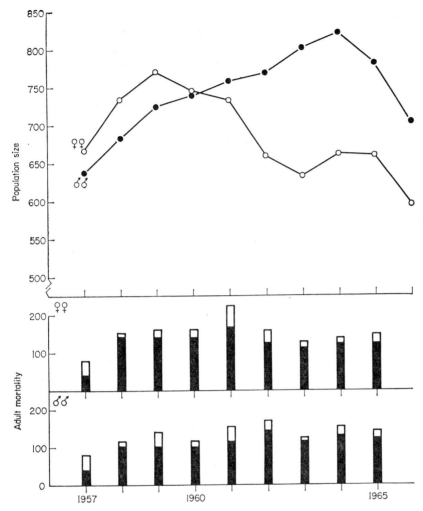

Figure 4. Population changes in adults (above) and annual mortality (below) on Rhum, 1957–66. ■ culled, □ natural deaths.

The number of deer, culled and dying naturally (Fig. 4) exceeded the number of calves surviving to become yearlings in only four of the nine years (1957–65). The total mortality was therefore normally within the limits of recruitment. The latter was 44·0 ± 4·9 per 100 hinds during the first 4 years and probably exceeded 45 per 100 hinds during the whole period. (Lowe 1969). The sex ratio of the foetuses in hinds culled during the period was 0·81 ♂♂:♀ (n = 268), and of calves caught for marking was 1·16 ♂♂:♀ (n = 492). Therefore, female recruitment should have been sufficient as a rule; in fact, it only failed in years like 1958, 1960, 1962 and 1967 (1·56 ♂♂:♀, n = 215 calves), following bad conditions during the previous autumn and winter. Of these years, 1967 was probably the worst for female recruitment, only 24 out of 71 calves caught for marking being females. Male recruitment, on the other hand, was not affected (Lowe 1969). But, because the counts were not corrected for misclassification when the numbers to be culled had to be estimated, culling which was intended to take one-sixth of the adults of each sex each year, fell more heavily on the hinds. An average of $19 \cdot 3 \pm 1 \cdot 29$ per cent of the latter were culled annually in contrast to $15 \cdot 2 \pm 1 \cdot 37$ per cent of the stags. This naturally led to an imbalance in the sex ratio, which changed from 0·96 ♂♂:♀ in 1957 to 1·27 ♂♂:♀ in 1963 and then to 1·18 and 1·19 ♂♂:♀ in 1965 and 1966 respectively. The later change in the ratio occurred despite the continuing pressure from the cull tending to increase the number of stags still further. In an earlier publication (Lowe 1969) I suggested this might be due to stag emigration. After including the data from the dead deer recorded in 1966 and 1967 and having reconstructed all six of the first counted populations (three of them are shown in Fig. 5), I find this evidence confirms stag emigration as the most likely explanation (see discussion).

Discussion and conclusions

The effect of the removal of the 1,700 sheep from Rhum in 1957 on the subsequent performance of the deer was not at first predictable. It was argued by some people that, so long as deer numbers were kept down by culling, some improvement in their quality should be expected in response to the increased food supply and reduction in competition for all resources in general. On the other hand, those who had been concerned with the former management of the sheep predicted that without moor-burning the deer would decline in performance along with their grazings, i.e. the economic density of the deer would increase as the areas of closely grazed pasture decreased in relation to a constant number of deer, unable to keep open their grazings unaided; and the nutrient status of their grazings would decline. Broadly this latter view appears to have been upheld, though the results were complicated by the effects of the culling on deer dispersal (p. 452).

Antlers

Though stags with inferior antlers were culled each year, leaving few heads with less than 10 points (tines) by the end of each shooting season, yet by the following year there were just as many poor heads as at the beginning of the previous season. An exception was 1962 (Fig. 1), when, for some unknown reason, there were very few stags with less than 10 points at the beginning of the season; shape was often the only criterion which could be used to select

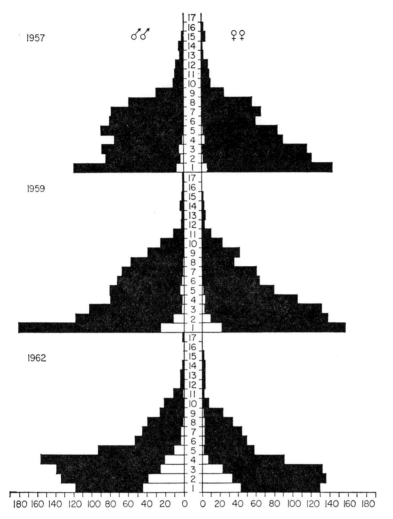

Figure 5. Deer populations on Rhum as at 1 June 1957, 1959 and 1962, reconstructed from subsequent deaths (shaded areas) and estimated survivors (open areas) up to May 1968.

stags for the cull that year. This result appears to be exactly similar to Andersen's (1961) experience with selective culling of roe deer (*Capreolus capreolus* (L)) in Denmark, and supports his contention that selective culling will do nothing to improve the trophy qualities of antlers.

Body weight and fecundity

Breeding must clearly be dependent to some extent on body size and, therefore, body weight and fecundity could be expected to be positively correlated within limits. The age by which puberty was attained could thus have depended mainly on achieving a critical body size, but it is not clear how the mature classes, with their much heavier body weights, were affected. Whether the decline in their fecundity was due to a reduction in the nutrient status of grazings, no longer being supplied with top dressings of ash fertilizer after moor-burning, or to the increasing physical difficulty the deer were having in obtaining the young grass shoots beneath the steadily accumulating layers of dead grass, still remains to be determined.

Similar increases in fertility, associated with burning, have been described by, among others, Evans (1890) for the red deer on Jura (another Hebridean island off the west coast of Scotland), and by Taber & Dasmann (1957, 1958) for the black-tailed deer (*O. h. columbianus* (Richardson)) in west coast chaparral (U.S.A.). Taber & Dasmann attributed the increase in fertility to changes in the quality of the food rather than to its increased availability. Daniel (1963), who found mature Graafian follicles in the ovaries of even calves of red deer in New Zealand, where the deer had access to exceptionally nutritious crops, also attributed such precocious sexual maturation to the quality of the food. In none of these studies was it established whether it was an increase in the proteins, or minerals, or both, which was responsible.

Changes in population numbers

The effect of the differential culling of the sexes (15·2 per cent of the stags, 19·3 per cent of the hinds annually) was, as stated earlier, to increase the numbers of stags and reduce the number of hinds, but the stag: hind ratio did not seriously exceed parity before 1962, when it reached the level of 1·17 ♂♂:♀ (Fig. 4). Thereafter, the sex ratio rose to 1·27 ♂♂:♀ in 1963 and 1·24 ♂♂:♀ in 1964 before declining to 1·18 and 1·19 ♂♂:♀ in 1965 and 1966 respectively.

Population estimates, based on figures which include the extra two years' mortality data (June 1966–May 1968) are generally lower than the estimates made in 1966, which suggests there may have been a further unaccounted loss of deer since that time, but again there were no serious discrepancies between the counted and calculated figures before 1962, when the difference reached 8·3 per cent (Table 2).

If one examines the year-class frequencies of the reconstructed populations for the first six years (1957, 1959 and 1962 are shown in Fig. 5), the hinds show a reduction in numbers, which is more or less evenly distributed throughout the classes. Only the yearlings in the 1962 population were disproportionately fewer than expected, and this was due to the unusually heavy mortality they suffered as calves during the 1961–2 winter. On the other hand, whilst stags increased in numbers up to 1963 as a result of the culling policy, the

Table 2. Comparisons between counted populations (adjusted to 1 June) and populations reconstructed from subsequent deaths and estimates of survival to 1 June 1968

Year		♂♂	♀♀	Calves	Total	Shot and natural mortality ♂♂	♀♀	Calves	% of population counted, known to be dead by May 1968	Difference assessed in 1968 % of counted	Difference assessed in (1966) % of counted
1957	Counted	564	741	279	1584	616	637	247	94·7	3·0	(3·4)
	Reconstructed	627	647	262	1536						
	Difference	+63	−94	−17	−48						
1958	Counted	598	818	295	1711	647	694	245	92·7	4·7	(1·1)
	Reconstructed	664	708	258	1630						
	Difference	+66	−110	−37	−81						
1959	Counted	626	871	236	1733	642	673	290	92·6	2·0	(2·2)
	Reconstructed	667	694	337	1698						
	Difference	+41	−177	+101	−35						
1960	Counted	624	862	314	1800	660	644	289	88·5	3·2	(1·7)
	Reconstructed	706	696	340	1742						
	Difference	+82	−166	+26	−58						
1961	Counted	669	824	319	1812	677	626	221	84·0	2·3	—
	Reconstructed	761	708	302	1771						
	Difference	+92	−116	−17	−41						
Mean difference between counts and reconstructions (% dead > 80)										3·0 ± 1·3	(2·1 ± 1·6)
1962	Counted	709	719	274	1702	623	507	159	75·7	8·3	—
	Reconstructed	728	585	258	1561						
	Difference	+19	−134	−26	−141						

increases were evenly distributed throughout the year classes only up to 1959. Thereafter increasing numbers of stags, from cohorts born in 1960 and later, appear to have vanished from Rhum without trace (see 1962, Fig. 5), and before they reached the age of 4 years, the lower age limit of the main cull. This progressive reduction in cohort numbers cannot be explained by fewer calves being produced because there was no similar trend in hind recruitment; nor by selective shooting by poachers because these age classes are not only difficult to distinguish in the field but are, like the hinds, less vulnerable to poaching, being mainly on higher ground and further from the sea than the older stags, which are the poachers' more usual quarry. In the light of this evidence, it now seems that the most likely explanation is that increasing numbers of the surplus young stags must have emigrated each year after 1962. Whether correcting the bias in the culls from 15·2 per cent of the stags and 19·3 per cent of the hinds to 18·0 per cent of both sexes (by shooting 20·0 per cent of the stags and 16·0 per cent of the hinds counted each spring) would have contained stag numbers and maintained the original numbers of hinds must remain speculative.

However this rather unexpected result did not obscure the two most important effects of the change in habitat management.

1   Whilst culling prevented any substantial increase in deer numbers after the removal of the sheep, there is no evidence to suggest that the subsequent deterioration in the structure and probable nutrient status of the grazings has reduced the carrying capacity, in terms of deer numbers, to a lower level than that obtaining in 1957.

2   The overall performance of the deer did not benefit from the reduction in grazing pressure, and certainly some properties, e.g. body weight and fertility, declined significantly, probably due to the deteriorating quality of the grazings.

Parallels with the Kaibab North and Jura

The management of the Kaibab North, an area of 526,200 ha consisting of forest, scrub and grassland, was rather different, but the results illustrate a situation where the stock was reduced and the deer were left unculled. Initially there were 20,000 cattle and 200,000 sheep on the reserve (1887–9). These were reduced to 4,356 and 3,508 head respectively by 1924 (Russo 1964). Meanwhile the 3,000–4,000 deer on the reserve in 1906 (Rasmussen 1941) were left unculled and increased in numbers to an estimated peak of 50,000–100,000 in 1924. Subsequently, deer numbers decreased, rapidly to begin with and then more slowly, to 30,000 in 1926, 25,000 in 1931 and 14,000 in 1932–42.

Whilst deaths of fawns were observed to be abnormally common in 1924–

5, the decline in the total population was not detected immediately. It is possible, therefore, that emigration occurred and that the decrease was largely due to this factor rather than to natural mortality; adult corpses are usually more obvious and persistent than those of calves and should have been found in large numbers if present.

After this, some culling was introduced but, until 1955, none of the culls would have altered materially the levels of population. Following the removal of the remaining 1,280 sheep in 1945 and another period of 'no does' shooting (1946–9), the population again reached a peak, this time of 57,000 in 1949, before declining. This time, numbers fell to about 12,000 by 1955, after which the culling level was increased to prevent further irruptions.

In such a situation, it appears, therefore, that cattle and sheep and/or their management by man can modify the habitat, so that it provides more nutritious feeding, but, in their absence, deer are unable to maintain these conditions. Each time, therefore, deer numbers fell to a similar and probably a more natural stocking level. On Jura, the change in management was different again, but the results illustrated the situation where there was no stock to compete with the deer and moor-burning was introduced only after the situation had been studied for six years. Throughout the twelve years' study, Evans (1890), who had leased the deer forest for 21 years, shot the deer only lightly (*c.* 10 per cent per annum).

During the first six years of little or no burning, deer numbers remained remarkably constant. After 1883, when regular annual moor-burning was introduced, deer numbers (particularly hinds) increased greatly (Table 3).

It appears, therefore, that fire can be used as an alternative to stocking with cattle and/or sheep, but in the absence of fire only cattle appear able to modify the habitat to benefit sheep or deer. As Cameron (1923) wrote (p. 196) . . . 'Cattle keep the black land trimmed, and sheep keep the green land green, and deer, which from their fickle feeding habit cannot improve pasture for themselves, reap the benefit of both.' Whether highland pastures can sustain such a regime indefinitely and without having recourse to moor-burning has, however, still to be demonstrated; and what number and quality of deer can be maintained on Rhum in the absence of stock and without moor-burning has also still to be determined.

Summary

1   The island of Rhum was first stocked with sheep in 1828 and was then managed in their interest for the greater part of the next 130 years. Red deer were introduced in 1845 and, thereafter, became part of the regime.

2   In 1957, the Nature Conservancy acquired the island as a National Nature Reserve. The sheep were removed and the associated management practice

Table 3. Estimates of the deer population in the deer forest on Jura, 1887–9, based on annual counts (Evans 1890)

Class	With little or no moor-burning						With regular moor-burning					
	1878	1879	1880	1881	1882	1883	1884	1885	1886	1887	1888	1889
Stags	525	490	478	461	444	453	429	445	471	499	548	581
Hinds	579	573	592	614	603	635	652	710	764	856	946	1008
Calves	205	201	209	217	213	224	230	251	271	302	334	355
Totals	1309	1264	1279	1292	1260	1312	1311	1406	1506	1657	1828	1944

of moor-burning was discontinued to try to rehabilitate the habitat. This paper describes the more important effects of this change in management on the quality and numbers of red deer after monitoring as many of the properties of the deer and their performance as possible during the first nine years (1957–66).

3   Selective culling of stags with inferior antlers proved ineffectual in increasing the average number of points (tines).

4   The average weights of mature deer of both sexes declined significantly (p <0·001). Stags decreased by a calculated 6·5 kg or 7·3 per cent and hinds decreased by 5·4 kg or 8·7 per cent.

5   The fecundity of all age classes of hinds declined significantly (p <0·001). Two-year-olds and hinds, nine years of age or older, were most affected.

6   The validity of the annual censuses was tested by contrasting the counted totals with the numbers calculated to have been present after ageing all the deer subsequently recovered dead. By 1966 the error was calculated to have been 2·1 ± 1·6 per cent. By 1968 the error was re-calculated to have been 3·0 ± 1·3 per cent. Errors in classification also showed little change.

7   Because of misclassification during counts, culling was more severe on hinds (19·3 per cent) than on stags (15·2 per cent) and this led to a distorted sex ratio reaching a peak of 1·27 ♂♂:♀ in 1963. Thereafter it fell to about 1·19 ♂♂:♀, which was thought to be due to emigration by young stags, since these classes were found to be unaccountably and progressively under-represented in population reconstruction after 1960.

Acknowledgements

I am particularly grateful to G.McNaughton, L.A.K.Stewart, P.Macrae, G.Sturton, G.Mackay, J.Ferguson, K.R.Duff, and D.Cameron, without whose assistance in the field little of this work would have been possible. I am also indebted to Mr R.W.Youngson for help with ageing mandibles and tabulating data. Mr D.A.Kempson prepared the plate and the Viscount of Arbuthnott, Dr W.J.Eggeling, Mr J.N.R.Jeffers and Mr H.N.Southern made a number of most valuable and constructive criticisms of the manuscript.

References

ANDERSEN J. (1961) Biology and management of roe deer in Denmark. *Terre Vie* 1, 41–53.

CAMERON A.G. (1923) *The Wild Red Deer of Scotland.* Edinburgh and London.

DANIEL M.J. (1963) Early fertility of red deer hinds in New Zealand. *Nature, Lond.* 200, 380.

DZIECIOLOWSKI R. (1969a) *The quantity, quality and seasonal variation of food resources available to red deer in various environmental conditions of forest management.* Warsaw.

456   *V.P.W.Lowe*

DZIECIOLOWSKI R. (1969b) Growth and development of red deer calves in captivity. *Acta theriol.* XIV, 10, 141–51.

EGGELING W.J. (1964) A nature reserve management plan for the Island of Rhum, Inner Hebrides. *J. appl. Ecol.* 1, 405–19.

ELTON C.S. (1957) *The Ecology of Animals.* Methuen, London and New York.

EVANS H. (1890) *Some account of Jura Red Deer.* Privately printed by Francis Carter of Derby.

LOWE V.P.W. (1966) Observations on the dispersal of Red deer on Rhum. *Symp. zool. Soc. Lond.* 18, 211–28.

LOWE V.P.W. (1967) Teeth as indicators of age with special reference to red deer (*Cervus elaphus*) of known age from Rhum. *J. Zool. Lond.* 152, 137–53.

LOWE V.P.W. (1969) Population dynamics of the red deer (*Cervus elaphus* L.) on Rhum. *J. Anim. Ecol.* 38, 425–57.

RAESFELD F.Von (1964) *Das Rotwild.* Hamburg and Berlin.

RASMUSSEN D.I. (1941) Biotic communities of Kaibab Plateau, Arizona. *Ecol. Monogr.* 3, 229–75.

RUSSO J.P. (1964) The Kaibab North deer herd—its history, problems, and management. *Arizona Game and Fish Dept. Wildl. Bull.* 7. 195 pp.

TABER R.D. & DASMANN R.F. (1957) The dynamics of three natural populations of the deer *Odocoileus hemionus columbianus. Ecology* 38, 233–46.

TABER R.D. & DASMANN R.F. (1958) The black-tailed deer of the chaparral. *Bull. Dep. Fish Game St. Calif.* 8, 1–163.

Part 6
The Influence of Biotic Factors on Wildlife Conservation

The effects of public pressure on the vegetation of chalk downland at Box Hill, Surrey

D.T.STREETER *University of Sussex*

Introduction

Box Hill forms that part of the chalk escarpment of the North Downs in Surrey standing on the east side of the Mole gap about 1–2 km north of Dorking. Rising to a height of over 180 m, it affords splendid views across the Weald to the South Downs 38·5 km to the south. It has long been known as a beauty spot and at the present time experiences one of the highest visitor densities at week-ends of any comparable area within a similar distance of London.

The Hill, which is owned by the National Trust, forms part of the Surrey Hills Area of Outstanding Natural Beauty. In addition it has been notified to the local authority as a Site of Special Scientific Interest by the Nature Conservancy. The main A24 London–coast road runs along the foot of the river cliff that forms the western edge of the Hill and the centre of London, which is about 30 km away, is a 40 minute journey by train (Fig. 1). The National Trust manage much of the top of the Hill as commercial woodland. The whole area, therefore, exhibits in a major way the problems that arise when it is necessary to integrate the often conflicting requirements of amenity, forestry and nature conservation. In the areas that experience the highest visitor pressure the chalk turf is already showing signs of advanced damage and erosion and some of the rarer chalk species are declining in abundance.

In 1969 we initiated a long-term study of the effects of visitor pressure on the Hill in order to assess the extent of the visitor, induced changes and the rates at which these were occurring. In particular we were concerned to accumulate information on the numbers of people per unit area of ground per unit time that produce specific levels of change; the final objective being to acquire sufficient objective data to help in the planning of the future management of the Hill. In addition it was hoped that some of the results might have

459

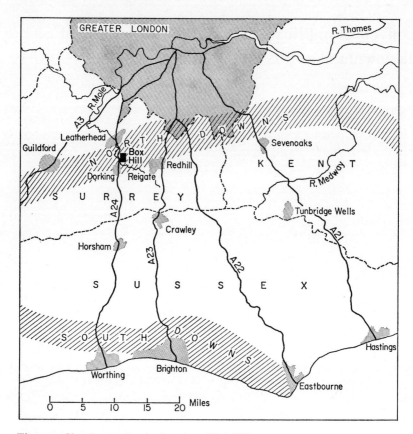

Figure 1. Sketch map showing location of Box Hill.

wider relevance to other amenity areas with similar problems. At present the investigation is planned in three parts; a long-term investigation into soil and vegetation changes, estimates of visitor density on different parts of the Hill to correlate with the ecological results, and a visitor census. The work presented here represents the initial results of the soil and vegetation studies on a limited part of the Hill.

Area of study and methods

The main focal point of the Hill is the Saloman Memorial which stands toward the top of the south scarp face of the Hill overlooking the Weald. There are car parks and a cafe within 180 m. The slope around and below the Memorial is showing signs of intensive wear and is much used by picnickers as well as general sight-seers. A path which runs along the top of the slope passes the foot of the memorial. The soil is a dark, friable rendzina moder, varying in depth from 0 to 14 cm with a mean pH of 7·5. The angle of slope is about 17°.

There is no detectable influence of the Plateau Deposits which cap the summit of the Hill and the upper parts of the dip slope.

For the purposes of permanent recording, the slope has been divided into a permanent grid of 50 m × 50 m units. The coarse distribution of each plant species is recorded on a 10 m × 10 m basis and detailed vegetational analyses are carried out by means of permanent 100 m transects, 10 m apart laid out at right angles to the contours (Fig. 2). Per cent cover is estimated by

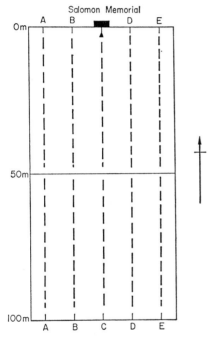

Figure 2. Arrangement of permanent 100 m transects on the south scarp face of Box Hill.

point quadrat analyses, recording 2 frames of 10 pins each, placed at right angles to each other, at 5 m intervals along each of the transects. Total nitrogen and citric acid-extractable phosphorus are similarly measured at 5 m intervals and soil compaction, as measured by the reciprocal of the total porosity, measured at 10 m intervals. In addition we are making annual photographic records of permanent 1 m² quadrats.

Results

The distribution analyses illustrate the progressive disappearance of the more sensitive chalk downland species such as *Thymus drucei* and *Asperula cynanchica* from the area of highest visitor pressure. On the other hand such species as *Medicago lupulina* appear relatively tolerant. Conversely it is

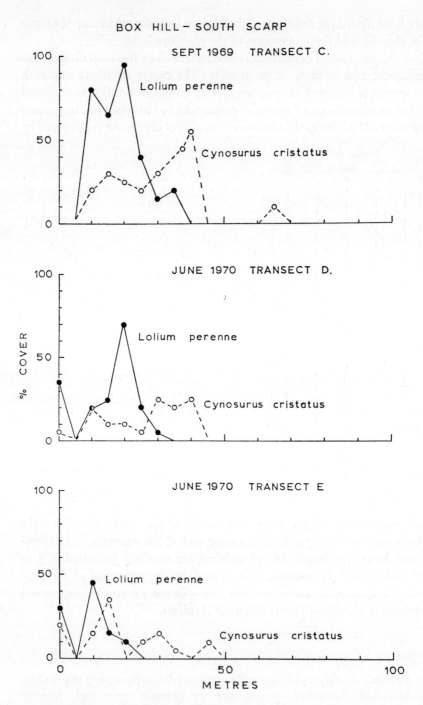

BOX HILL — SOUTH SCARP

SEPT 1969 TRANSECT C.

Lolium perenne

Cynosurus cristatus

JUNE 1970 TRANSECT D.

Lolium perenne

Cynosurus cristatus

% COVER

JUNE 1970 TRANSECT E

Lolium perenne

Cynosurus cristatus

METRES

Figure 3. Transects, C, D and E. Changes in cover percentage of *Lolium perenne* and *Cynosurus cristatus.*

interesting to note the appearance of a number of characteristic 'weed' species such as *Plantago major* and *Taraxacum officinale* in the turf around the Memorial.

One of the more interesting results of this initial survey is the appearance of *Lolium perenne* and *Cynosurus cristatus* as major constituents of the turf in the disturbed areas. This shows up in detail in the transect results (Fig. 3). These reveal a common pattern in the progression from the least to the most disturbed areas of an initial appearance of *Cynosurus* followed by *Lolium*, which may achieve complete dominance.

In transect C, which is the nearest of the three to the café and immediately below the Saloman Memorial, *Cynosurus* makes an appearance 65m from the top of the transect, whilst in transects D and E it first becomes apparent 50 or 55m from the top. Furthermore, in transect C it achieves a cover value of 55 per cent compared with 25–35 per cent in transects D and E.

Similarly *Lolium*, which achieves its maximum performance higher up the slope than *Cynosurus*, increases in cover value with increasing proximity to

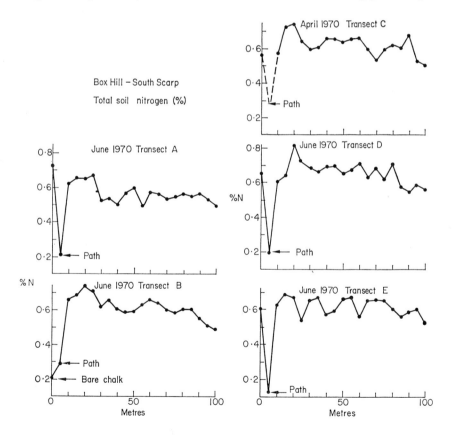

Figure 4. Transects A, B, C, D and E. Soil nitrogen expressed as per cent total nitrogen.

the areas of highest disturbance, with maximum cover values of 45 per cent in transect E, 70 per cent in transect D and 95 per cent in transect C. *Lolium* in particular is known to be a species with high nutrient requirements and neither it nor *Cynosurus* are characteristic components of these typically nutrient deficient chalk swards. This suggested that these two species were either responding to some degree of nutrient enrichment of the soil or were at a competitive advantage in respect to the other more typical downland species under conditions of soil compaction brought about by trampling. The results of the soil nitrogen and phosphorus analyses are shown in Figs. 4 and 5, and for the soil compaction in Fig. 6.

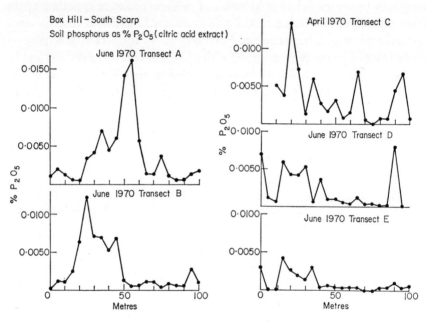

Figure 5. Transects A, B, C, D and E. Soil phosphorus expressed as per cent P_2O_5 (citric acid extract).

The values for soil compaction are generally higher in transects A and B, which are the closest to the café, whilst high values are only recorded for the upper parts of the slope in transects C, D and E; the values then rapidly falling off to a more or less constant low level.

The phosphorus results all show an initial low level, except for transect C where at the base of the Salomon Memorial the value rises to 0·05 per cent and consequently is not plotted on the graph. The initial low levels, which correspond to the position of the paths, are followed by a peak which is most pronounced in transects A and B and decrease in amplitude to transect E, the one most remote from the café. The down-slope values, falling to less than 0·005 per cent P₂O₅, emphasize the extreme nutrient-deficient status of these chalk soils.

The nitrogen results exhibit a similar pattern to the phosphorus analyses, although the peaks are less marked. Low values at the top of the transects correspond, as in the phosphorus figures, to the position of the paths. The highest values, in excess of 0·7 per cent, generally occur between 15m and 25m from the top of the transects whilst at the bottom ends the values fall to between 0·5 per cent and 0·6 per cent or less.

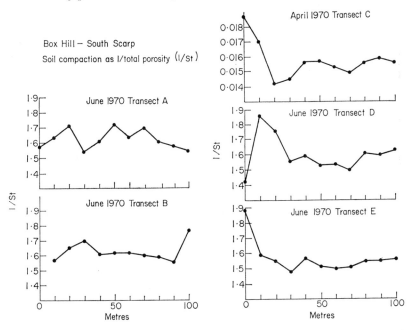

Figure 6. Transects A, B, C, D and E. Soil compaction expressed as reciprocal of total porosity.

Discussion

The soil analyses would appear to illustrate a three-phase character:

1 an initial low value at the bottom ends of the transects representing the normal levels in these very nutrient-deficient rendzina soils;

2 A zone of nutrient enrichment which is least marked in the areas that apparently experience the lower levels of pressure;

3 A zone of nutrient depletion at the top ends of the transects representing the erosion levels on and around the paths resulting from extreme visitor use.

Regression analyses reveal no significant correlation between the performance of *Lolium* and the degree of soil compaction, although the grass is clearly capable of tolerating quite high levels of trampling. There is, however, a positive correlation between the phosphorus levels and the performance of *Lolium* and a less convincing relation between *Lolium* and soil nitrogen levels (Figs. 7 and 8). It is interesting to note that the order of appearance of *Cynosurus* and *Lolium* on the transects is in accord with the experimental results of Bradshaw *et al.* (1960 and 1964) on the differential response of several grass species to increasing nitrogen and phosphorus levels.

There is now increasing evidence that many species characteristic of nutrient deficient soils are physiologically adapted to such conditions by an

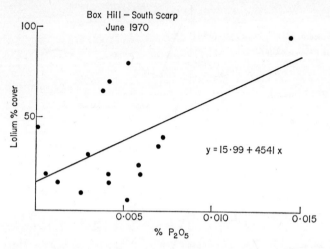

Figure 7. Relation between per cent total soil nitrogen and per cent cover of *Lolium perenne*.

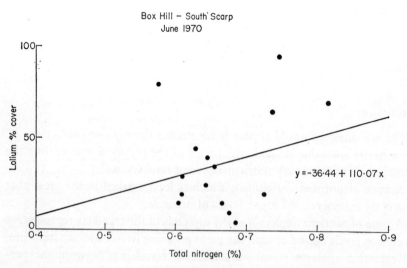

Figure 8. Relation between per cent extractable soil P_2O_5 and per cent cover of *Lolium perenne*.

inherently low growth rate, e.g. Rorison (1969). This results in a relatively low level of inter-specific competition within the community which is at least in part responsible for the remarkable species richness of grasslands on nutrient deficient limestone soils. However, these same physiological characteristics place these species at a disadvantage under conditions of trampling pressure. To tolerate such conditions, a high replacement rate or high rate of production would appear to be one of the necessary physiological characteristics. It might thus be expected that more vigorous species such as *Lolium* and *Cynosurus* would be better able to tolerate such conditions and would clearly be placed at a considerable competitive advantage under conditions that combined a degree of trampling with significant soil enrichment. Increasing pressure inevitably results in the total destruction of the vegetation cover and the concomitant soil erosion that is evident at the upper ends of the transects.

It would seem from these preliminary results that, at least on chalk downland, the interesting paradox arises that although visitor pressure reduces the botanical richness of the sward and hence its scientific value, a degree of use actually produces a sward that is better adapted to withstand the visitor pressure to which it is subjected. From a practical point of view what now needs to be established is the actual degree of use in terms of numbers of visitors per unit area per unit time that results in the optimum sward resistance for different combinations of recreation use and soil type. When this kind of information is available we shall be in a better position to marry, more objectively, our ecological resources to recreational demands.

The conflict between amenity and recreational use and the maintenance of scientific interest or wildlife conservation in the restricted sense, in areas where these two forms of land use meet, is clearly not irreconcilable. It is now a recognised fact that the behaviour pattern of the urban visitor to the countryside is such that the majority stay within a relatively small radius of the car park or other focal point. The rest of the area constitutes 'the view' into which relatively few intrepid explorers venture, e.g. Burton (1966). The spatial zoning of such areas is therefore a practical possibility; the planning of car parks, cafés and so on, determining the points of highest visitor pressure.

As most amenity areas are, of necessity, situated in marginal areas of low fertility it would appear possible to increase their visitor carrying capacity by artificially increasing the nutrient status of the soil and by selective seeding in the immediate areas around picnic sites and beauty spots, rather than waiting for the visitors themselves to produce the same result more slowly by a kind of pollution, that I suppose should be called 'terrestrial eutrophication'. What is important is that these areas should be so planned as to ensure that the level of pressure does not exceed the carrying capacity imposed by the prevailing complex of ecological factors, both 'natural' and artificial, else erosion problems will inevitably result. Also, it must be ensured that the areas of maximum use are so planned as to be sufficiently distant from areas of highest scientific value that damage to vulnerable ecosystems is minimal.

Acknowledgements

It is a pleasure to acknowledge the continuous encouragement given by the National Trust and the help of the staff of the Juniper Hall Field Centre of the Field Studies Council.

References

BRADSHAW A.D., CHADWICK M. J., JOWETT D., LODGE R.W. & SNAYDON R.W. (1960) Experimental investigations into the mineral nutrition of several grass species. Part III. Phosphate level. *J. Ecol.* 48, 631–7.

BRADSHAW A.D., CHADWICK M.J., JOWETT D., LODGE R.W. & SNAYDON R.W. (1964) Experimental investigations into the mineral nutrition of several grass species. Part IV. Nitrogen level. *J. Ecol.* 52, 665–76.

BURTON T.L. (1966) A day in the country. *Chart. Surv.*, January 1966.

RORISON I.H. (1969) Ecological inferences from laboratory experiments on mineral nutrition in *Ecological Aspects of Mineral Nutrition of Plants*. Symp. Br. Ecol. Soc., No. 9, 155–75. Blackwell Scientific Publications, Oxford.

Some effects of walking and skiing on vegetation at Cairngorm

NEIL G.BAYFIELD *Nature Conservancy, Blackhall, Banchory, Kincardineshire*

Introduction

There has been a great increase in skiing activity on Cairngorm since about 1960, when a road was made to about 650 m and permanent uplift facilities were installed to 1100 m. The chairlift has since catered for a considerable volume of summer tourists as well as for winter traffic. One of the consequences of these developments has been the local occurrence of destructive changes in the indigenous vegetation and soils, resulting from the increased activities of people and the use of vehicles on the hill. The changes include reduction of plant cover with the elimination of some species, and modification of the growth form of others. In the short term, an increase in the amount of litter may be noted, but further change often leads to exposure of bare soil. Signs of disturbance on the ground vary widely according to circumstances, but normally include bruised, broken or dead vegetation, patches of bare ground, and erosion of both plants and soil. Much of the affected ground is above 750 m, on acidic gravelly soils of low fertility. The combination of low fertility and severe climate (Baird 1957) means that recovery of damaged ground is slow, and reseeding with grass has been necessary on areas completely stripped of vegetation, both for amenity and to prevent erosion. Whilst much of the surface disturbance can be attributed to the use of tracked vehicles, considerable damage has also been caused by the trampling effect of people walking and skiing on the hill. This paper describes two approaches in a study of the cause and effect of damage due to trampling on Cairngorm; first by field observations of gradients of damage, and associated distributions of people, and second by means of simulated trampling experiments.

General description of damage

Methods

Skiing on Cairngorm is largely confined to the north-west slopes of the hill round Coire Cas, which are serviced by a variety of uplift facilities. A survey was made of the area bounded by the top and bottom chairlift stations, the Car Park Tow and tows serving the Coire Cas, Fiacaill and White Lady runs (Fig. 1). A base map made in autumn 1968 was revised every six months until spring 1970. The extent of disturbed ground was recorded using a combination of aerial photographs and ground measurements taken with a surveyor's wheel and tapes. Assessment was difficult above 750 m as the indigenous plant cover was patchy, much of the ground being covered with infertile granitic gravel (Watt & Jones 1948).

Transects were laid across the hill to help define the extent of the disturbed areas. Along each transect a 1·0 m² quadrat was dropped every three paces, and damage estimated visually on a three point scale:

Score 1: up to half of the quadrat showing signs of damage;

Score 2: more than half of the quadrat damaged;

Score 3: as for 2, but with bared ground on a tenth or more of the quadrat.

The mean score for each homogenous area was then classified as representing either 'slight', 'moderate', or 'severe' disturbance. 'Slight' damage was gauged as ground with a mean transect score of 0·4 to 0·8, 'moderate' more than 0·9 and 'severe' more than 2·0. Background scores of 0–0·4 were common on apparently undisturbed ground. These scores represented natural dieback of plant parts, erosion and solifluction, that could not be readily distinguished from the effects of disturbance. Two further categories, 'bared' ground (completely stripped of vegetation) and 'buried' ground (vegetation partly or completely buried by erosion sediment) were estimated by direct measurement.

Results

The most serious damage was 'bared ground', frequently showing compaction or disturbance of soil profiles to depths of up to 1 m. The area affected (8·8 ha) included dirt roads and tracks, bull-dozed pistes and ground inadvertently stripped during servicing of ski tows and other incidental activities involving tracked vehicles (Table 1).

Areas of vegetation buried under sediment (2·8 ha) occurred mainly on ground above 750 m. Most plants that were buried failed to grow through the sediment if it was more than 5 cm thick.

Most 'severe' damage on the White Lady ski run and above the Middle

Table 1. Summary of areas and causes of damage
(See text for explanation of damage categories)

Type of damage	Area (ha)	Apparent Cause
Bare ground	8·8	Tracked vehicles
Sediment burial	2·8	Natural erosion of bare ground
Severe	$\begin{cases} 1\cdot3 \\ 1\cdot0 \end{cases}$	Machines, skiers and walkers Skiers
Moderate	6·4	Skiers
Slight	2·9	Skiers

Station resulted from the combined action of tracked vehicles, and heavy foot and ski traffic. An area (1·0 ha) below the Middle Station, however, appeared to have been damaged exclusively by heavy skiing. 'Moderate' damage (6·4 ha) also appeared to be caused largely by skiing, and was confined mostly to areas near the Beginners' Tow, and a short section up Coire Cas and the White Lady runs.

Although bare ground was readily attributable to machines and most moderate and slight damage to skiing, in some places the causes were less clear because of multiple use of the hill. Use of the hill has also changed over the period of observation: some damage to vegetation on the White Lady run may have been caused by walkers, who used it as a direct route to the summit prior to 1969; since then most walkers have been diverted along an indirect dirt road to the summit. Also, footpaths outside the area mapped, such as that from the Top Station to the summit, and various peripheral paths, became noticeably wider and more worn in the period of the survey.

Traffic and damage on a small study area

Methods

Observations of winter and summer traffic and associated damage were made on a sample area of 3·9 ha hear the Car Park Tow (Fig. 1). The area contained a depression where snow lay for several weeks after surrounding snow had melted. A main path to a neighbouring mountain, Ben MacDhui, and one or two subsidiary paths, crossed the area. The vegetation over most of the site consisted of *Calluna-Trichophorum* heath, of a similar general composition to that examined in more detail in a trampling trial. The main exception was a small area of bare peat at the base of the snow hollow partly colonized by

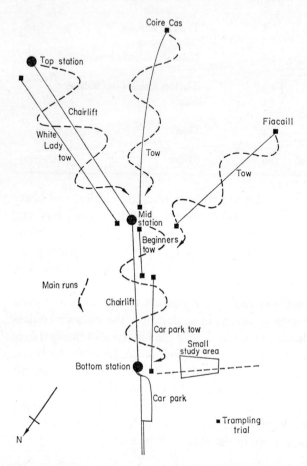

Figure 1. Ski tows and study area on Cairngorm.

cotton-grass (*Eriophorum angustifolium*). Elsewhere deer-grass (*Trichophorum cespitosum*) and heather (*Calluna vulgaris*) were present, though in widely varying proportions. Because of this variation, specific parameters of damage were useful only over short distances, and more general criteria were required for the area as a whole. The parameters chosen were the proportion of total damage (to either plants or soil) and of bare ground. Bare ground included all areas denuded apparently by trampling but excluded areas of natural bare peat. Data collected were visual estimates of cover by two observers working together. Contiguous quadrats were laid along two sample transects, that were also used in the assessment of pedestrian traffic in summer. Damage along these transects was recorded after counts of skiers in 1969, and just prior to observations of walkers in July 1969.

(a) Monitoring of walkers in summer

This was done using two 'thin wire trampleometer' transects across the area at right angles to the main paths. These trampleometer transects consisted of lines of fine wires about 5 cm long projecting vertically from the ground (Bayfield in press). Walkers standing on the wires bent them over. Repeated reading of the transects provided a detailed picture of relative differences in foot traffic along their length. The interval between wires was 30 cm except across paths, where it was 10 cm.

(b) Distribution of skiers

This was recorded by time-lapse photography from a point overlooking the sample area. The sampling programme allowed for photographs to be taken every 30 min. between 1000–1500 hrs. once every ten days in February–May 1969 and 1970, when skiers were present on the area. On four of the twelve sampling days in 1969, no photographs were obtained due to bad weather. In 1970, bad weather prevented observations on six occasions, and on three others only a few skiers were using the study area. In addition, snow cover was more complete this year, and fewer skiers were recorded on ground with broken snow cover. In 1970, additional information was obtained from the two trampleometer transects, which were set before skiing began in December and read at the end of May as the last snow was melting. These data provided an indication of relative differences in foot pressure at ground level over the winter months.

The photographic and trampleometer observations of skier distribution were given rankings of 'zero', 'low', 'medium' or 'high'. These corresponded with 0, 0.7, 3.4 and 11.4 skiers/ha/day for the photographic data and < 5, 6–49, 50–79 and 80–100 per cent bent pins for trampleometer data. In all cases the ranked data related to sections of the sample transects that were selected on the basis of ground topographic features and of the positions of paths. In interpreting the time lapse photographs, only skiers on or close to broken snow cover were counted.

Results

Data for transect 1 are given in Fig. 2. The second transect provided closely similar information and is not illustrated.

In summer 1969 trampleometer data were collected over a continuous

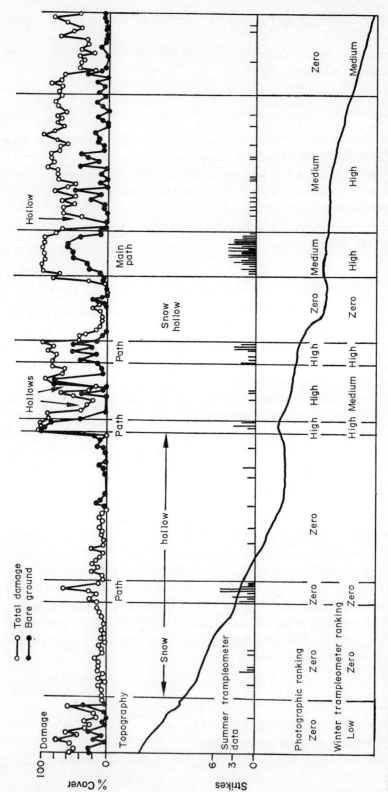

Figure 2. Traffic and damage on the small study area (Transect 1). Trampleometer pin interval 30 cm. Damage as cover of 0·25 m² quadrats. For rankings see text.

period from 13 August to 10 October. (Data for this period only are given in Fig. 2.) Most bent wires were recorded on paths crossing the sample transects. The total number of wires recorded during this period was 164 on the first transect and 127 on the second (counting only the wires spaced at 30 cm apart). Of this total, 81 per cent in the first and 78 per cent in the second transect were on one or other of the paths.

In mid-October, the *Trichophorum* and *Eriophorum* died back to a uniform yellow colour, which made the paths less conspicuous. A reading (10 October–1 November) during this period recorded 60 bent wires. Of this total, only 51 per cent were on the paths, compared with 81 per cent during the preceding (summer) period. A further reading was taken 1–15 June 1970 during the spring flush of growth, when the paths were again slightly obscured. A total of 110 bent wires was recorded, of which only 41 per cent were on the paths. The distribution of walkers in spring and autumn is surprisingly different from that found in summer. However the small area occupied by paths (relative to surrounding ground) meant that even the highest recorded proportion of bent wires off paths represented a considerably lower density of traffic than on the paths. Nevertheless the greater deviation of walkers from paths in spring and autumn may have made a significant contribution to the overall damage on the study area. Further work is necessary to clarify this point.

Over the main path, trampleometer pins inserted at 10 cm intervals provided a more detailed picture of the pattern of trampling than in other sections of the transects (Fig. 3). Observations were also made of the cover of

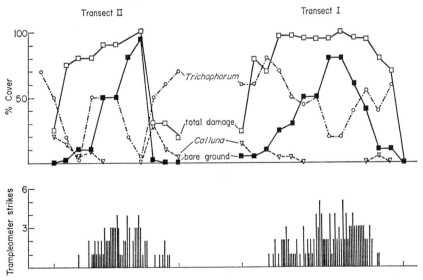

Figure 3. Detail of trampleometer strikes and damage across the main path. Trampleometer pin interval 10 cm. Damage parameters as cover of 0·25 m² quadrats.

Trichophorum and *Calluna* (live plants damaged or undamaged) in the quadrats used to assess 'total damage' and 'bare ground'. The peaks of trampleometer scores agreed quite well with those of 'bare ground'. Over much of the width of the path the surface appeared disturbed, and 'total damage' values were close to 100 per cent. *Trichophorum* tussocks were present in all the sample quadrats, but *Calluna* was recorded only at the edges of the path where the trampleometer scores were minimal.

The protection afforded to vegetation by unbroken snow cover during winter is well illustrated by the small amount of damage recorded in the two large snow hollows. The mean value for disturbed ground ('total damage') was 8 per cent, and bare ground 1 per cent. These data appeared similar to those recorded on vegetation remote from human trampling, but low levels of damage to vegetation were difficult to assess accurately, and made such direct comparisons of doubtful value.

Although large numbers of people skied on snow in the hollows, broken snow cover rarely occurred during the skiing season except in late spring, and both photographic and trampleometer rankings were zero. Summer trampleometer data (Fig. 2) indicated that use by pedestrians in summer was largely confined to a single small path across the larger of the two snow hollows.

Round the lower edge of the snow hollow was a marginal area of uneven hagged peat, broken by numerous small depressions and run-off channels (Fig. 2). The hummocks present showed signs of severe disturbance, with, in places, almost complete removal of the vegetation, and erosion of the peat beneath. By contrast, damage in the depressions was relatively low (minimum 20 per cent 'total damage'). The hummocks soon became exposed above the snow following a thaw or as a result of snow erosion by wind, and were favourite spots for skiers to gather on. (The ranking from photographic data was 'high'.) In the depressions snow lay longer, affording some protection to the vegetation. Consequently many of the trampleometer pins here were not struck, and the overall trampleometer ranking for the section was 'medium'.

The section of transect below the main path was gently sloping and lacked marked undulations (except for a single small depression next to the path). Here there were high values for 'total damage' (mean 67 per cent), but the proportion of 'bare ground' exceeded 40 per cent only in a single quadrat, so disturbance was not as severe as on the hummocks described previously. Because of the lack of depressions to hold the snow, the whole of this section became rapidly exposed in a thaw and consequently a larger proportion of the ground was affected by trampling than in the hummock section, in spite of a lower density of skiers. (The winter trampleometer ranking was 'high', but the photographic ranking only 'medium'.)

The adjacent, terminal section of transect was also a smooth slope. In this case the mean 'total damage' (47 per cent) was lower than the previous example as were the traffic estimates, with the trampleometer ranking 'medium' and the photographic one 'zero'. Skiers must have been present at some time during the winter to strike the trampleometer wires in this section, but the photographic sampling failed to record these people. A similar discrepancy between the two techniques was seen at the other extremity of the transect, at the top edge of the large snow hollow, where the photographic ranking was 'zero', and trampleometer ranking 'low'. In both cases, the numbers of people involved were probably quite small, and pressure only occasional. A larger sample of photographs would have made this method more sensitive. In many respects trampleometers are more suitable for detecting the presence of skiers as they measure trampling activity at the ground surface, but they have the disadvantage that only a binary indication is obtained. Some form of integrating trampleometer would be preferable.

Simulated trampling experiments

Methods

Snow trampling experiment

A simple comparison was made of the impact of a mechanical foot transmitted through various depths and types of snow. Circular mats of cork were studded with 16 equidistant drawing pins inserted into the cork to within 2 mm of the surface. The mats were placed inside cylindrical metal cans with a diameter and height of 15 cm. Blows from the mechanical 'foot' (faced with a rubber cleated climbing boot sole diameter 13 cm), striking the mat drove pins into the cork. The number of pins depressed increased linearly over the range 0·25 mkg to 1·25 mkg. Snow, carefully sprinkled into the cans, was subjected to single direct impacts of the foot, calculated to provide 1 mkg of energy at the surface of the cork in the absence of snow. The foot was dropped from a constant height above the cork rather than above the snow, as approximating most closely to natural trampling. The number of pins pressed into the cork was recorded after melting the snow. Occasional tiny fragments of snow trapped under the pins did not appear to prevent them being knocked into the cork.

Greenhouse experiment

S50 Timothy (*Phleum pratense*) was chosen for this work because it is a convenient experimental plant and is an important component of reseed mixtures used on Cairngorm (Watson, Bayfield & Moyes 1970). Seedlings grown in John Innes No 2 compost were transplanted singly into 15 cm plastic pots containing a mixture of one part sharp sand and two parts John Innes compost. After growth for a further seven weeks the plants had an average of 12 tillers, and were subjected to eight trampling treatments. There were ten replicates. The range of trampling treatments was 0, 1, 5, 10, 20, 40 and 100 impacts of the mechanical foot. The plants were left for three weeks before being examined to allow for dieback of damaged tissues.

Trampling trial in the field

The site chosen was a wet *Calluna-Trichophorum* heath community near the Car Park Tow, infrequently visited by either walkers or skiers. The vegetation consisted, in order of relative abundance, of *Trichophorum cespitosum, Calluna vulgaris, Eriophorum vaginatum, Erica tetralix, Eriophorum angustifolium, Narthecium ossifragrum, Potentilla erecta* and club mosses (*Lycopodium* spp.). In addition, there were large quantities of lichens (particularly *Cladonia* and *Peltigera* spp.), and bryophytes (*Sphagnum rubellum, Rhacomitrium lanuginosum, Hylocomnium splendens, Dicranum* spp. and various leafy hepatics). Plots in three randomised blocks were subjected to five different trampling treatments provided by two 70 kg men walking at random up and down the plots wearing British size 9 climbing boots. Each plot measured $1 \cdot 2$ m $\times$ $4 \cdot 6$ m with a minimum $0 \cdot 3$ m wide margin between plots. The treatments were as follows:

(*a*) 40 walks ('tramples') across each plot—7 July 1968;
(*b*) 80 walks across each plot—7 July 1968;
(*c*) 120 walks across each plot—treatment provided as three sets of 40 walks on 7 July, 10 August, 3 September 1968;
(*d*) 240 walks provided as in (*c*) but with 80 walks on each occasion;
(*e*) control—no trampling.

Visual cover estimates of botanical composition and of the extent of disturbance were made by the same two people on each occasion with each plot split for the purpose into five equal sub-plots. Analyses were made before trampling, and 12 and 23 months afterwards.

Data were recorded only for species present in every plot (though not always in every sub-plot), and observations were confined to aerial parts as examination of roots was impracticable. Assessment was concerned with the extent and not the severity of disturbance. Thus in estimates of *Calluna*, dead, broken, bruised, and leaf-stripped shoots all counted as damage. In the case of *Trichophorum* both tussocks which had strongly appressed stems, and those with a central eroded portion were recorded.

Results

(*a*) Snow trampling experiment

The impact transmitted through snow fell rapidly with increasing depth (Fig. 4) and even a few centimetres of snow had an appreciable cushioning

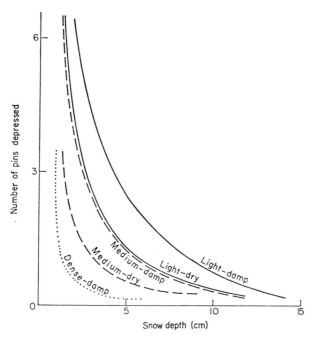

Figure 4. Impact of a mechanical foot transmitted through various depths and qualities of snow. Impact measured as the number of pins depressed per blow. Snow density, light o·09 medium o·17 and dense o·58 g/ml.

effect. Dense snow (o·58 g/ml) had more absorptive effect than light snow (o·09 g/ml) and damp snow more than crisp, dry snow. A more exhaustive study would be necessary to relate the experiment to the field situation. A great variety of conditions occurs after snow has lain for more than a few days (Rikhter 1954) and the action of skis on snow consists more of sliding and slicing than of direct impacts. Nevertheless this preliminary experiment and subjective evidence suggest that when ski pistes are covered in snow, considerable protection is given to the vegetation beneath.

The ski runs on Cairngorm are frequently broken by large snow-free patches, or small hummocks or ridges of uncovered ground, caused by general snowmelt or wind erosion of the snow cover. These exposed patches are particularly susceptible to damage from skiers travelling across them. The vegetation often turns brown, presumably as a result of dehydration after bruising (Watson, *et al.* 1966).

Snow compaction by skiers and by tracked vehicles tends to conserve snow cover since compacted snow melts more slowly than loose snow. Increases in the size of patches of late snow-lie due to compaction might contribute marginally to vegetation damage by snow moulds (*Fusarium* spp).

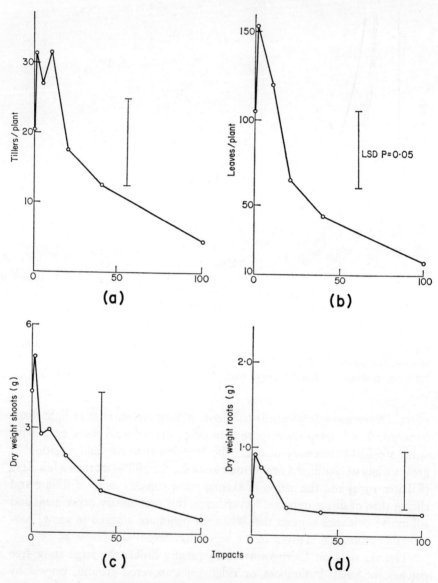

Figure 5. Effects of simulated trampling on S50 Timothy. (*a*) Tillers, (*b*) leaves, (*c*) dry weight aerial parts, (*d*) dry weight roots, per plant.

(b) Greenhouse experiment

Timothy plants subjected to simulated trampling showed immediate signs of damage in the form of broken and bruised leaves and tillers. Die-back of some of these parts took several weeks, but at the same time growth of new shoots continued. Consequently the analysis three weeks after trampling reflected not only immediate damage but also the growth response of the plants after trampling (Fig. 5). Treatments in excess of ten impacts depressed the total number of tillers, and the oven-dry weights of aerial and root parts. Two of the ten replicates treated with 100 impacts died; the others had all their leaves destroyed by the treatment, and produced a few small new shoots only after an interval of more than a week. By contrast, many plants subjected to the three lowest treatments (1, 5, 10 impacts) had higher values for some of the measured parameters (particularly numbers of tillers, and oven-dry weight of roots) than the controls.

(c) Trampling trial in the field

Although the 120 and 240 walk treatments were staggered over three months, the effects appeared to be essentially additive and were assumed for purposes of analyses to be directly comparable with the 40 and 80 walk treatments which were trampled on a single occasion. At the analysis four months after the first treatments, the amount of damaged *Trichophorum* was clearly related to trampling pressure (Fig. 6), with a maximum value of 34 per cent on the most heavily trodden plots. After twelve months this figure had dropped to 12 per cent, and a further slight reduction was noted at the final analysis in June 1970. Recovery of *Trichophorum* was fairly rapid probably because of its deciduous habit and basal growth apices. Although most trampled tussocks showed damage in the first year, very few were killed, and damage was difficult to distinguish at the final examination. The mean cover of live *Trichophorum* (heaviest treatment plots) before trampling was 33 per cent and at the final examination 35 per cent.

Damage to *Calluna* tended to be more severe than that to *Trichophorum*. At the first examination, signs of damage included dead, broken, bruised and stripped stems. The amount of damage increased steadily with number of tramples, to a maximum of 18 per cent. Detached stems represented the most serious effect of disturbance. During the winter following the treatments, most broken stems were blown away and this resulted in reduced values for damage (maximum 10 per cent cover) at the second and third analyses. In addition, most bruised and leaf-stripped stems died during the twelve months after treatment, and the second and third analyses were based on a single indication of damage—dead stems. *Calluna* regrowth after trampling appeared

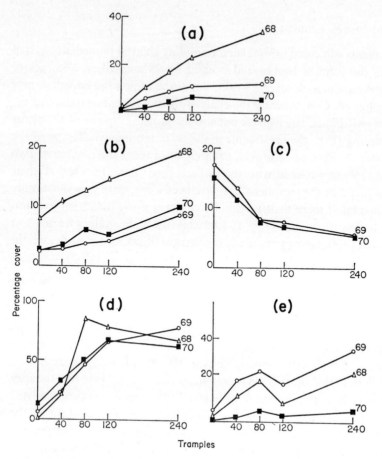

Figure 6. Effects of trampling on *Calluna Trichophorum* heath. (*a*) Damaged *Trichophorum*, (*b*) damaged *Calluna*, (*c*) intact lichens, (*e*) bare ground, as percentage cover per plot, (*d*) damaged *Sphagnum* as percentage damage per tussock.

to be extremely slow and the amount of live heather (heaviest treatment) at the final examination (18 per cent) represented a considerable reduction on that present before trampling (35 per cent).

Sphagnum was present in only 33 out of the total of 75 sub-plots but the data suggested that considerable damage (crushed or detached shoots) occurred, even at a relatively low level of trampling (80 walks), and there was little sign of recovery even after 23 months. *Sphagnum* shoots appear to be alive only near the apices, so the recovery of a broken *Sphagnum* tussock to a compact cushion is often a lengthy process.

The proportion of bare ground increased between 1968 and 1969, possibly due to wind erosion exposing ground hidden initially by moribund plant remains. The very low values for bare ground in 1970 (max. 5 per cent cover) appear to be the result of colonization by mosses and crustose lichens. Damage to foliose lichens was not assessed in 1968, as broken particles covered the trampled plots, and were difficult to distinguish from whole plants. By 1969, the loose fragments had blown away, and the total lichen cover remaining varied from 17 per cent on the untrampled to 5 per cent on the heaviest trodden plots. As lichens are generally slow growing plants, little change in these values was expected or observed in the final analysis.

Discussion

Trampling experiments with a mechanical foot or tamp (Wager 1964) have the advantage that repeatable trampling conditions can be imposed over a wide range of experimental conditions. Although artificial, such devices are quite suitable for modelling investigations in the greenhouse. This approach can certainly be considered for examination of any problem where the quantity and not type of trampling is a variable.

Experiments where people trample on plots simulate field conditions much more closely than those relying on a mechanical foot. However simulated trampling of any kind is only an approximation of that experienced in the field (Edmond 1958). The pressures transmitted to the ground by feet are in fact very complex, involving twisting as well as direct impact, and they vary both with the pace and activity of the walker (Harper *et al.* 1967). Trampling in the field is also variable both in respect of volume, continuity and classes of traffic. No comprehensive study of the comparative effects of intensity and frequency of trampling appears to have been published.

The simulated trampling experiments showed that in assessing the effects of disturbance, it is necessary to consider not only the immediate signs of damage, but also the ability of species to recover. Thus complete defoliation as a result of trampling might not be considered severe if the plant is able to replace quickly the damaged tissues. The responses to, and recovery from, disturbance are specific characteristics that may have profound competitive advantages or disadvantages for species growing in mixtures, and subjected to trampling. Within the limits of the treatments provided, *Trichophorum* and S50 Timothy appeared to be much less seriously affected by trampling than *Sphagnum*, lichens or *Calluna*. The relative tolerance of *Trichophorum* was borne out by its presence (and the absence of *Calluna*) right across the main path on the small study area.

Both simulated trampling studies and field observations demonstrated accumulative relationships between volumes of traffic and detectable damage, although individual species showed saturation of response after varying amounts of trampling. In the field trampling trial, *Sphagnum* showed signs of saturation at about 80 tramples, and *Trichophorum* at 240 tramples (little further change was possible as nearly all plants were damaged). In the small study area, increases in amounts of 'bare ground' continued after saturation of the parameter 'total damage'. It is likely that further changes take place after 'bare ground' saturation, particularly in soil structure and underground plant parts.

Simulated trampling experiments might be designed to compare the responses of different vegetation types to trampling. Information of this kind could form the basis of an index of relative tolerance to trampling. Such data are however of limited value in studies of cause and effect in field sites such as the small study area, where homogeneity of trampling or vegetation is rare. The criteria of damage identified for *Calluna-Trichophorum* heath in the adjacent trampling trial were found to be only applicable to small sections of the study area. Even with the more general damage parameters adopted, the relationship between amounts of traffic and disturbance varied with the type of vegetation. An example was the lack of recorded vegetation damage on the *Eriophorum angustifolium* stand at the bottom of the main snow hollow by comparisonwith low but detectable damage to adjacent *Calluna-Trichophorum* heath when both stands were exposed to similar amounts of trampling. Also, correlations between distributions of people and damage were in part confounded by variations in surface topography. Not only may hummocks and hollows modify patterns of walking and skiing, but the greater depths of snow in hollows confer come protection from disturbance. In this respect the distribution of damage may relate more to the ground topography than to the apparent activity of people. Consequently in any evaluation of the amount of traffic that a site such as this can tolerate, it will be necessary to relate observations to the parts of the site most liable to actual damage, even though overall damage may be at a much lower level. Although it may eventually prove possible to improve the tolerance to, or recovery from trampling of vegetation by for example application of fertilizers, in many cases a more direct approach may be a reduction of the incidence of damage by modifying the distribution of people by signposts, fences or other means.

Summary

On Cairngorm, damage has resulted both from the use of tracked vehicles, and from trampling by walkers and skiers. Two approaches were used to study cause and effect of the latter disturbance, first by field observations of gradients of damage and associated distributions of people, and second by means of simulated trampling experiments. Both approaches demonstrated accumulative relationships between trampling and damage. Extrapolation from simulated trampling studies to the field was found to be difficult because of heterogeneity of species cover, and wide variation in the extent and variety of trampling on the study area. In addition, ground surface topography was found to exert a considerable modifying influence on the relationship between skier traffic and damage.

Acknowledgements

I am indebted to Drs D.Jenkins, G.R.Miller, A.Watson and Mr I.A.Nicholson for valuable criticisms of the manuscript, and for discussions and suggestions during the course of the work.

Plant names follow Clapham A.R., Tutin T.G., and Warburg E.F. (1962) *The Flora of The British Isles*, 2nd Ed., Cambridge; Watson E.V. (1969) *British Mosses and Liverworts*, 2nd Ed., Cambridge.

References

BAIRD P.D. (1957) Weather and snow on Ben Macdhui. *Cairngorm Club J.* 17, 147–9.

BAYFIELD N.G. Thin wire trampleometers—a simple method for detecting variations in walker pressure across paths. *J. appl. Ecol* (in press).

EDMOND D.B. (1958) Animal treading and pastures. *Agric. Rev., Lond.* July 1958.

HARPER F.C., WARLOW W.J. & CLARKE B.L. (1967) *The forces applied to the floor by the foot in walking.* National Building Studies Research Paper 32. H.M.S.O.

RIKHTER G.R. (1954) *Snow cover, its formation and properties.* SIPRE Translation No. 6. U.S. Army, Illinois.

WATSON A., BAYFIELD N. & MOYES S. (1970) Research on damage and rehabilitation of Scottish mountain tundra, soils and animals, in *Productivity and Conservation in Northern Circumpolar Lands.* (Ed. by W.A. Fuller and P.G. Kevan). I.U.C.N. new series 16, 256–66.

WATSON A., MILLER G.R.M. & GREEN F.H.W. (1966) Winter browning of heather (*Calluna vulgaris*) and other moorland plants. *Trans. Proc. bot. Soc. Edinb.* 40: 195–203.

WAGA J.A. (1964) The carrying capacity of wild lands for recreation. *Forest Sci. Monogr.* 7.

WATT A.S. & JONES E.W. (1948) The ecology of the Cairngorms. *J. Ecol.* 36. 283–304.

The influence of sheep grazing on limestone heath vegetation on the Baltic island of Öland

ERIK SJÖGREN *University of Uppsala, Sweden*

In Sweden, work on nature conservation has increased considerably during the last decade. The work is now divided into fields concentrating on preserving air, water, wildlife and terrestrial habitats. Statens Naturvårdsverk, as the State Department for Nature Conservation is called, governs these efforts. In the terrestrial field, interest has been centred on conservation of the vegetation in alpine areas, on bogs and on the banks of large northern rivers. During the last few years there has been lively public debate on whether or not to conserve the rivers of the north which have not so far been exploited for hydro-electric power. Increasing attention has also been paid to preserving the old cultivated landscape. Its open character has for centuries been dependent on grazing and haymaking, in meadows as well as on heaths, and in deciduous forests. Grazing of pastures with low productivity decreased rapidly after the war. Nowadays spruce plantations are more profitable, at least in the short term. The decrease in numbers of deciduous trees in the landscape is considerable. Even former arable land has, to a large extent, been planted with coniferous trees in areas of low productivity. Soil acidity gradually increases to the value it had before the land was laboriously cleared of forests. The subject of this paper, namely changes in the vegetation on the limestone heath on Öland resulting from overgrazing, is part of the aspect of nature conservation dealing with changes in the cultivated landscape. A serious situation has developed in the unique vegetation on Öland as a result of the intensive sheep grazing there that began in the early 1960s.

First, a short introduction to Öland. This island is situated close to the south-east of Sweden. The wet summer winds are mainly south-westerly, so the island is situated in the rain shadow of the mainland. The climate on Öland is therefore semi-arid and the annual rainfall seldom exceeds 450 mm.

The type of climate is unique in this part of Europe. The temperature is more maritime than that of the mainland near by. Spring comes later, and temperatures in autumn and winter are higher.

The granitic bedrock of the mainland has been replaced on Öland by limestones, mostly Ordovician. In the so-called Alvar areas, which cover about 30 per cent of the island, this limestone is covered by a thin layer of soil, seldom deeper than 10 cm. The geological strata are inclined towards the east, so the limestone bedrock of the flat Alvar heath is younger as one progresses eastward.

The southern half of the island has a large deciduous forest, now the largest continuous decidous forest in northern Europe; and the largest European limestone heath. Cultivated areas are concentrated in the coastal regions with deeper soils. The deciduous forest consists predominantly of *Quercus robur* and *Betula verrucosa*, with *Corylus avellana* always present. Pure *Corylus*, *Fraxinus-Ulmus* or *Carpinus* woods are dominant in small areas. In the northern part of the island, geologically younger than the southern, there is a dense mixture of deciduous woods, small limestone heaths, pastures near the coasts, plantations of coniferous trees and arable fields. There are a few small lakes and swamps on the limestone heath. These are mostly dry in periods of the year with no rain. Small rich fens are found all over the island. The vegetation in the fens is often dominated by *Schoenus ferrugineus* and *Cladium mariscus*, with a large number of orchid species. Many of these fens have been drained in the recent centuries and have been planted with trees or used as arable land. The coast vegetation is very varied because of very different kinds of topography and soil. On steep limestone cliffs there are practically no vascular plants. Nitrophilous vegetation dominates on long shelving shores, in and around banks of algae, with dominant species such as *Rumex crispus*, *Chenopodium* spp., *Atriplex* spp., *Artemisia vulgaris* subsp. *coarctata*. Fragments of sand dune vegetation can also be found.

Öland is a purely agricultural area, with few industries and today fishing is only a subsidiary means of livelihood. Up to 1890, pastures were the dominant form of cultivated areas but, subsequently, cattle gradually lost their economic importance. Natural pastures close to the coast are now used only to a small extent and the grazing areas in the deciduous forests are no longer kept open. Until 1910, before the introduction of fodder plants, wooded meadows were economically essential natural resources. An average-sized farm with only a small animal stock experiences serious economic difficulties in the Sweden of today. The tendency is either to create larger farming units or to keep a large animal stock under rational management. On Öland, farming units now require additional animal stock and this is one of the reasons why sheep grazing has been introduced to natural pastures on the limestone heath. One of the most important motives was the probable high profit to be made from sheep breeding, since the Alvar heath provided large areas of natural pastures. In addition the annual cost of management was not high. This development is restricted to Öland and is unique in Sweden, where the general tendency is towards recolonization of old pastures and fields by trees and bushes.

The history of grazing on the Alvar probably goes back thousands of years. The Alvar was the common land of the nearby villages. Grazing there was carried on to a small extent, regulated by local laws. Before 1850, there were few fences. Small flocks of sheep were tended by shepherds over large areas. The pressure of grazing was less than 0·1 ewe per ha. Flocks of sheep were to be found mostly in the south-eastern parishes. This light but long-lasting grazing may possibly explain the type of vegetation in the area: it has fewer species and is less of a mixture of plant communities than the vegetation in the western parts, although other ecological conditions are the same. Up to the beginning of the twentieth century, grazing by young cattle, cows and horses was fairly intensive on the Alvar.

After 1900, use of the Alvar for grazing by young horses and heifers increased temporarily, after coastal meadows and wooded meadows largely ceased to be used for this purpose. The population decreased at that time, because of considerable emigration to the United States of America. In recent decades the number of horses has decreased because of increased mechanization on the farms. Cattle stocks were also moved away from the meagre pastures on the Alvar as these yielded insufficient fodder. The grazing, as a whole, up to the 1940s, was responsible for the absence, on the limestone heath, of dense groups of shrubs and trees which would otherwise have become established on deep gravel soil. The decrease of grazing after 1940 allowed conspicuous invasion of shrubs on to areas of gravel soil. New colonization by *Betula*, *Juniperus* and *Potentilla fruticosa* was considerable. Comparatively undisturbed development of lichen and moss communities, which are readily affected by grazing, was possible. Acidification around *Juniperus* shrubs resulted in increased expansion of species that sociologically do not belong there. Furthermore, the Seslerietum and Scorpidion associations close to swamps that periodically dry out became stabilized in undisturbed succession in large areas. In 1960 intensive sheep grazing began. From the very beginning it affected 30 per cent of the total Alvar area. During the first three years the pressure of grazing was raised to 1 ewe per ha. and this has been maintained ever since. Sheep breeding on the limestone heath is considered to be economically profitable at this grazing pressure. Activity has been concentrated on meat production, with wool and hides providing only a subsidiary income. Grazing is allowed for no more than 7 months during the summer season. During the rest of the time the sheep stock is fed in small pens with hay and straw and tops from sugarbeet and beans. The number of lambs per ewe has, on an average, been 1·3 per year. Water supply has been a major problem especially during extremely dry periods.

Conditions for sheep grazing on a large scale on the limestone heath are best illustrated by a short description of the vegetation and some of the ecological characteristics. The climate and the predominantly shallow layers of soil create conditions suitable only for vegetation that is highly tolerant of drought. Grasses dominate over herbs. Mosses and lichens are an important component in the plant cover. It is only around ephemeral swamps that groups of species less susceptible to drought are found. The drainage water from swamps or lakes reappears mostly in subterranean joint systems. The small amount of precipitation is quickly evaporated or drains down into joints in the limestone. The temperatures on the surface of the ground are high in the summer, as the rock easily absorbs warmth. Basic soils, with a pH value higher than 6·5, dominate. Thus calciphilous and basiphilous species are predominant. All the year round, the more or less strong winds are an important limiting ecological factor to shrub and tree vegetation. They serve to intensify the dry climate indirectly. Soil erosion is also maintained by the winds. In the winter the snow cover is usually very thin, less than 10 cm in areas with no shrubs. The snow disappears quickly in the spring and the daily temperature fluctuations at the surface of the soil are very large. Alternate freezing and thawing is therefore common and results in polygons and hummocks, as in alpine areas. The polygons in thin weathered material are colonized by a sparse vegetation, consisting of only a few species with strong root systems.

About 15 per cent of the heath vegetation consists of the Avenetum on gravelly ridges. Roughly 25 per cent consists of *Festuca ovina* heath on thin weathering material. The rest is made up of *Helianthemum* heath with lichens, bare rock surface with *Tortella* mosses, usually without vascular plants, and the Seslerietum community around Alvar swamps, small brooks and joints in the limestone.

Avenetum consists of a large number of herbs, up to 40 species per m². Predominating species are, for example *Avena pratensis*, *Thymus serpyllum*, *Filipendula vulgaris* and, in the bottom layer, *Camptothecium lutescens*. Festucetum and Seslerietum are grass communities with few species. The *Helianthemum* community on thin weathering material is rich in species, especially in the bottom layer, where there may be more than 30 species of lichens and mosses per m². The dominants in the Festucetum are *Festuca ovina* and *Festuca rubra* var. *oelandica*. The dominants of the *Helianthemum* heath include *Helianthemum oelandicum*, *Gypsophila fastigiata* and *Globularia vulgaris*. In the bottom layer, *Cladonia* and *Cetraria* species dominate. In occasionally moist habitats the Seslerietum, with grasses dominant, alternates with shrubs of *Potentilla fruticosa*. Dominant species include *Sesleria coerulea, Molinia caerulea* and *Carex flacca*, and *Ctenidium molluscum* and *Scorpidium* spp. in the bottom layer. From a plant geographical point of view the combination of species in the plant cover of the Alvar heath is very heterogeneous. There are several alpine species, mixed with pontic, sibiric and mediterranean species. There are a few endemic species and sub-species on the Alvar. *Helianthemum oelandicum* is especially worth mentioning.

Of these communities, the sheep graze the Avenetum preferentially. The grazing tolerance of this community is rather high, but after two seasons of intensive grazing, sheep may then graze the Festucetum and Seslerietum. Especially in the autumn, when the shortage of food becomes more acute, they graze *Juniperus, Prunus spinosa* and *Potentilla fruticosa*. The impact of grazing pressure on the Alvar vegetation is influenced by the fact that between 20 and 50 per cent of the plant communities on the heath are of practically no grazing value to the sheep.

Alvar vegetation is damaged by the intensive grazing by sheep, directly through grazing and trampling and indirectly in several other ways. Not all species tolerate grazing year after year. After a few seasons *Globularia vulgaris, Gypsophila fastigiata, Anthericum ramosum* and orchids almost disappear. Recolonization by these species is extremely slow. Species with a weak root system are often pulled up by the sheep and thus heavily reduced in numbers in overgrazed areas. Such species are *Viola pumila, Satureja acinos, Veronica spicata, Luzula campestris* and *Anthyllis vulneraria*.

All limestone heath is poor in nitrates. Sheep grazing has brought about considerable manuring of large areas. As a consequence, a strong competitive pressure from anthropochorous species has developed. These species are normally seldom found in the Alvar heath vegetation, but they appear frequently where there is continuous grazing. The natural calciphilous vegetation succumbs to these competitors. Close to pens, there is often a 100 per cent dominance of such anthropochorous species including *Cirsium arvense, Polygonum aviculare, Poa annua, Stellaria media, Urtica dioica, Capsella bursa pastoris* and *Geranium robertianum*.

The shrub layer, consisting of *Juniperus, Prunus* and *Potentilla fruticosa*, is affected by extensive grazing after about three years. In the long run, the vegetation mixture becomes more and more uniform. Acidiphilous groups of species round *Juniperus* shrubs disappear. The protection from exposure for the Avenetum is reduced on gravelly ridges. After grazing has ceased in an area, *Juniperus* regenerates very slowly, and *Potentilla fruticosa* somewhat faster. In the winter, considerable amounts of snow accumulate round the shrubs. Close to *Juniperus* shrubs about 1 m tall, there may be snow drifts about 10 m long. Snow melting normally takes place 2 weeks later around shrub vegetation than on shrubless Festucetum. This gives protection against large temperature fluctuations during early spring. There is therefore a more varied mixture of vegetation in areas with Avenetum rich in shrubs, because of the greater variation of ecological conditions.

Soil erosion is the most serious harmful effect of sheep grazing. It is most destructive as it is reversible only after a very long time. Soil erosion appears mainly in heavily grazed areas where Festucetum dominates on thin layers of weathered material. The soil cover around *Festuca* tufts is worn away by the trampling of the animals, and the tufts remain loosely attached to the ground on pillars of soil. They readily come away altogether and soil erosion can go on unrestrained. Tussock vegetation is also damaged by the trampling of the sheep. After the soil on one side of the tussocks has been exposed, erosion continues rapidly all round. As the bottom layer is an important stabilizing component in all Alvar vegetation, the elimination of mosses and lichens opens the way to erosion in the vascular plant cover and then of the thin layer of soil on the rock. The cover of mosses and lichens on bare limestone rock is quickly broken up by the grazing flocks of sheep. Primary colonization by cryptogams on these rocks is slow. The length of time required for the colonization of vascular plants there can be estimated as more than 100 years. When the weather is extremely windy and dry, fragmentation of mosses and lichens causes the distribution by the wind of a great number of diaspores. These conditions influence the plant cover far outside intensively grazed areas. In the bottom layer as well as in the field layer there are changes in the calciphilous species because of overgrazing. Such mosses as *Pohlia nutans* and *Bryum argenteum*, with a wide ecological amplitude and a weak differential value, increase explosively to dominance that may be total in some places. In some areas these species give a typical landscape colour to areas that are intensively grazed. As a result of soil erosion, species with low competitive ability, such as *Erophila verna*, *Hornungia petraea* and *Bromus hordeaceus*, may invade large areas of limestone heath. *Plantago lanceolata* often colonizes such bare habitats, forming dense carpets.

Every decade there is at least one extremely dry summer with less than half the normal precipitation. This affects the vegetation of the Alvar, and causes great difficulties in ensuring a sufficient water supply for the grazing animals. Often the farmers and tenants have to blast reservoirs in the rock where there are water-carrying joints. Such emergency measures may have long-term effects on the vegetation of large areas outside pastures where springs are usually to be found. Dry summers like 1969, when there were only a few mm of rain during June–July, naturally affect the vegetation with extremely low tolerance to grazing and soil erosion readily begins. Grazing during an extremely dry season has been observed to cause the same large changes in the vegetation as four normal seasons of the same grazing pressure. The distribution of diaspores from mosses and lichens increases.

Fragments of *Tortella* spp., *Schistidium apocarpum*, and *Ditrichum flexicaule* will then often be found carried by the wind to the edge of bare rock surfaces.

Intensive grazing on the limestone heath of Öland has now been going on for nearly a decade. In areas where the pressure of grazing has been maintained at 1 ewe per ha, the natural vegetation has changed and been destroyed to the extent that sheep farming can hardly be maintained at a profitable level for more than 7 seasons. Expensive supplementary fodder has become necessary and the additional amounts required have increased considerably. The result is that Alvar vegetation on Öland is now visibly damaged by only a short period of intensive grazing. The effect is similar to that in Mediterranean and Atlantic natural pastures which have been exposed to intensive grazing over a long period of time. Regeneration will take a very long time, in moss communities certainly more than 100 years. The speed of growth of primarily colonizing lichens is fairly well known. A plant of *Lecanora calcarea* with a diameter of 20 mm took 25 years to grow.

In the early sixties, investigations of limestone heath vegetation on Öland began in order to provide data on which to base future action in the field of nature conservation. These investigations could not be intensified until 1968. Total prohibition of sheep grazing was not considered possible, nor was it desirable except within a few reference areas that have not yet been exposed to intensive grazing. The investigations have the aim of recording the annual net primary aerial production of the most common grazed plant communities. The figures obtained will be related to the fodder requirements of sheep and lambs. Suitable grazing pressure will then be recommended, together with the amount of compensation to be paid to sheep farmers who will be recommended to reduce grazing pressure on their land. The grazing pressure should be regulated in such a way that the field layer of the limestone heath vegetation regenerates completely after every grazing season. Indirect changes in the vegetation as a consequence of damage to the ground and manuring should also be avoided as much as possible.

So far the following values have been obtained after one season's investigations of productivity. In a medium dense Festucetum, the annual net primary production amounts to 1000 kg dry weight per ha; whereas the Avenetum produces 2500 kg. About 25 per cent of the Alvar heath is covered by highly productive Festucetum and 15 per cent by Avenetum. The rest produces only small amounts of material for grazing, i.e. about 625 kg dry matter per ha, of which 75 per cent might be regarded as available for sheep grazing.

A ewe is said to graze 2·5 kg grass dry matter per day, for 6 months of the year. The lambs graze an average amount of 2·5 kg dry matter for an equivalent time, provided that their rate of growth is 200 g per day, the rate which is considered to be economically profitable. Altogether, this means about 5 kg grass dry material for ewe + 1·3 lamb, or 20 kg fresh weight. The pastures on the Alvar have been calculated to supply only two-thirds of the energy content of a good pasture grass, whereas the dry matter per kg is 20 per cent higher than that of a good grass. Ewe + lamb on the Alvar therefore have a daily requirement of 20 kg fresh weight of Alvar grass but only about 16·5 kg fresh weight of a high quality grass.

The figures above lead to the conclusion that Alvar vegetation can stand a maximum intensity of sheep grazing of 0·65 ewes with lamb per ha each year. It is taken into consideration that there are 6 months without additional feeding. If this intensity is maintained year after year, the growth of the vegetation will probably decrease progressively. Soil erosion, deficit of diaspores and killed and eroded bottom and shrub layers, are important results of damage by grazing. A suitable grazing pressure cannot here be recommended as providing a balance between the grazing requirements of the sheep stock and the production of the pastures, since sheep graze intensively and thus cause erosion to the plant cover to a far larger extent than a number of cows and horses with the same requirement for fodder. The final recommendation for grazing pressure on Alvar vegetation on Öland should then be 50 per cent less than the point of balance between production and fodder requirement. The Alvar vegetation can therefore preliminarily be estimated to tolerate a maximum grazing pressure of only 0·35 ewes + lamb per ha. This is 3–4 times less than that now considered to be profitable.

The vegetation of the Alvar has reached its present combination and dense mixture of communities as a result of extreme ecological conditions combined with the influence of long-term light grazing. Large areas of European meadow, heath and forest vegetation have been influenced for centuries by grazing. These types of vegetation, which in their way are living natural monuments, are threatened either by overexploitation or recolonization by shrubs and trees in highly industrialized countries. In both cases, urgent action by nature conservation authorities is necessary. In Sweden, the main problem is the recolonization by forest of the cultivated landscape, but there are examples, as on Öland, of present-day overgrazing. Severe overgrazing is today an important problem in other parts of the world, for example in Mediterranean countries and East Africa.

The value of protection of the old cultivated landscape from over- or undergrazing, is varied. In the work aiming at nature conservation, consideration should be given to future research in the fields of natural science and the history of culture, education and open-air activities.

A conserved area might be of most value if managed in various ways. A reserve can be used partly for regulated tourist activities, but part should be totally protected for research. In a cultivated type of landscape research should be started to find out how intensive and regular cultivation affects soil and vegetation and also the influence of no cultivation. A reserve on the limestone heath on Öland should thus occupy small areas that are grazed to various degrees, and also areas where grazing is totally prohibited. The requirements of research as well as of education can be satisfied in reserves of this kind.

A comparison of the effects of sheep grazing and mechanical cutting on the structure and botanical composition of chalk grassland

T.C.E.WELLS *Monks Wood Experimental Station,*
Abbots Ripton, Huntingdon

Introduction

Chalk grassland in lowland England is a biotic plagioclimax which has been maintained in the past by grazing animals of which the principal kinds have been sheep, cattle and rabbits. The type and breed of animal used at any particular time have varied considerably and it is doubtful if the traditional picture of large flocks of sheep drifting across open downland in the summer is entirely correct, except for a limited period in agricultural history, and then only in certain regions. It seems far more likely that stocking densities, time of year of grazing and type of animal used varied according to the season, availability of other pasture, size of human population and economic conditions.

Although the biological richness of chalk grasslands is well known (Lousley 1950) and has attracted the attention of the ecologist and naturalist for many years, few studies have been made of the effects of different management treatments on chalk grassland, probably because grazing by sheep and rabbits was observed to maintain a short, open, generally species-rich turf which supported a characteristic insect fauna. The importance of the rabbit in the grassland ecosystem was further emphasized when rabbit populations were greatly reduced after 1954 following myxomatosis. In his study of the effects of myxomatosis on chalk vegetation, Thomas (1960, 1963) showed that in the absence of rabbit grazing chalk grassland was colonized by scrub and coarse grasses which quickly led to a loss of species of low competitive ability and a fall in floristic richness. Similar changes occur when grazing by sheep or cattle ceases.

The influence of systems of management upon the botanical composition of permanent downland have been studied by Norman (1957) and Kydd (1964), using sheep and cattle. Continuous cattle grazing and close, rotational, cattle grazing in the first experiment resulted in a sward with a high proportion of forbs. With sheep under the same grazing systems, grasses predominated. An intermediate grass/forb balance was attained under lenient rotational cattle grazing. In the second experiment with cattle, Kydd (1964) showed that changes in ground cover were small under systems of continuous, frequent, and rotational grazing. These trials were carried out on a north-facing slope which had been ploughed during the second world war and resown to grass two years later, and therefore differed considerably in floristic composition from older chalk grassland which is usually of more interest to the conservationist. Apart from these two trials and a simple fertilizer combined with cutting trial by Warne (1934) there has been little study of the effect of sheep grazing, or cutting, on chalk grassland. In this paper some effects of cutting and sheep grazing on the botanical composition of chalk grassland are considered, with particular reference to the management of chalk grassland nature reserves.

Methods

Site details and layout

An area of heavily sheep-grazed downland on the Barton Hills, Bedfordshire (N.G.R. 52/090207), was selected for its apparent uniformity of structure and absence of scrub. The recent land-use history of this site has been described elsewhere (Wells 1968) and there is no evidence that it has ever been ploughed. It may therefore be regarded as a representative sample of old chalk grassland. A sheep and rabbit proof exclosure, 45 × 12 m, was erected on a steep (27°), south-facing slope on 15 May 1963. The exclosure was laid out so that its long axis extended over the gently sloping top of the spur down the steep slope to take advantage of the range of soil depths found there.

The soils varied from a shallow rendzina, 5 cm deep, on the steepest part of the slope to a grey calcimorphic loam, 18 cm deep, towards the bottom of the slope. Towards the top of the slope the soil was 13 cm deep, of a calcimorphic loam type. Throughout this paper they are referred to as shallow, deep and medium soils respectively. All were highly calcareous, with an average pH of 7·8 in the top 5 cm.

Within the exclosure, 48 plots, each 0·56 m², were marked out in 6 blocks. Two blocks, each of eight plots were marked out on each of the three soil depths. Outside the exclosure, in the grazed downland, 48 plots were similarly laid out (Fig. 1).

Seven cutting treatments and a control (not cut) were allocated at random to each block within the exclosure. The treatments were:

Control—not cut
Cut in spring (April)

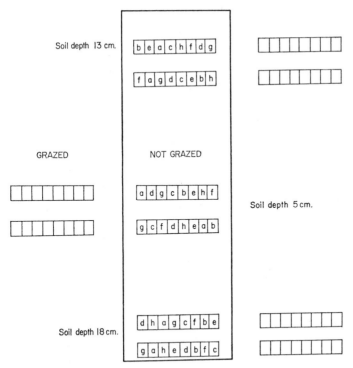

Figure 1. Plan of the cutting experiment within the exclosure and distribution of plots in the grazed downland. a, uncut; b, cut in spring (April); c, cut in summer (July); d, cut in autumn (September); e, cut in spring and summer; f, cut in spring and autumn; g, cut in summer and autumn; h, cut in spring, summer and autumn.

Cut in summer (July)
Cut in autumn (September)
Cut in spring and summer (April and July)
Cut in spring and autumn (April and September)
Cut in summer and autumn (July and September)
Cut in spring, summer and autumn (April, July and September)

Plots were cut with hand-shears as close to the ground as possible on the following dates:

1963—8 July, 30 September
1964 8 April, 15 July, 4 September
1965 8 April, 12 July, 15 September
1966 21 April, 22 July, 26 September
1967 12 April, 21 July, 12 September
1968 8 April, 31 July, 25 September

Cut material was removed from the plots and stored in polythene bags at −12°C until required.

Grazing regime

Border-Leicester × Cheviot ewes have grazed on the Hills since 1954 at a density of about 7·4 sheep/ha for roughly 9 months of each year. Regular counts have been made of sheep grazing on the 43·2 ha of chalk grassland since 1963 (Fig. 2). Grazing occurred at all seasons of the year but was not

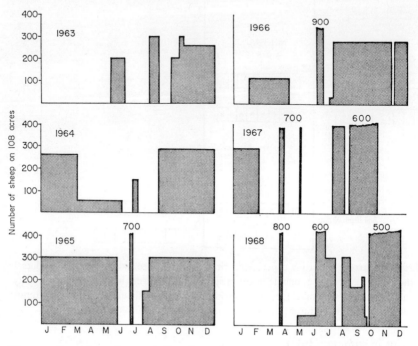

Figure 2. Intensity and pattern of grazing on the Barton Hills, Bedfordshire, 1963–8.

continuous, the grazing period being determined by the availability of other grassland on the farm and the amount of herbage on offer on the Hills. In general, the site of the 'grazed' plots outside the exclosure was intensively grazed throughout the experiment, apart from May, June and July 1967.

Estimation of botanical composition

The standard 10-pin point quadrat, with pins of 2 mm diameter and spaced at 5 cm intervals on the frame, was used to give an estimate of cover repetition (and hence performance (Greig-Smith 1964)) of all species in each plot. The point quadrat frame was placed in four positions in each plot, the same position being recorded in successive years. Each plot within the exclosure and in the grazed downland outside was recorded annually in July, immediately before the summer cuts were made.

Estimation of structure of vegetation

Ground cover was estimated by eye in July in each plot. The average height of the vegetation was estimated by placing a measuring rod at random four times in each plot and recording the height attained by the uppermost leaves of the vegetation, excluding leaves on the culms of grasses or on other inflorescence stalks.

Flower counts

The effect of cutting and grazing on flower production was determined by counting individual plants in flower of 6 dicotyledons in all plots on 12 July 1967. The species studied were: *Linum catharticum, Helianthemum chamaecistus, Thymus pulegioides, Poterium sanguisorba, Lotus corniculatus* and *Centaurea nigra.* Nomenclature of plants in this paper follows Clapham, Tutin & Warburg (1962).

Results

Initial botanical composition

The mean botanical composition of the plots within the enclosure, at the start of the experiment, is given in Table 1 in terms of percentage composition. The two blocks of plots on the medium soil depth contained considerably more grasses and sedges than forbs, with *Festuca ovina* more abundant than on the shallow and deepest soils. *Zerna erecta* was less abundant on the medium soil depth plots, but nevertheless contributed 19·4 per cent of the total cover. On the steep part of the slope, with the shallow rendzina soil, *Zerna erecta* (38·8 per cent) and *Poterium sanguisorba* (21·0 per cent) accounted for more than half the total cover. Twenty-five other species occurred although in small quantity. On the deepest soils at the bottom of the slope, *Zerna erecta* was dominant while *Cirsium acaulon, Carex flacca, Centaurea nigra, Poterium sanguisorba, Helianthemum chamaecistus* and *Filipendula vulgaris* were the next most abundant species. Mosses were infrequent in all plots, *Campylium chrysophyllum* and *Pseudoscleropodium purum* being the more common species.

In the grassland where *Festuca ovina* was dominant, the cover value reached 100 per cent, but on the steeper slopes 10–15 per cent bare ground was recorded at the start of the experiment.

The grazed plots, which were first recorded in July 1964, had a similar floristic composition to the plots within the exclosure. However, on the

Table 1. Initial botanical composition of plots in June 1963 before application of cutting treatments. (Percentage composition based on 640 points at each soil depth).

M = medium soil depth (13 cm)
S = shallow soil depth (5 cm)
D = deep soil depth (18 cm)

	M	S	D
Briza media	2·5	1·2	tr.
Dactylis glomerata	—	—	tr.
Festuca ovina	31·4	4·03	2·1
Helictotrichon pratense	2·2	1·0	0·4
Koeleria cristata	7·0	4·2	3·1
Zerna erecta	19·4	38·8	44·8
Carex caryophyllea	2·6	0·9	0·9
C. flacca	3·9	2·6	7·4
Asperula cynanchica	—	0·6	—
Campanula rotundifolia	2·6	0·5	1·0
Centaurea nigra	1·6	1·0	5·9
Cirsium acaulon	1·4	3·0	7·2
Filipendula vulgaris	2·3	4·7	3·6
Galium verum	0·4	1·0	tr.
Helianthemum chamaecistus	6·0	6·5	3·6
Hieracium pilosella	1·4	0·3	tr.
Hippocrepis comosa	0·9	0·3	—
Leontodon hispidus	0·1	0·6	3·1
Linum catharticum	0·3	0·3	1·1
Lotus corniculatus	2·7	0·9	tr.
Pimpinella saxifraga	—	—	0·3
Plantago lanceolata	0·4	0·6	—
Polygala vulgaris	0·3	0·1	0·3
Poterium sanguisorba	3·5	21·0	10·5
Prunella vulgaris	0·4	—	—
Primula veris	tr.	—	—
Pulsatilla vulgaris	tr.	1·4	—
Ranunculus bulbosus	0·4	0·1	—
Senecio integrifolius	0·6	—	—
Succisa pratensis	0·4	—	—
Thymus pulegioides	1·5	2·6	1·8
Viola hirta ssp. *calcarea*	tr.	0·3	tr.
Mosses	3·2	0·4	1·7
Total No. species	30	27	24
Height (cm)	3·3	4·2	6·6
Cover (%)	100	85	90
Total grasses and sedges	69·3	52·6	59·0
Total forbs	27·5	46·4	39·2
Total mosses	3·2	0·4	1·7

medium soil depth plots, grasses, especially *Festuca ovina*, contributed proportionately more to the total cover than in the plots within the exclosure.

Botanical changes in cut plots, 1963–8

Figures 3–7 show changes in the most frequent species in the plots measured

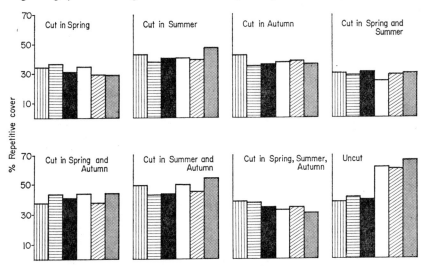

Figure 3. Performance of *Zerna erecta*, 1963–8, under 7 cutting treatments and in uncut controls. Soil depth 5 cm.

Key for Figs. 3–7: vertical lines, 1963; horizontal lines, 1964; solid black, 1965; open, 1966; diagonal lines, 1967; dots, 1968.

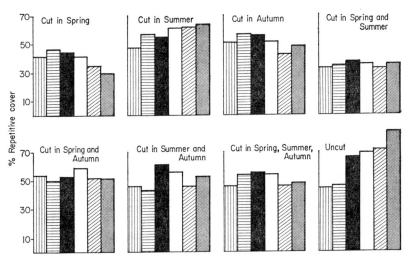

Figure 4. Performance of *Zerna erecta*, 1963–8, under 7 cutting treatments and in uncut controls. Soil depth 18 cm.

as a proportion of the total repetitive cover within each plot in the period 1963–8. In the plots on the deep soil, in which *Zerna erecta* contributed between 32·5 and 53 per cent before treatment, cutting in spring resulted in a gradual reduction in the cover of *Zerna* from 41·9 per cent in 1963 to 29·7 per cent in 1968. In contrast, in plots cut in summer, *Zerna* increased from 46·9 per cent in 1963 to 63·4 per cent in 1966. Plots cut in spring and summer,

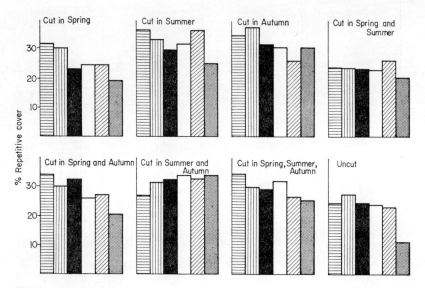

Figure 5. Performance of *Festuca ovina*, 1963–8, under 7 cutting treatments and in uncut controls. Soil depth 13 cm.

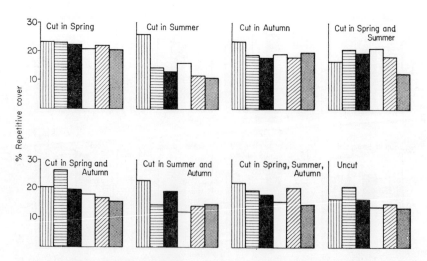

Figure 6. Performance of *Poterium sanguisorba*, 1963–8, under 7 cutting treatments and in uncut control. Soil depth 5 cm.

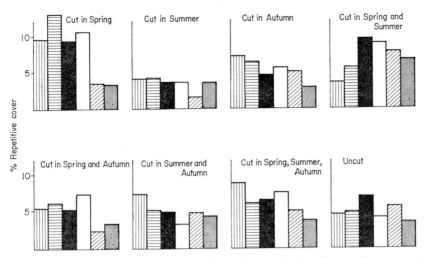

Figure 7. Performance of *Helianthemum chamaecistus*, 1963–8, under 7 cutting treatments and in uncut controls. Soil depth 13 cm.

spring and autumn, and in spring, summer and autumn showed little change in cover of *Zerna*. This is surprising in view of the decrease in *Zerna* in plots cut only in spring. Cutting twice or three times a year promotes tiller production and it seems likely that the increased tillering in these plots resulted in a higher total cover than in plots cut in spring alone. In plots on the shallow soil, *Zerna* remained relatively constant in all treatments, although in plots cut three times a year there was some reduction in cover. In plots on the medium-depth soil, in which *Festuca ovina* was dominant, or co-dominant with *Zerna*, cutting in summer resulted in an increase in cover of *Zerna* from 14·7 per cent in 1963 to 42·3 per cent in 1968 and in autumn from 9·2 per cent to 15·7 per cent. Cutting in spring caused no change in the cover of *Zerna*. Cutting twice or three times a year resulted in *Zerna* remaining at about the same level as it was in 1963.

On the medium soil depth, cutting in spring resulted in a reduction in the cover of *Festuca ovina* from 31·9 per cent in 1963 to 19·3 per cent in 1968, a trend which was followed in all other treatments with the exception of plots cut twice in summer and autumn, in which *Festuca* showed an increase from 27 per cent in 1963 to 34 per cent in 1969. In the blocks on the shallow and deepest soils, *Festuca* was present in such small quantities that it was not possible to discern trends.

Changes in the cover of *Helictotrichon pratense* and *Koeleria cristata* in the cut plots were small and insignificant. On the other hand, *Briza media*, although present in only small quantity, increased considerably in the cut plots, apparently benefiting from the less intense competition from *Bromus* and *Festuca*.

Carex flacca and *Carex caryophyllea* which were present in only small quantities in the plots showed no significant response to any cutting treatment, although *Carex caryophyllea* increased slightly in plots cut once in spring and autumn.

Twenty-four species of dicotyledons were recorded in the plots, 70 per cent of which contributed less than 20 per cent to the total cover of the plots. Although the total cover of these species fluctuated from year to year no significant changes in individual species were noted in the period 1963–8 except for the following. *Hippocrepis comosa*, which was only common on the medium-depth soils, increased considerably in plots cut once in spring and also in plots with combinations of cutting in spring with other seasons of the year. It was noticeable that in these plots, where competition from *Zerna* had been reduced, *Hippocrepis* assumed a more prostrate habit of growth and competed successfully with other dicotyledons present. Similarly, *Asperula cynanchica*, another species of low competitive ability with a prostrate habit of growth, increased in plots in which competition from grasses was reduced by cutting.

Poterium sanguisorba, the most abundant herb in the plots, was clearly reduced by cutting in summer and in combinations of other treatments which included a summer cut. This was especially noticeable on the shallow soils where *Poterium* was most abundant and a similar trend was noted on the other soil depths. *Poterium* was unaffected by cutting in April probably because it had produced few, if any, leaves by that time of year.

The behaviour of *Helianthemum chamaecistus*, the second most frequent herb in the grassland, varied considerably. On the shallow and medium soil depths, in plots cut in spring, it decreased from a mean of 9·5 per cent in 1963 to 3·6 per cent in 1968, while on the deep soil it increased from 1·6 per cent to 4·40 per cent in the same period. Cutting in autumn produced a decrease on all soil depths while in plots cut in summer there was no significant change in cover from 1963 to 1968.

Table 2. Mean height (cm) of vegetation in uncut controls 1963–8

	1963	1964	1965	1966	1967	1968
Soil depth 5 cm	4·5	8·3	8·9	16·5	22·4	17·9
Soil depth 13 cm	3·2	7·6	8·9	14·1	14·6	13·4
Soil depth 18 cm	6·4	14·1	17·9	22·0	26·9	29·7

Botanical changes in uncut plots, 1963–8

Following the cessation of grazing in 1963 growth by grass species was the most noticeable feature of the uncut control plots resulting in a considerable accumulation of litter. On the deep soils *Zerna erecta* increased from 44 per cent in 1963 to 83·5 per cent in 1968, forming a litter 7–12 cm deep. Changes in height of the vegetation were also considerable (Table 2). Competition for light became important in the uncut plots after 1966 and only those species which were able to increase their leaf area to compensate for the lower light intensities were able to survive on the plots on the deep soils. *Cirsium acaulon*, *Poterium sanguisorba* and *Filipendula vulgaris* were the most successful competitors with *Zerna* in these plots although small, often etiolated plants of *Thymus pulegioides*, *Helianthemum chamaecistus*, *Centaurea nigra* and *Campanula rotundifolia* survived. Their contribution to the total vegetation was, however, extremely small. Other grasses, and sedges, notably *Koeleria cristata*, *Festuca ovina* and *Carex flacca* increased in leaf length in response to the increased height of *Zerna erecta* in the uncut plots and survived in small quantities. In the uncut control plots on the shallow soils, *Zerna* increased from 38·2 per cent in 1963 to 66·2 per cent in 1968 with the productivity of the vegetation being controlled presumably by soil, water and nutrient factors. The height of the vegetation increased from 4·5 to 17·9 cm in the same period and the number of species which were able to survive in the uncut plots was greater in the shallow soils than elsewhere, although *Poterium sanguisorba* and *Filipendula* were again the most abundant species.

On the medium depth soils, which had a broader spectrum of species than plots on other soil depths, *Zerna erecta* increased from 24·8 to 40·5 per cent from 1963 to 1968. *Festuca ovina*, *Briza media*, *Ranunculus bulbosus*, *Lotus corniculatus* and *Plantago lanceolata* decreased while other herbs remained at about the same level. The mean height of the vegetation increased from 3·2 to 13·4 cm in that period.

The accumulation of litter was much less on the medium and shallow soil depths than on the deeper soils.

Botanical changes in the grazed plots, 1964–7

Mean botanical changes in the 48 plots in the grazed downland from 1964 to 1967 are shown in Fig. 8. The proportion of grasses and sedges increased from 64·7 per cent in 1964 to 74·8 per cent in 1967 with a corresponding decrease in the proportion of dicotyledons and mosses from 35·3 to 25·5 per cent. The increase of *Zerna erecta* on the deep soils and similar increases in *Festuca ovina* on the medium soils accounted for most of this change. *Koeleria cristata*, *Helictotrichon pratense*, *Carex flacca* and *Carex caryophyllea* changed little during the 4 years. During this period, particularly in 1966 and 1967, the numbers of sheep grazing the area varied more than in previous years, 900 sheep being put to graze for a short period from mid-June to end of July in 1966 immediately before the plots were recorded. In April and

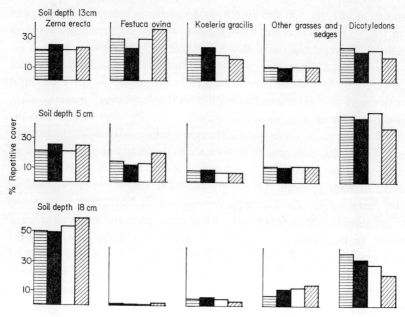

Figure 8. Changes in the botanical composition of sheep grazed plots, 1964–7. Recorded in July of each year. Symbols the same as Figs. 3–7.

May 1967, 700 sheep grazed the Hills, but, in the 2 months before the plots were recorded in July 1967, no sheep grazed on the Hills, and it may be that the previously heavily grazed grasses produced new leaves more quickly than did the dicotyledons. This was reflected in the 1966 and 1967 botanical records. Moreover, there was a general reduction in the cover of most of the dicotyledons present in the grazed grassland, especially on the deeper soils, which suggests that either the dicotyledons were being more heavily grazed than grasses, or some other factor in the environment, such as rainfall, was favouring the grasses.

Nevertheless, despite the changes in the proportions of species in the grazed downland, this work has emphasised the relative stability of heavily grazed grassland, especially the balance achieved between the species of dicotyledons, the status of each changing relatively little as a result of grazing. This suggests that selection by sheep under these conditions is unimportant, the scarcity of herbage on offer forcing them to eat species which under other conditions they reject.

The height of the vegetation in the grazed plots did not exceed a mean of 2·5 cm, except on the deeper soils, when in 1966 and 1967 a mean maximum height of 8·9 cm was recorded. For much of the 4-year grazing period, the vegetation rarely exceeded 1·2 cm. Litter accumulation did not occur during the 4-year period because the herbage produced was all consumed during grazing. As much as 25 per cent bare ground was recorded in some of the grazed plots, especially in the *Zerna* dominant areas in 1964 and 1965, and, although this became less in 1966 and 1967, nevertheless 5–15 per cent bare ground was frequently recorded in July of each year. The importance of this in relation to seed germination of chalk grassland annuals and perennials is discussed below.

Effect of cutting and grazing on flower production

One year after enclosure, the ungrazed grassland was conspicuous with the flower heads of many species, particularly *Helianthemum chamaecistus*, *Lotus corniculatus*, *Asperula cynanchica*, *Leontodon hispidus* and *Linum catharticum*. The profusion of flowers within the enclosure contrasted strongly with the paucity of flowers in the grazed downland. In 1965, two years after enclosure, counts of flowers were made on 21 July along transect lines, in grazed and ungrazed grassland, and it was found that there were about $2\frac{1}{2}$ times as many flowers in the grazed grassland as there were in the ungrazed grassland. This apparent reversal of the previous year's observation is explained by the absence of sheep from the Hills for two weeks before the counts were made, enabling many species to flower which otherwise would have been grazed. Within the enclosure a layer of leaf litter, in some places 17 cm deep, had already accumulated and this prevented the flowering of low-growing species such as *Asperula cynanchica* and the annual *Linum catharticum*. With the gradual build-up of litter and the increased dominance of grasses, especially *Zerna erecta* in the enclosure, only the more vigorous species, such as *Poterium sanguisorba* and *Centaurea nigra* were able to flower. By 1968, flower heads of dicotyledons were few, in contrast to the abundance of inflorescences of *Zerna erecta*.

The effect of cutting on flower production was investigated in July 1967 by counting the numbers of flowers of six species within the cut and uncut plots. Similar counts were made in the grazed plots. The results are shown in Table 3.

Linum catharticum was significantly more numerous in all plots receiving a cutting treatment than in the uncut controls ($P < 0.01$). Plots cut twice a year, in spring and summer, and plots cut three times a year, in spring, summer and autumn, contained significantly more plants of *Linum* than other cutting treatments ($P < 0.05$). In the grazed downland a mean of 51.5 plants/0.56 m^2 was recorded, which compares favourably with a mean of 66.6 plants/0.56 m^2 in the cut plots. The creation or continued presence of bare ground is essential for the success of this species and favourable conditions for establishment are provided by a variety of cutting and grazing treatments. Similar results with *Linum* have been obtained elsewhere (Wells 1969).

Table 3. Mean number of flowers in 0·56 m² plots given 7 different cutting treatments, compared with uncut plots and grazed plots.
(Means of 6 plots in the cut and uncut treatments, mean of 48 grazed plots)

	Linum cartharti-cum	Helianthe-mum cha-maecistus	Thymus pule-gioides	Poterium sangui-sorba	Lotus corni-culatus	Centaurea nigra
Uncut	5·0	2·3	2·5	4·0	1·3	0·5
Cut in spring	36·8	2·0	7·2	9·8	0·2	3·3
Cut in summer	40·3	7·8	6·3	7·6	4·5	1·0
Cut in autumn	59·5	1·1	5·6	9·6	4·2	1·2
Cut in spring, summer	108·3	12·2	13·1	10·5	2·2	2·2
Cut in spring, autumn	48·5	9·7	11·8	14·6	1·3	1·5
Cut in summer, autumn	80·3	4·5	30·5	5·3	2·0	1·0
Cut in spring, summer and autumn	92·6	3·0	8·0	13·5	10·5	1·7
S.E. mean	2·65	1·02	1·28	1·45	0·82	0·64
Grazed plots	51·47	3·56	18·50	23·14	1·30	1·90
S.E. mean grazed plots	4·42	1·07	3·98	3·41	0·27	0·36

Flowers of *Thymus pulegioides* and *Lotus corniculatus* were significantly more numerous in the cut plots than in the uncut controls. Cutting twice, in spring and summer, summer and autumn, and three times, in spring, summer and autumn, produced the highest number of flowers in *Thymus*. The highest response with *Lotus* was obtained in plots cut three times a year. Both species appeared to flower more profusely in grassland in which competition from grasses was minimal. *Poterium sanguisorba* and *Centaurea nigra* showed no significant response to any cutting treatment. In the grazed downland, flowers of *Poterium* were more numerous than in the cut plots, which suggests that inflorescences of this species may be avoided by sheep. The behaviour of *Helianthemum chamaecistus* was more erratic; cutting in spring and summer, spring and autumn produced the highest number of flowers per plot, but cutting in spring, summer and autumn resulted in few flowers per plot.

In general, cutting had a differential effect on species with regard to flowering, cutting in spring removing flower buds of early flowering species such as *Pulsatilla vulgaris* but not affecting species which flowered later. Similarly, cutting in autumn prevented species such as *Succisa pratensis* from flowering but did not affect species such as *Pulsatilla vulgaris*, *Hippocrepis comosa* or *Lotus corniculatus*, which by then had completed flowering and seed dispersal. Cutting in summer has a greater influence on flowering of the chalk flora than other treatments because most species flower at this time. Nevertheless, most species produced flowers later, if defoliated in summer, and although total flower production may be less, there is no evidence that flowering is completely prevented by cutting once or twice in the year. On the other hand, the results show that in the uncut controls, flower production of many species ceased completely.

Discussion

Many physiological and agronomic experiments have been conducted to investigate the behaviour of pasture associations in response to defoliation by cutting or grazing. In the past attention has been directed towards the effect of these treatments on stored reserves, particularly the utilization of carbohydrates in pasture plants after defoliation. May (1960), in a review of this subject, states that 'there is widespread agreement that the effects of repeated defoliation are cumulative, and that the more intensive and frequent the defoliation the lower the levels of carbohydrate reserves will be'. However, he qualifies this generalization by stating that many environmental factors, for example, nutrients, water content and temperature, influence this process and results obtained from pot experiments are likely to differ significantly from field experiments. Other workers, notably Brougham (1958) and Donald & Black (1958), have examined the relation of leaf area to the rate of regrowth after defoliation, while publications by the Commonwealth Bureau of Pasture and Field Crops (1970) show the interest in yet other aspects of defoliation.

In the 6-year study reported here attention has been given to the effects of cutting and grazing on the floristic composition of chalk grassland with the object of managing this type of grassland for the purposes of nature conservation. No studies were made on the physiological aspects mentioned previously, nor on changes in root/shoot ratios prevailing under the different treatments, attention being centred on the performance of individual species in the grassland in relation to other species. The results clearly show that cutting can be an effective substitute for grazing and, apparently, causes no loss of species from the vegetation, at least in the short term. This result appears at first surprising, since defoliation by mowing differs from grazing in being non-selective, so that all parts of a plant above the level of cutting are removed while sheep may graze leaves on the same plant to different extents. Furthermore, in this experiment all cut material was removed from the plots so that there was a net loss of nutrients, while in the grazed plots nutrients were returned in the dung and urine of the sheep. In addition there was no substitute for the treading action of sheep in the cut plots.

Figure 1 shows that the intensity of grazing by sheep during 1963–8 was high with the vegetation kept short for most of the time. Under these conditions of low availability of herbage sheep appear to be less selective and, at times of extreme shortage of pasture, non-selective in respect of the species listed in Table 1. Sheep were observed to eat species with spiny leaves such as *Cirsium acaulon*, plants with hairs such as *Leontodon hispidus*, *Zerna erecta* and *Koeleria cristata*, and even aromatic species such as *Thymus pulegioides* were eaten when young.

A further unexpected result of this trial was the relative stability of heavily grazed downland. Although there were changes in the proportion of grasses to forbs, especially in 1966 and 1967 when the grazing intensity was eased for a short period, changes were small and the proportions of more than twenty dicotyledons remained remarkably constant. The explanation for this undoubtedly lies in the life form of plants found in grazed downland. Nearly all (more than 90 per cent) are short- or long-lived perennials adapted to continual defoliation by having the growing point at or near the ground surface. Provided competition from coarse grasses is controlled by grazing, a balance can be achieved between species by means of vegetative reproduction and occasional seed germination. These results agree closely with those of Kydd (1964), who found that on cattle-grazed downland cover of species was modified, but not altered fundamentally, by variations in grazing management.

It has been stressed that control of the dominant grass, *Zerna erecta*, is the most important factor in maintaining a species-rich grassland. In the uncut plots, the growth of *Zerna* and the occasional accumulation of leaf litter to a depth of 10 cm caused the elimination of low-growing species and a considerable reduction in other species such as *Poterium sanguisorba* and *Centaurea nigra* which were the only species able to compete effectively with *Zerna erecta*.

Soil depth was an important factor in determining the amount of competition from *Zerna* in the ungrazed plots. On the deepest soils, growth of *Zerna* exceeded 20 cm and consequently competition was intense, in contrast to its growth on the shallow soil, where growth was less and light was able to reach the lower levels of vegetation. Similar changes were recorded by Kydd in ungrazed plots in which grasses increased from 37 to 79 per cent.

Cutting in spring (April) was the most effective treatment in reducing the competitive ability of *Zerna* on all three soil depths while cutting three times a year, in spring, summer and autumn, was also effective. *Zerna* begins vegetative growth early in March, presumably utilizing food reserves stored in the perennial stem. Removal of leaf area in the period April to May, when leaf growth is at a maximum, causes a severe check to this plant and it was noticeable that regrowth by the end of July, in plots cut in April, was small, usually producing a stubble 5–6 cm high. Other species, both grasses and herbs, were able to utilize this period when competition from *Zerna* was reduced, *Briza media* and *Hippocrepis comosa*, in particular, increasing considerably.

Defoliation acts differentially on species according to the time of year when they produce leaves, flowers, set fruit or are dormant with no above-ground parts. Although cutting at a certain time of the year caused a decrease in certain species initially, it was noticeable that this trend did not continue

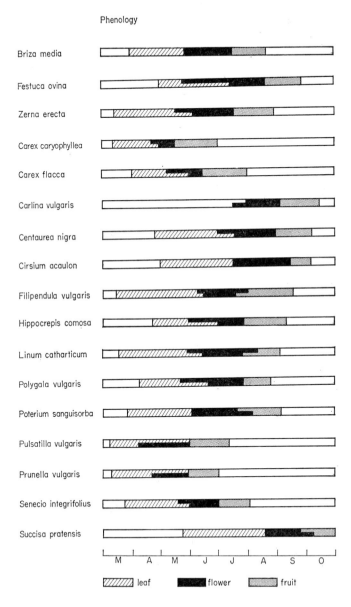

Figure 9. Phenology and development of seventeen chalk grassland species. Data derived from observations of marked plants 1964–6.

and after 4 years of cutting each species had achieved a fairly constant level in the contribution it made to the vegetation in any plot. This suggests that the effect of cutting on the total flora is to produce a balance in the vegetation, which may be different from that achieved by grazing but which nevertheless appears to maintain a similar degree of richness and diversity.

The development and phenology of 17 of the most frequent species present on the Barton Hills is shown in Fig. 9. By reference to this chart it should be possible to predict the effect of cutting, at a particular time, on the flowering and reproductive success of these species. For example, it is clear that cutting in mid-May is likely to remove the flowers and fruits of *Pulsatilla vulgaris* and probably prevent its establishment by seed. Cutting in August or September, on the other hand, will not affect the reproductive performance of this species although it will change its competitive relationships with other species. Similar reasoning applied to other species shows that there is no 'best' time for cutting or grazing for the conservation management of chalk grassland because time of application of treatments affects individual species differently. For this reason it is essential that the objectives of management should be clearly defined before management begins. This is especially important when grassland is managed for particular species of insects (Morris 1967) which depend for part of their life cycle on flowers or fruiting bodies for success. It may be equally important for certain species of plant especially annuals which depend on occasional establishment by seed for their success.

Finally, it is necessary to assess the practical application of these results to the management of chalk grassland. Grassland nature reserves in lowland England are usually small and are often on steep slopes. The cost of management of small reserves, using sheep, is high and for economic reasons these animals are unlikely to be widely used. Mowing is an attractive, alternative proposition but conventional mowers drawn by tractors are not always suitable because of the steepness of the slopes and often uneven nature of the terrain. It seems likely that mowing machines which float on a cushion of air, and which have recently been developed commercially, will be increasingly used in the future for grassland management on small reserves.

Acknowledgements

Thanks are due to Mr R.Farr for permission to erect an exclosure on the Barton Hills. Considerable assistance in the field was given by Miss L. Farrell, Miss T.Clay and Miss J.Williamson. It is a pleasure to acknowledge the helpful criticisms and discussions of many colleagues, particularly Mr D.A.Wells, Dr M.G.Morris and Dr E.A.G.Duffey. I wish to thank Mr P.H. Cryer for statistical advice.

References

ANON (1970) *Ann. Bibl. 838.* Commonw. Bur. Past. Fld Crops.

BROUGHAM R.W. (1958) Interception of light by the foliage of pure and mixed stands of pasture plants. *Aust. J. agric. Res.* 9, 39–52.

CLAPHAM A.R., TUTIN T.G. & WARBURG E.F. (1962) *Flora of the British Isles.* Cambridge.

DONALD C.M. & BLACK J.M. (1958) The significance of leaf area in pasture growth. *Herb. Abstr.* 28, 1–6.

GREIG-SMITH P. (1964) *Quantitative Plant Ecology.* London.

KYDD D.D. (1964) The effect of different systems of cattle grazing on the botanical composition of permanent downland pasture. *J. Ecol.* 52, 139–49.

LOUSLEY J.E. (1950) *Wild Flowers of Chalk and Limestone.* London.

MAY L.H. (1960) The utilization of carbohydrate reserves in pasture plants after defoliation. *Herb. Abstr.* 30, 239–43.

MORRIS M.G. (1967) Differences between the invertebrate faunas of grazed and ungrazed chalk grassland. I. Responses of some phytophagous insects to cessation of grazing. *J. appl. Ecol.* 4, 459–74.

NORMAN M.J.T. (1957) The influence of various grazing treatments upon the botanical composition of a downland pasture. *J. Br. Grassld. Soc.* 12, 246–56.

THOMAS A.S. (1960) Changes in vegetation since the advent of myxomatosis. *J. Ecol.* 48, 287–306.

THOMAS A.S. (1963) Further changes in vegetation since the advent of myxomatosis. *J. Ecol.* 51, 151–83.

WARNE L.G.G. (1934) Intensive treatment of a Wiltshire Down pasture. Effect on botanical composition. *J. Minist. Agric. Fish* 41, 470–5.

WELLS T.C.E. (1968) Land-use changes affecting *Pulsatilla vulgaris* in England. *Biol. Conserv.* 1, 37–43.

WELLS T.C.E. (1969) Botanical aspects of conservation management of chalk grasslands. *Biol. Conserv.* 2, 36–44.

Some effects of grazing on the population ecology of the Cinnabar Moth (*Tyria jacobaeae* L.)

J.P.DEMPSTER *The Nature Conservancy, Monks Wood Experimental Station, Abbots Ripton, Huntingdonshire*

Several papers during this Symposium have described the effects of grazing, or cutting of vegetation, on flora and fauna. What I wish to do is to show some of the more detailed effects of grazing on the population dynamics of one species, namely the Cinnabar Moth. The results from a 7-year study of the factors determining the distribution and abundance of this moth are being published elsewhere (Dempster in press). In this paper I shall describe only those aspects of the population ecology which are affected by grazing.

Cinnabar Moth has a single generation each year and overwinters in the pupal stage. The adult moths emerge in May and lay their eggs in clusters on the underside of the basal leaves of their food plant. This is usually ragwort (*Senecio jacobaea* L.), but may occasionally be groundsel (*Senecio vulgaris* L.). Normally about thirty or forty eggs are laid in a cluster, but up to 150 may be found. On hatching, the young caterpillars are greyish-green in colour and they stay together on the leaf on which they hatched during their first instar. After this, however, they move up the plant and frequently feed on the developing flower buds. By then they have developed their characteristic black and orange banding. There are five larval stages and the total larval period takes just over a month. When fully grown, the caterpillar leaves the plant in search of a pupation site. This is in the superficial layers of the soil, often amongst moss or grass roots, or under a stone. The pupa then survives the autumn and winter and produces an adult in the following spring.

Most of the data presented here are from a population of Cinnabar Moth on a heavily grazed area at Weeting Heath National Nature Reserve in Norfolk. Some less detailed information is also given from two populations at Monks Wood. One of these is a natural population in one of the clearings in the wood (East Field). The other is an introduced experimental population on the edge of cultivated land at the Experimental Station.

The Weeting Heath Reserve is one of the last remaining fragments of the once extensive Breckland. On the southern half of the Reserve an exceedingly high rabbit population occurs in an area of 19 ha (47 ac) within a rabbit-proof enclosure. This enclosure was built in 1956 in an attempt to maintain a rabbit-grazing pressure similar to that on the Reserve prior to myxomatosis. The vegetation is a very heavily grazed 'Grassland B' of Watt's classification (Watt 1940) and ragwort is abundant over the whole area.

Within the enclosure the Cinnabar population fluctuates violently. Occasionally it occurs at such high densities that it completely defoliates its food plants and many caterpillars die from starvation. This happened in 1960 and 1961 and again in 1967 and 1968. Figure 1 shows the changes in numbers

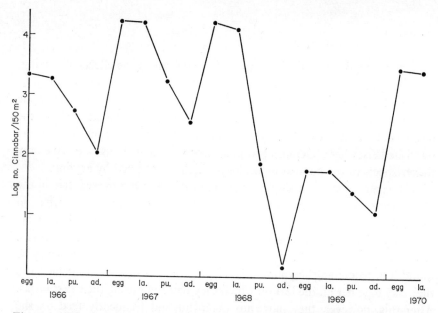

Figure 1. Changes in the number of Cinnabar Moth at Weeting Heath.

since 1966 when accurate counts began. Since that date adult numbers have fluctuated between 1·5 and 362·0/150 m². Egg numbers have varied to an even greater extent from 62 to 17110/150 m².

In East Field, Monks Wood, the Cinnabar population does not fluctuate to anything like this amount, and it never reaches such high densities that it eats out its food supply. East Field (4·2 ha, 10·4 ac) was cleared of trees and brought under cultivation during the last war, in 1943. The soil is a heavy boulder clay and although land drains were installed, the field frequently became waterlogged and in 1952 cultivation was abandoned, leaving a crop of potatoes in the ground. Ridges in the soil, left by this crop, are still present over the greater part of the field. It is now under rough grassland and is lightly grazed in places by rabbits. In most years since 1964 the vegetation has been cut to prevent the growth of woody plants. Occasional plants of ragwort occur throughout the field.

Cinnabar numbers are always low. In the two years, 1965 and 1966, when accurate counts were made, there were 126 and 143 eggs/150 m² laid. A straight comparison cannot be made between these figures and those from Weeting Heath, since plant densities differ so greatly in the two localities. In East Field ragwort occurs at about one plant/10 m², but the plants are large and each produces several flowering shoots. At Weeting ragwort is always at least 100 times as abundant as this, but as will be seen later, plant numbers fluctuate violently. On the light sandy soil at Weeting the plants are small and usually produce only a single flowering shoot of about 30–45 cm high.

The third population of Cinnabar Moth studied was an artificial one, created by releasing adult moths on to ragwort on the edge of an arable field at Monks Wood. The plants were at the base of a south-facing hedge within tall mixed herbaceous vegetation. This population did not survive in any year and new adults were released each May from 1964–6.

The violent fluctuations in Cinnabar numbers at Weeting Heath owe their origin to the heavily overgrazed condition of the vegetation. Overgrazing not only leads to an abundance of ragwort, it also increases the chance of the plant surviving after defoliation. Ragwort cannot become established and survive in a close grass sward (Cameron 1935). Bare patches created by rabbits enable seedlings to become established, while grazing reduces competition by grasses. Ragwort is normally not eaten by rabbits.

Ragwort is usually a biennial which flowers in its second year and then dies. Most seed germinates in the autumn and the young plants overwinter as small rosettes. Only rarely do plants flower in their first year, usually they pass their second winter as a rosette and flower in the following summer. If it is damaged and prevented from flowering, ragwort can behave as a perennial by repeated regeneration. Regeneration after defoliation may take two forms. If the plant is large and has ample food reserves, secondary flowering shoots may be formed from the crown of the plant in the autumn following defoliation. Seed production is, however, usually less than from an undamaged plant. Besides regrowth from the crown, regeneration may also occur from root buds (Harper & Wood 1957). This type of regeneration is particularly vigorous from the roots of rosette plants. The young plants resulting from regeneration from root buds are difficult to distinguish from seedlings, since the connection with the parent root is soon lost. Vegetative reproduction in this way may easily be confused with reproduction from seed.

Table 1 shows the average number of ragwort plants per m² at Weeting Heath since 1966. These figures are based on counts in 150 m²-quadrats. In

Table 1. Number of ragwort/m² at Weeting Heath

	3/5/66	19/4/67	13/9/67	9/4/68	14/8/68	25/4/69	12/6/70
Rosettes	5·27	3·96	3·56	5·53	38·75	59·5	33·9
Flowering	4·39	4·14	1·42	0·05	0·00	8·4	18·4
Total	9·66	8·10	4·98	5·58	38·75	68·1	52·3

Plants defoliated   Plants defoliated

1966 there were about 10 plants/m², of which just under half were of flowering size. The number dropped slightly in 1967 to about 8/m² and these were completely defoliated by Cinnabar caterpillars. When a thorough search was made on 10 July, no green remains of ragwort were found. Many caterpillars died from starvation. There was no secondary flowering, but by mid-September there had been some regeneration from root buds. By the following spring there were just over 5 plants/m², but the majority of these were small rosettes. These were again defoliated by Cinnabar and no green remains of the plants could be found on 26 June. Counts made in August showed, however, that there had been a tremendous regeneration by the plants (39/m²). This re-growth continued throughout the autumn and by the following spring a count of 68/m² was obtained. Approximately 8/m² flowered. By 1970 the number of plants started to drop, as the larger plants died after flowering. About a third of the plants flowered in 1970, i.e. about 18/m².

No seed was set on the area in 1967 or 1968 and yet the number of plants increased in the following year. This was probably due almost entirely to regrowth from root buds. In 1968 careful digging showed the connection of some plants with old root fragments, but one cannot be certain that some plants did not originate from seed left in the soil since 1966. Poole and Cairns (1940) have, however, shown that the viability of seed is low (3·5 per cent) when kept in soil for two years. The greatest amount of regeneration took place in 1968, the second year of defoliation. This was probably partly the result of the very wet summer in that year. During the period June–September 371 mm rain fell, compared with only 152 mm during the same period in 1967. The increased regeneration in 1968 was probably also due to the fact that the plants that were defoliated in that year were mainly small rosettes. These have greater powers of regeneration from root buds than have flowering sized plants.

This ability of ragwort to regenerate after defoliation is dependent upon the overgrazed condition of the vegetation at Weeting. The small rosette plants produced from root buds would not survive in a dense sward of grass.

Cinnabar numbers dropped almost to extinction as a result of shortage of food in 1968. It is estimated that only about 1·5 adults/150 m² survived from 16,493 eggs (99·99 per cent mortality). the few survivors that emerged in 1969 found a superabundance of their food plant, so that the moth was able immediately to build up in numbers again. If the plants had not regrown so spectacularly in 1968, the Cinnabar population would have taken far longer to recover and may well have become extinct.

Besides this effect of grazing on the food supply of Cinnabar Moth, the height and density of the vegetation has another important effect on its numbers. This is through the effect of the vegetation on the moth's natural enemies.

During early larval life there is a heavy mortality due to the action of arthropod predators. These were studied most intensively at the introduced Cinnabar population at Monks Wood. This population occurred on a small area of ragwort in which every plant could be searched every day. That is, the total population of Cinnabar could be counted every day during egg and larval development. Whenever an individual egg or larva was missing from the plants, a search was made and any possible predator that was found in the vicinity of the plant was caught. These were brought into the laboratory and their gut contents tested against anti-Cinnabar serum by means of the precipitin test. This test can detect small quantities of Cinnabar material in the gut of a predator, by its interaction with blood serum of a rabbit which has been inoculated with an extract of the moth (Dempster 1960). These tests identified twenty-eight species of predator feeding on Cinnabar eggs and caterpillars (Table 2), and over the three years 1964–6, a positive reaction was obtained from a predator on just over 60 per cent of the occasions when individuals were missing off the plants. Many of the species involved are nocturnal and there is little doubt that this percentage would have been even higher had searches been made at night. If it is assumed that all disappearances which were unaccounted for by other known causes (parasites, disease, drowning, etc.) were due to predators, a rough estimate of mortality caused by predation can be obtained. At this introduced population of Cinnabar it is estimated that between 83 and 89 per cent of the larvae were killed by predators (Table 3). The bulk of this mortality occurred in the first two larval instars.

An intensive study of predation was not possible at Weeting Heath owing to its distance from the laboratory. There is no doubt, however, that arthropod predators had a far smaller effect on that Cinnabar population than at Monks Wood. Precipitin tests of predacious arthropods trapped at Weeting identified only nine species feeding on Cinnabar Moth (Table 4). A very small percentage of positives was obtained from these tests, due to the fact that many of the predators were collected by pitfall traps which were emptied only

Table 2. The percentage of various predators giving a positive reaction to anti-Cinnabar serum, Monks Wood 1964–6

	Number tested	% positive
Arachnida Phalangida		
Phalangium opilio	73	50·7
Araneida		
Spiders (unidentified)	39	28·2
Theridion ovatum	9	88·9
Xysticus cristatus	7	42·9
Meta segmentata	2	50·0
Pachygnatha degeeri	3	(100·0)
Lycosa amentata	28	7·1
Acarina		
Anystis agilis	7	14·3
Insecta. Coleoptera		
Harpalus rufipes	96	18·8
Abax parallelopipedus	18	11·1
Feronia melanaria	54	14·8
F. cuprea	6	33·3
Harpalus brevicollis	9	11·1
Trechus quadristriatus	24	25·0
Notiophilus biguttatus	28	7·1
Bembidion lampros	64	3·1
Amara aulicus	2	(100·0)
Anthicus antherinus	6	50·1
Tachyporus spp.	11	9·1
Rhagonycha spp.	5	40·0
Heteroptera		
Heterotoma merioptera	7	28·6
Calocoris norvegicus	30	6·7
Anthocoris nemorum	13	30·8
Nabis rugosus	4	75·0
Dermaptera		
Forficula auricularia	6	33·3
Neuroptera		
Chrysopa larva	1	(100·0)
Mecoptera		
Panorpa spp.	1	(100·0)
Crustacea. Isopoda		
Woodlice (unidentified)	7	28·6
Armadillidium spp.	40	22·5
Philosia muscorum	25	32·0

once a week. It must also be remembered that at Monks Wood the predators
were collected only when eggs or larvae were missing. Several species which
were shown to feed on Cinnabar Moth at Monks Wood also occurred at
Weeting, but gave no positives in the tests. It is estimated that between 32 and
64 per cent of the larvae at Weeting were taken by arthropod predators
(Table 3), a far lower percentage than at Monks Wood.

Table 3. Mortality due to Arthropod Predators (% No. Larvae Hatching)

Monks Wood (introduced population)

1964	1965	1966
87·8	88·8	82·7

Monks Wood (East Field)

1965 (cut)	1966 (uncut)
62·9	71·2

Weeting Heath

1966	1967	1968	1969
60·7	63·7	47·8	32·3

Table 4. The percentage of various predators giving a positive reaction to anti-Cinnabar serum, Weeting Heath 1966–9.

	Number tested	% positive
ARACHNIDA		
Araneida		
Oxyptila scabricula	11	9·9
Xysticus cristatus	10	10·0
Acarina		
Erythraeus phalangoides	635	1·7
Phalangida		
Phalangium opilio	13	7·7
INSECTA		
Carabidae		
Metabletus foveatus	134	0·7
Amara spp.	19	10·5
Harpalus rufitarsus	1	(100·0)
CRUSTACEA		
Isopoda		
Armadillidium vulgare	30	6·7
Porcellio scaber	1	(100·0)

No precipitin tests were done from East Field, but the mortality attributable to predators was intermediate between the other two sites (Table 3). Of the two years for which data were obtained, mortality was highest in 1966, when the vegetation in East Field was not cut.

A rough measure of the importance of different species of predator at the three sites is given in Table 5. This shows the average number of predators trapped in pitfalls during the Cinnabar larval period on the three sites. Pitfall catches are influenced by a number of factors including the length and density of the vegetation and this makes comparisons between sites of uncertain value. Vegetation was shortest and sparsest at Weeting and longest and densest at the introduced population at Monks Wood. Differences in vegetation would, therefore, have tended to lead to higher catches at Weeting and lower catches at Monks Wood. The number of predators caught is a function of both their population size and their activity, and since these parameters determine rates of predation, pitfall traps may give a useful index of predation.

At Weeting, the mite *Erythraeus phalangoides* is probably the most important predator, while the ground-beetles (Carabidae), which are abundant at Monks Wood (introduced population), are almost missing. Of the twenty species in Table 5, nine species occur at all three sites and a further five are shared by two of the sites. The biggest differences between sites are then due primarily to differences in the abundance of shared species. The data in Table 5 show differences in the abundance of ground-living predators. Many plant-living species such as spiders (*Theridion*, *Meta* and *Pachygnatha*) and Heteroptera (*Anthocoris*, *Heterotoma* and *Nabis*) are not caught in pitfalls. These were far more abundant in the mixed herbaceous vegetation of the introduced population than on the other sites.

The high mortality caused by arthropod predators undoubtedly contributed to the inability of the introduced population to persist. On the other hand, this was not the whole reason. If all of the larvae which pupated had survived to the adult stage each year, the population would have survived. Pupal mortality was, however, exceedingly high.

Pupae are killed if kept in overmoist conditions. In the laboratory an increase in weight by as little as 10 per cent by absorption of water results in death. In contrast, pupae can lose up to 30 per cent of their weight by desiccation and survive, provided they are later allowed contact with water. The heavy clay soil at Monks Wood frequently becomes waterlogged and this causes high mortality of pupae. In East Field, pupal mortality is also high, but the species survives probably because of the ridges in the soil left by an earlier potato crop in the field. It is likely that only those individuals which pupate on the tops of the ridges survive.

At present, Cinnabar Moth is not a species which requires management for conservation. This study has, however, some practical application, since

Table 5. Mean number of predators trapped in 50 pitfalls per day

	Weeting Heath	Monks Wood (East Field)	Monks Wood (Introduced)
Insecta. Coleoptera			
Harpalus rufipes	0·01	0·11	14·77
Harpalus rufitarsus	0·10	—	—
Harpalus brevicollis	—	—	2·89
Abax parallelopipedus	—	0·07	3·71
Feronia melanaria	0·01	0·09	14·61
Feronia cuprea	—	0·11	1·68
Amara spp.	0·05	0·09	1·09
Bembidion lampros	0·04	0·32	5·94
Notiophilus biguttatus	—	0·07	0·51
Metabletus foveatus	2·17	—	—
Trechus quadristriatus	—	0·36	2·11
Anthicus antherinus	—	—	0·08
Dermaptera			
Forficula auricularia	0·03	0·04	0·55
Crustacea Isopoda			
Armadillidium spp.	2·28	1·71	6·02
Porcellio scaber	0·15	—	—
Philoscia muscorum	0·10	21·21	2·42
Arachnida Phalangida			
Phalangium opilio	0·17	0·93	0·86
Araneida			
Oxyptila scabricula	0·18	—	—
Xysticus cristatus	0·04	4·19	0·04
Acarina			
Erythraeus phalangoides	29·99	12·92	—
	36·22	42·22	57·28

Cinnabar has been used in a number of countries as a means of controlling ragwort in pasture. These attempts at biological control have had rather limited success (Bornemissza 1966; Frick & Holloway 1964; Hawkes 1968; Wilkinson 1965). The results reported here go some way towards explaining why failures in control have occurred. Firstly, Cinnabar Moth can only build up in numbers sufficiently to defoliate the plant on areas with well-drained soil. Secondly, while overgrazing allows the moth to develop high densities, it also enables ragwort to recover, and in fact to multiply, after defoliation. Only by reducing grazing at the time of defoliation is it likely that Cinnabar will control the weed.

The effect of grazing on the persistence of Cinnabar populations is of greater relevance to the subject of this Symposium. Here we find that both under- and overgrazing may lead to extinction of the moth. Undergrazing will reduce the availability of its food and will greatly increase mortality from arthropod predators. Overgrazing, on the other hand, may lead to such violent fluctuations in number that the moth fails to survive the periodic crashes due to starvation. Size and heterogeneity of the habitat play a role in persistence. The moth would almost certainly have failed to survive at Weeting Heath in 1968 had the area been smaller, and the distribution of the plants and the moth been more even. As it was, some patches of ragwort survived long enough for a few caterpillars to complete their development.

The effects of grazing on the population dynamics of a species may be extremely complex, and its use in management for conservation is only likely to succeed if it is based on a detailed knowledge of the requirements of the species which you wish to conserve.

References

BORNEMISSZA G.F. (1966) An attempt to control ragwort in Australia with the Cinnabar Moth. *Aust. J. Zool.* **14**, 201–44.

CAMERON E. (1935) A study of the natural control of ragwort (*Senecio jacobaea* L.). *J. Ecol.* **23**, 265–322.

DEMPSTER J.P. (1960) A quantitative study of the predators on the eggs and larvae of the broom beetle, *Phytodecta olivacea* Forster, using the precipitin test. *J. Anim. Ecol.* **29**, 149–67.

DEMPSTER J.P. (in press) The population ecology of the Cinnabar Moth, *Tyria jacobaeae* L. (Lepidoptera, Arctiidae).

FRICK K.E. & HOLLOWAY J.K. (1964) Establishment of the Cinnabar Moth, *Tyria jacobaeae*, on tansy ragwort in the Western United States. *J. econ. Ent.* **57**, 152–4.

HARPER J.L. & WOOD W.A. (1957) Biological flora of the British Isles, *Senecio jacobaea* L. *J. Ecol.* **45**, 617–37.

HAWKES R.B. (1968) The Cinnabar Moth, *Tyria jacobaeae*, for control of tansy ragwort. *J. econ. Ent.* **61**, 499–501.

POOLE A.L. & CAIRNS D. (1940) Botanical aspects of ragwort (*Senecio jacobaea* L.) control. *Bull. N.Z. Dep. Scient. ind. Res.* **82**, 1–61.

WATT A.S. (1940) Studies in the ecology of Breckland, IV The grass heath. *J. Ecol.* **28**, 42–70.

WILKINSON A.T.S. (1965) Releases of Cinnabar Moth (*Hypocrita jacobaeae* L.) on tansy ragwort in British Columbia. *Proc. ent. Soc. Br. Columb.* **62**, 10–12.

The management of grassland for the conservation of invertebrate animals

M.G.MORRIS *Monks Wood Experimental Station, Abbots Ripton, Huntingdon*

Introduction

Lowland grasslands are plagioclimaxes which are maintained by one or more of a small number of factors which are often under the direct control of man. Grasslands have been important to man throughout most of his history because they support the large herbivorous mammals which man has either hunted or farmed for food. Because of their agricultural and economic importance these aspects of grassland have been studied for some time and to a large extent this work has influenced the thinking of conservationists even where the conservation of wildlife rather than agriculture has been their primary concern. Although the flora and fauna of grasslands have been perpetuated because of past land use it is equally true to say that they have been maintained in spite of such past land use. The economic quality of pasture and the relationships between pasture and grazing animals continue to be studied. Research is being done into the basic ecology of grasslands, because these aspects have importance in relation to the functioning of all ecosystems. A more recent development has been the study of the management of grassland for the conservation of wildlife. Such studies have been undertaken particularly where natural and semi-natural grasslands are under threat from changes in agricultural practice in which increasing emphasis is being placed on arable farming and intensive methods of rearing stock. Countries in which this is happening are usually those which are developed and industrialized to such a degree that resources can be expended on the conservation of wildlife. This is particularly true of areas where a consideration of the invertebrate fauna of grasslands is appropriate. It is equally true that the invertebrate fauna must be relatively well known, taxonomically and ecologically, if its consideration is to be a factor in management of grasslands for wildlife conservation. Thus in reviewing the field of grassland management for the conservation of invertebrate animals this paper draws heavily on experience in northern Europe, particularly Britain, and North America.

Management of grasslands

Grasslands may be managed or maintained by several different factors, either singly or in combination. It is of basic importance to formulate the objects of management before actually managing an area of grassland. In Britain since myxomatosis and during the period of change in farming methods it has been convenient to distinguish two types of grassland management for wildlife conservation—the *reclamation* of grassland overgrown by coarse grasses, or even scrub, and the *maintenance* of those grassland biotopes or habitats which are ecologically desirable in the eyes of the conservationist. In the former type of management it is often unnecessary to be specific about individual species or groups of species of animals and plants. On many nature reserves in Britain, particularly National Nature Reserves, a phase of reclamation management is now passing into one of indefinite maintenance of specific biotopes for the continued conservation of particular species and assemblages of species of both plants and animals.

The many different types of lowland grassland in Britain have been very unequally studied. Although particularly true of the invertebrate animals, this also applies to the plant ecology of the grasslands as well. At the present time very little is known about the invertebrate faunas of the wetter British grasslands (washes, water meadows, flood meadows, etc.), particularly in relation to management. Most ecological information relates to the dryer grasslands, among which in Britain, calcareous grasslands, especially those developed on the chalk, are known to be particularly rich, botanically (Wells 1969, quoting several authorities) as well as zoologically (Richards 1964, Duffey & Morris 1966). The dryer lowland grasslands of Britain are usually managed by burning, mowing, or grazing, in increasing order of importance. Other methods, such as rotovating or ploughing, are considerably important as methods of altering grasslands, but most interest attaches to the reversion of ploughed or rotovated grassland back to grassland, with particular emphasis on the rate at which this is achieved. Thus these methods are not generally thought of as methods of management. In any case, there appears to be little information on the effects of ploughing and rotovating on the invertebrate faunas of grassland. In some areas of high public pressure trampling of the grassland is effective in maintaining a short turf. Again, there is little information about the effects of human trampling on the invertebrate faunas of grassland, although some effects on vegetation have been considered by Streeter (this volume).

All methods of managing grassland have in common the effect of reducing the amount of plant material present in the managed area and of lowering the mean height of the vegetation. The ways in which these two effects are produced may vary considerably between the methods used. The sequence of events in time may also be different, as may the relative proportions of dead and living plant material retained under different methods of management. Other effects may be more specific to the methods used. Daubenmire (1968) has recently reviewed the ecological effects of burning grassland, while Arnold (1964) emphasizes the three primary effects of grazing—defoliation, trampling and fertilizing (dunging). Wells (this volume) has compared the effects on vegetation of sheep grazing versus mechanical cutting.

The reduction in amount of plant material and of height of vegetation on managed grassland is responsible for a complex of factors affecting the distribution and abundance of the animals there. In many cases only the effects produced have been recorded, not the precise way in which the effects have been caused. Only a few of the more readily appreciated factors in the complex produced by reducing the plant material and height of vegetation by management have been studied. For instance the important microclimatological effects on invertebrate animals of managing grasslands have been given little attention, although Waterhouse (1955) provides some important information of a general character bearing on this problem.

Effects of management on the structure of individual plant species

One effect of the reduction of plant material by management is to reduce the numbers of aerial structures of particular plant species available to specialist insect feeders, particularly monophagous species. This is particularly important since floristic changes induced by managing, or ceasing to manage, grassland, are usually slow (Wells 1969). Such floristic changes may be irrelevant or insignificant to the fauna compared with structural changes. Morris (1967) recorded some of the initial effects on some selected invertebrate species of allowing an intensively grazed grassland to grow up. He drew attention to the structural differences between plants of the same species under grazed and ungrazed conditions by reference to a hypothetical plant. More realistically, an actual example may be given, although this is based on preliminary and incomplete data (Fig. 1). At the Barton Hills, Bedfordshire, *Centaurea nigra* supports a number of more or less specialist monophagous or oligophagous invertebrate species, but only one of these has (doubtfully) been found in association with *Centaurea* rosettes on the intensively grazed grassland. The abundance of individual plants of *Centaurea*, as measured by their mean distance from a randomly-chosen sampling point, was not significantly different in the ungrazed exclosures compared with the grazed grassland. However, the structure of the plants, measured by the size of the leaves, and the dry weight of plant material produced, was significantly greater in the

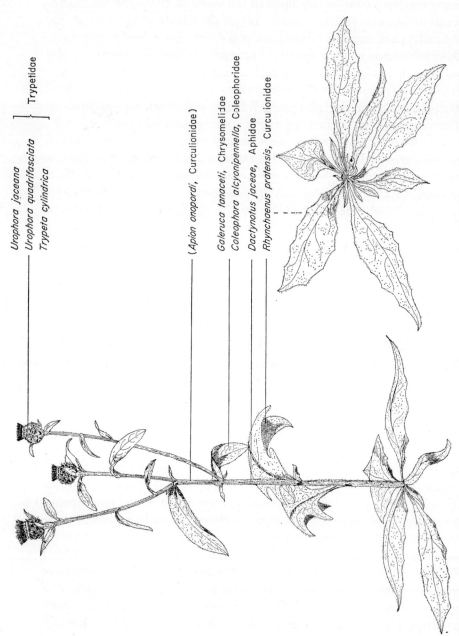

Urophora jaceana
Urophora quadrifasciata } Trypetidae
Trypeta cylindrica

(*Apion onopordi*, Curculionidae)

Galeruca tanaceti, Chrysomelidae
Coleophora alcyonipennella, Coleophoridae
Dactynotus jaceae, Aphidae
Rhynchaenus pratensis, Curculionidae

Figure 1. *Centaurea nigra* plants under ungrazed and grazed conditions, showing phytophagous invertebrates recorded (record of *Rhynchaenus pratensis* on grazed plant doubtful, that of *Apion onopordi* not based on larval record), Barton Hills, Beds.

exclosures. The mean number of leaves produced per plant was slightly, but significantly, higher on the grazed grassland. It is interesting to note that even the relatively less specialized feeders on or in the foliage were found almost exclusively on the ungrazed grassland, suggesting that for these species the overall structure of the grassland habitat may be of importance, as well as the structure of the foodplant. On the other hand, the rosette leaves of *Centaurea* plants on the grazed grassland frequently showed evidence of feeding by invertebrates, mainly molluscs, Auchenorhyncha and lepidopterous larvae. It is likely that the damage was caused by predominantly polyphagous species, though none has so far been found and identified.

The effects of cessation of management on specialist phytophagous invertebrates and their foodplants are often rapid and of considerable magnitude (Morris 1967). Succeeding phases of population development may be almost equally dramatic, such as those recorded for some species of Heteroptera (Morris 1969*a*). A better-documented series of changes in foodplant status is that of the flower production of *Campanula rotundifolia* recorded at the Barton Hills, Bedfordshire, in ungrazed exclosures and grazed control plots, in 1965 and 1966 (Morris 1967) and in succeeding years. The mean populations per

Table 1. Mean calculated total production of *Campanula rotundifolia* flowers in o·1 ha. plots, Barton Hills, Bedfordshire

	Grazed	Ungrazed
1965	915	27562
1966	5002	39785
1967	16502	8557
1968	3185	557
1969	2425	2541

plot (two plots per treatment) in each year since 1965, the year of exclosure, are given in Table 1. In the exclosures the initial flush of flowers in 1965 was maintained and increased in 1966 but in 1967 production fell considerably. In 1968 flowers were extremely scarce, but there was a slight but significant recovery in 1969. The causes of this recovery in 1969 are obscure, but may be related to the more tussocky and uneven nature of the ungrazed grassland in that year, or perhaps to mole activity in providing open ground for *Campanula rotundifolia* to colonize. The numbers of flowers in each of the ungrazed plots in 1968 and 1969 were very consistent. Table 1 also shows the variation in numbers of flowers produced each year on the grazed control plots. These differences can be attributed to the grazing pressure before and during the flowering period. In 1965 the exclosure of the ungrazed plots had the effect of concentrating the population of *Miarus campanulae*, a weevil feeding in the larval stage in the seed capsules of *C. rotundifolia*, within them, larvae being about 100 times more numerous per unit area in the exclosures than in the grazed control plots, in response to the far greater number of seed capsules there (Morris 1967). Since 1965, the year of fencing off the ungrazed plots, the rate of infestation of *Campanula rotundifolia* seed capsules by *Miarus campanulae* has always been greater in the exclosures than in the grazed plots (Table 2). Infestation has been highest when small numbers of capsules were available for oviposition, and vice versa.

Table 2. Mean % infestation of *Miarus campanulae* per seed capsule of *Campanula rotundifolia*, Barton Hills, Bedfordshire

	Grazed	Ungrazed
1965	17·3	11·5
1966	3·1	8·9
1967	11·1	31·4
1968	19·7	66·7
1969	36·2	51·9

Some plants under managed conditions may not fail to flower, but may produce smaller numbers of flowers on shorter inflorescences. Although there is no research which shows that these effects are critical for any actual invertebrate species, work done on populations of *Primula veris* at the Barton Hills, Bedfordshire, shows the type of differential effect on plant populations growing in grazed and ungrazed grassland. At this site flowers of *P. veris* are the preferred food of the adults of the weevils *Phyllobius viridicollis* and *P. parvulus*, although these species are normally regarded as polyphagous. Total populations of flowers could not be calculated but counts were made and inflorescences measured on phenologically similar dates in each year. A progressive increase in mean height of inflorescences on the ungrazed plots was recorded (Table 3) and the mean number of flowers per inflorescence was also greater. Presumably the increased height of the inflorescences is a response to the general increase in vegetation height on the ungrazed plots.

It is important to appreciate that the effects of management, or of ceasing to manage, grassland, influence different plant species at very different rates. Wells (1969) states that after cessation of grazing all annuals and the low-growing perennials are eliminated after about four years, although some broad-leaved herbs are able to compete successfully with grasses. Some species, such as *Centaurea nigra* appear to be structurally most diverse in the older types of grassland and to persist unless closed-canopy scrub dominates an area. If grassland-scrub-woodland be regarded as a successional continuum

Table 3. *Primula veris:* means per 0·1 ha plot, one sampling date in each year

| | Number of inflorescences | | Height of inflorescences (cm) | |
	Grazed	Ungrazed	Grazed	Ungrazed
1966	295	1460	6·5	12·0
1967	263	681	4·5	13·2
1968	161	956	5·9	16·7
1969	4	1623	5·0	22·0

| | Number of flowers | | Flowers/inflorescence | |
	Grazed	Ungrazed	Grazed	Ungrazed
1966	645	4756	2·2	3·3
1967	324	2088	1·2	3·1
1968	—	3307	—	3·5
1969	5	8547	1·4	5·3

then clearly the maturity and maximum structural diversity of different species will be achieved at very different points of time in the succession.

Effects of management on overall structure of the vegetation

The effects of management, or the lack of it, on populations of phytophagous insects restricted to particular structures of single plant species are relatively easily observed and understood. Many differences in the occurrence of populations of more generalized plant feeders and predacious species on managed and unmanaged grassland have a complex cause, but may be thought of as being mediated through the general structure of the vegetation. It is not always easy to distinguish monophagous and oligophagous species from polyphagous ones, while in many groups of animals species with different kinds of feeding habits are found. The representation of any taxonomic group of phytophagous animals on managed and unmanaged grassland can be thought of as being caused by differences in overall vegetation structure, since the foodplants of the different animal species together make up the vegetation. The importance of vegetation structure to predacious species of invertebrate has long been recognized and forms the basis for the classification of 'animal habitats' of Elton & Miller (1954). An example is the spider fauna of limestone grassland described by Duffey (1962a, b).

A recent extensive survey of the Auchenorhyncha (Hemiptera; leaf-hoppers) of limestone grassland sites in Britain, using a 'vacuum net' apparatus (Dietrick 1961), suggests that there is in general a relationship between the height of grassland vegetation and the numbers of animals inhabiting it, at least in certain taxonomic groups. The importance of stratification in determining the composition and abundance of leafhopper faunas in meadows was shown by Andrzejewska (1965). Prior to the survey leafhopper numbers had been studied on the grazed and ungrazed chalk grassland plots at the Barton Hills, Bedfordshire (Morris 1971). Here, two samples of 2 m² of grassland were taken from each plot at fortnightly intervals from 1 June to 7 November 1967 and 5 April 1968 to 25 March 1969. From these it was clear that most species of chalk grassland leaf hoppers are in the adult stage during the period July to September, so that this period was chosen for the extensive sampling from limestone sites. The work at the Barton Hills compared intensively sheep-grazed grassland with grassland where management had ceased for about $2\frac{1}{2}$ to 4 years. The numbers of species and adult individuals recorded are much greater in the exclosures than on the grazed controls (Table 4). Of the 45 species recorded two were more numerous on the grazed

Table 4. Numbers of species (*S*) and adult individuals (*N*) in 2 m² samples from experimental plots, Barton Hills, Bedfordshire. Means of six sampling dates July–September, per plot

| | Grazed | | Ungrazed | |
	N	*S*	*N*	*S*
1967	35·3	7·0	255·8	17·2
1968	31·8	6·0	621·6	18·4

plots and 22 more abundant in the exclosures, though these differences could not always be attributed to the treatments statistically. For each sample a value for species diversity was calculated, using the Brillouin index based on information theory and given by

$$D = \frac{1}{N} \log_2 \frac{N!}{N_1!N_2!N_3!\ldots N_s!}$$

where *N* is the total number of individuals and N_1, N_2, $N_3 \ldots N_s$ are the numbers of individuals of species 1, 2, 3…s in the sample (Margalef 1958, Pielou 1967). The diversity of leafhopper samples on the grazed grassland is zero during the winter months, because no species overwinters in the adult stage there, and rises rapidly from early June to reach a maximum in late August; from this values of *D* decline rapidly to zero by December. In the exclosures diversity is maintained at a value greater than 1 for most of the winter by species, mainly Typhlocybinae, which overwinter there as adults. Diversity increases from April–May onwards and reaches a maximum in September, falling to its winter level by December. At all times of the year diversity is greater on the ungrazed grassland than on the grazed. The relationship between *N*, *S* and *D* is not entirely simple and in some cases at least a direct measure of *S*, the total number of species present or breeding in a nature reserve or other area is a more readily appreciated index to its biological interest. The value of indices of diversity in management research, and the choice of indices to be used, have been discussed by Morris (1971).

Of the limestone grassland sites sampled during the extensive survey (1968–70) only the samples from chalk grassland sites have been fully identified and processed. Each sample was taken from 2 m^2 of grassland, to conform to the standard samples taken at the Barton Hills. Figure 2 shows the approxi-

Figure 2. Sampling sites for Auchenorhyncha: each figure indicates a site, its magnitude the number of samples taken. X indicates the Barton Hills, Beds. (reference site). Chalk outcrop stippled except where overlain by drift (shaded).

mate location of the sites, each number showing its geographic position and the number of samples taken. X represents the location of the Barton Hills, samples from which have been used as a basis of reference for the whole survey. The sites included were those which were potentially 'elite' grade 1 or 2 sites in the 'Reserves Review' conducted by the Nature Conservancy in 1968–9. Most of these sites are in Wiltshire, which contains most of the large areas of chalk grassland extant today, but the survey covered the entire chalk outcrop except for those parts, principally in East Anglia, where the chalk is overlain by pleistocene drift deposits. Some samples, not included in Fig. 1, had to be omitted because of insufficient ancillary information relating to the site.

Figures 3–5 show the values of *N*, *S* and *D* respectively plotted against mean vegetation height for each sample. Vegetation was measured to the nearest 5 cm, except for the shorter swards which were measured to the nearest 2–3 cm. For *N*, *S* and *D* there are highly significant correlations between increasing vegetation height and increasing values, and linear regression lines have been calculated for each on vegetation height. From inspection of Figs 3–5 it is evident that values of *N* (in particular) are lower than expected for samples taken from grassland 30 cm and more in height. It is quite possible that the actual relationship of *N* (and *S* and *D*) to vegetation height is non-linear, but an alternative explanation is that the sampling efficiency of the vacuum net is poorer for the taller grasslands than for the

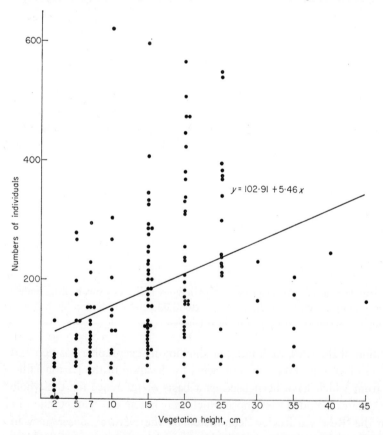

$$y = 102 \cdot 91 + 5 \cdot 46 \, x$$

Figure 3. Numbers of individuals (*N*) of Auchenorhyncha in samples, plotted against vegetation height, with linear regression equation for numbers on vegetation height.

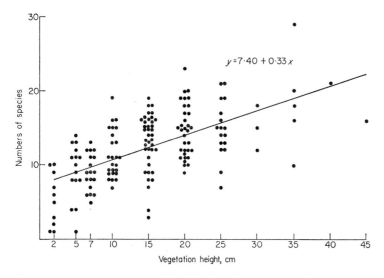

Figure 4. Numbers of species (*S*) of Auchenorhyncha in samples, plotted against vegetation height, with linear regression equation for number of species on vegetation height.

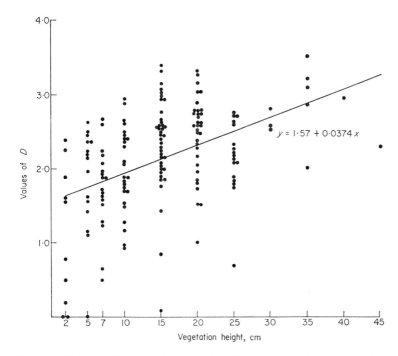

Figure 5. Values of *D* (see text) for samples of Auchenorhyncha plotted against vegetation height, with linear regression equation for *D* on vegetation height.

shorter. This point needs to be investigated. As all the samples were taken in July, August or September the samples taken in each month were plotted separately. No outstanding differences between months were found, although values of S and D tended to be uniformly slightly higher in August than in July or September. No distinction has been drawn at this stage between the methods of management which have maintained the vegetation at the different sites at their particular heights. However, most of the swards 2 cm high were heavily trampled by people. It will be noted that values of N, S and D for these swards tend to be lower than would be expected from the regression equation.

Of the other animals taken in the samples only the Heteroptera (Hemiptera) and Curculionoidea (Coleoptera; weevils) were identified. Regression lines for N, S and D on vegetation height for these two groups have not been calculated but Figs 6–8 (Heteroptera) and 9–11 (Curculionoidea) show that in general there are similar correlations between these parameters and height of the vegetation. In the case of the Curculionoidea fewer species and individuals appear to be present in the taller grasslands (30 cm tall and over). This is probably because weevils are feeders on herbs rather than grasses.

Although it is usually possible to measure the mean height of a grassland sward in fact such swards are nearly always mixtures of vegetation of different heights. In its extreme form 'patchiness' is an ecological problem which has long been recognized (e.g. Elton & Miller 1954). One extreme form of patchiness in grassland is the formation of tussocks. Luff (1965) has described the

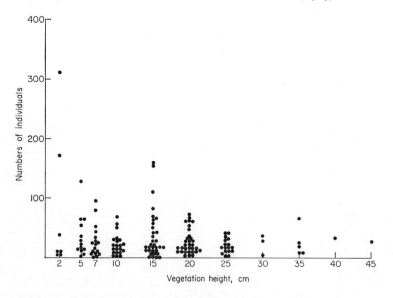

Figure 6. Numbers of individuals (N) of Heteroptera in samples plotted against vegetation height.

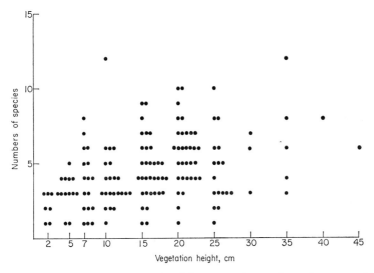

Figure 7. Numbers of species (*S*) of Heteroptera in samples against vegetation height.

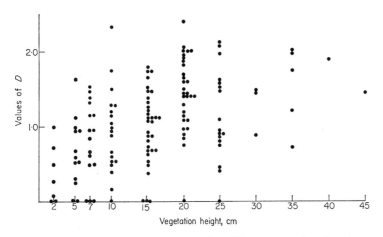

Figure 8. Values of *D* (see text) for samples of Heteroptera plotted against vegetation height.

morphology of *Dactylis glomerata* tussocks; and he has shown (1966) that the coleopterous faunas of such tussocks and the grass cover between them are similar, and that although the density of beetles in tussocks is greater than that in the grass between them, even in winter tussocks contain less than half the total coleopterous fauna of a rough grassland. This may well be because the grassland between tussocks was itself relatively tall. In samples taken over the course of one year three times as many beetles were found in ungrazed grassland as on short, intensively grazed chalk grassland (Morris

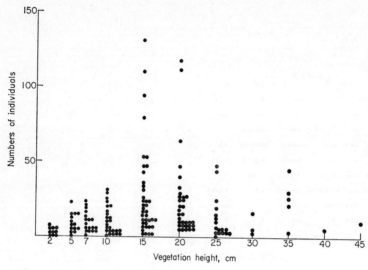

Figure 9. Numbers of individuals (*N*) of Curculionoidea in samples plotted against vegetation height.

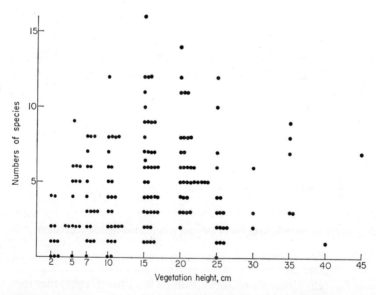

Figure 10. Numbers of species (*S*) of Curculionoidea in samples plotted against vegetation height.

1968). The differences between treatments were especially marked in winter, being indeed reversed for some of the summer samples (Fig. 11). 125 species were recorded, of which 20 were found only on the grazed plots and 57 on the ungrazed. The importance of tussocks or of any small patches of longer

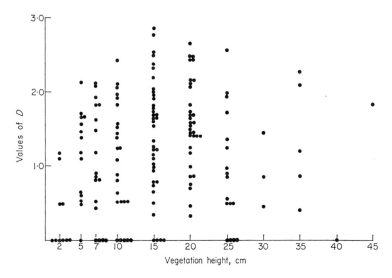

Figure 11. Values of *D* (see text) for samples of Curculionoidea plotted against vegetation height.

vegetation would seem to be greatest where the general height of the vegetation is very low.

Specific effects of different management methods

Burning

The burning of grassland is an important means of natural maintenance and of management by man in N. America, Africa and other parts of the world (Daubenmire 1968). In Britain, burning ('swaling') grassland is a traditional form of management in the West, on oolitic limestone sites, and on acid upland grasslands as a concomitant to 'muirburn', the management of ericaceous plant communities by fire (Grant *et al.* 1963). Few studies have been made on the effects of burning grassland on populations of invertebrate animals. Crawford & Harwood (1964) studied the effects of burning on lepidopterous larvae, particularly 'webworms' (Crambidae) in Washington and recorded a fifteenfold reduction in numbers on burned plots compared with unburned ones, though burning did not invariably reduce the size of the population. It was suggested that most of the mortality was indirect, fire destroying litter in the grassland and thus exposing larvae to the rigours of overwintering under relatively open conditions. Tester & Marshall (1961) studied the effects of burning at two different times of the year and of grazing on numbers of Orthoptera and Coleoptera. No identifications were made below the level of order and sweepnet samples were used to determine differences in numbers between treatments. Individuals of both orders were found to be more numerous on plots with sparse litter than on those treatments with deep litter. Taxonomically more precise data combined with more effective methods of assessing differences between treatments are required before these results can be accepted as confirmed.

Mowing

Rather more information is available about the effects of mowing or cutting on populations of invertebrate animals than about the effects of burning. Some species of invertebrates, such as the leafhopper *Macrosteles laevis*, seem to be well adapted to exploit cut and other disturbed grasslands quickly after treatment (Andrzejewska 1962). Southwood & Jepson (1962) have shown that in general 'short' grasslands are more productive of *Oscinella frit* and related species of Chloropidae (Diptera) than 'long' grasslands, the treatment applied to most of their experimental areas being mowing. It would be interesting to know to what degree disturbance caused by large ground-living invertebrates reduces oviposition in long grassland, since Jones (1968) reported that such disturbance was significant in reducing oviposition in the laboratory. Southwood & van Emden (1967) found more animals on cut grassland than on uncut, although biomass was generally slightly greater on the uncut grassland. For many taxonomic groups, e.g. Araneae (spiders), Acarina (mites), Collembola, Homoptera and Coleoptera, more individuals were found on the cut grassland than on the uncut, although in nearly all these groups, and others, the differences between treatments were small.

It is of considerable importance to determine why these results differ from those of other authors working on grasslands which have been managed by different methods, usually grazing, but which have essentially conformed to the 'short' versus 'long' grasslands into which cut and uncut grasslands can be classified. Some of the differences, both of vegetation height and of age of the different grasslands, between these studies of cut grasslands and his own work on grazed and ungrazed grasslands were discussed by Morris (1968). Cutting differs from grazing in a number of respects, but as far as defoliation is concerned the chief difference is in the non-selectivity of the mowing machine and the fact that it produces a sward of uniform height, whereas grazing is selective and, unless very intensive, produces a 'patchy' vegetation. There is an urgent need for these factors to be examined and for the effects of cutting to be re-assessed, particularly in comparison to grazing as an alternative method of management. At the present time it appears possible that cutting a grassland may have rather different effects on its invertebrate fauna than grazing it.

Grazing

Because grazing is the most usual form of grassland management in Britain there is rather more information relating to it than to other forms of management, and this includes the effects on invertebrate animals. The most obvious difference between grazing on the one hand and mowing and burning on the other is the presence of the grazing animal. Although almost no work has been done on the contribution that invertebrate animals associated with large herbivores and their products make to the total fauna of grazed grassland this contribution must clearly be very considerable. Morris (1969*b*) discusses this in general terms, suggesting that four types of invertebrate animal can be distinguished, those associated with the living grazing animal, with carrion, with dung, and with discarded fur and wool. Of these the dung-inhabiting animals (mainly Coleoptera and Diptera) probably make the greatest contribution to the diversity and variety of the grassland fauna, but the magnitude of this is not known, nor are the details and importance of successional effects within dung. There is also no information on whether natural and semi-natural grasslands have a different dung fauna from leys and improved pastures.

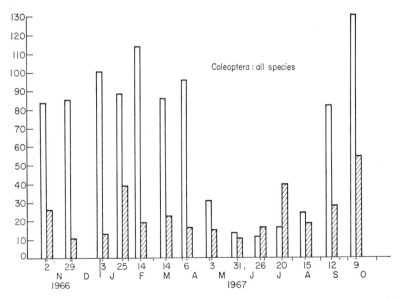

Figure 12. Mean numbers of Coleoptera recorded in turf samples (0·29 m² per plot) on grazed (shaded columns) and ungrazed (open columns) grassland, Barton Hills, Beds.

The other main specific effects of grazing as distinct from other methods of management are its selectivity and the effects of trampling by grazing animals. Selectivity is clearly likely to operate against invertebrate animals associated with particularly palatable plants, but there is as yet no evidence to show that this is so. Selectivity tends to produce patchy vegetation in a grazed situation, although under intensively grazed conditions such patchiness is not usually well developed. The production of patchy vegetation is probably one of the most important features of grazing in distinction to other forms of management, particularly in those areas where rotational grazing is not practised.

Trampling by grazing animals compacts the surface of the soil and tends to produce a uniform soil surface, which on a small scale is less undulating and uneven than the surface of an ungrazed grassland. Both types of surface are probably important to different animals. Many Orthoptera oviposit in compacted soil (Richards & Waloff 1954, Dempster 1963), while burrowing invertebrates are more likely to be found on the more friable surface of an ungrazed grassland. The other important effect of trampling is to break up the litter layer of the grassland. From a botanical point of view the accumulation of litter tends to reduce the diversity and interest of the chalk grassland flora (Wells 1969); but there are many litter-dwelling invertebrate animals. The resolution of different methods of approach is an important part of research into management for wildlife conservation.

The effects on invertebrates of disturbance or interference by grazing animals have received no attention, but should be investigated, since Jones (1968) has shown that disturbance by large beetles is an important factor in reducing oviposition by *Oscinella frit* on oats in the laboratory. If disturbance on this scale is significant it could well be that the movements of grazing animals through relatively tall grassland could reduce oviposition or other activities even though defoliation of the grassland were slight and not significant.

Other methods

Disturbance by large mammals is also a possible factor in grassland which is 'managed' by the trampling of human beings. Generally such trampling is thought of as having an important effect only when the vegetation is beginning to be worn down. As with so many other aspects of management for wildlife conservation, more research is needed.

As stated earlier, when grassland is ploughed most interest attaches to its reversion to grassland, since ploughing is not generally regarded as a suitable method of management. Experience in some areas suggests that not infrequently rotovating or ploughing of established grassland produces stands of tall herbs, often of weed species, rather than the desired pioneer grassland communities. Individual site characteristics are important here. The invertebrate animals associated with both pioneer communities and with areas of tall herbs are of interest to the conservationist but the treatment of such vegetation, or even whether to retain it at all, may be decided by other considerations.

Seasonal effects of management

In considering populations of invertebrate animals it is clear that the effects of a particular treatment applied at one time of year will seldom be equivalent to the same treatment applied at a different time of year. Traditionally, most methods of managing grassland are applied at particular times of the year because they have been derived from agricultural practices which have had nothing consciously to do with wildlife conservation. Thus mowing (for hay) tends to be done in early summer, and burning in late autumn or spring when the vegetation is neither full of sap (and being grazed) nor sodden with winter rain. Grazing has normally been practised at all times of year because stock has to be fed throughout the whole twelve-month period, although frequently stock are taken under cover during the winter and fed on hay. In reclamation management sheep have often been put onto grassland in winter in order to reduce quantities of coarse grasses because in summer with more palatable pasture available these coarse grasses would have been ignored.

If management treatments are applied annually it is inevitable that effects will be produced on populations of most invertebrate animals. Thus summer grazing will reduce the numbers of floral and other aerial structures in particular plant species and will lower the general height of the vegetation, while winter grazing will interfere with overwintering populations of animals. The conservationist needs to be able to recommend a particular time of year for treatment, if an annual treatment must be applied, and to demonstrate the effects of management at different times of the year on actual species of invertebrate animal, the representation of species in particular taxonomic groups, and, if possible, on animal communities.

Some preliminary results have been obtained from sampling invertebrate animals from chalk grassland plots grazed for exactly three months in each year at Aston Rowant National Nature Reserve, Oxon. This is a field experiment replicated once in which the zoological sampling is complementary to the primary study of the floristic changes induced in the vegetation by seasonal grazing. Standard samples, using a vacuum net, from 2 m² of grassland have been taken at six-weekly intervals from each plot and from two lightly and irregularly grazed areas which have served as controls. Thus samples have been taken at the beginning, end and mid-point of each grazing period. Because each plot is grazed at a different time of year the results should be examined for all treatments at each of the four seasons. It is more convenient and concise, however, as far as the representation of species within taxonomic groups is concerned, to compare autumn (October–December) and winter (January–March) grazing with spring (April–June) and summer (July–September) grazing. As has been stated previously, faunas of Auchenorhyncha reach their maximum numbers of adult individuals and species about mid-August. Samples taken at this time in two years show that mean species representation (S) is greater on autumn and winter grazed plots than on spring and summer grazed plots (Table 5). The mean number of individuals

Table 5. Mean values of number of individuals (N), number of species (S) and diversity (D) for samples of Auchenorhyncha from seasonally grazed plots

	N	S	D
13 August 1968			
Autumn and winter	224·0	16·8	2·62
Spring and summer	102·0	11·5	2·51
13 August 1969			
Autumn and winter	450·5	17·3	2·61
Spring and summer	220·0	16·0	2·78
'Control'	786·5	20·0	2·81
24 February 1970			
Autumn and winter	0·3	0·3	0·00
Spring and summer	7·5	1·3	0·20
'Control'	118·0	3·5	1·17

per sample on the spring and summer grazed plots is half that recorded on the other plots. On the other hand, diversity was slightly higher in 1969, slightly lower in 1968. Higher mean values of N, S and D were recorded on the 'control' plots than on the treated ones. In mid-winter numbers of Auchenorhyncha were so low that the values of N, S and D are scarcely meaningful. Diversity was zero on all treated plots except one. Thus grassland grazed for only three months of the year appears to be unsuitable for overwintering adult Auchenorhyncha, and long grass appears to be important in supporting populations of these species. In general the Heteroptera and Curculionoidea showed similar patterns of occurrence as the Auchenorhyncha (Table 6), but they were less abundant at all times of year.

As most invertebrate animals are highly mobile the interplay of the populations of the plots as grazing takes place on each in turn is important in assessing the results of an experiment such as has been described. If seasonal grazing treatments were applied uniformly to large areas of grassland very different results might be obtained from those recorded at Aston Rowant, where the populations of those plots not being grazed at any one time can be reservoirs for re-colonization of plots where grazing has just finished. In the experiment described here it is likely that there will always be a tendency

Table 6. *Mean number of species (S) in samples of Heteroptera and Curculionoidea from seasonally grazed plots*

	Heteroptera	Curculionoidea
13 August 1968		
Autumn and winter	4·0	3·5
Spring and summer	1·8	1·8
13 August 1969		
Autumn and winter	6·0	4·3
Spring and summer	2·8	2·5
'Control'	8·5	5·0
24 February 1970		
Autumn and winter	1·0	0·5
Spring and summer	0·0	0·5
'Control'	1·5	1·5

for the populations of different species to even out on those plots where grazing is not taking place. It may be expected that the results described as being caused by the treatments would be accentuated in situations where one seasonal treatment was applied over the whole of an area.

An exception to the 'evening out' process surmised above is afforded by the leafhopper *Zygina scutellaris*, which overwinters in the adult state. Samples were taken from May 1969 to February 1970 and the numbers of *Z. scutellaris* recorded have been presented as if they had been taken from January to November in a single year (Fig. 13). *Z. scutellaris* was most abundant in those

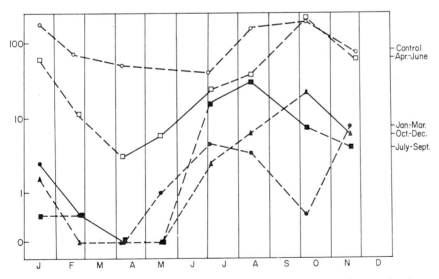

Figure 13. Numbers of *Zygina scutellaris* taken in samples from seasonally grazed and 'control' plots, Aston Rowant, Oxon.

samples taken from the 'control' grassland plots. On the plots grazed in summer, in autumn and in winter numbers were low and fell to zero during the winter. The numbers recorded on the spring-grazed plots were closer to the 'control' grassland populations, with numbers high in autumn, falling steeply during the winter and, surprisingly, rising during the period of grazing. Although these results are preliminary and their explanation tentative the trend seems to be clear cut and is presumably to be explained in terms of the interaction between the grazing periods and the life-history of the species (which has not been studied in detail). However, it is not entirely clear from the numbers recorded that this is so; although numbers generally fell during a period of grazing they did not always do so.

The development of management systems

The aim of research into management for wildlife conservation is to produce a scientific basis for the most effective conservation of animals and plants and the communities and ecosystems of which they form part. Using this scientific basis a technology will be developed for practical conservation. Research is orientated particularly towards conservation in nature reserves because these areas are those whose *primary* function is the conservation of wildlife and may be regarded as those places where the details of an ultimately complex technology can be put into operation. On other areas wildlife conservation may be of importance, but is usually only secondary to other kinds of land-use, and on such areas a much simpler, more traditional technology, derived at closer hand from agricultural practice, is likely to be appropriate.

There is no inherently right or wrong way to manage a nature reserve or any other area of grassland. The aptness of any method of management must be related to the objects of management for any particular site. The formulation of objects of management is the first important operation in the management of any reserve and is often the most difficult. In most cases it will be necessary to distinguish between primary and secondary objects and to assess priorities. Only when objects of management have been formulated can results of scientific management research be applied in the practical managing of a reserve. The more detail which can be included in the objects of management the better. The more general and vague the objects of management are the simpler and less specialized need the methods of management be to realize them. It is wasteful of scientific resources, effort and opportunities if the most important nature reserve is managed in exactly the same way as the nearest similar piece of land managed for a different purpose from wildlife conservation.

Objects of management on many reserves have been formulated in respect of reclamation, but where this has been achieved they should now be revised to give guidance for the maintenance of the biological interest and importance of the reserve. It has usually been possible to reclaim grassland from an overgrown state, or from scrub, without any detailed consideration of actual species of animals and plants. Such an approach is hardly possible in the 'maintenance and development' stage of management.

Most objects of management refer to the biological interest of a reserve either in general terms or in relation to particular species or communities. The general principles to be followed for the conservation of the richness of the floristics of calcareous grassland vegetation are fairly well known (Wells 1965, 1969). The concept that grassland is a plagioclimax and that its interest is maintained by management is an oversimplification, even in strictly botanical terms, as Wells (1969) points out. When animals, associations of animals, and animal communities are also considered the oversimplification is even grosser. Because in so many ecosystems the functionally important animal and plant species are so few it is sometimes forgotten that a major feature of nearly all ecosystems is the enormous number of species of animals and plants which are characteristic of them.

It is to be expected that only some reserves will have as one of their primary objects of management the specific maintenance of populations of named invertebrate species. In most reserves, however, the perpetuation of a rich invertebrate fauna will be a secondary object of management. Many of the effects of management described in this paper are examples of what may happen to species populations under certain circumstances, and as such are a guide to the management of other species populations where no better indications exist. Not all the actual species mentioned are important for conservation, but they provide examples of the ways in which species with similar life-histories and other characteristics may be affected.

Figure 14 is an idealized representation of the vegetation succession from pioneer communities to forest climax and grassland plagioclimax with representations of various systems of management. In general terms the botanical interest of lowland grassland is restricted to a small part of the succession and may be maintained by annual management, or by reclamation followed by annual management. The zoological interest of grassland extends over a far longer part of the succession, from the short grass communities maintained by grazing or other management, through the long coarse grassland stage into the mature scrub stage. It is probably theoretically possible to maintain coarse grassland and scrub communities by management, but this is not necessary, as there are already more than enough areas of both types of community. It is easy to clear these communities completely and start the succession afresh.

This starting afresh at an earlier successional stage is a feature of rotational regimes of management. In earlier papers (Morris 1967, 1969*a*, *b*) rotational grazing was recommended as being the best method of preserving and

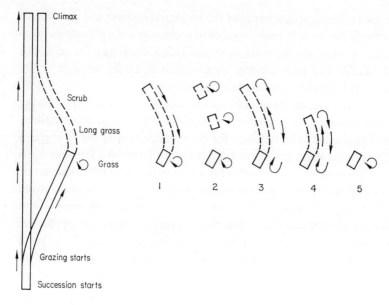

Figure 14. Diagrammatic representation of natural and managed successions on grassland: 1, reclamation of coarse grassland and scrub followed by annual management; 2, theoretical management of short grass, long grass and scrub; 3, management of short grass, long grass and scrub (long rotation); 4, management of short and long grass (short rotation); 5, annual management. (Arrows indicate direction of change.)

enhancing faunal richness on nature reserves. Essentially, rotational grazing regimes maintain longer parts of the 'natural' succession in a reserve than can be maintained by regular annual or continuous management (Fig. 14), and they maintain different successional stages simultaneously in time. It is important to have these different stages of the rotation present on a reserve at any one time, since otherwise some species and associations of species might not be represented. In theory rotations could be of considerable duration and could include scrub or even woodland. In practice a short rotation (about three years) and a longer one (about 10 years) are probably adequate on a strictly grassland reserve. Although grazing has been specified, other methods of management may be used in rotational management regimes. There is no reason to think that either burning or mowing is ineffective in producing an interesting succession of invertebrate animals.

On reserves where rotational management cannot be practised it may be necessary to decide on a particular form of seasonal management, or a regime of light management may be put into operation. It is probably easy to diversify and enrich the invertebrate faunas even of intensively grazed sites by providing quite small, portable exclosures to ensure the production of even a very small quantity of taller grassland. It is probable that if rotational grazing regimes of management are increasingly adopted, much less permanent fencing will be required in nature reserves and much larger quantities of temporary and movable fencing will be used. The dynamic nature of reserve management needs to be emphasized. It is also possible that machinery will be developed specifically for the management of nature reserves. On dry grassland reserves this would probably take the form of specialized mowing machines.

Acknowledgements

It is a pleasure to thank my colleagues Drs E.Duffey, Lena Ward and J.Sheail and Messrs T.C.E. and D.A.Wells for much stimulating discussion about grassland management problems. I am indebted to very many owners and occupiers of chalk grassland sites for permission to undertake research or collect samples from their land, and I am equally indebted to many Regional Officers and other members of the Conservation Branch of the Nature Conservancy for obtaining such permission. Many people have assisted with field and laboratory work and in the preparation of this paper and I would like to thank particularly Miss S.Murrell and Mr G.S.Tew.

References

ANDRZEJEWSKA L. (1962) *Macrosteles laevis* Rib. as an unsettlement index of natural meadow associations of Homoptera. *Bull. Acad. pol. Sci. Cl. II. Ser. Sci. biol.* **10**, 221–6.

ANDRZEJEWSKA L. (1965) Stratification and its dynamics in meadow communities of Auchenorhyncha (Homoptera). *Ekol. pol.* (A) **13**, 685–715.

ARNOLD G.W. (1964) Factors within plant associations affecting the behaviour and performance of grazing animals. In *Grazing in terrestrial and marine environments.* (Ed. D.J.Crisp, 133–54, Oxford.

CRAWFORD C.S. & HARWOOD R.F. (1964) Bionomics and control of insects affecting Washington grass seed fields. *Tech. Bull. agric. Exp. Stn Wash. St.* **44**, 25 pp.

DAUBENMIRE R. (1968) Ecology of fire in grasslands. *Adv. ecol. Res.* **5**, 209–66.

DEMPSTER J.P. (1963) The population dynamics of grasshoppers and locusts. *Biol. Rev.* **38**, 490–529.

DIETRICK E.J. (1961) An improved backpack motor fan for suction sampling of insect populations. *J. econ. Ent.* **54**, 394–5.

DUFFEY E. (1962*a*) A population study of spiders in limestone grassland. The field-layer fauna. *Oikos* **13**, 15–34.

DUFFEY E. (1962*b*) A population study of spiders in limestone grassland. Description of study area, sampling methods, and population characteristics. *J. Anim. Ecol.* **31**, 571–99.

DUFFEY E. & MORRIS M.G. (1966) The invertebrate fauna of the chalk and its scientific interest. *Handbk a. Rep. Soc. Promot. Nat. Reserves* 1966, 83–94.

ELTON C.S. & MILLER R.S. (1954) The ecological survey of animal communities with a practical system of classifying habitats by structural characters. *J. Ecol.* **42**, 460–96.

GRANT S.A., HUNTER R.F. & CROSS C. (1963) The effects of muirburning *Molinia*-dominant communities. *J. Br. Grassld Soc.* **18**, 249–57.

JONES M.G. (1968) The effect of moving carabids on oviposition by frit fly (*Oscinella frit* L.). *Entomologist's mon. Mag.* **104**, 85–7.

LUFF M.L. (1965) The morphology and microclimate of *Dactylis glomerata* tussocks. *J. Ecol.* **53**, 771–87.

LUFF M.L. (1966) The abundance and diversity of the beetle fauna of grass tussocks. *J. Anim. Ecol.* **35**, 189–208.

MARGALEF R. (1958) (trans. W. Hall) Information theory in ecology. *Gen. Syst.* **3**, 36–71.

MORRIS M.G. (1967) Differences between the invertebrate faunas of grazed and ungrazed chalk grassland. I. Responses of some phytophagous insects to cessation of grazing. *J. appl. Ecol.* **4**, 459–74.

MORRIS M.G. (1968) Differences between the invertebrate faunas of grazed and ungrazed chalk grassland. II. The faunas of sample turves. *J. appl. Ecol.* **5**, 601–11.

MORRIS M.G. (1969a) Differences between the invertebrate faunas of grazed and ungrazed chalk grassland. III. The heteropterous fauna. *J. appl. Ecol.* **6**, 475–87.

MORRIS M.G. (1969b) Populations of invertebrate animals and the management of chalk grassland in Britain. *Biol. Conserv.* **1**, 225–31.

MORRIS M.G. (1971) Differences between the invertebrate faunas of grazed and ungrazed chalk grassland. IV. Abundance and diversity of Homoptera-Auchenorhyncha, *J. appl. Ecol.* **8**, 37–52.

PIELOU E.C. (1967) The use of information theory in the study of the diversity of biological populations. *Proc. Berkeley Symp. math. Statist. Probab.* **5**, 163–77.

RICHARDS O.W. (1964) The entomological fauna of southern England, with special reference to the country around London. *Trans. Soc. Br. Ent.* **16**, 1–47.

RICHARDS O.W. & WALOFF N. (1954) Studies on the biology and population dynamics of British grasshoppers. *Anti-Locust Bull.* **17**, 182 pp.

SOUTHWOOD T.R.E. & VAN EMDEN H.F. (1967) A comparison of the fauna of cut and uncut grasslands. *Z. angew. Ent.* **60**, 188–98.

SOUTHWOOD T.R.E. & JEPSON W.F. (1962) The productivity of grasslands in England for *Oscinella frit* (L). (Chloropidae) and other stem-boring Diptera. *Bull. ent. Res.* **53**, 395–407.

TESTER J.R. & MARSHALL W.H. (1961) A study of certain plant and animal interrelations on a native prairie in northwestern Minnesota. *Occ. Pap. Univ. Minn. Mus. nat. Hist.* **8**, 51 pp.

WATERHOUSE F.L. (1955) Microclimatological profiles in grass cover in relation to biological problems. *Q. Jl R. met. Soc.* **81**, 63–71.

WELLS T.C.E. (1965) Chalk grassland nature reserves and their management problems, *Handbk a. Rep. Soc. Promot. Nat. Reserves* 1965, 62–70.

WELLS T.C.E. (1969) Botanical aspects of conservation management of chalk grasslands, *Biol. Conserv.* **2**, 36–44.

Part 7
Management Policy and Practical Problems of Conservation

The size and surroundings of nature reserves

M.D.HOOPER *The Nature Conservancy, Monks Wood Experimental Station, Abbots Ripton, Huntingdon*

A variety of criteria for the selection of Nature Reserves, the assessment of the relative importance of sites, or even the evaluation of wildlife resources in terms of monetary values have been suggested in the past. Sometimes there has been an explicit listing of the suggested criteria, as for example by Holdgate (1970), sometimes the criteria are implicit as for example in the list of proposed Reserves for England and Wales in Cmd 7122 (Anon. 1947) and in N.W.Moore's work on the Dorset Heaths (Moore 1962).

Two criteria, the extent of the site and variety of species occurring within it, are common to all lists but the way in which both area and diversity criteria are to be applied is sometimes confused. Holdgate (1970) requires reserves to be of sufficient extent to be invulnerable but suggests that sites which are vulnerable should become reserves. He also uses the word diversity to indicate a number of ecosystems on one site rather than the more usual relationship between numbers of species and individuals. Smith & Streeter (1970) commenting upon Holdgate's diversity criterion accept a more usual definition when stressing that high diversity is not necessarily of greater interest than low diversity. They also state that diversity of habitats on a site is only desirable if the size criterion is satisfied for each habitat.

In general, if 100 objects are all the same, diversity is at a minimum; if the 100 are all different, diversity is at a maximum, but how to express the intermediate levels in a single index is not entirely clear. Various indices have been proposed, all have been criticized. In terms of conservation, diversity is significant for two reasons. First, the greater the diversity the more there is to see and, of greater theoretical importance, diversity is said to create stability. The diversity which is said to create stability, however, is either the multiplicity of food chains (Elton 1958) or the number of links in a trophic web (MacArthur 1955), neither of which is truly measured by an index of diversity calculated from samples of a few taxonomic groups.

555

Even if the investigator were able to label all species and could hence calculate indices of diversity for a number of sites which truly reflected the stability of those sites, is it always this that a conservationist wants? He may want Red Squirrels and deplore Brown Rats or prefer Red Admiral Butterflies to Cabbage Whites. A conservationist will require the persistence through time of *all* species but as a human he will require the persistence of pest species to be at a very low number of individuals. This implies management for the stability of populations at predetermined levels.

Management for diversity and hence an inherent stability may mean no more than that the loss of a few species will not materially alter the abundance of each of many other species present. Probably the species which could be lost without affecting a system would be those least abundant at any single trophic level. That is, the rare species are expendable. Management for diversity could, by removing individuals of the most common species without any increase in the rare species, increase diversity without any real advantage.

The number of species and numbers of individuals in each species may be usable criteria, but cannot be compounded easily in an index of diversity which is applicable to all cases. However, both number of species and number of individuals are commonly related to area on sites that are at an equilibrium. For example in climax plant communities there is an equilibrium where, on average, one individual of a species is replaced by another individual of the same species upon death of the first. There may be an internal cycle as described by Watt (1947), but provided the site is of sufficient area to embrace all stages of the cycle at one time, there should be no major fluctuation in numbers of individuals of species participating in all stages of the cycle.

It is a common observation that of any assemblage of species, individuals of some species are frequent and others are rare. This has been given mathematical expression by Preston (1962) and by Williams (1964). Whether one accepts the logarithmic or lognormal distribution as reflecting the natural situation more closely, one must accept that for habitat reserves which are limited in area there must be an upper limit on the incoming energy from the sun and hence a theoretical upper limit on total number of individuals characteristic of that habitat which can be present upon the site.

The number of species and their density per unit area has been of particular interest in studies on island biogeography where the formula

$$S = CA^k$$

has been applied to the relationship between the number of species (S), their density per unit area (C) and area (A), where k may be regarded as a reciprocal index of diversity.

If the lognormal distribution of individuals is accepted then k should be a constant with a value of about 0·27. Values of this order have been found for islands (Preston 1962) and a similar relationship has been found for contiguous areas by Dony (1963) and in individual habitats in this country by Hopkins (1955) and in the U.S.A. by Kilburn (1966).

In effect if one increases the area of a reserve by a factor of ten the number of species present will be approximately doubled. A series of small reserves, each of a different habitat type, therefore, appears to be better in terms of total number of species conserved. This could lead to the establishment of reserve size criteria unaffected by ecological considerations. A criterion such as the variation in the capital cost per unit area with the area to be purchased might be used. For agricultural land in England at the present time, the price per unit area of small parcels of land is high but the price per unit is more or less uniform for parcels larger than about 32 ha. If the pattern of land prices for reserves is at all similar, one might therefore suggest a reserve size of 32 ha. Smith & Streeter (1970) give some evidence that the price per unit area of reserve land is much lower than for agricultural land and it is probably only coincidence that the average local nature reserve is just over 32 ha in extent. Obviously it would also be possible to evolve size criteria by consideration of management costs rather than capital costs.

Van der Maarel (this symposium and in Adriani & van der Maarel 1968) has used the logarithmic transformation of $S = CA^k$ and compared areas on the basis of various multiples of C assuming k to be constant at 0·28. But neither C nor k are constants.

The value of C, the number of species per unit area, must depend upon the size of the individuals of the species concerned and is likely to differ between, say, bogs, grassland and woodland. That C values do vary between communities is obvious from Hopkins's data where mean numbers of species per square metre varied between 1·17 and 19·76 for different communities (Hopkins 1955). Hence it appears that Van der Maarel's use of the C values of different sites is not entirely satisfactory for ranking communities since those which are species poor will be excluded despite any intrinsic interest.

It is also difficult to envisage the use of this criterion for ranking a series of sites of the same community or habitat type since it depends upon k being a constant. In Jack Pine woodland, C values ranged between 7·5 and 16 for different stands, but at the same time k varied between 0·28 and 0·33 (Kilburn 1966). Now diversity is roughly represented by $1/k$ and unfortunately in Kilburn's examples high C values go with high k values and hence low diversity. The two criteria of number of species per unit area and diversity counteract one another.

Both C and k may be expected to vary with changes in the environment but the only environmental factor, the effects of which on C and k have been investigated in any detail, is isolation. Where k is measured in contiguous sample areas as by Dony (1963) in England the value is 0·177, and as by Cailleux (1952) in France is 0·21, but for isolated islands the more usual values are larger, 0·3 and above, and C also may be expected to decline with isolation (MacArthur & Wilson 1967). Hence a habitat reserve which is within an area with many similar habitats in the neighbourhood will be better in terms of species density, but less amenable to improvement in number of species present by increasing its size than one which is isolated from similar habitats. This has the corollary that a large reserve within an area of similar type can, with advantage, be divided by management into a number of sub-units. For example, Monks Wood, an 150 ha National Nature Reserve with a number of other woodlands near by, is managed by dividing it into compartments, each with different management regimes such as coppicing.

Monks Wood is not truly contiguous with the other woods near by, although the distance from its nearest neighbour is only a matter of metres. Is such a distance effective isolation? Evidence indicating the measure of isolation needed in an English habitat was first provided by Moore (1962) on heathland where more isolated areas were found to have a poorer fauna. A distance of the order of 5 km from the main heath areas was found to be effective in preventing the occurrence of certain animal species. With higher plants, however, much smaller distances appear to be effective.

In the boulder clay area of Huntingdon and Cambridge there are a number of woodlands of various sizes roughly 0·8 km apart, whereas in the Rockingham Forest area of Northamptonshire, there is a similar group of woods, of various sizes, roughly 0·4 km apart. For each of these two situations I have calculated the C and k values from the areas and lists of the species of the ground flora. Timber species were excluded from the computation on the grounds that they were more subject to the planting policies which differ in the two areas. Under these conditions the k for the Rockingham Forest area is 0·188 and for the Cambridge and Huntingdonshire area nearer 0·5 which, if increasing k does indicate increasing isolation as MacArthur & Wilson (1967) suggest, implies the critical distance for constituents of the ground flora of woodland in this part of England is something under 0·8 km.

This should not be overemphasized, for, besides showing differences in distances apart at the present time, these two areas show differences in the duration over which the separation has existed. The Rockingham Forest woods were practically contiguous into the eighteenth century (Pettit 1968), whereas at least the west Cambridgeshire woods have had much the same degree of separation since the thirteenth century (Rackham 1967).

I infer from this that species have been dying out at random through time in all woods in both areas but, where the woods have been sufficiently close for long enough, recolonization has taken place. Where time has been too short, or distance too great for recolonization, some species have become extinct.

Indeed, it can be shown that extinction is a certainty if the time scale is infinite for any organism to which there is an upper limit in number (Skellam 1955). But for finite intervals of time the probability of extinction varies with the number of individuals and their life span. For a large population this probability is very small indeed but on a single reserve site, where there are common, frequent, occasional and rare species the probability of random extinction for some species will be large. Rare species will depend upon re-immigration to the reserve site for their survival there for even short periods of time. This will in turn depend upon the distance from a neighbouring population and the dispersal power of the species in question.

A choice exists: either (i) these rare species need not be conserved, or (ii) their populations on a single isolated reserve must be very large, or (iii) several sites within their normal dispersal distances may be conserved, or (iv) constant reintroduction from artificially maintained populations should be used.

These species which are in low numbers on reserves and other sites, whether the reason for the restricted number be the energy available, predation, or territorial behaviour, may experience genetic change as well as the possibility of random extinction. In fact the basic problem of conservation, that of ensuring the persistence of individual species in time, could be re-stated as the problem of ensuring the persistence of individual genes in time. Two types of processes affect this persistence of genes: systematic processes such as selection which change frequencies in a predictable manner and the dispersive process which results from inbreeding effects in small populations.

Inbreeding has three major consequences: differentiation of populations, genetic uniformity within populations and an increase in the frequency of homozygous genotypes (cf. Falconer 1960). If there is a large number of such populations, as for example, on a large number of small reserves, the differentiation between populations need cause no loss of genetic information over all. There may, in fact, be some advantage in the differentiation of local populations adding to the diversity of the area in which the populations occur. Increasing genetic uniformity, however, will make a population more responsive to changes in selective pressures. If these changes occur in both directions at random then population numbers may fluctuate more widely and the probability of random extinction of a population on a particular reserve may be increased. Increase in the frequency of homozygous genotypes also plays a part in this but as there is also a general tendency for deleterious genes to be recessive there may be a loss of fertility and viability which again could lead to a decline in population numbers.

The effect of selection upon an individual gene can quite easily overcome the effects of inbreeding on that gene. Very high selection pressures have been found but it is clear that all genes in a population are not subject to similar selection pressures at any one time. In a small population inbreeding will affect all genes.

It should be noted that the genetically effective population size is not necessarily the number of individuals in an area. Possibly the most important case in the situations discussed here is where there is a fluctuation in population numbers between generations. Here the generations with the fewest numbers have the most effect; they contribute most to the inbreeding.

These inbreeding effects in small populations can be counteracted quite readily by immigration or gene flow. If one accepts a critical coefficient of inbreeding of 0·333 (where all gene frequencies are equally probable among the isolated populations) then it can be shown that only one immigrant in every second generation is necessary to balance the population differentiating appreciably in gene frequency (Wright 1951). Hence it appears that reserves should be sufficiently close together to allow more than a single successful immigrant every second generation to balance genetic drift. Although a recognizable point a coefficient of inbreeding of 0·333 cannot be truly said to be critical since differentiation can occur at a coefficient of 0·05 or even to a small degree at 0·005. There is no truly critical coefficient of inbreeding any more than there is a minimum genetically effective population size above which inbreeding does not occur. There are only levels of probability which we can accept or not for a given species.

Similarly, the probability of random extinction of any species increases with time and there is no real minimum viable population size unless a period of time is defined and a small probability of extinction accepted. Given general agreement upon a time scale, a probability of random genetic change and a probability of random extinction, viable population sizes could be determined for the conservation of individual species.

The first practical problem for conservation is therefore to define acceptable levels of these three ultimate criteria. Only then can management of reserves be planned and carried out on a rational basis. But this will be species conservation rather than ecosystem conservation unless 'key' species in ecosystems can be identified as Moore (1962) suggested.

Moreover, if either the lognormal or the logarithmic distribution of species abundance is usual then whatever the size of a reserve, there will always be something so rare as to have a high probability of random extinction. The artificial maintenance of some species and their constant reintroduction to sites may be a necessity. For the less rare but still uncommon it may be more expedient in terms of cost to arrange for reserves to be linked by stepping stones for re-immigration rather than, or as well as, specialized management on reserves. Management policy must therefore take cognizance of the current trends on the surrounding agricultural lands which, in eastern England at least, include the decline of semi-natural habitats such as permanent grassland, hedges and small woods which might in the past have assisted in the dispersal of organisms.

References

ADRIANI M.J. & VAN DER MAAREL E. (1968) *Voorne in de branding.* Oostvoorne.

ANON. (1947) *Conservation of Nature in England and Wales. Cmd 7122 H.M.S.O.* London.

CAILLEUX A. (1952) *Richesse de Flores.* Not seen, quoted from Williams (1964).

DONY J.G. (1963) The expectation of plant records from prescribed areas. *Watsonia* 5, 377–85.

ELTON C.A. (1958) *The ecology of invasions by animals and plants.* London.

FALCONER D.S. (1960) *Introduction to quantitative genetics.* London.

HOLDGATE M.W. (1970) The national strategy for nature reserves. *S.P.N.R. County Trusts Conference Proceedings 1970.*

HOPKINS B. (1955) The species area relations of plant communities. *J. Ecol.* 43, 409–26.

KILBURN P.D. (1966) Analysis of the species area relation. *Ecology* 47, 831–43.

MACARTHUR R.H. (1955) Fluctuations of animal populations and a measure of community stability. *Ecology* 36, 535–6.

MACARTHUR R.H. & WILSON E.O. (1967) *The theory of island biogeography.* Princeton.

MOORE N.W. (1962) The heaths of Dorset and their conservation. *J. Ecol.* 50, 369–91.

PETTIT P.A.J. (1968) *The Royal Forests of Northamptonshire.* Northampton.

PRESTON F.W. (1962) The canonical distribution of commonness and rarity. *Ecology* 43, 182–215 and 410–32.

RACKHAM I. (1967) The history and effects of coppicing as a woodland practice. In *the biotic effects of public pressures on the environment* (Ed. E.Duffey), *Monks Wood Symposium No. 3,* 82–93.

SKELLAM J.G. (1955) The mathematical approach to population dynamics. In *The numbers of man and animals,* J.B.Cragg & N.W.Pirie (eds.) London.

SMITH A.E. & STREETER D.T. (1970) The role of the county trusts in the national strategy for nature reserves. *S.P.N.R. County Trusts Conference Proceedings 1970.*

WATT A.S. (1947) Pattern and process in the plant community. *J. Ecol.* 35, 1–22.

WILLIAMS C.B. (1964) *Patterns in the balance of nature.* London.

WRIGHT S. (1951) The genetical structure of populations. *Ann. Eugen.* 15, 323–54.

Historical studies and woodland conservation

OLIVER RACKHAM *Corpus Christi College, Cambridge*

Introduction

The present time is critical for woodland conservation in Britain. Deciduous woods are being destroyed for arable land or clear-felled and replanted with conifers at an alarming rate.

Table 1 (due to C.E.Ranson) shows that in Mid-Suffolk (area defined in Fig. 1) less than half of the deciduous woodland existing in 1837 remains as such. Much of the surviving woodland is threatened with destruction in the next few years.

At the same time, despite the mass of ecological literature on certain woodland types, especially those represented in existing nature reserves, there is a regrettable lack of systematic information, even at the descriptive level, about lowland woods as a whole. Suffolk, for instance, was almost unrecorded until the Nature Conservancy's woodland survey began in 1966. Ecological classification must therefore be incomplete and attempts at conservation haphazard.

Table 1. Woodland in Mid-Suffolk expressed as a percentage of the total land area

Deciduous woodland in 1837	4·4
Deciduous woodland in 1837 now destroyed	2·0
Deciduous woodland in 1837 now conifers	0·7
Surviving deciduous woodland	1·8
Woods established since 1837	0·5

Little attention has been paid to the origin and development of individual woods, largely because vegetational historians have concentrated on stratigraphical methods which have little to say on this subject. Writers from

Tansley (1939) onwards have assumed that present-day British woodlands are in some way related to the floristically comparable forests of the later postglacial, but there is not much definite evidence on the nature of this relationship.

Historical evidence enables the ecologist to see the current destruction of deciduous woodland in its proper perspective. Public authorities often allege, for instance, that the loss of existing woods is (or could be) offset by new 'amenity' plantings. In practice, secondary woodlands in East Anglia may remain floristically depauperate for centuries (cf. Pigott (1969) for Derbyshire). Historical information enables us to look beyond the neglect or 'devastation' of much English woodland in the last few decades to the often more conservative management of past centuries. Without such information it is impossible adequately to assess the importance of individual woods and woodland types, or to draw up rational management schemes without awaiting the results of long-term experiments.

Although historical studies have a place in the conservation of single species, this paper is concerned with the maintenance of as great a range as possible of the ecosystems thought to be characteristic of an area. Logically this should proceed in three stages:

Stage 1. General survey of all the woodlands within a geographical area.

Stage 2. Selection of sites meriting particular attention, e.g. by forming reserves.

Stage 3. Detailed research on selected sites and the drawing up of management plans.

This sequence, of course, is often impracticable. Stage 2 decisions, for instance, are often precipitated by a particular wood coming on the market or being threatened with destruction; the decision to buy the wood or to oppose the destruction may have to be taken at short notice on inadequate information.

East Anglian woodlands

Apart from large modern plantations, the woods of East Anglia (Fig. 1) are scattered blocks mainly of under 100 ha. The 'heavy' *Quercus robur-Fraxinus-Acer campestre-Corylus* woodland type on chalky boulder clay is described by Adamson (1912), Valentine (1948), Abeywickrama (1949), Martin (1968), and others. On sandy more acid Pleistocene deposits there is an undescribed* 'light' type with *Quercus robur, Tilia cordata,* and *Betula pubescens.* Each type occurs in several variants, and there are transitions to the *Alnus-Salix* carr of fen valleys and to the Essex *Carpinus* woods (Christy 1924), both of which are outside the scope of this paper. Woods often show much internal variation.

* Adamson's 'loam area' is a variant of this type.

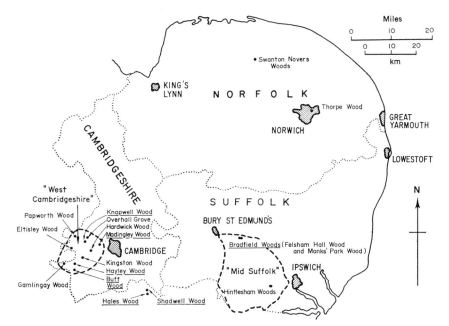

Figure 1. East Anglia, showing boulder-clay wood reserves (underlined) and woods mentioned in the text.

Many East Anglian woods appear to be historically continuous with the prehistoric forest on sites which have never been cleared.* Others are wholly or partly secondary woodland originating in various ways and at various times on former open land. The original forest was fragmented in Anglo-Saxon times and surviving woods were maintained for intensive timber production under a coppice-with-standards system which went on for at least 700 years (Rackham 1967). Coppicing was abandoned in most woods between 1890 and 1930, but a few are still coppiced and nearly all the older woods show some trace of the practice.

In an area in which human intervention has been a relatively stable ecological factor for many centuries, conservation management and experimentation should start from a knowledge of what 'traditional' management consisted of, and what variation there was from place to place and from time to time.

Types of historical information

This is a brief outline of the methods of investigating woodland history, with the suitability of each method for particular stages of an investigation

* Another East Anglian ecosystem which may in some cases be derived from prehistoric forest is parkland (Peterken 1969).

based on the time and specialized knowledge which it demands. Further
information will be published in Rackham (in press).

As far as possible, a group of comparable woods should be studied rather
than one or two sites. Much historical evidence is sporadic in its occurrence
and no one site is likely to provide complete information. All historical
material, except certain types of documents and the annual rings of living
trees, involves more or less circumstantial interpretation which can be carried
out with confidence only on the basis of a comparative study within a
geographical area. It is hazardous to apply such interpretations outside the
area where they have been tested, except where independent types of
evidence corroborate one another.

Pollen analysis

Iversen (1964) traces the history of Draved Forest in Jutland up to the
present day from pollen deposits within the wood. This is seldom possible in
Britain; suitable deposits inside woods appear to be rare, and because the
forest cover was fragmented by agriculture many centuries ago late pollen
diagrams contain information from many vegetation types within an ill-
defined area.

Available diagrams should be consulted at Stage 1 to provide general
information on local vegetation history and on what trees, particularly uncommon species, are likely to be native.

Documents

Documentary methods for woods are similar to those for other features of the
landscape (Hoskins (1959, 1967) gives a general account). Only the most
fruitful of the great variety of sources for East Anglia are mentioned.*
Documentary evidence is generally precise as to date but (apart from maps)
often imprecise as to site.

Maps

The first edition Ordnance Survey, published (except for Scotland and
northern England) in the first half of the nineteenth century, should be consulted at Stage 1, especially as reprints are now easily accessible. Map sources
for Stage 2 include the later O.S. editions (Harley & Phillips 1964), and
the large-scale enclosure, tithe, and estate maps of the sixteenth to nineteenth
centuries which exist for most parishes and are usually kept in the county

---

* Woods belonging to the Crown have their own documentation, which is outside the
scope of this paper. See Albion (1926), Hart (1966), and Tubbs (1968).

record office. The earliest known map showing East Anglian woods is for Hintlesham in 1595 (Ryan & Redstone 1931).*

National land surveys

Three relevant national surveys are sufficiently easily accessible for use at Stage 2. The entries of Domesday Book (1086) are conveniently summarized by Darby (1950, and in the regional volumes such as Darby (1952)), but Domesday woodland statistics are notoriously difficult and unreliable to interpret. The Hundred Rolls of 1279 (Rotuli Hundredorum 1818) are much more detailed and explicit and probably more reliable, but exist for only a few counties.† The Valor Ecclesiasticus (printed 1810–34) mentions the larger of the many woods owned by the church in 1535. These surveys give some information on woodland areas but seldom anything on management.

Local surveys

Estate surveys or 'extents' mentioning woodland occur in Anglo-Saxon wills, medieval monastic cartularies and inquisitions *post mortem*, leases and conveyances, and modern sale handbills, etc. Some of them are quite detailed and contain management particulars. Many are kept in county record offices and should be consulted at Stage 2. Finding and interpreting the earlier ones is a somewhat specialized study.

Accounts

The annual accounts of estates often contain particulars of timber and coppice sold, bought, or consumed on the estate, from which woodland management can sometimes be reconstructed in detail (Fig. 2). East Anglian examples so far known are mainly medieval. Such studies are suitable for Stage 3.

Court proceedings

Lawsuits about woods may result in a detailed survey being made of the wood and management details being recorded. The most fruitful source is the proceedings of the Court of Exchequer in the sixteenth and seventeenth centuries. For instance, the information in Fig. 2 is fortunately supplemented by a case concerning Hardwick Wood in 1589 (Rackham 1967). This is a source for Stage 3. The minor criminal proceedings of manor courts

---

* Thorpe Wood appears in the panoramic view of Norwich by Hoefnagel, *c.* 1580.
† In West Cambridgeshire, almost all the woods in the Hundred Rolls can be related in position and area to present-day woodland (Rackham 1968).

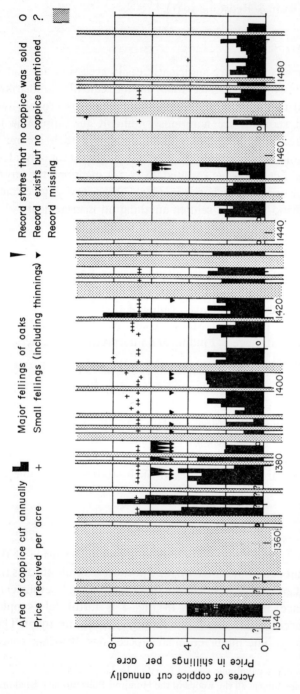

Figure 2. Quantities of coppice sold yearly from Hardwick Wood during the latter Middle Ages, together with the price received per acre and the years in which oaks were felled. The information is derived from the annual accounts of the manor, of which the wood formed only a small part, so that the missing records do not necessarily imply that no coppice was sold in those years. The existence of a record in which no coppice is mentioned probably does imply that no income was received from this source. The figures probably imply an average coppice rotation of about 4 years in the fourteenth century, increasing to 6½ years in the latter fifteenth century. See Rackham (1967) for further discussion.

sometimes contain isolated details of woods, but although picturesque these are seldom scientifically worth the labour of searching for them.

Sale advertisements

Sales of woods and timber are the main written source for woodland management in the otherwise poorly documented nineteenth century. Their study belongs to Stage 3, as it involves tedious searching of newspapers.

These sources combined provide incomplete information on woodland continuity, and more or less detail on felling, coppicing, grazing, and other management practices. Management information in East Anglia tends to be more complete for the Middle Ages than for later periods. Floristic information is usually limited to the names of the commoner trees.*

Archaeology

Woods, at least on the heavier soils, preserve earthworks within them. A wood is likely to contain all the ditches and other surface features that have been on the site since the wood was established. Some information about these should be collected at Stage 1 and a map should be made for Stage 2. They are precise as to place, but can seldom be accurately dated, and thus complement documentary evidence.

Wood outlines on heavy soils are very stable. Ancient woods nearly always have a slightly sinuous outline (Fig. 6) by which they can be tentatively recognized at Stage 1 on the 2½ in O.S. map. Perfectly straight edges generally result from comparatively modern addition or subtraction.

The earthwork most characteristic of woods is a boundary bank and ditch with the bank nearly always on the *wood* side. Wood-banks are frequently mentioned in medieval documents; they continued to be made into the nineteenth century but later ones are small. Internal coppice-banks of the kind found in the New Forest (Tubbs 1968) are rare in East Anglia, probably because grazing was seldom important in woods.

Numerous non-woodland types of earthworks, such as the ridge-and-furrow of former ploughland and the moats of former farmsteads, occur in woods and prove that their sites were at one time not wooded. Figure 3 shows the complex earthworks of Buff Wood, with old secondary woodland outside the wood-bank of a much smaller original wood.

---

* Uncommon trees are occasionally recorded: the Gamlingay court rolls of 1464 record a fine imposed for damaging 'arbores vocate crabtres', which is the earliest direct evidence for *Malus sylvestris*. Early botanical accounts are exceptional: Ray (1660) records numerous plants for Madingley and Kingston woods, from which it is known that Kingston has changed little floristically but Madingley is now much poorer.

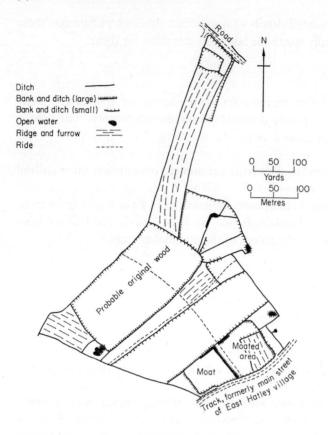

Ditch
Bank and ditch (large)
Bank and ditch (small)
Open water
Ridge and furrow
Ride

N

0   50   100
Yards
0   50   100
Metres

Road

Probable original wood

Moated area

Moat

Track, formerly main street of East Hatley village

Figure 3. The earthworks of Buff Wood. Correlation with woodland structure and vegetation and with some documentary evidence suggests that a small original wood increased in size at the expense of what had been arable and pasture. This took place, perhaps in stages, between 1300 and 1600, and was perhaps connected with the decline of the medieval village of East Hatley, of which two moats are now inside the wood.

Vegetation

Annual rings of living trees

An obvious source for the age-structure of the present woodland and for growth rates in the immediate past. The annual rings of ash stools sometimes provide a record of coppice cycles over the past 200 years.

Woodland structure

Provides evidence of whether the site was coppiced and how long ago coppicing ceased. Neglected ancient 'heavy' woodland typically has a three-layered structure (Fig. 4): standards of oak with a few ash (the latter often

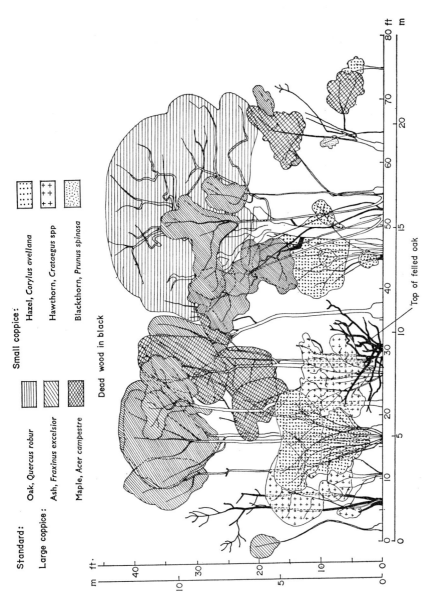

Figure 4. Measured profiles of all trees over 6 ft (2 m) high on a transect 25 m (80 ft) wide in Hayley Wood, last coppiced in 1897. Recorded with the help of P.J.Grubb, March 1968.

'promoted' coppice); large coppice of ash and maple arising from massive long-lived hollow stool bases; and small coppice of hazel and hawthorn with smaller underground stools. Woods with this structure are sometimes secondary but not less than 300 years old. 'Light' woodland has fewer characteristic features but giant stools of *Tilia* sometimes replace those of *Fraxinus*.

Plant species

Certain plants are associated with woods of particular historical types. For instance, within East Anglia, *Primula elatior* (Christy 1897), *Sorbus torminalis*, *Tilia cordata* (cf. Pigott (1969) for Derbyshire), *Campanula trachelium*, *Mercurialis perennis*, and *Platanthera chlorantha* are characteristic of ancient woodland; and *Hedera helix* (as ground cover), *Primula veris*, *Daphne laureola*, and *Anthriscus sylvestris* are characteristic of secondary woodland. Assemblages of these plants are more reliable than single species; thus *Primula elatior*, though rarely found away from ancient woods, occurs in several places within 600 m of the ancient Eltisley Wood (e.g. Kerr (1967), Valentine (1948), Abeywickrama (1949)), in several ancient hedges in East Cambridgeshire, and in a few fens (e.g. Galpin (1888), Woodell (1965)). Moreover, secondary woodland *adjoining* ancient woodland contains some characteristic species of the latter, and *vice versa*.

Building timbers

Timbers in medieval and sub-medieval buildings are often hewn from entire tree-trunks and provide evidence of the size and shape of the tree and its rate of growth. Wattle-and-daub material gives similar information about coppice. This is a difficult method, requiring a knowledge of vernacular architecture and means of establishing the provenance of the timber, but provides direct evidence of woodland management and thus deserves more detailed study.

Stage 1: Local woodland surveys

Existing methods in conservation surveys of woodland are rather unsatisfactory given the limitations of time and manpower. Visits often have to be hurried, incomplete, made by inexperienced persons and at unfavourable times of year. Even at the simplest floristic level, a reasonably complete assessment of a group of woods requires many visits to each site. Figure 5a shows the recording of vascular plants in Hayley Wood, a well-known site near Cambridge frequently visited by professional botanists for over a century, and Fig. 5b shows the progress of a more intensive study of the

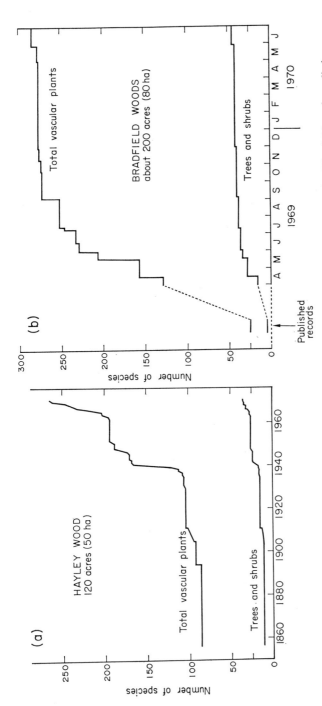

Figure 5 (*a*) History of the recording of vascular plants, and of trees and shrubs (excluding *Rubus*) in Hayley Wood. Note three distinct phases of recording activity. Compiled from many sources, chiefly Babington (1860), Babington's MS notes in Cambridge University Botany School, and the Cambridge Natural History Society's records.
(*b*) Similar diagram for the Bradfield Woods. Records up to April 1969 are due to Mrs A.Hart. Later records collected by the author with the help of Miss P.F.Cammell, Mr and Mrs F.L.Harris, Mrs Hart, and others.

Bradfield woods, an effectively virgin site for which few pre-1968 records were available. The Nature Conservancy's woodland record cards, with their emphasis on woody species, might be expected to suffer less from this disadvantage; this is not borne out either by Hayley or Bradfield, in both of which, despite the differences in recording procedure, the progress of recording trees and shrubs has been closely parallel to that for the total vascular flora. Two tree species were added to the Hayley Wood list in 1968–9, having been overlooked for decades, which is a warning against overreliance on presence-or-absence data.

Elementary historical material is an important part of the 'background' information necessary for the interpretation of such incomplete biological records. Apart from written evidence, surface features and other field data can be recorded at a single visit, by unskilled persons, and at otherwise unsuitable seasons.

Stage 2: Assessment and selection of sites

Several historical issues arise at this stage, especially where a wood is complex and it is possible to select only part of it for conservation management. It is necessary to know whether special features of importance are a transient result of succession or are likely to continue under suitable management. If a site is threatened with some undesirable change, it is important to know to what extent it is replaceable. Recent woodland is potentially replaceable whereas ancient woodland, particularly on sites which have never been ploughed, is not, although the distinction is more marked with some woodland types than others.

The importance of a site for future research depends to some extent on how much historical information exists. A wood with a detailed historical record has a greater potential for interpretation than one without, especially if there has been a long period of relatively unchanged management, or if different parts are known to have different histories.

There is also the political consideration that much conservation in Britain is done by amateur bodies and financed by public subscription. The interests of biological conservation often coincide with those of local archaeologists and historians. A project is likely to attract more support if it appeals to a wider range of interests than the specialist concerns of ecologists.

Stage 3: Management

Short-term: coppicing

The silvicultural neglect of many of the older English woodlands in the last few decades, and the decline of coppicing, are a drastic break with previous practice. Although the effects of coppicing vary widely (Rackham 1967), and Adamson's account for Gamlingay Wood (1912) is only partly representative even of East Anglian woodlands, there is little doubt that neglect results in the loss of many characteristic features and—at least in the first 50 years—a decline in variety of habitats.

Evidence on the length and regularity of the coppice cycle is provided by documents and (for the latter period) by annual rings. In East Anglia, the cycle was generally very short (four or even three years) and irregular (Fig. 2) in the Middle Ages; later it became longer and more regular (e.g. 15–16 years for Hayley Wood in the nineteenth century). Specimens of coppice from ancient buildings suggest that this change may be partly due to a decline in productivity, possibly because of depletion of soil phosphate (Rackham 1967). These long-term changes must be borne in mind when deciding on the length of a restored coppice cycle, an important decision biologically because the length of the closed canopy phase determines to what extent light-demanding herbs and saplings will be suppressed.

Middle-term: standard trees

Many woods have been seriously depleted of mature oaks by excessive felling during or between the World Wars. The following questions arise:
(i) How serious are the consequences, particularly for insects and epiphytes, of a break in the continuity of oaks?
(ii) What steps should be taken to restore the canopy of standards (e.g. by planting oaks or by 'promoting' large coppice)?
(iii) What is a suitable density of standards?

Documents show that the majority of standards in East Anglian woods were normally oak, but other species were sometimes present (e.g. Gamlingay and Hardwick estate papers *passim*). In the Middle Ages, standards were not managed regularly but were felled as demand arose, often in large numbers (e.g. 269 oaks on 40 acres of Gamlingay Wood in 1333). This went on into the seventeenth century at least.* It is probable that most woods have already been through phases when there were few large oaks.

It is often supposed (e.g. Tansley 1939) that the usual density of mature oaks was 12 to the acre (30 per ha), the basis being the statutes of woods (e.g. 1543), which purported to regulate coppice-with-standards management nationally. The assumption overlooks the fact that this density was laid down by statute as a minimum, and that the penalties for infringement were

* In Monks' Park Wood a 'great part of the Timber trees' was felled in 1656–7; in 1669 it was said that as a result the coppice 'is become of a greater value by a third part than it was when the timber was standing'. (Information kindly supplied by Mr A.R. Allan from Court of Exchequer depositions.)

lenient. Nevertheless, this minimum is sometimes written into leases (as late as 1768 at Gamlingay), and it is likely that it had some effect on management. Twelve mature oaks to the acre would normally produce about a 30 per cent canopy, and it is not surprising that this number was often exceeded.* Hayley Wood in the 1920s had an average of about 30 to the acre, whereas Felsham Hall Wood probably had about 9 to the acre.† Similar variations are found in the middle ages. Hardwick Wood had at least 24 oaks to the acre in 1380 (Rackham 1967); Beevor (1924) gives 5 to 40 per acre for various Norfolk woods in the fifteenth century.

Long-term successions

Pollen analysis and documents show that the tree composition of the older East Anglian woods has not changed much in historic times. *Pinus* and *Fagus* apparently became extinct as native trees in the later Middle Ages,‡ probably because in mixed woodland they did not withstand intensive coppicing. *Alnus* is now very rare in boulder-clay woods, probably because the better-drained sites where it is recorded in the Middle Ages have since been cleared. *Tilia* is rarer and more calcifuge than its abundance in pollen diagrams (e.g. Godwin (1968)) leads one to expect, and this may be because it does not compete well with *Fraxinus* and other coppice species.

It is natural to regard oak, as Tansley (1939) does, as the climax dominant of East Anglian woodlands. Although this may have been so in the past, most oak woodland is at present a plagioclimax which can only be maintained in the long run by active management.§ The well-known, though still somewhat obscure, failure of oak to regenerate from seed inside woods will lead in the long run to its replacement by ash. That this has not happened in the past may be due partly to artificial planting, but also to the practice of replacing oak by coppicing; there is considerable evidence from documents and building timbers that oak was formerly widely grown as long-rotation coppice, which would reduce the need for seed regeneration.

But the climax dominant in East Anglia, at least on calcareous soils, is probably not *Fraxinus* but *Ulmus carpinifolia agg.* Many woods show a varying degree of invasion by elm. In the early stages this takes the form of circular patches produced by suckering (Plate 1). Several genotypes are involved. In some cases, the elm coexists with the existing 'heavy' woodland

---

* The notion that oaks were deliberately grown widely spaced in order to provide natural bends for shipbuilding does not apparently apply to East Anglian woods, which are not known to have supplied timber for shipyards, still less to have been managed to this end.
† Figure deduced from sale particulars kindly supplied by A.R.Allan.
‡ Beech was cut commercially in North Norfolk as late as the thirteenth century (Saunders 1930, p. 77).
§ The Bradfield woods, in which oak regenerates excellently, are an exception.

Plate 1. Mosaic aerial photograph of the eastern side of Hayley Wood, Cambs, taken by Cambridge University Department of Aerial Photography in 1963. The large roughly semicircular area is an almost pure stand of *Ulmus carpinifolia* agg. which has largely replaced the *Quercus–Fraxinus–Acer* woodland surviving in the rest of the photograph. There is a zonation in age-structure within the semicircle: the large elms in the interior and near the wood margin are about 200 years old, while the small dense elms near the curved front are much younger and derived from suckers.

trees, at least for a time, but in Hayley Wood and elsewhere it overtops and shades out the oak. In some woods the process is beginning, but others (e.g. Papworth Wood and Overhall Grove) are completely overrun by elm and retain only traces of the former structure. The origin of the process is obscure: it appears to have begun in the eighteenth century or shortly before.* Succession to elm is the natural fate of 'heavy' boulder-clay woodland, although it may be postponed by the isolation of individual woods, and this fact must be considered in long-term management.

An Example—the Bradfield Woods†

Felsham Hall Wood and Monks' Park Wood (Fig. 5) are some 10 km south-east of Bury St Edmund's. Along with Swanton Novers woods (Petch and Swann 1968), they are the most outstanding of the East Anglian woodlands. 'Light' and 'heavy' woodland types occur together; there is an exceptionally rich flora, especially in trees and shrubs; and commercial coppicing still continues. Up to 1968 they were to all practical purposes unknown, earlier work having been forgotten.

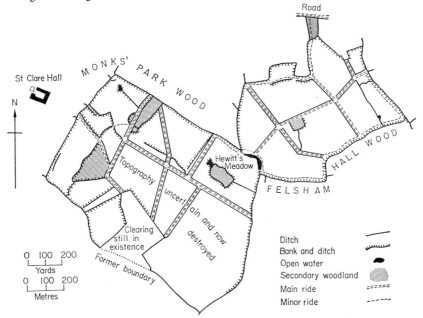

Figure 6. Topography of the Bradfield Woods. Recent changes are ignored.

* It is tempting to attribute the elm invasion to the artificial introduction of new elm genotypes (cf. Richens (1958); but Richens studied *village* elms which are not necessarily genetically related to the nearby woodland elms).

† An outline of work done in collaboration with D.P.Dymond and A.R.Allan, to be published shortly in more detail.

The following is a summary of the historical evidence. A Stage 2 survey was begun at very short notice when the woods were threatened with destruction, and the main outlines emerged within two days (one spent in the field, the other in libraries). Felsham Hall Wood and part of Monks' Park are now owned by the Society for the Promotion of Nature Reserves and further evidence is being sought for management and research.

In the Middle Ages the woods, which appear to have had roughly their present outlines, belonged to Bury St Edmund's Abbey, and are described in its cartularies.* The estate containing Monks' Park Wood was leased at times to the St Clare family and appears in secular records as well. An agreement of 1269 shows that a deer park had been formed in the existing wood and was used for hunting, which strongly suggests that clearings existed in it. Otherwise there is abundant evidence of woodland continuity from 1252 onwards.

Management evidence, both for coppice and standard timber, exists at many points in the same period. Coppicing appears to have followed the usual course, but production has remained high. The early nineteenth-century rotation was regularly 10 years;† but no coppice was cut between 1848 and 1853,† and management has since been less regular. The records of Whelnetham Woodworks Ltd, which coppices the woods, show that the average rotation since 1938 has been about 11 years. The fluctuations in oaks have already been mentioned. The drastic felling of 1669 was repeated in 1929, and there are now only about three mature oaks to the acre (but numerous saplings and stools).

Felsham Hall Wood has a massive wood-bank, which follows most of the irregular northern boundary. Internally it has few surface features apart from the ride ditches and irregular sinuous hollows which may be natural features of the unploughed boulder-clay.

The whole of Monks' Park Wood appears to have been a deer park. It has a broad flattish wood-bank which doubtless carried a high fence. The compact outline and rounded corners suggest economy in fencing. Some of the internal earthworks define four former clearings, which are mentioned in seventeenth century documents and may date from the deer-park period. Hewitt's Meadow, with its pond, is of particular conservation interest because it remained a clearing until about 1900; its partial reopening is being considered. Other internal banks may be copse-banks necessitated by the juxtaposition of coppicing and deer.

Apart from known clearings, the woodland structure and vegetation of the whole area are typical of ancient woodland.

St Clare Hall, a timber-framed house of several medieval and later

* Preserved in Cambridge University Library and consulted at Stage 2.
† *Bury and Norwich Post* sale advertisements, 1853-5.

periods, provides an unusual opportunity for studying datable building timbers of almost certain provenance. Monks' Park was the only wood of any size on the Bradfield St Clare estate. The wood must have provided a much wider range of sizes of oaks in the Middle Ages than it has done recently.

The historical evidence suggests that these woods had a greater diversity of structure and habitat in past centuries than in recent decades. This has probably contributed to their unusual biological interest. A return to such variation, together with continuing the coppicing tradition, would appear to be the most rational principles of future management.

Acknowledgements

I wish to thank the custodians of archives which I have consulted, especially the Librarians of Merton College, Oxford (for Gamlingay), and Pembroke College, Cambridge (for Hardwick), and landowners who have allowed me to visit their woods. I am most indebted to Mr A.R.Allan, Mr D.P.Dymond, Mrs A.Hart, Dr G.F.Peterken, and Mr C.E.Ranson for held with field-work and for discussion and information, and to Dr G.C.Evans for comments on the draft of this paper. I am grateful also to Mr and Mrs J.F.Bayton, of St Clare Hall, and to Mrs N.Litchfield and Mr Cullum, of Whelnetham Woodworks.

References

ABEYWICKRAMA B.A. (1949) *A study of the variations in the field layer vegetation of two Cambridgeshire woods*. Ph.D. dissertation, Cambridge.

ADAMSON R.S. (1912) An ecological study of a Cambridgeshire woodland. *J. Linn. Soc. (Bot.)* 40, 339–87.

ALBION R.G. (1926) *Forests and sea power. The timber problem of the Royal Navy 1652–1862*. Harvard.

BABINGTON C.C. (1860) *Flora of Cambridgeshire*. London.

BEEVOR H.E. (1924) Norfolk woodlands, from the evidence of contemporary chronicles. *Trans. Norfolk Norwich Nat. Soc.* 11, 488–508.

CHRISTY M. (1897) *Primula elatior* in Britain: its distribution, hybrids, and allies. *J. Linn. Soc. (Bot.)* 33, 172–201.

CHRISTY M. (1924) The hornbeam (*Carpinus betulus* L.) in Britain. *J. Ecol.* 12, 39–94.

DARBY H.C. (1950) Domesday woodland. *Econ. Hist. Rev.* 2nd ser. 3, 21–43.

DARBY H.C. (1952) *The Domesday geography of Eastern England*. Cambridge.

GALPIN F.W. (1888) *An account of the flowering plants, ferns and allies of Harleston*. London and Harleston.

GODWIN H. (1968) Studies of the post-glacial history of British vegetation. XV. Organic deposits of Old Buckenham Mere, Norfolk. *New Phytol.* 67, 95–107.

HARLEY J.B. & PHILLIPS C.W. (1964) *The historian's guide to Ordnance Survey maps*. National Council of Social Service, London.

HART C.E. (1966) *Royal forest. A history of Dean's woods as producers of timber*. Clarendon, Oxford.

HOSKINS W.G. (1959) *Local history in England*. Longmans, London.

HOSKINS W.G. (1967) *Fieldwork in local history*. Faber & Faber, London.

IVERSEN J. (1964) Retrogressive vegetational succession in the post-glacial. *J. Ecol.* **52** suppl. (*Jubilee Symposium*), 59–70.

KERR A.J. (1967) A new oxlip locality in Cambridgeshire. *Nature Cambs.* **10**, 26–7.

MARTIN M.H. (1968) Conditions affecting the distribution of *Mercurialis perennis* L. in certain Cambridgeshire woodlands. *J. Ecol.* **56**, 777–93.

PETCH C.P. & SWANN E.L. (1968) *Flora of Norfolk*. Jarrold, Norwich.

PETERKEN G.F. (1969) Development of vegetation in Staverton Park, Suffolk. *Fld Stud.* **3**, 1–39.

PIGOTT C.D. (1969) The status of *Tilia cordata* and *T. platyphyllos* on the Derbyshire limestone. *J. Ecol.* **57**, 491–504.

RACKHAM O. (1967) The history and effects of coppicing as a woodland practice. In *The biotic effects of public pressures on the environment* (Ed. E. Duffey), Monks Wood Experimental Station Symposium **3**, 82–93.

RACKHAM O. (1968) Medieval woodland areas. *Nature Cambs.* **11**, 22–5.

RACKHAM O. (in press) The History of Hayley Wood. *Hayley Wood* (Ed. O. Rackham), Cambs & Isle of Ely Naturalists' Trust.

RAY J. (1660). *Catalogous plantarum circa Cantabrigiam nascentium*. Cambridge.

RICHENS R.H. (1958) Studies on *Ulmus*. II. The village elms of southern Cambridgeshire. *Forestry*, **31**, 131–49.

Rotuli hundredorum temp. Hen. III & Edw. I in Turr' Lond' et in curia receptae Saccarij Westm. asservati. Vol. **2** (1818). H.M.S.O., London.

RYAN G.H. & REDSTONE L.J. (1931) *Timperley of Hintlesham*. Methuen, London.

SAUNDERS H.W. (1930) *An introduction to the obedientiary and manor rolls of Norwich Cathedral Priory*. Jarrold, Norwich.

TANSLEY A.G. (1939) *The British Islands and their vegetation*. Cambridge.

TUBBS C.R. (1968) *The New Forest: an ecological history*. David and Charles, Newton Abbot.

VALENTINE D.H. (1948) Studies in British Primulas. II. Ecology and taxonomy of primrose and oxlip (*Primula vulgaris* Huds. and *P. elatior* Schreb.). *New Phytol.* **47**, 111–30.

Valor ecclesiasticus temp. Henr. VIII auctoritate regia institutus. Vols 1–6. H.M.S.O., London.

WOODELL S.R.J. (1965) *Primula elatior* in Norfolk: immigrant on relic? *Proc. bot. Soc. Br. Isl.* **6**, 37–9.

The Management of Woodwalton Fen: a multidisciplinary approach

ERIC DUFFEY *The Nature Conservancy, Monks Wood Experimental Station, Abbots Ripton, Huntingdon*

Introduction

The total number of National Nature Reserves in Britain is now 129, covering an area of 110,500 ha. Of these nearly a half (62) are in England, although they account for only just over 23 per cent of the total N.N.R. area. The criteria for the selection of these reserves are based primarily on scientific factors, mainly ecological, geological and representation of species of plants and animals of special conservation interest. 'Naturalness' of the wildlife communities has always been accepted as an important factor, but no definition of this term was attempted during the late 1940s when most of the present National Nature Reserves were selected (Cmd 7122, 1947). Although it was realized that many of the reserves were areas which had been greatly modified by man's activities, precise historical data on the type of use were generally lacking.

In 1947 it was generally assumed in Britain that the scientific management of wildlife on nature reserves could be practised successfully by applying the classic concepts of plant and animal ecology. These, however, had been derived largely from a study of the least disturbed sites, which in many instances had been allowed to develop for a long period without major modification. Most nature reserves, especially in lowland England, are not of this type and may have been exploited for centuries for agriculture, forestry or in other ways. Such reserves are generally described as 'semi-natural', but this term is used loosely for a wide range of conditions from little to greatly modified formations. The definitions proposed here are adapted from Westhoff (1968).

Natural Formations

Completely uninfluenced by man, either directly or indirectly. It is doubtful whether any still survive in Britain but one might include very localized areas such as mountain tops, types of snow-bed vegetation, inaccessible ledges, rock crevices, some cliff-face vegetation and a few isolated water bodies.

Near-Natural Formations

The spontaneous development of native species in a community very similar to the potential natural ecosystem. This formation differs from the above in that it has been used or influenced by man but without the natural succession having been deflected. No species will have been deliberately introduced or eliminated. Examples would include climax forest from which timber has been taken, climax grassland or moorland which have been grazed, but in neither case would the natural succession have been significantly altered. Here again such areas are scarce in Britain but would include certain dune, shingle and saltmarsh formations, more extensive upland areas above the natural treeline, raised bogs and other wetlands. It is possible, but less certain, that any woodlands or fens in Britain achieve this status.

Semi-Natural Formations

Associations of plants and animals consisting entirely or almost entirely of native species, but in formations whose structure and development have been greatly modified by man's activities. Succession has been diverted away from its natural course so that the existing formation bears little or no relation to the potential natural ecosystem. Well-known examples in Britain are the extensive calcicolous grasslands and heathlands of lowland England, whose climax vegetation would be forest. It also includes fens, scrub, coppice and most woodlands. In the case of woodland the term semi-natural accepts that extensive planting of native species may have occurred. Most British nature reserves, especially those in England, consist of formations of this type. It will be shown below that Woodwalton Fen is a comparatively well-studied example.

Artificial Formations

Entirely man-made or arising directly out of human activities; usually bearing no relation to the previous flora and fauna on the site. Obvious examples are disused gravel, clay and chalk pits and quarries; disused railway tracks, banks of road and rail cuttings; canals, reservoirs, land flooded by mining subsidence; spoil tips; planted hedgerows, etc. Many of these sites are colonized by native species and subsequent development has been little interfered with by man. In such cases a local nature reserve of considerable scientific interest may develop.

5. Agricultural Formations

Crops, sown grassland, orchards, plantations and other features of the farmed landscape created by man for economic production. (Permanent pastures grazed by cattle or sheep are Semi-Natural Formations.)

The History of Woodwalton Fen

This National Nature Reserve (213·3 ha) in Huntingdonshire became a private reserve in 1910, was presented to the Society for the Promotion of Nature Reserves in 1919 and leased to the Nature Conservancy in 1953. It was formerly part of a much larger wetland area in the Fenland Basin of East Anglia and it was not until the mid-nineteenth century that reclamation of the surviving section became possible. In 1924, 2,240 ha of fen country remained, together with a large shallow lake, Whittlesea Mere, which when full covered another 640 ha (Duffey 1968). The relationship of Woodwalton Fen to this mere and the surrounding unreclaimed fen in 1824 is shown in Fig. 1. At this time the area may have been close to a Near-Natural Formation because the vegetation cover had survived largely in its aboriginal condition. The surface is unlikely to have been broken, except perhaps in small local areas, because of seasonal flooding, but it is almost certain that it was used for summer grazing, cutting of hay and litter and the harvesting of reed (*Phragmites communis*) in the winter. Mid-nineteenth century plant records of the Whittlesea Mere area (Druce 1926, Miller & Skertchley 1878) clearly indicate that a surface acid peat had developed with an oligotrophic vegetation, including *Drosera anglica, D. intermedia, D. rotundifolia, Vaccinium oxycoccos, Anagallis tenella, Pinguicula vulgaris, Liparis loeselii, Narthecium ossifragum, Eriophorum angustifolium, Rhynchospora alba, Calluna vulgaris, Erica tetralix, Myrica gale, Salix repens, Molinia caerulea* and *Sphagnum* spp. In addition there were many species more characteristic of mesotrophic conditions, suggesting that there were local areas of fen flushes (Poore 1956).

An examination of the peat stratigraphy (Godwin & Clifford 1938) has shown that in general the surface acid peat has developed over a fen peat including *Phragmites, Typha, Schoenoplectus lacustris* and *Juncus*. Beneath this layer is a zone of wood peat over the Oxford Clay, which forms the floor of the Fenland Basin.

In 1851 Whittlesea Mere was drained and extensive reclamation began, both of the exposed mere bottom and the surrounding land. The usual practice was to burn off the surface vegetation and spread gault (calcareous clay) prior to cultivation (Wells 1860, 1870). It is not known how the Woodwalton Fen area was first reclaimed, and although by 1870 peat-cutting for fuel was widely practised there is no direct evidence of extensive arable farming.

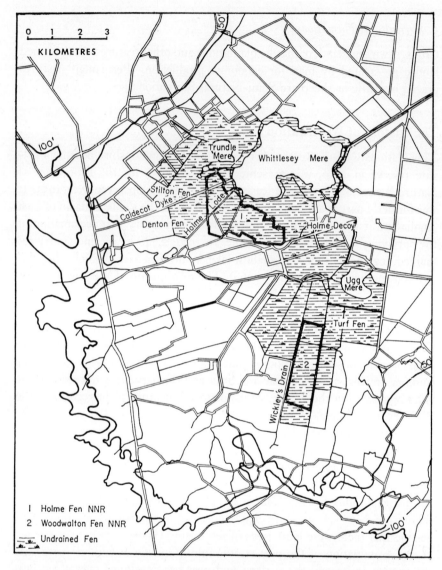

Figure 1. The location of Woodwalton Fen in relation to undrained fenland in 1824

During this time the series of cross-drains were dug (Fig. 2), in order to remove the peat by boat to the larger Great Raveley Drain. Peat-cutting continued until the beginning of the twentieth century, by which time most of the peat suitable for fuel had probably been exploited over the northern two-thirds of the Fen. The southern third had become part of a farm; some areas on the west side were probably cultivated and the remainder was used for grazing, hay-making and as a rough shoot. This area has no cross-drains

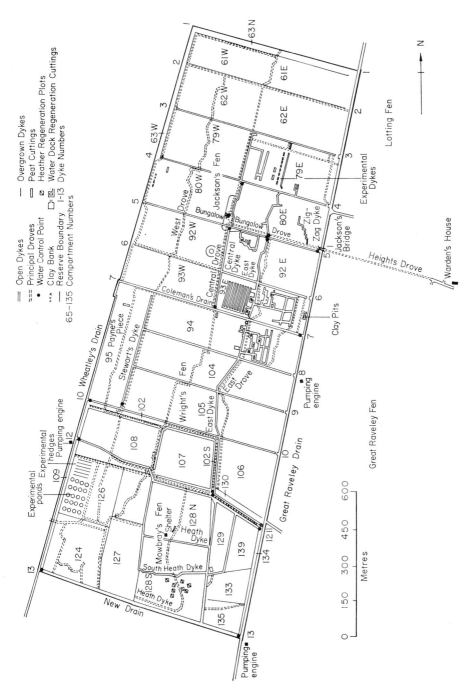

Figure 2. Woodwalton Fen. Drains, ponds, peat cuttings, droves, pathways and experimental areas.

of the type found further north so that peat-cutting may have been of short duration.

Poore (1956) has shown that during the peat-cutting period nearly all the surface acid peat was removed from the northern two-thirds of the reserve exposing a more base-rich fen peat beneath. Acid peat still remains, however, over a substantial area in the south of the reserve (Fig. 3). Towards the end of the nineteenth century peat-cutting declined. A contemporary map held by the Middle Level Drainage Authority shows most of the Fen as rough grazing or marsh, although absence of symbols from compartments in the southwest and southeast compartments suggests some form of agricultural use.

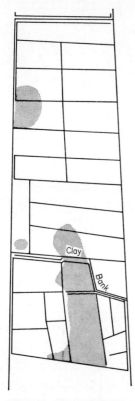

Figure 3. The distribution of acid peat (dotted area) with *Molinia* (after Poore 1956).

Fryer (1936) saw the Fen in about 1905 and describes the vegetation as mainly herbaceous, including large areas of *Phragmites*. Other areas were more open and described as 'litter fen', while bush growth was very local. Reed-cutting became an important occupation and was continued until 1939 when the last commercial crop was taken. By this time bush growth was extensive and in 1952, when the first aerial photograph was taken, very few areas of herbaceous fen remained. In addition the dyke system, apart from two sections, had become silted up and overgrown.

The present vegetation cover

This has been described in detail by Poore (1956), who distinguished two main seres based on differences in the dominant herbs: the *Calamagrostis epigejos* sere and the *Molinia* sere. He showed that there was a close correlation between the type of plant association and the nature of the surface peat. The *Molinia* sere with its characteristic associated species, *Myrica gale*, *Calluna vulgaris*, *Salix repens*, *Erica tetralix*, *Cladium mariscus*, *Potentilla erecta*, with a birch scrub, was only found where bog peat had survived, while the *Calamagrostis* sere with its associated common fen plants, *Phragmites*, *Filipendula ulmaria*, *Thalictrum flavum*, *Lythrum salicaria*, etc., with a sallow scrub, was found on the fen and wood peats exposed during peat-digging.

There is an almost complete absence of the rarer *fen* plants at Woodwalton, the only possible exception being *Ranunculus lingua*. However, a number of plants have been introduced in the past, mainly during the 1920s, notably *Sonchus palustris*, *Peucedanum palustre* and *Potentilla palustris*, all previously recorded for the Whittlesea Mere area in the nineteenth century. The native rarities have been well known from the Fen for many years and include *Viola stagnina*, *Viola canina* ssp. *montana*, *Luzula pallescens* and *Dianthus armeria*. None of these plants is found elsewhere in the East Anglian fens, although *V. stagnina* was formerly known on Wicken Fen and Lakenheath Poor's Fen. These species are small plants normally growing in relatively open situations, which cannot exist on the reserve today unless maintained artificially. The naturally developing herb cover of the Fen is tall and dense and scrub growth soon spreads everywhere unless periodically cut back. About 400 flowering plants and ferns are known from the Fen, excluding a few old or doubtful records. This total compares favourably with the more famous Wicken Fen, where 268 flowering plants and ferns have been recorded (since 1940), over a slightly larger area (Walters 1967).

Fauna

The animal life of the Fen has not been studied in the same detail as the vegetation. Nevertheless there is information available for 21 invertebrate and 5 vertebrate orders. The best known are the Lepidoptera, Coleoptera, Araneida and Hymenoptera (Symphyta). Some smaller groups have been well studied, notably the Odonata, Heteroptera and Diptera (Agromyzidae). Wicken Fen is richer in species in nearly all these groups, despite its plant list being substantially smaller. The main reason for this is probably because it has been more thoroughly studied by zoologists for a longer period of time.

Nevertheless, there are a number of striking differences which cannot be explained in this way. The Wicken spider fauna is particularly rich and includes a number of notable rarities which also occur in other East Anglian fens but are absent elsewhere, including Woodwalton Fen. A few, such as *Marpessa pomatia* and *Lycosa rubrofasciata*, are widespread in the herbaceous vegetation of these fens but have never been recorded at Woodwalton. On the other hand Woodwalton Fen has two species, *Lycosa paludicola* and *Synageles venator*, which are unknown at Wicken. Neither of the latter species has been recorded from true fens in Britain or elsewhere in Europe. The former is more characteristic of acid peat substrates and the latter of coastal dune formations, although it has been known for many years in the Whittlesea Mere area (Duffey 1968). This evidence supports the more detailed botanical, stratigraphical and historical data that an oligotrophic formation, very different from fen conditions, had developed in the Woodwalton Fen area prior to reclamation.

Although about 665 species of Lepidoptera and about 750 species of Coleoptera have been recorded from the Fen (Anon. 1964), none suggests the earlier presence of bog conditions. The rare moths *Hydrillula palustris* Hübn., *Perizoma sagittata* Fab. and *Perinethela perlucidalis* Hübn. are known from other East Anglian fens. The best known insect from the Whittlesea Mere/Woodwalton Fen area is the Large Copper Butterfly (*Lycaena dispar* Haw.). This species was well known in the early nineteenth century, particularly around the Mere, but became extinct in about 1851. Although it also occurred in certain Cambridgeshire fens, there are no records for Wicken Fen or for the extensive fens of the Norfolk Broads, in spite of the fact that its food plant, *Rumex hydrolapathum*, is common and widespread (Duffey 1968).

The diversity of animal habitats

Elton and Miller (1954) devised a habitat classification system for ecological survey which is particularly useful for assessing the *potential* faunistic richness of an area. The classification divides the structural components of the environment (living and non-living) into height zones, while water bodies are grouped according to size, water flow and whether shaded or not shaded. There are four main 'Systems', Terrestrial, Aquatic, Aquatic-Terrestrial Transition and Maritime. Within the Terrestrial System the land habitats are divided into the following Formation Types:

(*a*)   Open-ground type—all vegetation and other structures below 15 cm in height.

(*b*)   Field type—all vegetation (herbaceous and woody) below 1·8 m.

(*c*)   Scrub type—bushes and small trees not exceeding 4·5 m in height.

(*d*)   Woodland type—tree canopy exceeding 4·5 m in height.

Qualifying terms are applied to these types to distinguish different associations of plants to describe marginal areas known as 'edge' habitats. The Eltonian classification includes a total of 172 habitat types, of which 66 have been recorded on Woodwalton Fen. Although this is quite a high score, inspection of the habitat classification chart shows that certain important components are poorly represented or absent. The Open-ground Type exists only on the mown pathways, in places where excavations have been cut in the peat, or, temporarily, after bushes have been cleared. More important is the almost complete absence of the Aquatic-Terrestrial Transition zone; waterlogged marshy ground is not a permanent habitat on the Fen and is only created from time to time by periodic flooding. The old system of drains has now been largely reopened and new drains cut, but they are all approximately the same size and have steep sides so that no marsh zone has formed. Plants characteristic of this habitat are scarce and the same has been noted for insects; there are few species of *Stenus*, only one species of *Donacia* and none of *Plateumaris* spp. This may also be partly the reason why the Common Frog (*Rana temporaria*) is now completely absent, not having been seen since about 1953. Shallow water, necessary for spawning, is no longer available.

The water regime

Woodwalton Fen is situated in one of the driest parts of Britain with a mean annual rainfall of about 546 mm (21·5 in). The average *summer* rainfall (April–September) is 242 mm, but if the water table is to be held at a constant level a further 115 mm is required. This means that irrigation is needed in most years (Craig 1962). In the past the Fen has relied on the moderately base-poor upland water draining from the surrounding hills of Oxford Clay (Godwin & Clifford 1938). Impeded water flow across the Fen Basin to the outfall in the Wash permitted the development of raised bog conditions close to the higher clay land which was originally forest-covered. The Great Raveley Drain, which forms the eastern boundary of the reserve, was cut at an early date, probably before the seventeenth century, and because of its relatively large size it was an important navigation route. Wheatley's and Coleman's Drains may also be fairly early as they carried water from the higher land across the Fen to the Great Raveley Drain. All the other drains probably date from the second half of the nineteenth century, apart from a few new ones dug since 1954.

Although annual winter flooding must have been a regular occurrence before reclamation, Poore (1956) has shown that as water control of the external system became more efficient in the early years of the twentieth century, the mean level fell and floods became less frequent. The mean water level in the external system (Great Raveley Drain) in 1900 was −15 cm

Ordnance Datum and in 1962 it had fallen to −80 cm O.D., while the estimated desired water table level on the reserve is −45 cm O.D. Today an extensive system of open-water dykes has been restored to maintain a permanent aquatic habitat, to allow rapid flow of water to all parts of the Fen for irrigation and to act as a reservoir. The permeability of peat varies considerably according to structure. Poore (1956) has shown that wood peat offers least resistance while the compact acid peat is very resistant. However the upper 25–50 cm of the peat, whatever its origin, forms a worked and oxidized soil layer created by past peat-cutting or attempts at cultivation and this material is very permeable. When the water level in the drains reaches a level above the usually sharply defined undisturbed peat, lateral flow into the compartments is rapid.

The fen is now a self-contained unit with upland water flowing along its south boundary to reach the Great Raveley Drain instead of crossing the centre of the reserve as it did before 1967. Nevertheless the main supply of water must still come from the external system, and this is done by opening boundary valves when the Great Raveley Drain levels are high enough or by using a pump. The water from agricultural land is rich in nutrients and a progressive eutrophication of the Fens seems unavoidable. In general, drainage water has a pH of 8·0 or more, while peat water in many compartments is between pH 4·0 and 5·0. In addition the efficient upland drainage system now allows a faster run-off so that during periods of heavy rain levels rise rapidly and short-duration flooding is likely to occur at any time. Flood water may rise 90 cm in 24 hours but the fall is relatively slow because recent maintenance work on the reserve boundaries has effectively cut down the rate of water loss.

Some effects of summer flooding

Heavy rainfall in July, August and September 1968 (Table 1) caused extensive floods on the Fen, probably the worst since August 1912. From 10 July to 10 November the reserve was almost continuously inundated (Duffey & Mason 1970).

Table 1.

	July	Aug.	Sept.	Oct.	Nov.	Dec.
Estimated av. mon. rainfall (mm) (Monks Wood, 4·8 km from the Fen)	54·0	51·0	51·0	49·0	54·0	44·0
Monthly rainfall in 1968 Woodwalton Fen	157·0	86·0	78·0	40·0	43·0	45·0

Winter flooding, which for centuries was a regular feature of the seasonal variation in the water regime, causes no harm to wildlife which is adapted to it. Prolonged flooding of plant and animal life during the period of growth and reproduction may, however, have a disastrous effect on some species. In 1968 the flooding coincided with the first emergences of the Large Copper Butterfly (*Lycaena dispar batavus* Obth.) which lays its eggs on the Great Water Dock (*Rumex hydrolapathum*). After 10 July all the food plants were submerged apart from the topmost leaves of the largest plants and this continued while adult butterflies were on the wing. Consequently very few eggs were laid and only 10 larvae were counted in the spring of 1969 after hibernation. These produced 1 male and 4 female butterflies but no pairing took place and for the first time since 1928: when this species was re-introduced to the Fen, extinction took place. Fortunately a captive stock was maintained elsewhere and restocking was possible in 1970. Further evidence of the effects of the 1968 summer flood is as follows.

The wolf-spider, *Lycosa paludicola*, known from only four localities in Britain, is normally abundant on the central part of the reserve during April but in the spring following the flood only two specimens were seen in spite of extensive searches. Birch trees (*Betula* spp.) began to show browning of leaves in autumn 1968 and in 1969 large numbers failed to come into leaf. Not a single flower of the Fen Violet (*Viola stagnina*) was recorded in 1969, although it was widespread in May 1968.* No *Luzula pallescens, Cirsium dissectum* or fen orchids were seen in 1969, although well-established colonies were known up to 1968. The common grasses *Calamagrostis epigejos* and *C. canescens* were less vigorous. Luck (1964) has shown that these species do not grow well if the water table is less than 30 cm below ground level. On the other hand *Phragmites communis* and *Phalaris arundinacea* grew more vigorously than ever before. 1968 was clearly an exceptional year in the climatic records but it is possible that artificially induced summer floods may occur in the future as a consequence of increasingly efficient drainage on the surrounding agricultural land.

A survey of management and its effects since 1954

Bush clearance

In 1954 about 90 per cent of the reserve was covered by birch and sallow carr or incipient bush growth; the largest area of open herbaceous fen persisting on the old arable land of the southwest compartments. A programme of clearance was started, particularly of the sallow carr which was most

* In 1970 there was an excellent recovery.

widespread. This was done in the winter months by pulling out the rootstocks of sallow to prevent regrowth. The exposed ground was almost bare of vegetation and the surface was broken by numerous saucer-shaped depressions created by the removal of rootstocks. During the first growing season the open ground was rapidly colonized by plant species found nearby but two occurrences of exceptional interest were noted. In several areas *Viola stagnina* appeared in such numbers that swards covering several square metres were recorded. In the second season the species was much less common and by the third summer the other vegetation was so tall and dense that plants survived only on the sparsely vegetated sides of the saucer-shaped depressions. Prior to bush clearing *V. stagnina* had not been recorded in these areas for very many years and it is assumed that seed lay dormant in the surface peat, surviving from a much earlier period when open conditions prevailed.

A similar phenomenon was recorded (only once) in the case of *Luzula pallescens*, normally a very scarce plant found on mown pathways. In 1967 a very large number of plants appeared in an area which was previously covered with dense *Crataegus* scrub at least 40 years old. *L. pallescens* was first recorded in Britain at Woodwalton Fen in 1907 and is still only known from this site and from the nearby Holm Fen (Fig. 1). *V. stagnina* was a well-known plant around Whittlesea Mere before 1851 and has survived at Woodwalton but nowhere else in East Anglia. Although it frequently occurs in disturbed situations on the reserve, for example after bush clearing, on spoil from peat cuttings and newly dug drains, around sites of fires and on mown droves, it has never been recorded on the south section of the Fen. It is difficult to understand why it should be absent from the acid peat area where several other plants with direct lineage to pre-drainage days still survive and yet is widespread on that part of the reserve where all the surface peat has been exploited and the plant cover is a secondary development. Similarly neither *Lycosa paludicola* nor *Luzula pallescens* have ever been recorded in the acid peat area south of the clay bank (Fig. 3).

In the case of *V. stagnina* the explanation may be as follows. If we assume that this plant was formerly distributed over the whole area it is reasonable to suppose that it disappeared first from the southern part of the Fen which was drained and incorporated in a farm at an early date after reclamation. In the northern two-thirds of the reserve, however, regular peat-cutting maintained large areas of open wet ground, on which the fen violet could thrive. After peat-cutting ceased in the early part of the twentieth century this plant became very scarce. It survived, however, in rabbit-grazed areas and on mown pathways until 1954 when extensive clearance and dyke-digging restored open conditions and the plant once more became locally common.

Cattle-grazing

From 1964 to 1965 Friesian heifers grazed compartments in the south of the reserve, then in 1966 ten Galloway bullocks were purchased to graze selected southern compartments all through the year according to a pre-arranged plan. In the southwestern compartments the cattle were used to control the rank growth of *Arrhenatherum elatius*, *Phragmites communis* and *Calamagrostis epigejos* and prevent bush growth. This was successful in diversifying and opening up a species-poor area on old agricultural land.

In compartment 128 grazing was designed to control *Molinia* which was preventing the regeneration of *Calluna* and *Erica tetralix* and to create disturbed ground at the time these plants were shedding seed. In addition experimental plots were cleared of vegetation, by hand, adjacent to groups of heather and *Erica* plants. This work was initially successful. A year after such treatment 2,007 *Calluna* plants (15–22 cm in height) and 589 *Erica* seedlings were counted over an area of 5·9 m² (Anon. 1964). Subsequently, however, rapid invasion by *Calamagrostis epigejos* and *Chamaenerion angustifolium* smothered the young plants and few survived. In addition, the cattle had destroyed by trampling most of the old heather plants so that there was no longer an adequate source of seed. This work is now being repeated but measures will be taken to prevent the grass reaching a height greater than the heather seedlings.

The third object of grazing management was to improve the habitat conditions for the only well-established colony of *Dianthus armeria* on the Fen. This species has been known on the reserve for 65 years and grows on a rather dry peat soil of pH 4·6–5·3 in a species-rich grass heath (Wells 1967). Until 1955 the vegetation was kept short by rabbit grazing but after myxomatosis the grasses grew tall and rank and *Calamagrostis epigejos* began to invade. In 1964 only five *Dianthus* plants were found. Cattle grazing began in the winter of 1964/5 and the tall herbage was reduced from 45·7 cm to 61·0 cm in height to an average of 1·3 cm. In 1965 50 *Dianthus* were counted; in 1966 the total had increased to 336 plants and in 1967 900 plants but was much reduced in 1968 by prolonged flooding. Cattle grazing is regulated to a moderate level during the autumn, winter and spring and ceases before the plants come into flower. It is not resumed until the seed are shed.

The restoration of open water and primary fen

The restoration of the dyke system and the construction of new waterways was completed during the 1950s. A system of water control points was also built in order to maintain levels in different parts of the reserve according to conservation interest. The dyke system not only distributes water within the Fen, but provides, with shallow peat cuttings, the only aquatic habitats within the reserve. The aquatic invertebrate fauna is particularly rich and appears to require regeneration of the dyke system if diversity of species is to be maintained. Morris (1969) found that stagnant, old dykes typically supported an aquatic bug fauna poor in species and characterized by the corixid *Hesperocorixa sahlbergi*. In dykes with flowing water, even if the flow was slow and intermittent, a richer association of species was found. Shallow peat cuttings, dug for the establishment of *Rumex hydrolapathum* (see below), often supported very rich associations of corixid bugs, although there is some evidence that the species concerned were not breeding in them. The larger peat-cuttings were shown to be suitable for the surface-living bug *Gerris thoracicus* which was absent in the dykes where other, commoner, species occurred.

The creation of aquatic-transition zones was a more difficult, but equally urgent, problem, particularly in relation to the status of the Large Copper Butterfly. Since 1928 the food plant, *Rumex hydrolapathum*, had been regularly planted in the herbaceous fen because plants growing in or by the side of water in the dykes were generally avoided by the female insect when egg-laying. The seed of this plant only germinates on fairly open wet peat and because plants away from water in the thick growth of *Calamagrostis canescens* and *Phragmites* gradually lose vigour and die after a few years there is no natural replacement. Thus the optimum conditions for the germination and growth of *Rumex hydrolapathum* are different from the optimum conditions for the insect when selecting food plants for oviposition (Duffey 1968).

Primary fen was first restored by digging flat-bottomed depressions adjacent to certain dykes. These proved to be unsatisfactory because when the water table was higher than normal the *whole* area was flooded and when lower the whole area was too dry. A more satisfactory design, which was widely adopted, consisted of a shallow saucer-shaped cutting about 4 m wide and 25 cm deep with gently sloping sides, having standing water in the middle, and a graded margin reaching average ground level at its highest (and driest) part (Fig. 2). A network of these cuttings has been constructed over a 5-year period so that the vegetation is now in different stages of succession. The margins were seeded, in parts, with *Rumex hydrolapathum*, which produced fruiting plants after 2 years. At the same time other vegetation colonized the wide margins, many of which remained sufficiently open for the *Rumex* plants to thrive and regeneration to continue. As the herbaceous sward developed around these plants the habitat became progressively more favourable for the female butterflies. In this example, successful management for an insect of high conservation interest required the creation of an anthropogenic ecocline between open water and a secondary fen sere. The initial conditions permitted the growth and regeneration of the food plant and the succession which followed developed an environment in which the food plant was acceptable to the female insect for oviposition.

Criteria for a management policy on a semi-natural formation

Woodwalton Fen is a good example of the complexity of ecological management in a Semi-natural situation. It is postulated here that such formations
present the most difficult problems because the objects of management must,
to a considerable extent, be decided arbitrarily in relation to the various disturbance factors which have modified the ecosystem. Traditional forms of
land-use may be followed without alteration in the case of Near-natural
Formations, but they only constitute a guide to the management of Semi-
natural Formations. The established diversity of habitats and species on
Natural and Near-natural Formations form the main part of the scientific
interest and if modified would introduce instability and unpredictable ecological changes. On Semi-natural Formations the diversity of habitats and species
is to a considerable extent, subject to choice. Detailed ecological knowledge
will be required to maintain those habitats which are seral stages, in order to
control the status of species in these unstable conditions. The most difficult
aspect of such management problems is the accurate prediction of the response
of species to different habitat treatments.

One of the more important ecological problems in planning habitat
diversity in a Semi-natural area such as Woodwalton Fen is the maintenance
of marginal areas between different habitats. Natural formations have long
established ecoclines (used in the sense of Whittaker (1970) to describe a
gradation of vegetation types) in which the inter-relationships between species
are stabilized. Anthropogenic ecoclines are both difficult to create and to
maintain and yet constitute a vital part of a man-made habitat pattern which
attempts to simulate the diversity of a natural ecosystem. At Woodwalton Fen
the best example is the creation of an aquatic-terrestrial transition zone, a
formation which requires constant intervention by man to reverse the processes of natural succession.

The following table summarises and compares the criteria for management on Natural, Near-natural, Semi-natural and Artificial formations.

Criteria for a management policy on different formations

Formation

NATURAL   Non-intervention. Continuance of existing conditions.

NEAR-NATURAL Identification of human activity modifying environment.
               Usually a single factor which should be continued as closely
               to traditional methods as possible. *Status quo* to be main-
               tained for other environmental factors.

SEMI-NATURAL History of previous land-use often complex. Several factors
               responsible for modifying environment. The effects of

these must be determined. The choice of habitat pattern and species diversity determined by the 'land manager' in relation to surviving flora and fauna and prior condition of area. The environment can be manipulated according to the conservation interests and objectives.

ARTIFICIAL   Environment completely changed so that few or none of previous fauna and flora survive. Wildlife determined by secondary colonization. Vegetation cover and animal habitats can be arbitrarily selected by further modifications, including introductions of plants and animals to create a predetermined landscape pattern.

Acknowledgements

I would like to thank my colleagues at the Monks Wood Experimental Station, Dr M.G.Morris, Mr T.C.E.Wells, Mr D.A.Wells and Mr J.M.Schofield, for information about the Fen and for helpful discussions. I also acknowledge a special debt to the Warden, Mr G.Mason, who made available his very comprehensive knowledge of the reserve and its problems.

Plant names follow Clapham A.R., Tutin T.G., and Warburg E.F. (1962) *The Flora of the British Isles.* 2nd ed. Cambridge.
Spider names follow Locket, G.H., and Millidge A.F. (1953) *British Spiders.* Vol. II. Ray. Soc. London.

References

ANON. (1964) *Woodwalton Fen National Nature Reserve. Management Plan.* The Nature Conservancy. (Unpublished.)

CRAIG C.W. (1962) *A study of the hydrology and ecology of Woodwalton Fen N.N.R. Hunts.* Dissertation, University College, London.

DRUCE G.C. (1926) Botany. In *Victoria County History, Hunts.* 1.

DUFFEY E. (1968) Ecological studies on the Large Copper Butterfly *Lycaena dispar* Haw. *batavus* Obth. at Woodwalton Fen National Nature Reserve, Huntingdonshire. *J. appl. Ecol.* 5, 69–96.

DUFFEY E. & MASON G. (1970) Some effects of summer floods on Woodwalton Fen in 1968/69. *Ent. Gaz.* 21, 23–6.

ELTON C.S. & MILLER R.S. (1954) The ecological survey of animal communities: with a practical system of classifying habitats by structural characters. *J. Ecol.* 42, 460–96.

FRYER J.C.F. (1936) Woodwalton Fen. *Handbk. a. Rep. Soc. Promot. Nat. Reserves,* 1936, 11–20.

GODWIN H. & CLIFFORD M.H. (1938) Studies in the post-glacial history of British vegetation. I. Origin and stratigraphy of fenland deposits near Woodwalton, Hunts. *Phil. Trans.,* Series B. 229–323.

LUCK K. (1964) *Studies in the autecology of* Calamgrostis epigejos (L.) *Roth. and* C. canescens *(Weber) Roth.* Ph.D. Thesis, Cambridge University.

MILLER S.H. & SKERTCHLEY S.B.J. (1878) *The Fenland Past and Present.* London.

MORRIS M.G. (1969) Associations of aquatic Heteroptera at Woodwalton Fen, Huntingdonshire, and their use in characterising artificial aquatic biotopes. *J. appl. Ecol.* 6, 359–73.

POORE M.E.D. (1956) The ecology of Woodwalton Fen. *J. Ecol.* 44, 455–92.

WALTERS S.M. (1967) List of the vascular plants of Wicken Fen. In *Guide to Wicken Fen*, No. 3. The National Trust.

WELLS W. (1860) The drainage of Whittlesey mere. *J.R. agric. Soc.* 21.

WELLS W. (1870) On the treatment of the reclaimed bogland of Whittlesey mere. *J.R. agric. Soc.*, Series 2, 6.

WELLS T.C.E. (1967) *Dianthus armeria* L. at Woodwalton Fen, Hunts. *Proc. bot. Soc. Br. Isl.* 6, 337–42.

WESTHOFF V. 1968 Die 'ausgeräumte' Landschaft. Biologische Verarmung und Bereicherung der Kulturlandschaften. In *Handbuch für Landschaftspflege und Naturschutz.* (Eds. Buchwald, K. & Engelhardt, W.), Vol. 2, 1–10. Munich.

WHITTAKER R.H. (1970) *Communities and ecosystems.* New York.

The management of plant and animal communities in the Tatra Mountains National Park

ADAM ŁOMNICKI *Nature Conservation Research Centre, Polish Academy of Sciences, Krakow, Poland*

The Polish Tatra National Park is situated on the northern slopes of the Tatra Mountains and it constitutes about one fourth of the area of the whole massif. The southern and eastern part, across the border in Slovakia, is also managed as a National Park and there is co-operation between the Headquarters of both Parks.

Some features of the Tatras make them one of the most interesting areas from the scientific point of view (Szafer 1962). They form the highest part of the Carpatians, but are of a relatively small area, 51 km in length, 17 km in width; the total area being about 700 km². Within a few kilometres there may be a considerable difference in altitude, from the foothills at 1000 m above sea-level, to the highest peaks at over 2,600 m. The differences in altitude within a relatively small area, the steep slopes and deep valleys, a varied geomorphology and two different geological substrata contribute to the great diversity within the area.

During a day's walk in the Tatra Mountains it is possible to pass through deciduous forest, spruce forest, and above the timber line to the mountain pine (*Pinus mughus*) zone, the alpine meadow zone and the subnival zone of bare rocks.

Although altitude is the main factor differentiating natural habitats, other influences are also very easy to detect. The position of the timber line is a good indicator of these factors. The line is higher on the southern slopes, in the centre of the massif, due to the temperature inversion on the ridges. It moves down on some very steep stony slopes, because of snow avalanches and sometimes because of man's activities such as woodcutting and intensive grazing.

Plant communities are much more abundant and diverse on the limestone than on the granite soils. For example in the natural spruce woodland association (*Piceetum tatricum*) there are about fifty species on the limestone, but only a third of this on the granite.

The Tatra Mountains became a great tourist attraction more than a hundred years ago. From the scientific point of view they are one of the best known regions of Poland. Hundreds of papers dealing with this small area have been published concerning geology, hydrology, climatology, botany and zoology as well as the history and social anthropology.

It is impossible to discuss the conservation policy in the Tatra National Park without taking into account the fascination imposed by this piece of land both on its earlier visitors and the thousands of tourists today. As early as in 1868 due to the efforts of scientists, mainly those of Professor Maksymiliam Sila-Nowicki, zoologist at the Jagiellonian University, a bill was passed giving protection in the Polish Tatras to two species of alpine mammals, the chamois and the marmot. From the end of the nineteenth century until 1954, when the National Park was established, there was a strong voluntary movement with great pressure from scientists for the conservation of this area.

Among the scientists working towards the foundation of the Tatra National Park, there was a strong conviction that its main purpose should be the conservation of natural habitats and the elimination of changes induced there by human activity. This conviction has survived and has become part of the bill on which the foundation of the National Park is based. The idea is that only tourist movement and scientific research should be allowed in the Park.

Natural habitats and changes induced by man's activity

The botanical and zoological investigations carried on during the last hundred years have shown that in many parts of the Mountains changes induced by human activity were small or insignificant. On the other hand they have shown that many parts of the area are heavily damaged, due mainly to timber exploitation and intensive grazing.

The results of the phytosociological investigations and other data show that the natural plant community on the limestone soils in the lower part of the mountains between 700 to 1,250 m above sea-level, is the beech-fir (*Fagetum carpaticum*) woodland association. On the acid granite soils a spruce-fir woodland grows. Some rocky fragments below the timber line are devoid of tree cover.

Above 1,250 m up to the timber line there is the zone of spruce woodland (*Piceetum tatricum*) with a number of stone pines (*Pinus cembra*) near the timber line. The timber line is, on an average, at 1,540 m. Strictly speaking it is a belt, not a line. There is a gradual change from the well developed spruce woodland, through groups of smaller spruce trees and single spruce and stone pine trees, to a thick carpet of mountain pine (*Pinus mughus*). As the altitude increases, the mountain pine becomes smaller, grows in smaller patches and at about 1,800 m the alpine meadow zone begins.

There is no glacier or permanent snow in the Mountains but above 2,300 m the vegetation is very poor and different from the alpine meadows, and is called the subnival zone. It is characterized by bare rocks, but it has nevertheless about 120 species of plant.

The natural habitats in the Tatra Mountains were altered in many ways. Grazing by sheep and cattle, which according to some documents goes back to at least the thirteenth century, was the first factor inducing changes in the plant cover. Not only were the alpine meadows grazed, but the woodland and mountain pine were destroyed and artificial meadows were formed. Grazing took place in the forests adjoining the meadows and there was a tradition among shepherds to enlarge meadows by timber cutting and by burning the mountain pine scrub.

Grazing by sheep and cattle took place only during the summer months, from May to September. Shepherding in the Tatras had a very long tradition and there was an interesting folk culture connected with this activity. Nevertheless at the beginning of the twentieth century it became obvious that the mountain vegetation was overgrazed. Destruction of woodland and mountain pine with intensive grazing had led to soil erosion and to the complete elimination of soil cover in some parts of the area. Grazing had heavily damaged some forests so that the restoration of woodland was hardly possible and the existence of wild herbivores was in danger. The diminishing economic importance of sheep and cattle grazing, and the possibility of buying the land from private owners, have in the last few years helped to eliminate most of the shepherding in the National Park.

Considerable changes in woodlands were caused by intensive timber exploitation in the nineteenth century and at the beginning of the twentieth. Mines of silver, copper and later of iron ore were worked in the Tatras from the sixteenth to the second half of the nineteenth century and a great amount of timber was required, especially in the iron foundries. The exploited trees were replaced by the spruce trees of unknown origin. Because of this, only small areas of natural beech-fir woodland were left in the limestone areas.

The planted woodland and the forests in which timber exploitation and heavy grazing were taking place were subjected to further damage, mainly tree-fall due to winds and insect pests. The wind called 'halny' (of the same kind and origin as the Föhn in the Alps), blowing from the south and especially frequent during spring and autumn, is a great problem in woodland management. The most damaging wind ever described happened in May 1968. Out of 12,000 ha of woodland within the boundaries of the Park 470 ha were blown down. If the trees are not removed quickly after tree-fall, there may be a population increase of the spruce bark beetle (*Ips typographus*). This species is an important pest, and when abundant attacks standing spruce trees leading to further tree-falls in the next strong wind. Woodcutting near the timber line or any clear-felling which exposes a 'wall' of tree trunks to the wind is very dangerous, as it can start a chain of events which is not easy to stop.

Snow avalanches during winter and spring are another important problem. Although these are natural phenomena, it seems that snow mobility and avalanches are caused by poor plant cover due to the mountain pine destruction and the overgrazing of the areas above the timber line (Myczkowski 1962). Almost every year, due to avalanches, some woodland destruction is recorded and this is an important factor in the formation of the timber line.

The grazing of meadow and woodland areas has a harmful effect on the population of large herbivores. When competing with sheep and cattle chamois, marmots, red deer and roe deer are at a disadvantage.

It should be noted that the National Park within the boundaries of Slovakia was in a much better situation. Before the National Park foundation the bulk of its area was managed for hunting, without any grazing, so its natural habitats are in a much better condition.

Management

The above short account of the damage caused in the natural environment of the Tatra Park by human activity shows that the first object of its management is to prevent woodland destruction and soil erosion. This object has to be attained irrespective of wildlife conservation. It is part of a general programme of plant cover management in any mountainous area where strong erosion processes are at work and where it is very important to control water run-off in the area. However in the Tatra National Park, there are some other more specific problems of management for conservation, which will be discussed below.

An interesting and important problem is the restoration of the beech-fir forests on the limestone soils below 1250 m. There are many reasons for this. (1) It is a return to the natural plant association, which was the native community in this area, (2) It will increase the diversity of plant and animal communities which, in the present spruce monoculture, is rather poor, (3) It will eliminate damage due to the spruce bark beetle, which is the chief pest in these monocultures, (4) There are data showing that the beech-fir woodland is much more resistant to wind action than the spruce woodland. This probably results from a much shallower spruce root system compared with beech and fir root systems, (5) The beech-fir woodland restoration will increase the diversity of the whole mountain scenery.

The policy of replacing the spruce woodlands by beech and fir woodland with a smaller amount of spruce and sycamore (*Acer pseudoplatanus*) is followed in many parts of the National Park on the limestone. Beech, fir and sycamore are planted in many clearings made by the wind or by clear-felling after damage due to the spruce bark beetle.

A thorough study of how the conversion of the spruce woodland into the beech-fir woodland should be done was made by Fabijanowski and Oleksy (1959). The authors started with a phytosociological analysis of the herb layer in both the natural and spruce woodlands to find out whether there are appropriate conditions in the spruce forests for changing them into beech-fir forests. They suggested that the spruce should be removed gradually to avoid harmful effects of wind and soil erosion. It should start with the clear-felling of small patches, or narrow strips of spruce woodland, to permit the growth of the beech trees. The clear-fellings could then be enlarged at a later date. According to the authors such a conversion should last for 50 or more years.

Sheep and cattle were removed from the bulk of the area of the Tatra National Park only a few years ago, and the study of the result of this removal is still at an early stage. Therefore at present not enough data are available and only a short account of the work taking place can be given here.

It is believed that the removal of grazing will not bring any great changes in the composition of plant communities within the alpine meadow zone. It will stop soil erosion and it will have beneficial effects on the chamois and marmot populations. The chamois avoid sheep herds and it seems that sheep grazing was the main factor limiting their abundance in the Polish Tatras.

In the mountain pine zone the removal of grazing will eventually lead to an enlargement of the areas covered by this species. A similar process is expected in the meadows below the timber line where woodland will colonize. On the other hand it does not seem probable that the mountain pine and the woodland will cover the whole area within their zones. This will be prevented mainly by the action of physical factors of the mountain environment. Some very steep and rocky slopes, including places where snow avalanches often occur, and where wind action is pronounced, can prevent the mountain pine and the woodland from spreading over the whole area so that habitat diversity will be maintained.

The greatest changes are expected on the bottom of the valleys below the timber line, in the areas now covered by mown, grazed and manured meadows. They form the so-called Gladiolo-Agrostetum plant association whose origin and maintenance depend on human interferences. When left alone these meadows will be covered, eventually, by forest. The Gladiolo-Agrostetum plant association forms a very diverse and rich community. Early in the spring, just after the snow melts there is a mass flowering of crocuses (*Crosus scepusiensis*), which is a great attraction for visitors. During summer the meadows, if not grazed, are covered by the flowers of *Gladiolus imbricatus* and of many other species. These meadows also make a habitat for a rich insect community.

The question, 'What should be done with the Gladiolo-Agrostetum meadows?' is part of a more general problem, 'What shall we conserve— natural communities or the plant and animal diversity?' Fortunately, the association in question is also common outside the boundaries of the National Park, therefore for the time being it will not be entirely eliminated. Looking ahead it should be realized that modern methods in agriculture will eliminate this sooner or later along with many other plant and animal communities, whose existence depends entirely on primitive agriculture. We have to ask ourselves an important question, 'Should we simulate old agricultural methods, which are, or will soon be, no longer used, in order to preserve the Gladiolo-Agrostetum and other plant and animal communities?'

Finally I should add that in spite of many changes induced by man in the Tatra Mountains environment, the general policy of Park management, no interference where this is possible and the encouragement of a return to the natural communities, has proved reasonable. This is now part of management practice. The policy has necessitated applying a number of restrictions on access by visitors. One of these is that in the network of strict nature reserves within the National Park boundaries, no visitors are allowed. These reserves were carefully planned (Myczkowski 1967) and are very important, especially as refuges for large mammals. Nevertheless it seems that the general policy of the National Park management is approved both by the scientists and by the general public.

References

FABIJANOWSKI J. & OLEKSY B. (1959) Les méthodes de conversion de certain peuple- ment de l'étage montagnard inferieur dans le Parc National de Tatra. *Ochr. Przyr.* 26, 95–171. (Polish with French summary.)

MYCZKOWSKI S. (1962) The impact of snow avalanches on the forests of the Tatra National Park studied in the valleys of Rybi Potok, Roztoka, Waksmundzka and Panszczyca. *Ochr. Przyr.* 28, 83–109. (Polish with English summary.)

MYCZKOWSKI S. (1967) A project for the network of strict nature reserves in the Tatra National Park. *Ochr. Przyr.* 32, 41–88. (Polish with English summary.)

SZAFER W., ed. (1962) *The Tatra National Park.* 2nd ed. Krakow. (Polish with English summaries.)

The conservation of ecological diversity of Mediterranean ecosystems through ecological management

Z.NAVEH *Technion—Israel Institute of Technology, Haifa*

Introduction

The object of nature conservation is not only the preservation of certain plant and animal species, threatened by extinction, but also of the ecological diversity and stability of whole ecosystems endangered by urban and industrial expansion.

The purpose of this paper is to outline some of the problems encountered by the conservation of such ecosystems in the mountainous Mediterranean region of Israel and to re-evaluate some of the conventional assumptions on Mediterranean hill-land use.

Mediterranean mountain and hill land ecosystems and their anthropogenic nature

In Israel, as well as in other countries with a similar summer-dry subtropical climate of the Koeppen (1923) Cs, or the UNESCO (1963) xero- and thermo-Mediterranean type, and with a long history of intensive and destructive land use, the only true 'wildlands' are located in the mountainous regions. These are larger areas covered by natural vegetation and on sites too steep or rocky, with soils too shallow for arable farming.

Such untillable wildlands constitute about 40 per cent of the total area in northern and central Israel (Seligman *et al.* 1959), 57 per cent in Greece (Margaropoulos 1952), 64 per cent in Lebanon (Tisdale 1967) and probably not much less in other countries bordering the southern and eastern portions of the Mediterranean. They have been exposed to human activities for a very long period and at least since the Mousterian and Upper Paleolithic period, the primeval, Pleistocene forests of these uplands were influenced by fire, hunting, food gathering and human settlement. After the Late Mesolithic and Early Neolithic agricultural revolution, and particularly during historic times, grazing and browsing of domestic livestock, woodcutting, brush clearing and cultivation caused the extinction of big mammals—herbivores and most of their predators, the loss of the taller trees, the erosion of the upper soil profile and the impairment of watersheds, and, finally, in overall desiccation (Whyte 1961). Thus these climax forests have been turned into human-degraded and converted upland ecosystems of sclerophyll woodland, scrubland, savannas and derived grasslands. Probably only on the most remote and inaccessible niches such as steep, rocky cliffs and crevices, some artefacts of the original vegetation may have survived. We can assume that some time during the period of abandonment and neglect, following the Muslim Conquest in the Middle Ages, a new dynamic equilibrium has been established between these habitats (now more exposed and drier) and those components of the wildlife which have been best adapted to these semi-natural conditions. Others, succumbing to the pressure of fire, man, his livestock and cultivation, have been replaced by invaders, with broader ecological tolerances, from adjacent more arid regions.

In this way, the landscape has been moulded into a strikingly diverse vegetation pattern. This varies from more or less open multilayered strata of higher and lower phanerophytes, chamaephytes, hemicryptophytes, geo-phytes and therophytes, to closed, floristically and faunistically much poorer and almost impenetrable one- or two-layered brush thickets. Eig (1927) sub-divided this vegetation into 'Maquis', dominated by trees, 'Garigue', dominated by shrubs up to one metre in height and 'Batha', when dominated by a mixture of dwarf shrubs, hemicryptophytes and therophytes. Whereas most of the sclerophyllous hardwood species are considered of low economic value for forest production, the herbaceous layer contains many valuable pasture grasses and legumes and a profusion of beautiful, flowering winter annuals and flowering geophytes from the Liliaceae, Iridaceae, and Orchi-daceae families.

However, since the foundation of the State of Israel, this equilibrium has been disturbed again in those parts of the mountainous regions where year-round grazing and browsing of Arabic cattle and goats and the traditional patch-cultivation has been replaced by intensive, seasonal grazing of large beef-cattle and milk-sheep herds and by modern, mechanized methods of land preparation and hill cultivation. In recent years, the greatest impact on this landscape has been the large-scale afforestation by densely planted Allepo pines and the rapid process of urbanization, industrialization, water and road development which has reached the most remote Arabic villages in this region. Anagnostopoulos (1967) describes a similar situation in Greece.

In this way, great parts of these upland 'wildlands' have been lost alto-gether and most of the remaining are changing rapidly. Smaller but most significant portions, from the ecological and scenic point of view, have been declared as Nature Reserves or National Parks. Here, and in the remaining open areas, which are now the last resources for outdoor recreation and tourism in the Mediterranean, mountainous region of Israel and in other Mediterranean countries, the need for sound ecological management is very acute.

The need for a holistic and dynamic approach to ecological classification and management

Most of our present information on the vegetation of these wildlands is derived from extensive ecological and phytosociological studies (Zohary 1962). These have been inspired by the Zürich-Montpellier School in which subjective, pseudo-taxonomical and hierarchical classification of 'vegetation classes' and 'climax communities' are used. In addition to the basic objections to this method by Egler (1954), Poore (1955) and others, its drawback for our purpose lies in the emphasis on such preconceived concepts as 'climax communities'. This approach ignores the fact that in the Mediterranean region, fire, man, his axe and livestock have become inseparable and integral parts of these semi-natural ecosystems. Therefore, their exclusion cannot be regarded as creating a 'natural' situation, which will lead to the re-establishment of an hypothetical 'climax'. On the contrary it may lead to a less 'natural' situation—at least from the point of view of biological diversity and stability.

In Europe, where the human impact on natural vegetation has been shorter but not less intensive, this Clementsian climax concept is being replaced by a more realistic term, 'potential natural vegetation' (Tüxen 1956). Also, pseudo-taxonomic, phytosociological classifications have been replaced by broader and more objective ecological classifications (Ellenberg 1963).

The semi-natural status of woodlands and grasslands has also been recognized in conservation management and research in Great Britain (Ovington 1964). This dynamic and holistic approach should also be adopted in Israel and other Mediterranean countries. The object should be the conservation of the structural and functional continuity of these modified ecosystems and thereby their biological diversity.

For this purpose, a more comprehensive ecological classification will be necessary, subdividing the ecosystems into smaller landscape units and ecotopes on a basis of habitat, flora, fauna, biotic history, present and potential utilization. For the vegetation inventory, objective sampling methods should be developed to deal with the three main, closely integrated patterns of spatial variability in vegetation composition, density and structure. These include gradual 'continuum' changes along environmental gradients—similar to those defined by Whittaker (1960) for California, and more abrupt changes in parent material, soil, topography and rockiness. Superimposed on this environmentally conditioned variability are spatial changes induced by the differential biotic history.

The effect of human interference versus protection on Mediterranean upland ecosystems

Our present knowledge of the long-term effects of different modes and intensities of grazing, burning, cutting, etc., which could serve as a basis for management practices, is only fragmentary and has probably been influenced by many subjective impressions and misconceptions.

Our earlier work in connection with range management and improvement in the Galilee (Naveh 1955, 1960, 1962a, 1970) and our present ecological studies on Mount Carmel and the Samarian Hills indicate that the dynamic equilibrium between the taller, more aggressive woody species and hemi-cryptophytes and the lower herbaceous plants—including flowering geophytes and annual pasture plants—is very vulnerable and is regulated chiefly by the amount and kind of anthropogenic pressure exerted.

The adverse effect on woody Mediterranean vegetation of heavy, uncontrolled grazing, especially if combined with frequent burning and indiscriminate cutting, is well known. Depending on local site conditions and climate and on initial floristic composition, this is leading to domination by a few species of stunted trees and shrubs which are either thorny or aromatic and unpalatable. Germination is also encouraged by fire, for example *Rhamnus palaestina*, *Calycotome villosa*, *Poterium spinosum*, *Cistus and Salvia* spp., or else they are too resistant to grazing and fire to be killed out completely, as with *Pistacia lentiscus* (Naveh 1960).

The effect of 'overgrazing' on the herbaceous plants is much more complex and depends on the species of herbivore and on the timing and intensity of grazing pressure (Seligman *et al.* 1959). Typical pasture swards of mediterranean open woodlands, oak savannas and derived grasslands contain a great number of hardy and early-maturing annual, winter and spring growing grasses, legumes and forbs. These fluctuate in relation to climate and management and most are eaten at one time or another by Arabic cattle, goats, sheep or donkeys during year-round grazing. Because of frequent defoliation the productivity of these plants is low. After the first rains, during early winter germination and growth, when food is very scarce for herbivores and the soil is still bare, the greatest damage is inflicted on these pastures.

On the other hand, grazing by large beef cattle and milk-sheep herds in the vicinity of Jewish settlements is much more selective and confined chiefly to the winter and spring growth seasons. Therefore, if uncontrolled, it might be even more detrimental to the soil and may lead to the domination of a few less palatable and aggressive forbs and thistles and—because there is no browsing by goats—to reinvasion by woody plants.

Systematic studies in the Lower Galilee in typical Vallonea Oak savanna pastures have shown that by adjusting the timing and intensity of grazing in relation to the vegetative and reproductive requirements of *Avena sterilis* (the most valuable annual grass) this dynamic equilibrium can be shifted in favour of the more productive and nutritious grasses, clovers and medics. By such a rotational-deferred grazing system, the initial output of these degraded pastures has been doubled and, with additional improvements, such as NP fertilizers, selective spot-spray of weeds and perennial thistles and oak thinning, even trebled. (Naveh 1962*a*, 1970.) Similar integrated pasture ecosystem management in fenced paddocks has been adopted now by progressive farmers and collective settlements in Israel.

Although not yet measured quantitatively, it appears as if moderate and especially rotational-deferred grazing also has beneficial effects on many flowering annuals and geophytes, provided that no blanket spraying with 2, 4– is applied. In this respect, sheep seem to be less desirable than cattle because of their greater preference for broadleaved plants of the Compositae and other families. On several occasions we observed that sheep, developed a special liking for *Cyclamen persicum*, selecting their flowers systematically.

That complete and prolonged protection is by no means preferable to moderate grazing for the conservation of ecological diversity in these Mediterranean pastures is clearly demonstrated in Table 1. The higher cover percentages of tall hemicryptophytic thistles and shade tolerant perennial grasses and a reduction in the number of species is very typical in this respect. Sampling was not intensive enough to detect statistically meaningful differences in plants with very low coverage, such as *Ranunculus asiaticus* and *Cyclamen persicum*. But their greater frequencies in the grazed plot indicate that complete protection is not necessary for their conservation and might even be detrimental.

The important role of human interference in the encouragement of light-demanding geophytes and especially Orchidaceae in Mediterranean forests and shrublands was demonstrated on Site 1—a heavily browsed, previously burned and otherwise disturbed site (Table 2). Here, many other herbaceous perennials, as well as annual plants not listed in this Table, have been recorded. Site 2 is representative of the natural Allepo pine forests and open Maquis in the Carmel Park, which are being gradually invaded by taller woody plants, resulting in the reduction of frequency and vitality of geophytes. Site 3 is a typical example of the floristic impoverishment and the simplification of ecological diversity of natural upland ecosystems, induced by pine afforestation. Here, planted pine trees have replaced most of the Maquis trees, shrubs and their climbers, and from the profusion of geophytes only two, more shade tolerant, Orchidaceae, and five other geophytes have survived, chiefly on the edges of the forest. All of these Orchidaceae and most of the other geophytes, recorded by us in the Carmel National Park, prefer well-lighted niches and are mainly found in grassy or rocky openings, near pathways and edges of trees or shrubs or where the shrub canopy has been lowered and opened by browsing, cutting or burning. Apparently they can take immediate advantage of newly exposed sites and concentrate therefore in recently cleared picnic grounds on the forest edges and, as in Site 1, on previously burned areas.

Table 1. Comparison of botanical composition of two adjacent vallonea oak savanna pastures after 8 years of protection versus grazing. Neve Yaar (Lower Galilee) Spring 1962. Coverage percentages determined by 400 point quadrats along 4 transects.

	Protected pasture	Grazed pasture
Perennial grasses*	15·1	3·2
Annual grasses	32·3	40·6
Legumes	7·3	10·9
Forbs	28·7	37·7
Flowering geophytes:		
Ranunculus asiaticus L.	0	1·1
Cyclamen persicum Mill.	0·5	1·9
Perennial thistles:		
Carlina involucrata Pair	5·9	0·7
Echinops blancheanus Boiss.	1·2	0·9
Bare soil	1·0	3·0
	100·0	100·0

* In protected pasture, mainly *Dactylis glomerata*; in grazed plot mainly *Hordeum bulbosum* L.

Consequently the occurrence of a typical heliophytic orchid, *Ophris fuciflora*, is closely related to light intensity, as regulated by shrub density and height. This is shown in Fig. 1—a typical chart quadrat and profile transect from this site. Here, it appears mainly amongst the low *Pistacia lentiscus* canopy regenerating after fire, where light intensity is almost as high as in the open and reaches 1·35 g cal/cm min. Even where it grows amongst the taller and more dense *Genista sphacelata* shrubs, the light intensity is still above the threshold of 0·11 g cal/cm min found by us for Orchidaceae. This threshold is the same also for *Cephalanthera longifolia* which can be regarded as a facultative sciophyte. Therefore—as shown in Fig. 2—it appears in open

Table 2. Relative abundance of trees, shrubs, climbers and geophytes in three biotopes with different biotic history on Mount Carmel (Spring 1969)

Upper Tree Layer

	(1)	(2)	(3)
Pinus pinea L.	+		
Pinus halepensis Mill.	1	4	5
Quercus calliprinos Webb.	3		
Ceratonia siliqua L.	+		
Genista sphacelata Dec.		1	
Crataegus officinalis L.	+		

Lower Tree Layer

	(1)	(2)	(3)
Arbutus andrachne L.	+	3	1
Rhamnus alaternus L.		+	
Styrax officinalis L.	+	+	
Laurus nobilis L.		1	
Quercus calliprinos Webb.	+	4	2
Pistacia palaestina Boiss.	+	1	
Phillyrea media L.		2	1
Crataegus azarolus L.	+	2	1
Cercis siliquastrum L.		+	

Shrub Layer

	(1)	(2)	(3)
Pistacia lentiscus L.	2	1	3
Calycotome villosa (Doir) Lk.	1	2	
Genista sphacelata Dec.	2	2	2
Rhamnus palaestina Boiss.	+	+	1

Climbers

	(1)	(2)	(3)
Rubia tenuifolia D'Urv		1	+
Smilax aspera L.		1	+
Tamus communis L.		1	+
Asparagus aphyllus L.		1	+
Clematis cirrhosa L.		1	
Lonicera etrusca Santi.		+	
Prasium majus L.		1	+
Convolvulus scammonia L.		1	+
Bryonia syriaca Boiss.			+

Geophytes Layer (Orchidaceae)

	(1)	(2)	(3)
Ophrys sintenisii Fleisch et Bornm	3	+	
Ophrys dinsmorei Schltr	1	2	
Ophrys fuciflora Hal	3		
Ophrys bornmuelleri M. Scheuze	3	1	
Ophrys lutea Cav.	1	+	
Ophrys fusca LK.	1	+	
Ophrys iricolor Desf.	1		
Serapias vomeracea (Burm) Brig.	2		
Anacapiptis pyramidalis (L) Rich			1
Orchis papilionacens L.	2	+	
Orchis anatolicus Boiss		+	
Orchis gal:laeus Schltr.	3	+	
Orchis tridentatus Scop.	2	2	
Cephalanthera longifolia (Huds) Fritsch	3	2	
Limodorum abortivum (L.) Sw.			1

Other Geophytes

	(1)	(2)	(3)
Asphodelus microcarpus Viv.	2	1	2
Asphodelus tenuifolius Cav.	+		
Allium ampeloprasum L.		+	
Allium neapolitanum Cyr.	+		
Allium hirsutum Zucc.	2	1	1
Ornithogalum narbonense L.	1	1	
Iris sisyrinchium L.	1		
Iris palaestina (Bad) Boiss.	1		
Arisarum vulgare Targ.		1	
Arum dioscoridis S. et S.	+	1	
Anemone coronaria L.	1	1	1
Ranunculus asiaticus L.	2	1	
Cyclamen persicum Mill.	1	1	2
Thrincia tuberosa (L) Lam. et DC	2	1	2
Bellis silvestris Cyr.	2	1	

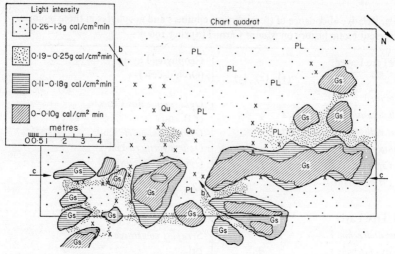

Figure 1. (*a*) Distribution of *Ophris fuciflora* (×) as related to light intensity in a disturbed *Genista sphacelata* (Gs) and *Pistacia lentiscus* (PL) stand at the Carmel National Park. The measurements were carried out in the spring of 1970 with solarimeter CM2 at 1030 h. The arrows point to the sites where the corresponding profile transects were made.

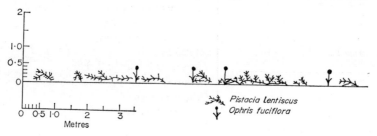

(*b*) Profile transect as indicated in Fig. 1(*a*).

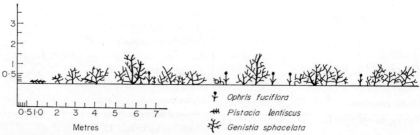

(*c*) Profile transect as indicated in Fig. 1(*a*).

niches or amongst the low *Pistacia lentiscus* canopy, but only where the horizontal branches of *Pinus halepensis* are not more than 4·0 m above the ground.

The attempt to convert the few remaining, natural and open Allepo pine stands on Mount Carmel into dense, artificial pine plantations and thereby

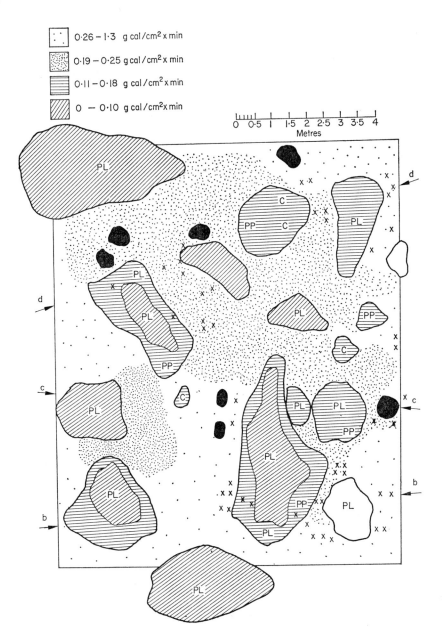

Figure 2. (*a*) Distribution of *Cephalanthera longifolia* (×) as related to light intensity in a *Pinus halepensis* (black area) and *Pistacia lentiscus* (PL) stand at the Carmel National Park. The measurements were carried out in the spring of 1970 with solarimeter CM2 at 0930 h. The arrows point to the sites where the corresponding profile transects were made. Other plants present are the *Pistacia palaestina* (PP) and *Cistus salvifolius* (C).

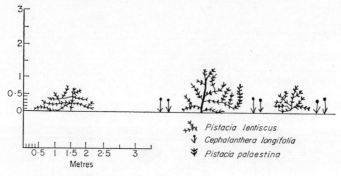

(*b*) Profile transect as indicated in Fig. 2(*a*).

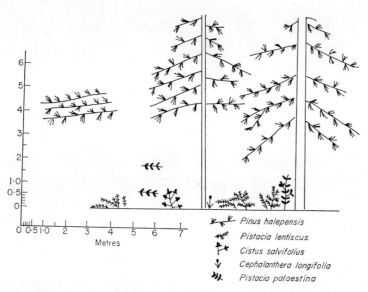

(*c*) Profile transect as indicated in Fig. 2(*a*).

to sacrifice much of their special scenic, recreational and wildlife values is most regrettable. This is especially so in view of the low timber and forest production potential of such rocky hill sites. The situation is even worse in regular, commercial pine afforestations, where up to 2,500 trees per ha are planted. Here, the lack of light and the accumulation of slowly decomposing needle leaf-litter, apparently containing germination-inhibition kolines (Yardeni & Evenari 1952), are even less inducive to the development of a herbaceous understorey. This correlation between the density of the pine canopy and needle-litter mulch and absence of a herbaceous vegetation was revealed also in a recent extensive forest survey in Israel (Duer, pers. comm.).

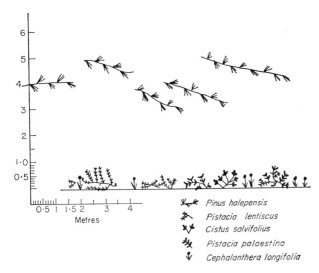

Pinus halepensis
Pistacia lentiscus
Cistus salvifolius
Pistacia palaestina
Cephalanthera longifolia

(*d*) Profile transect as indicated in Fig. 2(*a*).

In Table 3 an interesting example is presented of the 'natural potential vegetation' which might be expected after 50 years of complete protection of Maquis *Quercus calliprinos—Phyllirea media* in a Nature Forest Reservation, established by the British Mandatory Forest Service after World War I in the Samarian mountains. These vegetation records were collected only with the greatest difficulty because of the great density and inaccessibility of the tree and shrub canopy. From 20 woody species, listed altogether on the north (most mesic) slope, only 5 gained any importance and very few herbaceous plants found their last refuge near rock edges.

Recent studies on Mount Carmel (Rosenzweig 1969, Shachori *et al.* 1968) have shown that sclerophyll and evergreen, deep-rooted trees such as *Quercus calliprinos*, and to a lesser degree also *Pinus halepensis*, are, during the summer, depleting the water surplus stored in the karstic-limestone rocks down to 8–10 m. Their water consumption is therefore 100–350 cub. m. higher than that of the winter and spring growing herbaceous plants. Consequently, this water is lost for spring flow and ground water storage in the catchment areas of these brush-covered watersheds, and thereby for irrigation, wildlife and recreation.

Unfortunately, we lack reliable information on the trophic structure, energy flow and nutrient cycling in these ecosystems. But we can safely assume that in such closed, uniform and monotonous Maquis thickets there are fewer favourable niches and edge habitats available for insects, reptiles, birds and mammals, than in their unprotected, open and multi-layered counterparts. The loss of floristic and structural diversity will be reflected in

Table 3. Coverage and abundance of woody plants in closed maquis after 50 years of protection. 'Um Rechan Forest Preservation'—Samarian Mountains. Altitude 400–70 m; North slope 40–45 per cent, very rocky, dark Terra rosa soil.

Name of Species	% cover* in quadrate	Number† plants in transects
Trees (2–5 m ht)		
Quercus calliprinos Webb.	40	157
Phillyrea media L.	27	160
Pistacia palaestina Boiss.	8	86
Rhamnus alaternus L.	+	2
Quercus ithaburensis Bois.		24
Quercus infectoria Oliv.		2
Arbutus andrachne L.		3
Styrax officinalis L.	+	2
Crataegus azarolus L.	+	6
Cercis siliquastrum L.		
Shrubs (1–2 m ht)		
Pistacia lentiscus L.	75	48
Rhamnus palaestina Boiss.	3	29
Calycotome villosa (Doir.) Lk.	4	61
Dwarf shrubs—< 1 m ht		
Cistus salvifolius L.	13	93
Poterium spinosum L.		1
Climbers		
Rubia tenuifolia D'Urv	+	
Smilax aspera L.	+	
Asparagus aphyllus L.	+	
Clematis cirrhosa L.	+	

* Cover estimated in 13 quadrats of 10 × 10 m along 9 transects of 150–200 m.
† Number of plants in 7 transects, 1,340 m long (2 transects too steep and rocky for exact counting).

a lower efficiency of energy interception and transfer and a reduction in channels for nutrient and water circulation and storage capacity. In thermodynamic terms this means an increase of entropy at the cost of all-over productivity and stability. It might be manifested by the great vulnerability to fire of these dense Maquis stands, accumulating large masses of highly combustible, dead material, dry branches and sclerophyllous leaves. A similar situation has also evolved in the Californian Chaparral, where the artificial prevention of natural fires is increasing the hazards and only delaying their disastrous results (Naveh 1967, Schultz 1967).

The place of goat grazing and fire in integrated upland ecosystem management

Amongst the anthropogenic defoliation agents which seem to play such an important role as homeostatic controls, goat browsing and fire are most controversial, because they have been blamed as the chief culprits for Mediterranean land ruin. However, in scientific management of natural resources, this irrational, wholesale condemnation should be replaced by a more balanced and unbiased reassessment of their place in Mediterranean hill land use in general and specifically in conservation management.

The possibilities of rational and profitable utilization of milk and meat potential of the Mediterranean black Mamber goat in rugged and shrub-covered terrain, without endangering sustained productivity, have been discussed in a special FAO seminar (French 1965). Practical suggestions to bring about a rise in the standard of goat husbandry and pasture management have been made also in Israel (Laor pers. comm., Weitz 1964), on which improved and more conservative management practices should be based.

Of great interest for the controlled use of goat browsing in Mediterranean upland reserves and parks is the recent promising experience gained in Israel by the use of improved Angora goats from Texas for mohair and meat production in fenced Maquis pastures in Western Galilee (Naveh 1962*b*, 1968). With the help of these goats, problems connected with the need for daily milking and the difficulties arising from the control of the much more agile Mamber goats could be overcome. If the good economic prospects envisaged from high-quality Angora goats in well-managed brush ranges could be realized, they could become a very attractive proposition in modern, conservative Mediterranean hill farming. At the same time, they could be used as a valuable biological tool in the conversion of dense Maquis and Garigue into open woodland and savanna pastures, in combination with cattle. Between 1952 and 1960, brush conversions for range improvement were carried out in several collective settlements in the Western Galilee by integrated ecosystem management (Naveh 1960, 1967; Soil Conservation Service 1964). In this, the suppression of undesirable dwarf-shrubs and shrubs was achieved by fire and arboricidal treatment and the encouragement of valuable pasture plants by reseeding with perennial grasses and legumes in the brush ashes together with rotational-deferred grazing. At the same time, valuable trees, such as *Ceratonia siliqua, Pistacia palaestina, Quercus* spp., were protected from fire and spraying.

On the basis of these extensive field studies it was concluded that controlled burning can be used as an efficient tool for the quick removal of dense and well-developed brush cover on high potential sites and the creation of favourable conditions for the establishment and production of perennial grasses, such as *Oryzopsis miliacea* and *Phalaris tuberosa*, provided that the area is protected from grazing one year prior to, and after, the burning and that vigorous brush regeneration is checked.

Great objections have been expressed against the use of fire because of the danger of accelerated erosion. However, our studies revealed that in the first winter after burning dense shrubland, no trace could be detected of runoff and soil movement even on steep and rocky slopes and even after heavy early winter rain storms. Fire affects mainly the upper 5 cm of the Aoo and Ao soil profiles. These are converted into a 1–3 cm high layer of compacted ashes, charred leaf litter and humus, and provide an ideal seed-bed for broadcasted pasture plants. The organic matter content of these Maquis soils is very high, so that even after losing about a fifth by fire, 10 per cent is still retained in the total soil profile of about 30 cm and 13–16 per cent in the upper soil layer (Table 4).

Table 4. The effect of burning on organic matter of upper 4 cm of a dark brown rendzina maquis soil, beneath trees and shrubs. Mazuba—(Western Galilee). Fall 1953.

Name of plant in sampling location	Depth cm	Organic matter % Before burning	After burning
Quercus calliprinos Webb.	0–2	18·13	16·36
	2–4	16·22	13·28
Ceratonia siliqua L.	0–2	23·35	14·59
	2–4	18·27	12·05
Pistacia palaestina Boiss.	0–2	16·48	14·59
	2–4	18·27	12·32
Pistacia lentiscus L.	0–2	22·30	20·17
	2–4	16·31	14·25
Average	0–2	20·7	16·7 −4
	2–4	16·9	13·2 −3·7

This fact, together with the excellent granular structure of these Brown Rendzina and Terra rossa-Maquis soils, may explain their high infiltration capacity and stability. On poorer sites, however, with less fertile, calcareous soils, and a lower shrub cover, the danger of soil erosion is much larger, especially if these are grazed prior to and after the burn.

Together with the reseeded plants, naturally occuring, relic perennial grasses and many flowering geophytes, such as *Crocus, Ochrus, Ophyrys*,

Allium and *Colchicum* spp. spread after the fire (Loeb 1960, Naveh 1960). Our studies indicated that in addition to the opening of the shrub canopy and the release of soluble minerals (especially potassium), fire may fulfil vital functions in the removal of phytotoxic kolines and in the stimulation of germination and regeneration of these plants. If this is confirmed by our present study, fire may become an indispensible tool in conservation management.

Although good returns from such converted upland pasture ecosystems can be expected (Weitz 1964), heavy initial investments are likely to inhibit commercial application by private farmers and collective settlements. This would be less so if development schemes in mediterranean hill land were approached on a broader, regional scale and aimed at optimization of multiple use benefit for pasture, recreation, tourism, wildlife and watershed management (Naveh 1968).

Conclusions

On the basis of our present knowledge we can conclude that for the purpose of the conservation of structural, functional and biological diversity of mediterranean woodland, shrubland and grassland ecosystems, the continuation of active human intervention at one level or the other is essential.

In nature reserves a flexible and dynamic conservation policy should be adopted, similar to that proposed recently by Mörzer Bruijns for Israel (1969). In this, destructive disturbances, such as overgrazing and mass-recreation on one hand, and irreversible, non-ecological interventions, such as monospecies pine afforestations, should be avoided. Until more reliable information is gathered from systematic ecosystem and management studies, three main levels of anthropogenic intervention should be adopted:

1 Continuation of controlled 'conventional' defoliation activities—including moderate goat grazing and occasional fires—and confinement of 'modern' disturbances and activities to prescribed and restricted areas and footpaths. Buffer zones should be as large as possible.

2 Setting aside considerable portions of representative biotopes and landscape units for complete protection as control and study areas.

3 The reservation of other areas for the experimental manipulation of ecosystems, where long-term and overall effects of different intensities and modes of grazing, cutting, burning, spraying as well as planting could be tested systematically. The emphasis in these manipulation studies should be on conservation of maxium biological diversity, as outlined above, and the application of their results to larger, conventionally managed areas.

In national parks and other upland-wildlands which are open for public recreational use, our goal should be the optimization of landscape values to enable maximum enjoyment for visitors with minimum damage to natural resources. The creation of densely planted, fire-prone and monotonous 'production forests' or inaccessible Maquis 'protection forests' will minimize these values. On the other hand, the conservation and active stimulation of biological diversity by means of integrated ecosystem management will maximize these values by the creation of edge habitats and favourable niches through the conversion of Maquis, Garigue and Batha into open forests, woodlands and savannas with well-developed and ornamental shade and forage trees and a rich herb layer.

For the remaining open upland ecosystems, the alternative to the present misuse and neglect and the forestry production or protection approach should be multiple-land use patterns based on over-all dynamic planning of scientific, ecological and technological management. This should ensure the rational utilization of these renewable resources of vegetation, wildlife, soil and water on the basis of the current and anticipated needs of society and the biological potential of these ecosystems. Some of the choices for such alternatives have been indicated above and others are described elsewhere (Naveh & Ron 1966, Naveh 1970).

These choices can be made only after a systematic and comprehensive study of the ecological, socio-economical and hydrological implications and by provision of objective parameters for cost/benefit analyses of the various alternatives and combinations in different situations. Therefore mediterranean hill-land use should give first priority to integrated upland-ecosystem studies, guided by more enlightened and unbiased approaches than those prevailing, at present, amongst most planners, decision makers and administrators of these mediterranean wildlands.

Summary

One of the chief aims of conservation of untillable mediterranean upland ecosystems which have been influenced for long periods by anthropogenic pressure, is the preservation of their striking structural, functional and biological diversity. These are threatened at present by urban, industrial and agricultural expansion on one hand and by creation of dense and monotonous Allepo pine 'production' or inaccessible Maquis 'protection' forests on the other.

Both in oak savannas and in open Maquis and Garigue, the dynamic equilibrium between phanerophytes, chamaephytes, hemicryptophytes and the geophyte and therophyte understorey, containing many flowering plants and favourable niches and edge habitats for animals, can be maintained only by active human intervention.

Therefore, a dynamic and integrated ecosystem approach is necessary in which grazing, cutting, burning and other defoliation agents can be used as management tools. In nature reserves this implies the continuation of moderate, controlled and non-destructive intervention, together with protection and experimental manipulation of representative ecosystems. In national parks and open wildlands it implies optimization of landscape values for mass-recreation or for multiple use benefit for pasture, forest, recreation, tourism, wildlife and watershed management. This can be achieved by conversion of Maquis, Garigue and Batha into open forests, woodlands and savannas. For dynamic planning of these land-use patterns comprehensive and enlightened ecosystem research in mediterranean upland is urgently required.

References

ANAGNOSTOPOULOS G.L. (1967) Landscape planning in different areas: assessment and applications. *P.v. Rapp.* & *Réun. tech. Un. int. Conserv. Nat.* 1966, 52–73.

EGLER F. (1954) Philosophical and practical considerations of the Braun-Blanquet system of phytosociology. *Castanea* 19, 45–60.

ELLENBERG H. (1963) *Vegetation Mitteleuropas.* BdIV/2. Einfuehrung in die Phytologie (H. Walter). Stuttgart.

EIG A. (1927) On the vegetation of Palestine. *Institute of Agriculture & Natural History, Agr. Exp. Sta. Bull.* 7.

FRENCH H.H. (1965) *The goat in the Mediterranean climate zone.* Report on goat raising policies in the Mediterranean Region. Rome FAO.

KOEPPEN W. (1923) *Die Klimate der Erde.* Berlin.

LOEB H. (1960) Regeneration of Maqui shrubland after burning. In *The Western Galilee,* 271–7. Tel-Aviv (Hebrew).

MARGAROPOULOS P. (1952) Mountain range management and improvement in Greece. *J. Range Mgmt* 5; 200–6.

MÖRZER BRUIJNS M.F. (1969) *Proposals for the management of nature reserves in Israel.* Report to the Nature Reserve Authorities of Israel. Mimeo.

NAVEH Z. (1955) Some aspects of range improvement in a mediterranean environment. *J. Range Mgmt* 8; 265–70.

NAVEH Z. (1960) *Agro-ecological aspects of brush range improvement in the Maqui belt of Israel.* Ph.D. Thesis, Hebrew University, Jerusalem. (Hebrew.)

NAVEH Z. (1962a) The effect of rotational-deferred grazing, spraying and fertilizing on the output of a mediterranean hill pasture in Israel, Neve Yaar 1953/54–1958/59. *Hassadeh* 43, 655–68. (Hebrew.)

NAVEH Z. (1962b) Angora goats as a solution for Maqui-brush utilization. *The Shepherd* 43, 27–30. (Hebrew.)

NAVEH Z. (1967) Mediterranean ecosystems and vegetation types in California and Israel *Ecology* 48, 445–59.

NAVEH Z. (1968) Multiple use of mediterranean range land—new approaches to old problems. *Ann. arid Zone* 7; 163–76.

NAVEH Z. (1970) The effect of intensive ecosystem management on the productivity of a mediterranean oak savanna pasture in Israel. *Proc. XIIth. Int. Grassld. Congr.,* 59–63.

NAVEH Z. & RON B. (1966) Agro-ecological management of mediterranean ecosystems—the base for intensive pastoral hill-land use in Israel. *Proc. Xth Int. Grasld Congr.*, 872–4.

OVINGTON J.D. (1964) The ecological basis of the management of woodland nature reserves in Great Britain. *Jubilee Symp. Suppl. J. Ecol.* **52** 29–38.

POORE M.D. (1955) The use of phytosociological methods in ecological investigations. II. Practical issues involved in an attempt to apply the Braun Blanquet system. *J. Ecol.* **50**; 369–91.

ROSENZWEIG D. (1969) *Study of difference in effects of forest and other vegetative covers on water-yield.* Annual report No. 4 for the USDA of Project No. A–10–FS–13.

SHACHORI A.Y., ROSENZWEIG D., ISRAELI M. & STANHILL, G. (1968) *Study of difference in effects of forest and other vegetative covers on water yield.* Annual report No. 3 for USDA of Project No. A–10–FS–13.

SELIGMAN N., RAZ Z., TADMOR N. & NAVEH Z. (1959) *Natural pastures of Israel, vegetation, carrying capacity and improvement.* Tel-Aviv. (Hebrew).

SCHULTZ A.M. (1967) The ecosystem as a conceptual tool in the management of natural resources. *Quality and quantity in resources management.* Berkeley.

Soil Conservation Service, Israel. (1964) *Conversion of Maqui into pasture parks as a means of enrichment of ground water,* Ministry of Agric. Tel-Aviv. (Mimeo. Hebrew.)

TISDALE E.W. (1967) *A study of dry-land conditions and problems in portions of South-west Asia, East and North Africa and the Eastern Mediterranean.* Report 3, Dry-lands Res. Inst. Univer. California, Riverside. (Mimeo.)

TÜXEN R. (1956) Die heutige potentielle natuerliche Vegetation als Gegenstand der Vegetationskartierung, *Angew. PflSoziol.* **13**, 5–42.

UNESCO, Arid Zone Research Team. (1963) *A bioclimatical map of the Mediterranean zone and its homologues.* Paris.

WEITZ M. (1964) *Goat browsing in Maqui vegetation in Israel.* Soil Conservation Service, Israel, Report. (Mimeo. Hebrew.)

WHITTAKER R.H. (1960) Vegetation of the Siskiyou Mountains, Oregon and California. *Ecolog. Monogr.* **30**, 279–338.

WHYTE R.O. (1961) Evolution of land use in South Eastern Asia. *Arid Zone Res.* **16**, 57–118. Paris.

YARDENI D. & EVENARI M. (1952) The germination inhibiting and phytotoxic effects of certain leaves and leaf extracts. *Phyton, B. Aires* **2**, 1–17.

ZOHARY M. (1962) *Plant life in Palestine.* New York.

Indexes

Author Index

Bold figures refer to pages where full references appear

Abedi Z.H.   197 **200**
Abeywickerema B.A.   297 300 309 564
  572 **579**
Ackefors H.   178 **200**
Ackermann A.   389 **390**
Adamson R.S.   564 575 **579**
Adriani M.J.   46 58 59 60 61 557 **561**
Ahlgren C.E.   430 431 **433**
Ahlgren I.F.   431 **433**
Albion R.G.   566 **579**
Alexander G.   419 **422**
Alfred E.R.   297 **309**
Allen D.L.   420 **422**
Allen G.P.   27 **30**
Allen S.E.   96 97 102 156 164 **165**
Amirthalingam C.   297 **309**
Anagnostopoulos G.L.   606 **621**
Anderson J.   449 **455**
Anderson P.K.   189 193 **200**
Andrzejewska L.   534 542 **551**
Angus A.   319–**31**
Antonovics J.   180 **200**
Archer A.L.   394 **404**
Arnold G.A.   178 **200**
Arnold G.W.   529 **551**
Arnon D.I.   107 **113**
Assmann E.   42 **43**
Austin R.C.   430 431 **433**
Auten J.T.   430 **433**

Bailey-Watts A.E.   233 **238**
Baird P.D.   469 **485**
Baisinger D.H.   430 431 **433**
Baker H.G.   178 199 **200**
Ball D.F.   188 **132**
Bannikov A.G.   419 420 422 **423**
Barclay-Estrup P.   93 94 95 101 **102**
Barnett S.A.   418 **423**
Bartley D.D.   153 **165**
Batcheler C.L.   416 **422**
Batten J.L.   189 **200**
Bayer A.W.   360 **365**
Bayfield N.   473 478 485 **469–85**

Bayley R.W.   229 **238**
Beadle N.C.W.   431 **433**
Beauchamp R.S.A.   307 **309**
Beaufait W.R.   432 **433**
Beck G.   130 131 **132**
Beechey C.V.   189 **205**
Beeton A.M.   230 231 **238**
Beevor H.E.   576 **579**
Belcher J.H.   231 233 **238**
Bell J.   180 **206**
Bell R.H.V.   351 362 363 365 387 390 395
  404
Bellamy D.J.   58 **61**
Berndt C.H.   219 **220**
Berndt R.M.   219 **220**
Berry R.J.   177–**206** 181–3 185 187 189–
  94 197 199 **200** 201 204 **205**
Bews J.W.   337 **348**
Bielling P.   425 **434**
Bigger J.W.   226 **238**
Bindernagel J.A.   394 **403**
Bindloss M.E.   233 **238**
Birch L.C.   196 **201**
Birks H.J.B.   153 **165**
Bishop J.A.   181 **201**
Biswell H.H.   431 **435**
Bitterlich W.   35 **43**
Björk S.   252 **267**
Black C.A.   120 **132**
Black J.M.   511 **515**
Blair-West J.R.   371 **385**
Boam T.B.   191 **206**
Böcher T.W.   79 **89**
Bodmer W.F.   188 189 **201**
Bogdan A.V.   360 361 **365**
Bogner W.   72 **76**
Bole B.P.   431 **433**
Bonner J.   105 **113**
Bonomi G.   230 **238**
Bornemissza G.F.   525 **526**
Borthwick H.A.   347 **349**
Bott E.   371 **385**
Boughey A.S.   373 383 **385**
Braathe P.   105 **113**
Bradley R.T.   33 **43**

Bradshaw A.D.   72 76 77 183–4 196–7 201 203 204 466 468
Brantjes N.B.M.   313 315
Bredon R.M.   337 348 360 365
Breeze E.L.   188 201
Brereton J.leG.   207–21
Brian P.W.   106 113
Bridgewater P.   59 61
Brinkhurst R.O.   231 238
Brinkman K.A.   41 43
Brook A.J.   233 238
Brougham R.W.   511 515
Brown A.W.A.   197 200
Brown E.R.   426 433
Bruckert S.   130 132
Buechner H.K.   319 321 325 329 331 420 422
Bumpus H.C.   180 201
Burges N.A.   131 132
Burton T.L.   467 468
Buttery B.R.   265 267

Cadbury C.J.   193 204
Cailleux A.   558 561
Cain A.J.   180 183–4 189 190 201
Cairns D.   520 526
Calhoun J.B.   418 422
Cameron A.G.   438 453 455
Cameron D.   519 526
Camin J.H.   180 203
Cantlon J.E.   26 30
Carrick R.   218 221
Carson H.L.   199 201
Casebeer R.L.   351 361 365
Chadwick M.J.   72 76 466 468
Chapman S.B.   95 102
Charles A.H.   26–7 30
Chevrou R.B.   35 43
Chivu I.P.   265 268
Christy M.   564 572 579
Clapham A.R.   117 132 152 485 501 596
Clarke B.C.   180 185 193 202
Clarke B.L.   483 485
Clarke C.A.   189 190 202
Clarkson D.T.   74 76
Clausen J.   186 202
Clifford M.H.   585 589 596
Cochran W.G.   405 411
Coghland J.P.   371 385
Cole D.   431 433
Commonwealth Bureau of Pasture and Field Crops   511 515
Condon P.   110 113

Connaughton C.A.   431 433
Connolly D.   179 206
Cook L.M.   190 202
Cooke G.W.   226 238
Cooper C.F.   235 238
Cooper J.P.   188 202
Cooper R.W.   426 433
Corey R.B.   226 238
Cousens J.E.   36 43
Covarrubias R.   5 14
Craig C.W.   589 596
Cramer O.P.   432 435
Crampton H.E.   184 202
Crawford C.S.   451 552
Creed E.R.   178 182 202
Crocker J.   178 200
Cross C.   541 552
Crothers J.H.   181–3 191 199 201
Cumming B.G.   347 348
Cunia T.   35 43 44
Currey J.D.   185 201

Dallman A.A.   154 166
Dansereau P.   46 61
Darby H.C.   567 579
Darlington P.J.   297 309
Dasmann R.F.   395 403 404 420 422 426 427 434 450 456
Daubenmire R.   7 14 426 433 529 541 551
Davies G.E.   96–7 103
Davies L.J.   271–93
Davies M.   27 30
Davies W.   17 27 29 30 31
Davis K. P.   425–6 433
Davis P.E.   197 201
Davison E.C.   369 385
Dawkins H.C.   33–44 36 41–2 43 319 321 325 329 331
Day F.   298 309
Degerbøl M.   190 202
Dempster J.P.   517–26 517 521 526 544 551
Denton D.A.   371 385
Deraniyagala P.E.P.   297 298 309
Derksen J.W.M.   52 61
Dessauer H.C.   187 202
Di Castri F.   5 14
Dieren J.W. van   11 14
Dimbleby G.W.   130 132
Diver C.   184 202
Dixon M.J.   432 433
Dobzhansky T.   181 189 193 197 202
Dommergues Y.   130 131 132

Donald C.M.   129 133 511 515
Dony J.G.   557 558
Dowdeswell W.H.   180-2 193 202 203
Dowrick V.P.J.   189 203
Driessche R. van den   130 131 132
Driscoll R.S.   426 433
Droop M.R.   229 240
Druce G.C.   583 596
Drummond D.C.   179 203
Duchaufour A.   41 43
Duffey E.   199 203 528 533 551 581-97
    583 590 594 596
Dunn J.A.   179 197 203
Dykyjová D.   265 267
Dyson-Hudson N.   401 403
Dzieciolowski R.   438 440 456

Eddy A.   154 164 166
Eden T.   430 433
Edmond D.B.   483 485
Edmonds J.W.   179 206
Edmondson W.T.   230 239
Edwards D.C.   337 338 339 348 360 365
Edwards R.W.   286 292
Eggeling J.   361 365 437 439 456
Egler F.   607 622
Ehrlich P.R.   180 203
Eig A.   606 621
Einarsen A.S.   420 422
Elder E.N.   419 424
Ellenberg H.   66 76 607 621
Elliott R.J.   96 97 102
Elton C.S.   185 203 437 456 533 538 552
    555 561 588 596
Emden H.F. van   542 552
Ernst A.   189 203
Estes R.D.   414 422
Evans G.H.   235 239
Evans H.   438 453 456
Evans S.A.   27 30
Evenari M.   614 622
Ewart A.J.   337 348

Fabijanowski J.   603 604
Falconer D.S.   559 561
Fandeev A.A.   419 422
Fernando C.H.   295-310 295 297 301-2
    305 307 309
Ferrell W.K.   431 433
Fiala K.   241-69 245 249 251-2 257 268
Field C.R.   321 329 331 351 365 395 398
    403

Finney D.J.   35 43
Fish G.R.   230 239
Fisher R.A.   179 184-9 203
Fjerdingstad E.   274 292
Foenander F.   217 221
Folkes B.F.   85 89
Ford E.B.   181-2 184-6 190-3 197-8 202
    203
Ford H.D.   198 203
Forsberg C.   229 236 239
Foster J.   22 26 30
Fox H.M.   285 293
Fox J.E.D.   36 43
French H.H.   617 621
Frick K.E.   525 526
Frink C.R.   73 77
Fritschen L.J.   432 435
Fryer J.C.F.   586 596
Fryer J.D.   27 30
Fuller L.A.   413 422
Furtado J.I.   307 309

Gabrielson I.N.   14
Gaevskaya N.S.   245 265 267
Galazö G.I.   230 239
Galpin F.W.   572 579
Garman E.H.   431 433
Garren K.H.   431 433
Gates C.E.   405 410 411
Gaumann E.   110 113
Gee J.M.   178 203
Geist V.   403 413-24 414 416 419 420-1
    422
Gerletti M.   230 238
Gibson J.M.   431 434
Gigon A.   72 76
Gilchrist D.A.   16 30
Gillett J.D.   197 203
Gimingham C.H.   91-103 93-6 101 102
    103 164 166
Gingrich S.F.   41 43
Goddard J.   351 365
Goding J.R.   371 385
Godwin H.   583 589 596
Goodall D.W.   26 30
Goodall J. van Lawick   414 423
Goodhart C.D.   185 193 203
Goodrich E.S.   186 203
Gore A.J.P.   164 166
Gorham E.   265 268
Graham A.D.   393-404 429 434
Grant S.A.   93 96 102 541 552
Grant V.   186 203

Green F.H.W.   153 166 480 485
Green H.E.   115–18 122 124 127 129 132
Gregor A.   244 268
Gregory R.P.G.   183–4 197 201 203
Greig-Smith P.   500 515
Grier C.   431 433
Griffiths B.M.   237 239
Grime J.P.   67–8 76 77
Grubb P.J.   115–33 115–17 122 124 127
      129 132
Grzimek B.   360 365 400 403
Grzimek M.   360 365 400 403
Gulliver P.H.   401 403
Gunary D.   72 77
Gwynne M.D.   351 362–3 365 387 390

Haertl E.J.   236 240
Hafez E.S.E.   419 423
Haines F.M.   430 431 434
Haldane J.B.S.   179 203
Haller K.E.   36 43 411
Hallsworth E.G.   75 76
Hanawalt R.B.   346 349
Handley W.R.C.   109 111 113
Hare F.K.   153 166
Harley J.B.   566 579
Harley J.L.   66 76 131 132
Harlow R.F.   425 434
Harper F.C.   483 485
Harper J.L.   15–31 17 27 31 519 526
Harris H.   187 203
Harrison B.J.   188 205
Hart C.E.   566 580
Harthorn A.M.   395 403
Harwood R.F.   541 552
Hasel A.A.   34 43
Haskell G.   188 204
Haslam S.   258 260 265 267
Hasler A.D.   225 239
Hatchell G.E.   431 434
Hawkes H.A.   271–93 271 291 293
Hawkes R.B.   525 526
Haycock P.   179 206
Heady H.F.   360 365
Heeres E.   46 62
Hejný S.   241–2 244 248 251 256 258 262
      266 267 268
Held A.J. den   47 63
Hemingway P.   405–11
Hemming H.G.   106 113
Heptner V.G.   420 423
Herman S.G.   178 205
Heteša J.   244 268

Hiesey W.M.   186 202
Higgs D.E.B.   68 76
Higler L.W.G.   311–15 311 313 315
Hines W.W.   426 434
Hoagland D.R.   107 113
Hofstad J.G.L.   52 61
Holdgate M.W.   555 561
Holloway J.K.   525 526
Holmes P.   236 239
Holroyd J.C.   414 423
Holub J.   244 268
Hooper F.F.   236 240
Hooper M.D.   61 555–61
Hoover E.F.   431 435
Hope-Simpson J.F.   70 76 85 89
Hopkins B.   557 561
Hopkins H.G.   430 431 434
Hori S.   230 239
Horn E.E.   431 434
Horrell C.R.   360 365
Hoskins W.G.   566 580
Hubby J.L.   187 199 205
Hudec K.   245 268
Hulten E.   79 89 153 166
Hundt R.   66 76
Hunt R.   68 76
Hunt W.G.   187 190 191 205
Hunter R. F.   93 96 102 541 552
Hurst H.M.   131 132
Husák Š.   245 257–8 268
Hynes H.B.N.   227 239 271 293

Imber D.   199 206
Indrasena H.H.A.   305 307 309
Indri E.   230 238
Isaac L.A.   430 431 434
Isambaev A.I.   265 268
Israeli M.   615 622
Iversen J.   566 580

Jackson M.L.   117 118 132
Jacquin F.   130 132
Jain S.K.   183 204
James D.B.   68 76
James P.W.   152
Jefferies R.L.   68 72 77
Jeffrey D.W.   58 71 79–89 86 89 151
Jepson W.F.   542 552
Jerison H.J.   417 423
Johnson D.S.   304 309
Johnson W.E.   190 205
Johnston D.R.   33 43

Johnston R.F.   178 **204**
Jones E.W.   460 **485**
Jones Ll.L.   21 25 30 69 **77**
Jones M.G.   16 17 24 26 30 **5**42 544 **552**
Jowett D.   72 76 466 **468**
Juhren G.   431 **435**
Juhren M.C.   431 **435**

Karn M.N.   180 **204**
Kayll A.J.   96 **102**
Keay R.V.J.   41 **43**
Kempton D.P.   179 197 **203**
Kenworthy J.B.   94 96 **103**
Kern H.   110 **113**
Kerr A.J.   572 **580**
Kettlewell H.B.D.   178 180 186 189 **204**
Kilburn P.D.   557 **561**
King J.M.B.   190 **201**
Kirven M.N.   178 **205**
Klawitter R.A.   431 **434**
Klein D.R.   413 421 **423**
Klika J.   244 **268**
Klotzli F.   387 **390**
Knapp G.   387 **390**
Knapp R.   387–90 387–9 **390**
Koeppen W.   605 **621**
Kolak E.E.   431 **434**
Kolkwitz R.   274 **293**
Komarek R.   425 **434**
Koss G.   351 361 **365**
Kozhov M.M.   230 **239**
Krajicek J.E.   41 **43**
Krantz G.S.   422 **423**
Kravchenko D.   398 **404**
Krotkevich P.G.   252 **268**
Kuc J.   110 **113**
Kühme W.   414 **423**
Kuznetsov S.I.   230 **239**
Kvet J.   241–68 245 249 251–2 256–7 **268**
Kydd D.D.   497–8 512 **515**

Lack D.   181 189 **204**
Lack E.   181 **204**
Laing E.V.   106 **113**
Lamb H.H.   139 140 **152**
Lambert J.M.   265 **267**
Lamotte M.   184 **204**
Lamprey H.F.   360 363 **365**
Langdale-Brown I.   321 **331**
Laws R.M.   319 329 331 395 **403**
Lawton R.M.   **333–6**
Learner M.A.   286 **292**

Lebedeva L.S.   419 **422**
Ledger H.P.   395 400 **404**
Lee B.T.O.   188 **204**
Lee R.B.   394 **403**
Leentvaar P.   313 **315**
Leertouwer J.   49 57 **62**
Lees D.R.   192 **204**
Leeuwen C.G. van   5 13 14 47 54–8 61 **62**
LeGrande W.P.   431 **434**
Lehr J.J.   118 **132**
Leopold A.S.   200 204 425–7 **434**
Lerner M.   199 **204**
Leuthold W.   414 **423**
Levchenko F.I.   129 **132**
Levitan M.   189 **204**
Lewontin R.C.   187 199 **205**
Liddell H.S.   418 419 **423**
Lin S.Y.   305 **310**
Lindqvist G.   229 **239**
Ling S.W.   305 308 **310**
Lioucourt F. de   41 **43**
Lisle E.   16 **30**
Livens J.   130 **132**
Livingstone F.B.   192 **204**
Lloyd P.S.   67 77 80 84 **89**
Lock J.M.   320 331 **337–49**
Locket G.H.   **596**
Lockie J.S.   96–9 100 **103**
Lodge R.W.   72 76 466 **468**
Loeb H.   619 **621**
Loetsch F.   36 43 **411**
Łomnicki A.   **599–604**
Longhurst W.   426–7 **434**
Losos B.   244 **268**
Lotti T.   431 **434**
Loucks O.L.   57 **62**
Lousley J.E.   497 **515**
Lovat, Lord   93 **103**
Lowdermilk W.C.   431 **434**
Lowe V.P.W.   437–56 439 440 444 446–8 **456**
Lowe-McConnell R.H.   304 307 **310**
Luck K.   591 **596**
Luff M.L.   538 **552**
Lund J.W.G.   225–40 225 229 235 236 **239**
Lush I.E.   186 **204**
Luther H.   244 **268**
Lutz H.J.   425 430 **434**

Maarel E. van der   5 14 45–63 45–6 48–9 54 56–60 62 557 **561**
Macan T.T.   233 235 **237**

MacArthur R.H.   555 561
McBride G.   217 221
McCullough D.   420 423
McGarity J.W.   340 349
McGowan J.C.   106 113
Mackareth F.J.H.   226 235 239
Mackie D.W.   178 204
McLaughlin J.J.A.   229 240
McNeilly T.S.   180 183 197 201 204
McPherson J.K.   111 113 346 349
McVean D.N.   96–9 100 103 153 166
McWhirter K.G.   181–2 202 203 205
Maire R.   337 348
Manley G.   80 89
Mann K.H.   286 293
Manson-Baker P.   399 403
Margalev R.   5 7 14 55 62 534 552
Margaropoulos P.   605 621
Marks T.C.   153–66
Marshall B.   337 348
Marshall C.   58 61
Marshall W.H.   405 411 541 552
Marsson M.   274 293
Martin M.H.   564 580
Martin P.   110 113
Mason G.K.   590 596
Mason L.G.   181 205
Masson H.   340 348
Mather K.   188 201 205 206
May L.H.   511 515
Mayr E.   191 205
Merrell D.J.   180 205
Merrifield R.C.J.   115–18 122 124 127 129
    132
Meyer H.A.   34 43
Milburn T.R.   337–49
Miles J.   96 103 111 112 113
Miles S.C.   418 423
Miller G.R.M.   96 97 103 111 112 113 480
    485
Miller H.A.   425 434
Miller R.S.   533 538 552 588 596
Miller S.H.   583 597
Millidge A.F.   596
Milton W.E.J.   17 19–22 26 30 69 71 77
Mohamed B.F.   94 96 103
Moore A.W.   431 434
Moore N.W.   101 103 555 558 560 561
Moravec J.   244 268
Morgan N.C.   233 239
Morris M.G.   513 515 527–52 528–9 531–2
    534–5 539 542–3 549 551 552 594 597
Morzer Bruijns M.F.   619 621
Mossman A.S.   395 403 404

Moyes S.   478 485
Muller C.H.   111 112 113 346 349
Muller P.E.   105 113
Munro I.S.R.   295 299 310
Munro P.E.   110 113
Murbach L.   339 349
Murphy H.M.   192 199 201
Murphy J.L.   425–35 427 432 434 435
Murray J.J.   180 185 202
Myczkowski S.   602 604

Napier J.R.   189 205
Nasimovic A.A.   420 423
Naumann E.   225 239
Naveh Z.   605–22 608–9 616–17 619–20
    621 622
Naylor E.   178 205
Neilson-Jones W.   106 113
Neuhäusl R.   244 268
Nevo E.   187 202
Nicholson E.M.   177 205
Nicholson I.A.   96 103
Nichulescu C.   265 268
Nievergelt B.   414 423
Nishikawa Y.   419 423
Norman M.J.T.   497 515
Norton B.E.   340 349
Novak V.   244 268

Odum E.P.   5 7 14 45 47 55 62
Oleksy B.   603 604
Olsen C.   66 77
Olson D.P.   405 411
Orr-Ewing A.L.   431 433
Osmaston H.A.   41 43 321 331
Østgård O.   164 166
Ovington J.D.   130 132 607 622

Parer I.P.   217 221
Parker I.S.C.   319 329 331 393–404 393–4
    404
Parry R.   218 221
Parsons P.A.   188 201 204
Payne W.J.A.   395 400 404
Peakall D.B.   178 205
Pearsall W.H.   265 268
Pearson K.   180 206
Peaslee D.E.   73 77
Pelikan J.   245 268
Penrose L.S.   180 187 204 205
Perring F.H.   55 62 153 166

Petch C.P.   577 580
Peterken G.F.   565 580
Petrides G.A.   395 404
Pettit P.A.J.   558 561
Phillips C.W.   566 579
Phillips G.C.   193 204
Phillips W.   237 239
Picozzi N.   100 103
Pidgeon R.   210 213 221
Pielou E.C.   534 552
Pierlot R.   41 44
Pigott C.D.   58 62 79 80 84 89 564 572 580
Poole A.L.   520 526
Poore M.E.D.   45 62 587 589 590 597 607 622
Posselt J.   398 404
Prain D.   337 349
Prakash S.   187 199 205
Preston F.W.   58 62 556 557 561
Provasoli L.   229 240
Putwain P.D.   17 27 31

Quezel P.   337 349

Rackham O.   558 561 563–80 565–8 575 580
Raesfeld F. von   440 456
Ramel C.   178 205
Ranwell D.S.   54 62
Rasmussen D.I.   438 452 456
Ratcliffe D.A.   153 166
Rawes M.   154 163–4 165 166
Ray J.   569 580
Rayner M.C.   106 113
Raz Z.   608 622
Redeke H.C.   311 314 315
Reid R.L.   418 423 430 434
Reineke L.H.   41 44
Rendel J.M.   180 205
Rennie P.J.   99 103
Resvoll T.R.   154 166
Reynolds C.S.   237 240
Reynoldson T.B.   275 293
Richards O.W.   528 544 552
Richens R.H.   577 580
Rieche P.   178 205
Rikhter G.R.   479 485
Riney T.   394 404
Risebrough R.W.   178 205
Robertson R.A.   96 97 103
Robins E.   420 423
Robinson A.   218 221

Robinson R.K.   105–13
Rodell C.F.   180 205
Rodgers W.A.   410 411
Rodhe W.   230 240
Ron B.   620 622
Rorison I.H.   65–77 65 67 72 76 77 467 468
Rosenberg M.   233 240
Rosenzweig D.   615 622
Roth H.H.   394 404
Rothmaler W.   245 267
Rowlands I.W.   200 205
Rudescu L.   265 268
Rudolph V.J.   35 44
Rune O.   88 89
Russo J.P.   438 452 456
Rzoska J.   244 268

Sagar G.R.   27 28 31
Salisbury E.J.   130 133
Samarasinghe E.L.   301 310
Sampson A.W.   430 435
Santer S.   337 349
Saunder D.H.   367 385
Saunders H.W.   576 580
Savory C.A.R.   394 395 404
Scali V.   181 205
Schaller G.B.   414 423
Schelske C.L.   236 240
Schlich W.   33 44
Schroevens P.J.   314 315
Schultz A.M.   431 435 616 622
Schuster W.H.   297 310
Schutz F.   110 113
Scossiroli R.E.   189 205
Scott J.D.   360 365
Scotter G.W.   413 423
Searle A.G.   189 205
Segal S.   314 315
Selander R.K.   178 187 190–1 204 205
Seligman N.   608 622
Shachori A.Y.   615 622
Shain W.A.   35 44
Shaw N.H.   340 349
Sheppard P.M.   180 184–5 190 197 201 202 203
Shire J.G.M.   178 206
Shirley H.L.   431 435
Silker T.H.   425 431 435
Silveyra J.   287 293
Sjögren E.   487–95
Skellam J.G.   559 561
Skertchley S.B.J.   583 597

Slobodkin L.B.   196 206
Sloet van Oldruitenborgh C.J.M.   46 62
Smirenskij A.A.   252 265 266 268
Smirnov N.N.   230 239
Smirnova K.M.   130 133
Smith A.E.   555 557 561
Smith C.A.B.   193 201
Smith J.M.   189 191 206
Snaydon R.W.   20 31 72 75 76 77 466 468
Sobey W.R.   179 206
Soil Conservation Service   617 622
Soong M.H.H.   304 309
Southwood T.R.E.   542 552
Sowls L.K.   425 434
Spence D.H.N.   319–31
Spencer D.L.   425 434
Spickett S.G.   178 188 206
Sprague J.B.   285 293
Spurr S.A.   36 44
Stalder L.   110 113
Stanhill G.   615 622
Stebbins G.L.   178 197 200
Steel W.S.   394 404
Stewart D.R.M.   351–66 351–2 357 360–1
   363
Stewart J.   178 206 351–66 351–2 360 361
   363
Stoddard A.L.   425 435
Storer T.I.   425 435
Storey J.E.   231 238
Straškraba M.   230 240
Straškrabova V.   230 240
Streeter D.T.   88 459–68 528 552 555 557
   561
Suhanova N.P.   130 133
Sukopp H.   61 62
Surber E.W.   237 240
Suter M.B.   75 115–33
Sutton C.D.   72 77
Svoboda J.   245 249 251 252 256–7 268
Swank W.G.   395 404
Swann E.L.   577 580
Szafer W.   599 604

Taber R.D.   425–35 450 456
Tadmor N.   608 622
Talbot L.M.   360 363 387 390 395 400 404
Talbot M.H.   360 363 387 390 395 400 404
Tallis J.H.   153 166
Tansley A.G.   564 575–6 580
Taylor A.E.R.   285 293
Taylor C.R.   395 404
Taylor J.W.   184 206

Taylor K.   153–66
Taylorson R.B.   347 349
Teal J.J. Jr   420 423
Tester J.R.   541 552
Tevis L. Jr   431 435
Thalen D.   45 50 62
Thoday J.M.   188–9 191 200 206
Thomas A.S.   497 515
Thomas B.   68 77
Thomas E.A.   230 240
Thomas R.G.   367 385
Thompson E.Y.   180 206
Thompson W.R.   419 423
Thurston J.M.   17 31 70 77
Tickle W.M.   58 61
Tisdale E.W.   605 622
Tiurin I.V.   129 133
Tomlinson T.E.   226 235 240
Tonolli L.   230 238
Topachevski A.V.   230 240
Torrey J.G.   107 113
Tothill J.C.   337–8 340 346 349
Treus V.   398 404
Tricker B.J.K.   197 201
Trinder N.   68 77
Tryon E.H.   431 435
Tubbs C.R.   566 569 580
Turner M.I.M.   362 366
Tutin T.G.   117 132 152 485 501 596
Tüxen R.   607 622

UNESCO   605 622
Ursin E.   190 206

Valentine D.H.   564 572 580
Vampilov V.N.   265 268
Vanstellen R.   130 132
Van Valen L.   180–1 192 206
Veracourt L.D.   395 400 404
Vicherek J.   248 269
Vincent-Thomas R.G.   367 385
Vlamis J.   73 77 431 435
Vogle R.J.   430 435
Vollenweider R.A.   226 228 240

Waddington C.H.   180 206
Wager J.A.   483 485
Wahlenberg W.G.   431 435
Wallace B.   189 199 206
Waloff N.   544 552
Walsh B.   231 238

Walters S.M.   153 166 587 597
Walther F.   409 411 414 423
Warburg E.F.   117 132 152 485 501 596
Ward W.A.   519 526
Ware K.D.   35 44
Warlow W.J.   483 485
Warne L.G.G.   498 515
Waterhouse F.L.   529 552
Watkin E.M.   27 31
Watson A.   478 480 485
Watson G.V.   485
Watson R.H.   419 424
Watson R.M.   362 366 395 404
Watt A.S.   11 14 54 62 63 93 95 101 103
    137–52 137 139 140 143 148 152 164
    166 460 485 518 526 556 561
Weaver H.   426 435
Weber C.A.   225 240
Weerekoon A.L.J.   301 310
Weibel S.R.   226 240
Weir J.S.   367–85 369 373–4 382–3 385
Weiss R.A.   181 206
Weitz M.   617 619 622
Welch D.   154 163–5 166
Welcomme R.L.   307 310
Welles F.B.   414 424
Welles R.E.   414 424
Wells T.C.E.   497–515 498 509 515 528–9
    544 549 552 583 593 597
Went F.W.   431 435
Werf S. van der   55 63
West G.   233 240
West O.   320 331 337 349
Westhoff V.   3–14 45–7 51 62 63 581 597
Westlake D.F.   252 269
White M.J.D.   189 206
Whitehead F.H.   167–76
Whittaker E.   96 103
Whittaker R.H.   5 7 14 45 55 58 63 595 597
    607 622
W.H.O.   179 206
Whyte R.O.   606 622

Wiburg L.   229 239
Wigan L.G.   188 206
Wilde S.A.   129 133
Wilkinson A.T.S.   525 526
Willén T.   230 240
Willey A.   297 310
Williams C.B.   58 63 556 561
Williams C.H.   129 133
Williams D.E.   73 77
Williams R.J.B.   226 238
Williams T.E.   29 31
Williamson M.H.   185 206
Willis A.J.   53 63 68 70 72 77 80 84 85 89
    151 152
Wilson E.O.   558 561
Wilson J.G.   321 331
Wilson K.   130 133
Winch J.E.   27 31
Wing L.W.   425 435
Winton M.   371 385
Woodell S.R.J.   572 580
Woodford E.K.   17 31
Woodhead T.W.   75 77
Woods F.W.   105 113
Wright R.D.   371 385
Wright S.   560 561
Wynne-Edwards V.C.   189 206

Yang S.Y.   187 190 191 205
Yardeni D.   614 622
Yeatman C.W.   106 107 113
Yemm E.W.   70 77 85 89
Young J.O.   275 293

Zeuner F.E.   398 404
Zhirnov L.V.   419 422
Zigunov P.S.   418 424
Zohary D.   199 206
Zohary M.   607 622

Subject Index

Aberdeen 91
Aberystwyth 20
Abinger, Surrey 70 75
abortions 418
Abraxas grossulariata semilutea 186
absorption of embryos 418
Acacia 321 325 326 352
Acarina 522 523 542
Acholi, Uganda 394
acidification 19
  and *Ulex europaeus* 115–33
  and *Calluna* 115–33
acidity, soil 431
acid
  peat 586 592
  upland grasslands 541
Acris crepitans, protein variation in 187
Adriatic 172
Aedes aegypti, genetic change in 197
aerial dispersal 279
African swallow-tail butterfly 190
agricultural
  drainage 314
  fertilizers 226 229
  formations 583
  land 557 561
agricultural practice 548
  changes in 527
Agrimonia eupatoria 6
Agropyron repens 245
Agropyro-Rumicion crispi 46 48
Agrostis canina 51 139 145 147 148
— *stolonifera* 27 53 116 245
— *tenuis* 16 19 21 25 69 74 139 140 180
Aira praecox 140
air pollution 431
alarm reaction 417
aldrin 26
algae 96
algal production 236
Alisma plantago-aquatica 245
Allolobophora caliginosa 128
— *chlorotica* 128
allochthonous material 271
allogenic succession 9
alluvial flats 334

Alnus glutinosa 576
  soil improvement by 99
Alopecurus pratensis 70 75
alpine meadow 491 599 603
Alvar Heath, Öland 488ff
Alyssum sp. 388
Amathes glareosa, melanism and distribution 193
amenity plantings 564
ammonia 275 285 315
  concentrations 290
  toxicity 285
ammonium sulphate 19
Ammophila arenaria 11
Ammophiletum 11
Amphidasys cognataria 186 187
Aneilema hockii 353
animal
  behaviour 413ff
  habitats 533
  man as 400
animals
  burrowing 388
  domestic 395
  wild 396
annidative relationships 17
Anostraca 374
ant hills 18
Anthoxanthum odoratum 46 75
  morphological and physiological variation 20
anthropochorous species 491
anthropogenic ecoclines 595
Anthyllis vulneraria 491
antibiotics 106
Antilocapra americana 220
antlers 440 442 443 448
  pedicles 440
  tines 448 455
Apanteles tetricus 181
aphids, resistance to pesticides 179 197
Apodemus silvaticus 178
— *silvaticus hirtensis* 197
Araneae 522 523 542 587
archaeology of woodlands 569
arctic-alpines 58 79 80 83

Arctosa perita 178
Arenaria humifusa, on serpentine in S. Scandinavia 88
— *serpyllifolia* 70
Aristida adoensis 355
Arizona Chaparral 427
Armeria maritima 11
Arrhenatherum elatius 69 70 75
Artemisia vulgaris subsp. *coarctata* 488
artificial
    fertilizers 20 226–7 234
    formations 582
    grassland 24
    manuring 10
    waterholes 369
Asellus aquaticus 273 275 286 288 289 291
aspen 427 430
Asperula cynanchica 116 461 506 509
Aspilia mossambicensis 353 355
Aston Rowant NNR 545 546
Atlanticus testaceus 26
Atriplex spp. 488
— *hastata* 257
Auchenorhyncha 531 533 536 546
aurochs 420
    grazing 12
Australian magpie 218
Australopithecus 219
autochtonic swamp successions 312 314
autogenic succession 9
autoxicity 111 121
    and senescence 112
avalanches 602 603
Avena pratensis 490
Avenetum 488ff
Avon gorge 71

Baetis rhodani 280 283 291 292
Banff National Park 414
baobab 336
barium (barytes) 80 87
barley, as test plant 107
Barton Hills, Beds 498ff 529ff
base rich fen peat 586
base saturation and pH 121
Batha 606 620
bats 220
Bedgebury 130
beetles, dung 375 377
Bellis perennis 22 23 26
benthic communities 272 275 286 287 291
    saprobic 292
Berks, Bucks & Oxon Naturalists' Trust 42

Berkshire 184
Berwyn Mountains 153
Betonica officinalis 116
Betula spp. 489
    and *Calluna* 106 112
    and soil improvement 99
— *humilis* 12
— *verrucosa* 488
Betuletum, Querceto- 7
Bialowicza Nature Reserve 12
Bidens cernuus 8
— *tripartitus* 8 245 257
bighorn sheep 414 415 420
biochemical oxygen demand 275
birds and pesticides 178
Birmingham 274 291
Bison bison 220 397
Biston betularia carbonaria 180 186 189 200
bitter-brush 426
blanket bogs 9 153 154 163 164
Blelham Tarn 235
blowflies 179
bobwhite quail 430
bog
    blanket 9
    peat 587
    raised 8
    species density 557
Bolboschoenus maritimus 244
boreholes 368
Boschplaat 11 12
Bos sp. 220
Bothriochloa insculpta 340 353 355 361
Botrychium lunaria 6
boulder clay 558
Box Hill, Surrey 459ff
Brachypodium pinnatum 27
Bradfield Woods, Cambs 573 574 576 577
Braunton Burrows 70
Breckland 137–52 518
Brillia longifurca 280 282
Brillovin index 534
Briza media 70 505 507 512 514
Broads, as nature reserves 311
Bromus erectus 492
    response to phosphorus 71
— *tectorum* 427
browsing 329 335 387 425
Bryum argenteum 492
buffalo 322 329 333 369ff 388 397 398
Buff Wood, Cambs 569 570
burning
    bush 401
    controlled 384 431 432

effects on *Calluna* heath 91–103 105
effects on floristic composition 194
effects on invertebrate animals 550
effects on lepidopterous larvae 541
effects on *Rubus chamaemorus* 153–66
grassland 528 529 541–2
moor 437 439 444 448 450 453
prescribed 432
and *Themeda* 337 340
time of year 545
burrowing
animals 388
invertebrates 544
bush clearance 591
Bushmen 393 394

Cairngorm Nature Reserve 469ff
Calamagrostis epigeios 46 245 587 591 593
and rabbits 54
and water table 55
calcicolous (calcareous)
grassland 528 549
lakes 236
plants 70 72–5 115–16 124 129 131
soils 618
calcifuge plants 71–4 115–16 131
calciphilous species 490–2
calcium
loss from soil 123
immobilization in plant and litter 122–3
California 191
Chaparral 427 616
Calluna and *Calluna* heaths 11 51 91–103
105–13 115–33 137–40 143 148 150 153–
4 164 472 476 481 483 593
effect of management (burning and grazing) 94–8
effect on uptake and removal of nutrients
94–8
production of toxins 105–13
and *Pteridium* 97 137–40
Calluna/Trichophorum 471 478 484
Calluneto-Eriophoretum 153–5 164–5
Calthion palustris 52
camels 397
Campanula rotundifolia 507 531 532
Camptothecium lutescens 490
Capsella bursa-pastoris 491
carbohydrate reserves 511
carbon dioxide concentration 285
carboniferous limestone 71 80
Cardiganshire 17 19 20 25
Carex sp. 53

— *appropinquata* 12
— *arenaria* 11
— *buekii* 12
— *caespitosa* 12
— *caryophylla* 506 507 514
— *dioica* 6
— *disticha* 55
— *ericetorum* 149
— *flacca* 491 506 507 514
— *hirta* 5
— *hostiana* 6 51
— *hudsonii* 12
— *lasiocarpa* 12
— *lepidocarpa* 80
— *panicea* 80
— *pulicaria* 6 51
— *otrubae* 5
Carpatians 599
Carpinus sp. 488
carr 4
cattle 53 97 397 608
grazing 12 452 453 497 498 601
carrion 543
carrying capacity 467
Cenchrus ciliarus 355
censuses 369–70
Centaurea nigra 501 507 509 510 512 514
529 532
Cepaea nemoralis 180 185 190
Cetraria spp. 490
chairlift stations 470
chalk
downland 461 467
grassland 8 27 148 497ff 528ff
heath 115–33
management for nature conservation 511
chamois 388 419 600 603
Chaparral 427 428 616
effect of clearance of flora 111
chelate metals 236
chemical control 26
Chenopodium spp. 245 488
Chilopoda 95
chimpanzees 220 414
chironomid larvae 279 280 288 291
Chironomus riparius 280 285 287 291 292
Chloris gayana 340
Chloropidae 542
Chobe, Uganda 319
Cinnabar moth 517ff
Cirsium acaulon 507 512 514
— *arvense* 491
Cladium mariscus 488
Cladonia sp. 478 490

— *arbuscula* 142–3 148
— *foliacea* 46
Cladophora sp. 228 289
  balls 237
Clarias mossambicus 374
Clausilia laminata 180
clay pans 369
Clifton Park grass mixture 16
climax
  communities 9 607
  forests 606
coastal dunes 4
Cockle Park 16
Coke's hartebeest 351
College of African Wildlife Management
  405
Collembola 542
Coleoptera 522 538 539 542 543 587 588
Colophospermum mopane 335
Colorado forests 427
Combretum ghazalense 319 327 328 335
Commelina spp. 353 355
communal hunting 394
communities
  benthic 272 286 287
  climax 9 607
  cormophyte 7
  decomposer 286
  ochtohydrophyte reedswamp 241
  pioneer 544
  saprobic benthic 292
  xerophytic 11
  xerothermic plant 388
compaction of soil 464 470
competition
  Agrostis canina and *Galium hercynicum*
    147
  Agrostis canina v. *Luzula campestris* 148
  Calluna vulgaris v. *Pteridium aquilinum*
    97 137–40
  control by grazing 512
  Epilobium hirsutum and *Lythrum salicaria*
    168ff
Conchostraca 374
conifers 7 130 150
coppice 4 10 334
  banks 569
  oak 7
  rotations 568 570 575 578
  with standards 565 570–2 575
coppicing 565 568 569 572 574–5
Cornwall 181
Corylus avellana 488
Corynephoretum 11

Violo- 11
Corynephorus canescens 46
Cothill, Berks 184
Court of Exchequer 567
coypu, feeding on *Phragmites* and *Typha*
  171
Crambidae 541
Crose Mere, Cheshire 237
Crustacea 522 523
Ctenidium molluscum 491
culling 329 446–8 449 450 452 453
  selective 455
Curculionoidea 538 546
cutting
  compared with grazing 510
  effect on invertebrates 542
  and flower production 509
  for peat 583
  mechanical 497
  of reed 586
  times, effect of 505 506
Cyclamen persicum 609
cycling of bases 121–2
Cygnus olor 13
Cymbopogon pospischilii 353 355 361
Cynodon dactylon 353 355 360 362
Cynoglossum officinale 54
Cynosurus cristatus 462ff
Cyperus kilimandscharicus 355
Czechloslovakia 226

Dacelo gigas 218
Dactylis glomerata 16 69 70 75 539
dalapon 27
Dartford warbler 101
Dartmoor 153
DDT 26
deer 97
  black-tailed 426 450
  body weight 443 444 449 450 452
  density 429
  mule 220 414 415 425
  park 578
  Père David 196
  production 429
  red 388 419 437ff
  roe 449
  removal of nutrients by cropping 97
  sika 420
  white-railed 220 425 430
defoliation
  anthropogenic 617

of grassland   529 542 544
of ragwort   519
regrowth after   511
repeated   511 608
selective   24
timing of   22
Dendrocoelum lacteum   275
Denmark   99 190
Derbyshire   72
Dermaptera   522
Deschampsia flexuosa   25 68–75 143 148
deserts, semi-   7
detergent   228 229
Dianthus armeria   6 587 593
— *superbus*   6
diaspores   263–4 492 494
diatoms   284
Dicranum spp.   478
— *scoparium*   95
dieldrin   26
diel fluctuation   282 284 288 290
Digitaria macroblephara   353 355 361 362
— *scalarum*   353 355 361 362
Diptera   542 543 587
disease organisms   15
dispersal   557 561
aerial   279
range   149
Ditrichum flexicaule   493
diversity   8 15 321 555 556 557 602
biological   607 619 620
biotic communities   13
cormophyte communities   7
ecological   605ff
ecosystems   4 5
floristic   21 22
habitat   7 595
indices   535
of chalk grassland flora   544
of grassland fauna   543
species   12 17 29 46 53 56 58 534
and environmental gradients   46
structural   615
vegetational   17 513
Domesday Book   567
domestic animals   394–7
domestication   397–9 402
donkeys   397 608
Dorset heaths   555
Douglas fir   426 427
Dowles Brook   274 275
downs   4
chalk   461 467
semi-natural   10

drainage, agricultural   314
Draved Forest, Jutland   566
Drosera rotundifolia   49 50
Drosophila persimilis   187
— *pseudo-obscura*   181 187 197
dune
embryo   11
grassland   45 46 48 53 54
lakes   311
sand   6
scrub   11 45 54
slack   45 49 53–5 58 82 85
system   12
dung   18 19 511
beetles   375 377
deposition   374–6
fauna   543
fertilizer   529
removal   376
transport of   378–81
dykes
as nature reserves   311
old breaks   311
Dyschoriste radicans   353

ear tags   440
earthworks   569
earthworms   122 127 128 132
East Anglia   536 564
Echinochloa crus-gali   245
— *stagnina pyramidalis*   334
ecocline   5 13 56 595
anthropogenic   595
ecological
gradients   5
niche   12
economic value   383
ecosystems
aquatic   291
conservation of   560
diversity of   5 555
potential natural   582
oligotrophic   8
semi-natural   10
ecotone   5 56
effluents   292
organic   271 275
oxidized   286
sewage   287 288 289 290 291
toxic   291
eland   335 370ff 388 398
elephant   319 321–2 329 333 369ff 388 398
destruction by   380

elk 220 420
 grazing 12
Eltonian classification 589
Elytrigia juncea 11
— *pungens* 12
— *repens* 5
emigration 448 452 453 455
Empetrum nigrum 96
Enchytraeidae 285
endemic
 fish species 297 299 307 309
 organisms 230
English Lakes and eutrophication 226
enrichment
 artificial (eutrophication) 226ff
 organic 271 274 279 281 285–6 291 292
Ephemeroptera 285 291 312–13
Epilobium hirsutum 167–72
 day length 170
 genetic pattern of development 169
 nutrients 169 170
 seedling survival 172
 temperature 170
Eragrostis braunii 353 355
Erica cinerea 95 115–16
— *gracilis* 110
— *tetralix* 51 478 593
Eichhorn's hypothesis 42
endocyclic selection 193
Eriophorum angustifolium 8 478
— *vaginatum* 153 472 475 476 478 484
Erodio-Koelerion 48
Erophila verna 492
erosion 395 459 460 467 469
 after (uncontrolled) fire 428 618
 gullies 97 98 335
 soil 431 467 492 494 601 602
Erpobdella testacea 286 291
Erythraeus phalangoides 524
Esthwaite Water 275
Eukiefferiella hospitus 279 281 292
Euphrasia borealis 50
European steppe 388
Eustachys paspaloides 353
eutrophication 88
 of Fenland 590
 of lakes 225ff
 terrestrial 467
eutrophic
 conditions 13 286
 environments 6 7
 habitats 6
 lakes 236
 water 9 311

extinction, rescue from 196

faecal analysis 357
faeces 352 364
Fasciola hepatica 6
fattening farms 315
fecundity 444–6 449 450 452 455
Felsham Hall Wood 576 577–8
fen 12
 carr 175
 peat, base-rich 586
 primary 593
 Violet 591
Fenland Basin 583
fertilizers 15–31
 application 20 237
 agricultural 226 229
 artificial 20 226–7 234
 nitrogenous 226–7 236
Festuca/Agrostis 20 25
— *arundinacea* 5
— *ovina* 21 25 51 68 69 71 80 82 86 87 95
  139 140 143 147 150 490 501 505 514
 and grazing 20–1 140
 and growth requirements 74
 and lead 87
 and nutrients 20 21 82
 and rainfall 142
 and senescence 140 143
 and shade tolerance 95
— *pratensis* 16
— *rubra* 11 12 19 21 27 53–4 70–1 82 84
  116 118 119
 and grazing 27 54 116
 and *Lotus corniculatus* 71
 and nutrients 53 70 82
 and soil acidity 118
— *tenuifola* 46 50
Festuco-Galietum maritimi 46
Filipendula ulmaria, morphological response to habitat factors 172
— *vulgaris* 124 490 507 514
fire 319 320 334 376 377 379 383 425ff
  616 619
 ash 340
 control 427
 heat of 340
 and *Themeda* 337ff
firebreaks 320 330 340
fisheries 295ff 314
fish
 meal 19
 ponds at Lednice 244

production 307
Flintshire 184
flood
    control 301
    meadows 528
flooding 335
    summer 590
    winter 591
food
    availability 357 360 511
    chains 555
    digestion 359 364
    palatability 351
    preferences 351ff 387
forage utilization 360
forests
    communities 33–44
    coniferous 7
    deciduous 7
    mixed hardwood/coniferous 429
    pine 430
    Rocky Mountain 427
    temperate rain 426
formations
    artificial 582
    natural 581 595
    near-natural 582 595
    semi-natural 581 582 595
Foxhole Heath 148–9
France 91
Fraxinus sp. 488
freshwater arthropods 374
Freshwater Biological Association 233
frost 139
fungicides 26
fungitoxic compounds 105–6 110–13
fungus, sewage 271
Fusarium spp. 480

galah 208
Galium hercynicum (saxatile) 25 68 140
    143 144
    and *Agrostis canina* 147
— *verum* var. *maritimum* 46
game ranching 393ff 413 421
Gamlingay Wood, Cambs 569 575 576
Gammarus pulex 281 282 285 286 287 289
    292
Garigue 606 617 620
genetical constitution of populations and
    conservation 177–206
    pattern of development 169
    structure of populations 179

Geranium robertianum 491
Germany 101
Gentiana amarella 50
— *pneumonanthe* 51
Gerris thoracicus 594
Ghana 36
gibbon 220
giraffe 369ff
Gladiolo-Agrostetum 603–4
Glaux maritima 49
Glossiphonia complanata 286
Glycine javanica 323–5 328 329
Globularia vulgaris 490 491
goats 397 439 608
    grazing 617 619
Goeree 61
goose
    grazing 258 260
    grey lag 258 266
goral 420
gorilla 200 414
gradients, ecological 5
Grallina cyaneoleuca 218
Grant's gazelle 351 353 357 360 361–4
grass-heath 51
grassland 7 15–31
    acidiphilous 140
    acid upland 541
    artificial 24
    calcareous 528 549
    calcicolous 28 582
    chalk 8 27 497ff 539 545 561
    community 17
    East African 359
    ecosystems 619
    fauna, diversity 543
    flora, diversity 544
    meadow 19
    'natural' 16
    nature reserves 513
    neutral 27
    permanent 16 19 23 24 28
    plots 322
    reclamation 528
    reversion 528
    rough 539
    semi-natural 75
    sown 16
    species density 557
    systems 15
    trampling 528 529
    ungrazed 539
    upland 17 24 28
grassland management 319ff

burning 319ff 451-2
grazing 319ff
treatments 322
grazing 11 15-31 53-4 143 151 153-66
  319ff 387 528 542
  animals 15 24 25 28 542 543
  and flower production 509
  and *Tyria jacobaea* 517
  aurochs 12
  cattle 12 489 498 593 601
  compared with cutting 512
  continuous 498
  controlled 22 27
  elk 12
  frequent 498
  goat 617 619
  goose 258
  horses 12 489
  intensity 322-3 493
  muskrat 265
  pastures 487
  pressures 26 489 491 494 531 608
  rabbit 497
  rotational 498 549 550 609
  seasonal 545
  selective 252 608
  sheep 10 12 19 488ff 497 601 603
Great Basin area 427
Great Britain 10
Greece 605
greensand 70
ground water table 55
grouse moor 154
growth cycle of plants 25 26
Grzedy Nature Reserve 12
guanotrophic pools 8
Gwaii River 367
Gypsophila fastigiata 490 491

habitats
  diversity in 7 595
  eutrophic 6
  hyperoligotrophic 8
  heterogeneity of 18
  oligotrophic 6 231
  quality of 420
Hadza, Tasmania 393 394
Halimione portulacoides 12
Hard Hill 155
hardpan 97
Hardwick Wood, Cambs 567-9 575 576
Hardy-Weinberg equilibrium 179 191
hares 97 359

Haringvliet 61
Harpachne schimperi 353 355
hartebeest 361 362
Hatertse Vennen Nature Reserve 8
hayfields 4 22 314
Hayley Wood, Cambs 571-3 575-7
heather 137-40
heathlands 4 10 105 106 110-11
  Dorset 555
  effect of isolation 558
heavy metals, tolerance to 86-7 180 182
  183 184
hedgerows 4 29 561
Helianthemum chamaecistus 68 490 501
  505 506 507 509 510
— *oelandicum* 491
Helictotrichon pratense 505 507
Helobdella stagnalis 286
Hemiptera 533 534 538
herbicides 10 18 28
  and floristic composition 15 26 27
  selective 26
herbivores 25 543
Hesperocorixa sahlbergi 594
Heteropogon contortus 340 346 362
Heteroptera 522 531 538 546 587
Hickling Broad 237
Hierdense Beek 315
high forest 319
hill
  farming, Mediterranean 617
  pastures 20
Hippocrepis comosa 506 510 512 514
Hippophae rhamnoides 54
hippopotamus 319 321-2 329 333 336
  388 398
Hirudinea 285 291
historical information 565
Holcus lanatus 27 75 180
— *mollis* 111
Homoptera 542
hoofmarks 18
Hornungia petraea 492
horses 53 397
  grazing 12
houseflies 179
Hoveton Great Broad, Norfolk 237
human ecological limitations 393
human interference 608-9 619
Hundred Foot Bank 185
Hundred Rolls 567
hunting 334 422
  dogs 414
Hydrillula palustris 588

Hydrocotyle vulgaris 8 47
Hydroides norvegica 178
Hydrophilidae 374
hygroscopic behaviour 339
Hylocomnium splendens 478
Hymenoptera 95 587
Hyparrhenia spp. 319 323 328 334 340
   353 362
— *filipendula* 110
hyperoligotrophic habitats 8
Hypnum cupressiforme 95
— *cupressiforme* var. *lacunosum* 46
Hypocharis radicata 116
hypolimnion 232

ibex 420
Idaho forests 427
immigration 560
immobilization of calcium in plant and
   litter 122–3
impala 410
Imperata cylindrica 321
India 297
indicators, mesotrophic 8
indices of diversity 535
Indigofera volkensii 353
inhibitors 346
   root growth 106 112–13
insect feeders, specialist 529
insecticides 10 26
intensity
   light 610
   trampling 483
International Biological Programme 12
   230 233
invertebrates, effects of cutting on 542
Ireland 226
Iridaceae 606
Iris pseudacorus 172–5
Ischaemum afrum 353 360 362
island biogeography 556
isocenes 48
isolation 557
Israel 605 617

Jack pine 430 557
Jeallott's Hill 17
Juncetum gerardii 12
Junco-Molionon 52
Juncus spp. 53
— *effusus* 8
— *gerardii* 11

— *inflexus* 5
— *maritimus* 5 49
— *squarrosus* 97
Juniperus communis 92 96 489 491
Jura 450 453
Jurinea cyanoides 388

kaibab 438 452
Kalahari sand deposits 367ff
Kobresia simpliciuscula 79–89
Kochia arenaria 388
Koeleria cristata 68 505 512
— *glauca* 388
kolines 614
   phytotoxic 619
kookaburra 218
kudu 370ff

Lagopus scoticus 93 97 165
Lakenheath Poor's Fen 587
Lakenheath Warren 137
lakes, eutrophication of
   Baikal 230
   Blelham Tarn 231
   eastern European 230
   English 226 233
   Erie 226 231
   Esthwaite Water 231
   Japanese 230
   Kobylí 241ff
   Maggiore 230
   Michigan 231
   Ontario 226 231
   Rostherne Mere 231 237
   Scandinavian 230
   Swiss 230
   Washington 230
   Wisconsin 230
lakes,
   calcareous 236
   oligotrophic 235 236
Lancaster 80
landscape
   cultivated 3 13
   manmade 6
   natural 4
   newly created 311
   optimization of values 621
   semi-natural 4 9 10
   sub-natural 4 9 12
land use 400 548
   history 498 527

surveys, national 567
Large Copper butterfly 588 591
Larus ridibundus 8
Lathyrus nissolia 6
lead (galena) 80 85–8
  and inorganic phosphate 86
leaf litter 509 614 618
Lecidea uliginosa 96
Lednice, S. Moravia 241
  fishponds 244 266
Leguminosae 19
Leicestershire 178
Leontodon autumnalis 47
— *hispidus* 509 512
Lepidoptera 439 587 588
lepidopterous larvae, effects of burning on
  541
lichens 96
  crustose 483
  foliose 483
light
  effect of burning 340
  intensity 610
  penetration 347
Liliaceae 606
lime 19–21
limes convergens 5–8 49 56
  divergens 5–8 56
limestone 6 7
  grassland 50 51 71 535
  heath 487ff
  nutrient deficient 467
  oolitic 541
liming 19 20
Limnaea trunculata 6
limosal ecophase 248 257 262 263 266
Limulus polyphemus 187
Lintonia nutans 353
Linum catharticum 49 50 501 509 514
lions 414
litter 106 108–9 115 116 122–3 129–32
  141–3 151 507–8
  destroyed by fire 541
  layer 544
littoral ecophase 248 257
llamas 397
Llety-ifan-Hên 20
local nature reserve 557
Loch Leven 231 233
Lockinge, Berks 28
lodge pole pine 427
loess 129
Lolio-Cynosuretum 47
Lolium perenne 22 23 24 27 69 462ff

Lonchocarpus laxiflorus 325
Long Ashton 169
Lotus corniculatus 68 71 501 507 509 510
— *corniculatus* subsp. *corniculatus* 46
Luangwa Valley, Zambia 333
Lullington Heath 115–33
Luzula campestris 140 143 144 147 491
— *pallescens* 587 591 592
Luzula-Koelerion 49
Lycaena dispar 199 588 591
Lycopodium spp. 478
Lycopus europaeus 8 257
Lycosa paludicola 588 591 592
— *rubrofasciata* 588
Lymnaea pereger 291
Lysimachia vulgaris 51
Lythrum salicaria 167–72

machine mowing 23
Macrosteles laevis 542
magnesium 19
malaria 179 197
malathion 26
Malaya 36
Malham Tarn 236
management
  bush clearance 591
  cessation of 531
  effects of 532
  of grassland for nature conservation
    511 527ff
  microclimatological effects of 529
  objects 528 548 549
  policy criteria 595
  scientific 287
  seasonal effects of 545
  of small reserves 513
  systems 497
  of water 311ff
  of weather 432
  of wild ungulates 413ff
man as an animal 400
Manchester 6
Maniola jurtina 192
manmade
  landscapes 6
  habitats 301
man's ecological needs 401
manuring
  artificial 10
  by sheep 491 493
  liquid 315
maps, historical 566

Maquis   606 609 615 617 618 620
'marginal' lands   395
Mariscus macropus   353 355
Markhov   420
Malborough Downs   193
marmot   600 603
Marpessa pomatia   588
Masailand   361
May, Isle of   192
meadows   534
  flood   528
  grazed   603
  manured   603
  mown   603
  water   314 528
Mecoptera   522
Medbourne   29
Medicago falcata   149
— *lupulina*   461
Mediterranean
  hill farming   617
  woodland   619
Melampyrum lineare   26
melanism   177–98
Melilotus dentatus   257
Melitaea (*Euphydras*) *aurinia*   198
Melopsittacus undulatus   208 213
Merychippus primus   180
mesotrophic
  indicators   8
  swamps   12
metaldehyde   26
Metkovic   168
Miarus campanulae   531 532
mice   179
Michigan   26
microclimatological effects of grassland
    management   529
Michrochloa kunthii   340 353
milk hinds   440
Millfield   29
millipedes (Diplopoda)   95
millstone grit   72
mineral
  nutrients   18–27 65–77 161 162
  salts   371
minimum area and nature reserves   58 101
Miombo woodland, Tanzania   410
mires, ombrogenous   153 154
Missouri   200
Mitchell grass plains   216
moats   569 570
mole
  activity   531

and floristic composition   148–9
  hills   18
Molinia caerulea   8 20 21 51 69 97 164
    439 491 586 587
Molinietalia   51
molluscicides   26
molluscs   531
Monks' Park Wood   575 577–9
Monks Wood (Experimental Station)   517
    518
  National Nature Reserve   558
monophagous species   529
Montana forests   427
moor burning   437 439 444 448 450 453
moorlands   4 9 71
  oligotrophic   8
Moorea   184
Moorhouse National Nature Reserve   154
    155
mopane   335
mor   130
mosquitoes   179 197
mosses   483
mountain
  goats   414
  pine   599 601
  sheep   414 419
Mount Carmel National Park   610–13
mowing   19 23–4 51 54 70 116 122 151
  as management tool   513 528 550
  machine   23 551
  non-selectivity of   542
  time of year   545
'muirburn'   541
mulching   106
Murchison Falls National Park   319ff 398
musk oxen   420
muskrats   252 264
Mus musculus muralis   197
Mweya, Queen Elizabeth Park   321
mycorrhiza   106 109–11
myxomatosis   27 54 115 131 139 143 179
    497 528

Nairobi National Park   351
Nardo-Galion   49 51 52
Nardus stricta   21 25 68 97
Narthecium ossifragum   478
national land surveys   567
National Nature Reserves   455 528
  Aston Rowant   545 546
  Cairngorm   469ff
  Hickling Broad   237

Hoveton Great Broad 237
Loch Leven 231 233
Monks Wood 558
Moor House 154 155
Rostherne Mere 232
Weeting Heath 517ff
Woodwalton Fen 581ff
National Parks 413 607
Banff 414
Mount Carmel 610–13
Murchison Falls 319ff 398
Nairobi 351
Queen Elizabeth, Uganda 329 337ff 398
Serengeti 360 361 362 395
Tatra 599ff
Wankie 367ff
Waterton Lakes 415
National Trust 459
natural
ecosystems, potential 582
formations 581 595
grassland 16
pastures 488–9
purification plants 314
selection 179
succession 582
vegetation 26
Nature Conservancy 76 131 151 154 165 437 453 459 535 563 583
nature reserves 535 607
Bialowicza 12
Boschplaat 11
grassland 513
Grzedy 12
Haterste Venn 8
local 557
management of small 513
management of water in 311ff
selection 555
near-natural formations 582 595
né-né, Hawaiian 196
Netherlands 10 12 13 50–2 55 59 61 311ff
Neuroptera 522
Neusiedler See 266
New South Wales 207 219
New Zealand 413 419
niche, ecological 12
Nijmegen 51
nitrates 288 491
nitrification 110
nitrilotriacetic acid 228
nitrogen 19 24 227 229 233 461 465
from sewage 228

oxidized 275
soil 466
nitrogenous fertilizers 226 236
nitrophilous vegetation 388 488
North America 413
Notonectidae 374
Nucella lapillus 181
nutrient 311 380 511
content of grasses and herbs 68–69
deficient limestone 467
depletion 465
enrichment 465
and floristic composition 16 17 18–26 53 65–77
levels 431
and *Kobresia simpliciuscula* 79–89
and *Rubus chamaemorus* 156–63
status 28
nutrition, mineral 18
Nymphicus hollandicus 208 216

oak coppice 7
ochtohydrophyte reedswamp communities 241
Odocoileus hemionus 220 438
— *virginicus* 220
Odonata 374 587
Oenanthe aquatica 8 257
Öland 487ff
Oligochaeta 291
oligophagous species 529
oligotrophic
conditions 13
ecosystem 8
environments 6 9
habitats 6 8 231
lakes 235 236
moorlands 8
'vens' 311
water 6
Olpidium sp. and *Erica gracilis* 110
onager 420
Ontario 27
oolitic limestone 541
Opilionida 95
orang-utan 220
Orchidaceae 6 606 609
Oregon 426
organic
effluents 271 275
enrichment 271 274 279 281 285–6 291–2
pollution 272 274

sewage   226
organisms
    disease   15
    endemic   230
Origanum vulgare   6
Orkney   192
Orthoptera   544
Orthosiphon parvifolius   353
Oscinella frit   542 544
ostrich   359 398
Oude Maas   61
Outer Hebrides   192
ovaries   442
overgrazing   487 519 524 525 602 608 619
oviposition of invertebrates in grassland
    542
Oxford   105
oxidized
    effluents   286
    nitrogen   275

Pacific Northwest   426
palatability   25 26
Panaxia dominula   184 185 197
Panicum ?massaiense   355 361
— *poaeoides*   355 361
Papilio dardanus   190
paraquat   27
Park Grass plots   17–20 22 53 151
parkland   565
Parnassia palustris   49 50
parrots (Australian)   207–21
Partula sp.   184
Passer domesticus   178
pastures   4 16 24 527
    hill   20
    natural   488–9
    permanent   24 583
    semi-natural   10
patchiness   141
pattern and process   3 4 5 11
pcat
    acid   586 592
    base rich fen   586
    bog   587
    cutting   583
    permeability   590
    pits   312
pedestrian traffic   472
pellet groups   375
Peltigera spp.   478
Pembrokeshire   191
Pennines   153

Pennisetum mezianum   353 355 359 361
    362
Perinethela perlucidalis   585
Perizoma sagittata   588
pesticides   15–31
    and selection   15 26 27 178 197
pests   15
    insect   260
pets   396 402
pet-syndrome   397
Peucedanum palustre   8
phenology   513–14
Phleum arenarium   70
— *phleoides*   149
— *pratense*   16 69 477
phosphate   24 275 288
    soil   575
phosphorus   19 21 229 461 465 466
    from sewage   228
    radioactive   382
    soil   464
    utilization of   381
photography, time-lapse   473
Phragmites communis   168 170 171 244ff
pH values   19 275
Phyllobius parvulus   532
— *viridicollis*   532
phytophagous species   533
phytotoxic
    compounds   105–9
    kolines   619
Picea abies   105 108
pigs   315 397
Piliostigma sp.   328 335
pine forests   430
Pinguicula vulgaris   6
Pinus sp.   50
pioneer communities   544
Piscicola geometra   286
plagioclimaxes   527
Plantago lanceolata   27 28 492
— *major*   245
— *maritima*   80 83
— *media*   28
Plantaginetea maioris   6
plant cover, removal by fire   340
plant epidermis in faeces   352 364
Platanthera bifolia   51
Platycercus elegans   208
— *eximius*   216–18
Plecoptera   285 291
pleistocene drift deposits   536
poaching   334 330 452
Poa annua   491

— *pratensis* 27 53
— *trivialis* 27
podsolization 97 98 129–31
Pohlia nutans 492
Poland 12 599ff
polders 311
pollard growth 335
pollen analysis 566
pollution 88
  air 431
  control of 287
  organic 272 274
  and selection 177
  water 226 230 231 311 313
Polycentropodidae 312
Polygala vulgaris 46 514
Polygonatum odoratum 6
Polygonum aviculare 491
— *hydropiper* 8 257
polyphagous species 531
Polypodium vulgare 96
polyspecific forest 34
pond culture 304
ponderosa pine 426 427
ponies 439
Poo-Lolietum 47
pool, guanotrophic 8
populations
  development 531
  dynamics 517ff
  rabbit 27
  regulation in parrots 215
  rodent 431
  segregation of animal 369
  size 446
  stability 556
  structure 446–7
potassium 19 21 619
potential
  natural ecosystem 582
  natural vegetation 607 615
  water deficit 153
Potentilla anserina 5
— *erecta* 25 68 95 478
— *fruticosa* 489 490
— *reptans* 19 47
Poterium sanguisorba 68 116 124 501 504
  506 507 509 510 512 514
precipitin test 521
predators 521ff 524
pressures
  grazing 26 489 491 494
  public 80 528
  visitor 459 461 467

primary
  fen 593 594
  production 9 493
Primula elatior 572
— *veris* 70
— *vulgaris* 189
Procus literosa 191
Prodiamesa olivacea 280
production
  deer 429
  fish 307
  primary 9
  secondary 9
productivity 617
pronghorn antelope 220 420
protein deficiencies 399
Prunella vulgaris 514
Prunus sp. 491
Psephotus haematonotus 213
Pseudotsuga 42
Pteridium aquilinum 95 97 101 137–40 150
puberty 445 450
Puccinellietum maritimae 11 12
Puku 334
Pulsatilla vulgaris 510 513 514
purification plants, natural 314
Prymnesium parvum 237

Queen Elizabeth Park 329 337ff 398
Queensland 216
Querceto-Betuletum 7
Quercus 488
— *robur* 564 575 576
  density of 576–7 578

rabbit populations 27
rabbits 12 53 54 139 519
radioactive phosphorus 382
Radiola linoides 49 50
ragwort 517
  and overgrazing 520
rainfall
  and *Agrostis canina* 145
  and *Galium hercynicum* 143
  and *Luzula campestris* 143
  and *Pteridium aquilinum* 139
rain forest, sclerophyll 208
raised bog 8
Rana pipiens 180
Rangifer spp. 220
Ranunculus
— *flammula* 8

— *repens* 5
—*sceleratus* 175
Rattus rattus 179 181
raw humus 106 107 110–11 112
reclamation of grassland 528 545 548
recolonization of woodlands 558–9
recreation parks 311
reed
  culture 314
  cutting 586
reedswamps 4 9
  ochtohydrophyte 241
  unstabilized 260
refugia 374 383
regeneration
  Calluna 96–8
  ragwort 519
  shrub 328 493
regrowth after defoliation 511
  ragwort 519
reindeer 418 420
relative growth rate 68
reproductive performance 418
Research Institute for Nature Management, Zeist 311
'Reserves Review' 535
Rhacomitrium lanuginosum 478
rhinoceros 335 414
Rhodesia 110 394
Rhum, Isle of 437ff
Rhynchospora alba 8
richness of grassland 513
ridge and furrow 569
ring-barking 336
rivers, old branches as nature reserves
   311
River
  Cole 274ff
  Neretva 168
  Nile 319
  Ray 286–90
  Severn 274ff
  Thames 287
  Upper Rhine plains 389
  Upper Thames 288 289
Riverside 28
roan 369ff
Rockingham Forest, Northants 558
Rocky Mountains 151 427
rodent population 220 431
rooting depth 124
root secretions 105–13
Rostherne Mere NNR 231 237
rotational grazing 549 550

Rothamsted Experimental Station 17 19
  52 69 70 74 151
rotovating 528 544
Rotterdam 46
Rubus caesius 55
— *chamaemorus* 153–65
Rumex acetosa 19 27 71–3
— *acetosella* 27
— *crispus* 5 245 488
— *hydrolapathum* 588 591 594
— *tenuifolius* 140 148
rush culture 314
rustic moth 193
rye grass, perennial 24

sable 369ff
Salicornia stricta 11
Salicornietum 11
Salix/Myrica scrub 51
Salix repens 54
— *rosmarinifolia* 12
saltings 11
salt
  licks 372
  marshes 6 11 53 58 82 85
Salticus scenicus 178
Salvia leucophylla 111
Samarian Mountains 615–16
sampling
  continuous 33–6
  permanent plots 33–6
  populations 405ff
  recurrent 33–6
  stratified random 33–6
  sweepnet 542
  with partial replacement 33–6
sand
  diggings 311
  dunes 6
  Kalahari deposits 367ff
saprobia 274
saprobe system 315
saprobic benthic communities 292
  micro-organisms 271
Satureja acinos 491
Saturnia pavonia 439
savannas 110 606
  woodland 208 219
Scabiosa columbaria 72–4 124
Scandinavia 88 91
Schelde 61
Schiermonnikoog 45 49
Schistidium apocarpum 493

Schoenoplectus lacustris 244ff
Schoenus ferrugineus 488
— *nigricans* 49 50
scrub 4 532 606
Schwingmoor 237
Scilly Isles 181
Scirpus caespitosus 97
sclerophyll forest 207 208
Scotland 91 98 192
Scottish Highlands 153
sea lamprey 231
seasonal effects of management 545
secondary production 9
sedge
    swamps 9
    utilization of 364
seed
    burial (*Themeda*) 346
    germination 175
seepage water 314
segregation of animal populations 369
selection 559
    of nature reserves 555
    pressures 560
    by sheep 508
selective
    culling 455
    defoliation 24
    grazing 252 608
Selinum carvifolia 51
Selous Game Reserve 409–10
semi-arid regions 426
semi-deserts 7
Senecio integrifolius 514
— *jacobaeae* 71 517
senescence
    in *Calluna* 111 113
    in *Festuca ovina* 140–3
Serengeti National Park 360–3 395
serpentine 88 195
Sesleria coerulea 81 490
Setaria eylesii 319 328 330 334
sewage
    effluent 287–91
    fungus 228 271 284
    organic 226
    water 315
sex ratio 448 450
sheep 397 452 545 608
    Border Leicester x Cheviot ewes 500
    grazing 10 19 20 24 53 154 428 448
        453 487–8 497ff 601 603
    selection by 508
Sheffield 52

Shetland 193
shrub
    dwarf 617
    land 619
    regeneration 328
Sieglingia decumbens 25 116
Silene nutans 6
— *otites* 149
silica, role of 73
silver fir 105
simulated trampling 469 477 479 480–1
Sitka spruce 106
skiers 473 476ff
skiing, effect of 469 471
ski
    tows 472
    traffic 471
Skokholm 191 192 199
snow
    avalanches 602
    cover 80 476 480
    drifts 491
    trampling experiment 479
Snowdonia 153
Society of American Foresters 426
Society Islands 184
Society for the Promotion of Nature
        Reserves 151 583
social organization and behaviour 208–20
sodium 19
    content 372
    nitrate 19
soil
    acidity 431
    basic 490
    brown forest 130
    calcareous 618
    chernozem 129
    compaction 464 470
    depth 512
    erosion 431 467 470 492 494
    grood 129
    moisture 430
    nitrogen 466
    phosphate 575
    phosphorus 464
    rendzina 465 618
    temperatures 339 340 431
Solanum dulcamara 257
solifluction 460
South Africa 394
South Australia 151
South Downs 29
Southern uplands 153

spatial distribution 409
specialist insect feeders 529
Sphaeroma rugicauda 181
Sphagnum cuspidatum 8
— *rubellum* 478
— spp. 10 482 483
spider fauna 533 542
Sporobolus pyramidalis 323
— sp. 319 325 328 330
— *stapfianus* 340
sport hunting 396
spruce bark beetle 602 603
stability 4 7
    of ecosystems 5
    of grazed downland 512
    of populations 556
    in time 5
standing crop biomass 322
Staphylococcus 179
Statens Naturvårdsverk 487
Stellaria media 491
Steppe, European 388
Stercorarius parasiticus 197
Stigeoclonium sp. 284
Stipa sp. 339
Stockport 175
stone pine 600
stratification 533
Stratiotes aloides 312–14
subnival zone 599 601
succession 543 574 577
    allogenic 9
    autochtonic swamp 312 314
    autogenic 9
    cyclic 10–12
    ecological 288
    following myxomatosis 54 55 116 574
    long-term 576
    on molehills 148–9
    natural 582
    proceeding 10–12
    terminating 10
    vegetation 387
Succisa pratensis 510 514
Suffolk 563
sugar limestone 80
surface run-off 368
'swaling' 541
swamps 12
    autochtonic 312 314
    mesotrophic 12
    reed 4 9
    sedge 9
sward resistance 467

Sweden 487
sweepnet samples 542
swifts 181
Synageles venator 588

taming 414
Tarangire Game Reserve 360–1 363
Taraxacum officinale 19
Tatra National Park 599ff
techniques for long-term diagnosis and
    prediction in forest communities 33
Teesdale 29 58 79 84–8 151
Teesdale Trust of I.C.I. 88
temperate rainforests 426
temperatures, soil 339 340 431
Terminalia sp. 319 328 329
— *superba* 41
terminating succession 10
termites 377 383 384
terrestrial eutrophication 467
Terschelling 11 49
Tetraopes tetraophthalmus 181
Teucrium scordium 55
Themeda triandra 337ff 353 355 357 360
    362
    after-ripening period 344 347
    and burning 337–40
    clipping 340
    germination 337
    hygroscopic behaviour 339
    seedling establishment 337
thiram 26
Thomson's gazelle 351 353 357 360–4
    407–8 414
Thymus
— *drucei* 70 461
— *pulegioides* 46 501 507 510 512
— *serpyllum* 490
Tilapia mossambica 295ff
Tilia cordata 564 572 576
time, dispersion in 7
time-lapse photography 473
Timothy S50 480 481 483
tomato, as test plant 107–8
Tortella spp. 490 493
Tortulo-Phleetum arenarii 54
tourists 369 415
toxic compounds from *Calluna* 105–13
toxicity, ammonia 285
trampleometer 473ff
trampling 55 80 377 496ff
    effect on floristic composition 55
    effect of people 469 544

frequency 483
grassland 528 529
by grazing animals 543
intensity 483
mechanical foot 477 483
sheep 511
simulated experiments 469 477 479
  483–4
treatments 478
transport of dung 378–81
Trelogan mine 184
Trichophorum cespitosum 472 475 476 478
  481 483 484
Trichoptera 285 291 312–13
Trifolium medium 6
— *repens* 5 16 17 21 24 25 75
— *subterraneum* 129
Triphaena comes 192
trophic web 555
tropical rainforest 36
trout streams 287
tsetse fly (*Glossina*) 397
Tubificidae 285 288 291
Turbellaria 275
Turkey 200
2–4, D 609
Typha angustifolia 244ff
— *latifolia* 8 244ff
  rhizomes 171
Typhlocybinae 534
Tyria jacobaeae 517ff

Uganda 36
Ulex europaeus
  and Dartford Warbler 101
  and earthworms in soil 127–8
  mechanism of soil acidification under
    115–33
  rooting depth 124
— *gallii* 97
— *minor* 97
Ulex scrub 116
Ulmus carpinifolia 576
— sp. 488
ungulates 220 413
Unit of Grassland Research 76
unstabilized reedswamps 260
Upper Rhine plains 389
Urtica dioica 491
Utah forests 427
utilization of
  phosphorus 381
  sedges 364

Utricularia vulgaris 257

Vaccinium myrtillus 25 68
— *vitis-idaea* 51 95 96
vacuum net 533 536 545
Valor Ecclesiasticus 567 580
value, economic 383
variation, genetic and environmental
  selection 177–206
vegetation
  destruction of 373
  height 529 536 538 542
  natural 26
  nitrophilous 388 488
  'patchiness' 538
  succession 387
  tussocks 538–40
Venn diagram 18
'vens', oligotrophic 311
Veronica spicata 491
— *spicata* subsp. *spicata* 149
vertebrates
  selective effects of pesticides, drugs, etc.
    178–9
  social trends in gregariousness 220
Vikings 178
Viola canina ssp. *montana* 587
— *pumila* 491
— *stagnina* 587 591 592
Violo-Corynephoretum 11
Violon caninae 49
visitor pressure 459 461 467
Voorne 45 46 53 58 59 61

Wales 20 69 153
Wankie National Park 367ff
Wantage 28
wapiti 420 427
Warburg Reserve 42
warfarin 179
warthog 359 369ff
Warwickshire 178
washes 528
waste water 314
waterholes, artificial 369
water
  blooms 230 232
  management 311ff
  meadows 314 528
  oligotrophic 6
  quality 313 371
  seepage 314

sewage 315
supplies 367ff
table and floristic composition 55
waste 314
watershed cover 428
Waterton Lakes National Park 415
weather management 432
Weeting Heath NNR 517–19
western hemlock 426
western red cedar 426
western white pine 427
Wheat Fen Broad 171 174
Whin Sill 80
Whipsnade 200
Whittlesea Mere 583
Wicken Fen 587
Widdybank Fell 80 85 86
wild animals 396
wildebeeste 351 360–2 370ff 414
wild hog 388
wild horses 420
wildlife productivity 395
wild turkey 430
willows 427
Wiltshire 193 289 535
Winchester 181
Winterswÿk 50
wisent 420
wood-banks 569
woodland 319 439
  'amenity' planting 564
  ancient 565 574
  archaeology 569–70
  Crown 566
  destruction 563 601
  law-suits 567
  management, historical 567–9 572 578
  Mediterranean 619

Miombo 410
outlines 569
Quercus robur–Fraxinus–Acer campestre–
  Corylus 564
recolonization 558–9
recording 572–3
sales 569
sclerophyll 606
secondary 564 565 574 577
small 561
species density 557
structure 570
surveys 563–4 572–4 578
types in East Anglia 564 576 577
Woodwalton Fen NNR 581ff
Wyre Forest 274

xerothermic plant communities 388
xerophyte communities 11

yaks 397
yeld hinds 440
Yugoslavia 168

Zambia 333 394
zebra 351 359 360–2 370ff
Zerna erecta 27 71 501 503–4 509 512
  competition ability 512
  phenology 514
zinc 141 180 184
zones, transitional 5
zoos 398
Zürich-Montpellier School 607
Zygina scutellaris 547